Malawi Adventure Pack

Story • Colour-in village scene • Cut-out model Bible van • Maisie's 'Amaizing' Pancakes • Wordsearch • Learn a little Chichewa • Play the 'Scripture Safari' game

An Adventure Pack to help our children know more about life in rural Malawi - from minnows and monkeys to mud huts - and how children there would be delighted to have their own copy of the Scriptures.

Informative and educational activities to keep youngsters (primary school age) happily occupied during holidays, in the classroom, or in a Sunday school group.

Suitable for holiday camp use. All items are photocopiable.

Maisie, please send me/us a **Malawi Adventure Pack** as soon as possible

Name _____

Address _____

_____ Postcode _____

Group_____

Post or fax the coupon to
Maisie Rendall or email her at:
maisie.rendall@scottishbiblesociety.org

SCOTTISH
BIBLE SOCIETY
The Word for the world

The Scottish Bible Society
7 Hampton Terrace
Edinburgh EH12 5XU
Tel: 0131 337 9701 Fax: 0131 337 0641
www.scottishbiblesociety.org
e-mail:info@scottishbiblesociety.org
Scottish Charity No: SC010767

Donation Envelopes Ltd
The giving envelope specialists

REVOLUTIONARY NEW RANGE

Our new range of larger self adhesive envelopes mean more room for donations without the need to lick and stick.

Sets can now be ordered with extra envelopes to include special giving days such as Gift aid, Easter or Building and Maintenance.

for free samples and full details please contact:
market leaders in self adhesive collection envelopes

Unit 15, Telford Court, Clydebank Business Park, Clydebank G81 2NR.
Tel: 0141 951 1847 Fax 0141 951 1611
email: info@donation-envelopes.co.uk
web: www.donation-envelopes.co.uk
SEQUI is a registered trademark of Donation Envelopes Ltd

The Right Reverend Finlay A.J. Macdonald MA BD PhD DD

MODERATOR

The Church of Scotland
YEAR BOOK
2002/2003

Editor
Rev. Ronald S. Blakey
MA BD MTh

Published on behalf of
THE CHURCH OF SCOTLAND
BOARD OF COMMUNICATION
by SAINT ANDREW PRESS
121 George Street, Edinburgh EH2 4YN

THE OFFICES OF THE CHURCH

121 George Street	Tel: 0131-225 5722
Edinburgh EH2 4YN	Fax: 0131-220 3113
	Internet: http://www.churchofscotland.org.uk/

Office Hours: Monday–Friday 9.00 am–5.00 pm
Office Manager: Mrs Dorothy H. Woodhouse

PARISH EDUCATION
21 Young Street, Edinburgh EH2 4HU   Tel: 08702 415748

SOCIAL RESPONSIBILITY
Charis House   47 Milton Road East, Edinburgh EH15 2SR   Tel: 0131-657 2000
                    [E-mail: info@charis.org.uk]   Fax: 0131-657 5000

NATIONAL MISSION
Glasgow Office   59 Elmbank Street, Glasgow G2 4PQ   Tel: 0141-333 1948
Kirkcaldy Office   St Bryce Kirk Centre,
                    St Brycedale Avenue, Kirkcaldy KY1 1ET   Tel/Fax: 01592 646406

(Youth Adviser: Presbytery of Glasgow)
                    110 St James Road, Glasgow G4 0PS   Tel: 0141-400 7788

QUICK DIRECTORY

A.C.T.S. 01786 823588
Badenoch Centre 01540 651373
Board of Communication 0131-240 2236
Bridgeton, St Francis-in-the-East Church House 0141-554 8045
Carberry 0131-665 3135/7604
Christian Aid London 020 7620 4444
Christian Aid Scotland 0131-220 1254
Kirk Care 0131-225 7246
Lodging House Mission 0141-552 0285
Netherbow 0131-556 9579/2647
Media Relations Unit (Press Office) 0131-240 2243
Pathway Productions 0131-225 5722
Scottish Churches Parliamentary Office .0131-622 2278
Society, Religion and Technology Project 0131-556 2953

First published in 2002 by SAINT ANDREW PRESS, 121 George Street, Edinburgh EH2 4YN on behalf of the BOARD of COMMUNICATION of the CHURCH of SCOTLAND

Copyright © The BOARD of COMMUNICATION of the CHURCH of SCOTLAND 2002

ISBN 0 86153 347 X

British Library Cataloguing in Publication Data
    A catalogue record for this book is available from the British Library.
Printed and bound by Bell and Bain Ltd, Glasgow

Publisher's note: the photograph of the Moderator in the 2001–2002 *Year Book* was taken by Gary Doak.

CONTENTS

Prefaces xviii

SECTION 1   Assembly Boards and Committees
            including dates of meetings 1

SECTION 2   General Information 51

SECTION 3   Church Procedure 73

SECTION 4   The General Assembly of 2002 79

SECTION 5   Presbytery Lists 87

SECTION 6   Additional Lists of Personnel 259

SECTION 7   Congregational Statistics 2001 309

Index of MINISTERS.. 344
Index of PARISHES and PLACES 357
Index of FORMER PARISHES and CONGREGATIONS 363
Index of SUBJECTS.. 386
Index of ADVERTISERS 390

All correspondence regarding the *Year Book* should be sent to
The Editor, *Church of Scotland Year Book*,
Saint Andrew Press, 121 George Street, Edinburgh EH2 4YN
Fax: 0131-220 3113
[E-mail: cofs.standrew@dial.pipex.com]

GENERAL ASSEMBLY OF 2003
The General Assembly of 2003 will convene on
Saturday, 17th May 2003

FROM THE MODERATOR

I wonder whether Paul, when he wrote Chapter 16 of his letter to the Romans, had to hand a *Year Book* of the early Church. The chapter contains a fascinating list of names and reminds us not just that the apostle was concerned to articulate and impart Christian teaching but also that he clearly valued the work of individual believers and his relationships with them.

Our *Year Book* contains much useful information about the Church, but at its core are the names of people who serve the Church across Scotland and throughout the world – our presentday equivalents of Prisca and Aquila, Andronicus and Junia. How true it is that the Church is not so much a place as people. Thank God for the people of God!

This new volume has great value as an up-to-date guide to the Church of Scotland. It will also take its place as the latest in a long sequence of volumes which provide an invaluable part of our Church's record. Only recently, in my capacity as Principal Clerk, I received an enquiry from someone asking if there existed a photograph of a relative who had been Moderator in the 1940s. I was able to go straight to my bookshelves and locate the volume, and there was the photograph!

I am delighted to commend this 2002/2003 edition and, at the same time, to express the gratitude of the Church to the editor, the Rev. Ronald Blakey, and to all who work with him to provide this excellent and most useful publication.

Finlay A.J. Macdonald
June 2002

FROM THE EDITOR

The principal changes in this edition of the *Year Book*, as compared with immediate past editions, centre on the inclusion of two new sections and the omission of three former sections.

The new entries are:

* After a ten-year gap, there has been restored the section listing the senior ministers of the Church, which for this purpose has been deemed to be those who have been ordained for sixty years or more. This list (List S in section 6) has been compiled in response to a number of requests and enquiries. In that no single source seemed to contain all the necessary information, no guarantee is given that the list is complete. The hope is that it will be found to be of interest: as always, comments and fuller information will be welcomed.

* Last year's edition saw the inclusion for the first time of a Supplementary Index of lost parish names of Scotland. The widespread interest that this list occasioned has been remarkable: it has provoked more correspondence and been responsible for more appreciative comment than could ever have been imagined. This year, it has been expanded into an index of former parishes and congregations, and it now covers the towns and cities as well as the rural areas. It is not intended that this section should be reprinted every year, but the hope is that every few years it will appear in a suitably updated form which has taken account of relevant readjustment in the intervening period. As before, I am indebted to Roy Pinkerton for his assistance.

The omissions are these:

* On the advice of the Principal Clerk, the sizeable section dealing with Procedure in a Vacancy has been omitted. The Church is currently considering in detail proposals which, if approved, would see significant changes in this important area of the Church's life. Such changes would be likely to come into effect during the lifetime of this *Year Book*. It was understandably felt to be less than helpful to include here guidance which could prove to be at best misleading, at worst wrong. Consideration will be given in due course to restoring this section in an appropriate new form.

* The Board of World Mission has decided to withdraw the small section listing Overseas Appointments. It did not appear to provide any information which was not available in more detailed form in the section listing Overseas Locations.

- Following representation from some of those who were or might have been listed, the Secretary of the Committee on Chaplains to HM Forces concluded that there was little useful purpose in retaining the list of retired Chaplains to the Forces. In recent years, the list has been less than complete and more than a little out of date, in that retired Chaplains did not always think to inform the Secretary when they moved from one location to another. The standard Index of Ministers which the *Year Book* contains endeavours to be all-embracing and should enable the current whereabouts of former Chaplains to be ascertained.

The work of editing the *Year Book* is a privilege; mostly it is also a pleasure. Moments of exasperation this year have in the main been confined within two areas. Not all Board Secretaries and Presbytery Clerks have easily been persuaded that deadline dates for submitting material are in fact that: they are not arbitrary notions to be viewed with detached academic interest. The other main threat to blood pressure continues to be the challenge of deciphering the ever-increasing number of e-mail addresses which are desired within these pages. Where the illegible meets the unintelligible, there are bound to be some mistakes – and for these I apologise. It crossed my mind to ask if agreement had been reached by editors of like publications as to what might be an appropriate collective noun for such addresses. I was told there are at least two, used interchangeably depending on one's prevailing mood – an exuberance and an eczema.

There are, however, many lighter moments. Three in the past year stand out.

- Correspondence was continuing across a wide front as to whether female ministers, deacons, committee conveners and the like should be expected to declare which of the standard prefixes should be used of themselves – Ms, Miss or Mrs. Listening carefully and sympathetically to the arguments adduced, the editorial decision is that each individual should be free to choose, with the absence of any prefix an equally acceptable option. I have tried to reflect such individual wishes, and apologise for any sins of commission or omission. I was considerably diverted by a letter from one of our ministers affirming that, if she and her colleagues were asked to declare their marital status, every male should have to do the same. Following this up in a mixed group of Kirk folk in which women were in the majority, I was offered some interesting suggestions as to what might appear in brackets after a male name. The more printable included 'spoken for', 'one careful owner' and 'free to a good home'.

- Computers are wonderful – we all know that. We also know that, by and large, they produce answers based on information they have stored. They cannot, for example, reject the ludicrous simply because it is ludicrous. As I have indicated, I was seeking to draw up a list of those ministers who had been ordained for sixty or more years so that we might know the identity of the current 'Father of the Kirk'. The computer in the Department of Ministry was duly asked to produce the goods, and in double-quick time out came the show-stopping answer that we do not have a 'Father' but a 'Mother', despite the comparatively recent ordination of women. The explanation was that a particular minister's date of birth had inadvertently been entered as her date of ordination. I will spare Effie Campbell's blushes and go no further.

- Last year's *Year Book* was posted to parish ministers at the end of September. Two months later, I received a letter from a minister in Perthshire, thanking me for his copy which he had just received. For some reason which must have seemed good at the time, the postman had delivered the book not through the letterbox but through the cat flap. That particular cat flap leads into a hidden space behind the washing machine in the manse. The book only came to light when the cat's reluctance to go voluntarily to the vet for his annual MOT led him to hide in what he had hitherto regarded as his exclusive territory. It is salutary to realise that the presence of this priceless work had not hindered the cat in going about his daily business, nor had its absence discomfited the minister.

As always, I am indebted to those who have assisted in the preparation of this book. Presbytery Clerks play a considerable part in this, as do the Secretaries of Assembly Boards and Committees, and I am grateful for their co-operation. Sandy Gemmill and the staff of Saint Andrew Press are likewise key players, and I gladly place on record my thanks to them.

Ronald S. Blakey
August 2002

SECTION 1

Assembly Boards
and Committees

MEETINGS OF BOARDS AND COMMITTEES

The following Boards and Committees have indicated that they plan to meet on the dates listed.

ASSEMBLY COUNCIL
2002   24 October, 5 December
2003   23 January, 13 March, 1 May

BOARD OF MINISTRY
2002   17–18 September, 11 December
2003   12 February, 26 February (provisional), 18 June, 25 September, 10 December

BOARD OF PRACTICE AND PROCEDURE
2002   17 September, 19 November
2003   21 January, 18 February, 15 April, 17 June

COMMITTEE ON EDUCATION
2002   12 September
2003   12 February, 25 June

ECUMENICAL RELATIONS
2002   26–27 September
2003   23 January, 27 March, 26 June, 25–26 September

GENERAL TRUSTEES
General Trustees
2002   24 September, 22 October, 19 November, 17 December
2003   28 January, 25 February, 25 March, 29 April, 27 May, 8 July, 23 September

FABRIC AND CHAIRMAN'S
2002   3 September, 8 October, 5 November, 3 December
2003   14 January, 11 February, 11 March, 8 April, 13 May, 17 June, 29 July, 2 September

GLEBES
2002   4 September, 9 October, 6 November, 4 December
2003   15 January, 12 February, 12 March, 9 April, 14 May, 18 June, 30 July, 3 September

HOUSING AND LOAN FUND
2002   10 September, 10 December

NATIONAL MISSION
BOARD (Wednesdays 10am)
2002   4 September, 4 December
2003   5 February, 4 June, 3 September, 3 December

COMMITTEE ON PARISH REAPPRAISAL (Tuesdays 2pm)
2002   17 September, 15 October, 19 November, 17 December
2003   18 February, 18 March, 15 April, 17 June, 16 September, 21 October, 18 November, 16 December

COMMITTEE ON NEW CHARGE DEVELOPMENT (Wednesdays 10:30am)
(The location for these meetings can be variable.)
2002   16 October
2003   15 January, 18 June, 15 October

COMMITTEE ON PARISH ASSISTANCE (Wednesdays 10:30am)
2002   25 September (all day), 27 November
2003   15 January, 11 June, 24 September (all day), 26 November

COMMITTEE ON MISSION AND EVANGELISM RESOURCES (Thursdays 10:30am)
2002   31 October
2003   16 January, 13 March, 29 May, 20–21 August, 23 October

COMMITTEE ON CHAPLAINCIES (Wednesdays 2pm)
2002   6 November
2003   28 January, 11 June, 5 November

HOSPITALS, HEALTHCARE AND UNIVERSITIES SUB-COMMITTEE (Tuesdays 10:30am)
2002   24 September, 19 November
2003   14 January, 11 March, 27 May, 23 September, 15 November

CHURCH AND INDUSTRY SUB-COMMITTEE (Wednesdays 6:30pm)
2002   4 December
2003   15 January, 23 April, 25 June, 17 September, 19 November

PRISON CHAPLAINCIES SUB-COMMITTEE (Wednesdays 10:30am)
2002   2 October
2003   22 January, 28 May, 1 October

JOINT FAITHS ADVISORY BOARD ON CRIMINAL JUSTICE (Wednesdays 2pm)
2002   11 September, 11 December
2003   12 March, 4 June, 10 September, 10 December

PERSONNEL COMMITTEE
2002   12 September, 5 December

SOCIAL RESPONSIBILITY
BOARD
2002   30 October
2003   13–14 February, 19–20 June

EXECUTIVE
2002   23 October, 4 December
2003   13 February, 16 April, 19 June

STEWARDSHIP AND FINANCE
2002   13–14 November
2003   26 February, 26 March, 25 June

WORLD MISSION
2002   11 September, 27–28 November
2003   5 February, 2 April, 18–19 June

Assembly Boards and Committees

		Page
(1)	General Administration (Practice and Procedure)	5
(2)	Central Co-ordinating Committee	6
(3)	General Treasurer's Department	7
(4)	Information Technology Department	7
(5)	The Law Department	8
(6)	Office Manager's Department	8
(7)	The Personnel Department	9
(8)	General Trustees	9
(9)	Nomination	11
(10)	Church of Scotland Investors Trust	11
(11)	Stewardship and Finance	12
(12)	The Church of Scotland Pension Trustees	14
(13)	The Church of Scotland Guild	14
(14)	Assembly Council	16
(15)	Church and Nation	16
(16)	Panel on Doctrine	17
(17)	Panel on Worship	17
(18)	Committee on Artistic Matters	18
(19)	Department of Ministry	19
(20)	National Mission	22
(21)	Social Responsibility	29
(22)	World Mission	38
(23)	Ecumenical Relations	40
(24)	Parish Education	43
(25)	Education Committee	46
(26)	Communication	47
(27)	Church of Scotland Trust	49

[Note: Years, where given, indicate the year of appointment]

(1) GENERAL ADMINISTRATION
(PRACTICE AND PROCEDURE)

MEMBERSHIP
BOARD OF PRACTICE AND PROCEDURE
(38 members: 32 appointed by the Assembly, plus Moderator, Moderator Designate, Clerks, Procurator and Law Agent *ex officiis*)

Convener:	Rev. David W. Lacy BA BD (2000)
Vice Convener:	Rev. Alastair H. Symington MA BD (2002)
Secretary:	The Principal Clerk

COMMITTEE TO NOMINATE THE MODERATOR
(54 members: three surviving immediate past Moderators, three elders appointed through the Nomination Committee and one member from each UK Presbytery and the Presbytery of Europe)

Convener:	The earliest serving former Moderator present and willing to act
Secretary:	The Principal Clerk

JUDICIAL COMMISSION OF THE GENERAL ASSEMBLY

Chairman:	Sheriff J. Douglas Allan
Vice Chairman:	Rev. Alistair G.C. McGregor QC BD
Secretaries:	The Clerks of Assembly

STAFF

Acting Principal Clerk:	Rev. Marjory A. MacLean LLB BD
Assistant Secretary:	John D. McCulloch DL
Principal Administration Officer:	Mrs Alison Murray MA

REMIT: BOARD OF PRACTICE AND PROCEDURE

1. To advise the General Assembly on questions of Church Law and of Constitutional Law affecting the relationship between Church and State.
2. To advise and assist Committees of the General Assembly in the preparation of proposed legislation and on questions of interpretation, including interpretation of and proposed changes to their remits.
3. To make all necessary arrangements for the General Assembly each year.
4. To advise the Moderator anent his or her official duties, if so required.
5. To be responsible to the General Assembly for the care and maintenance of all Assembly buildings and its other property.
6. To compile the statistics of the Church, except Youth and Finance; and to supervise on behalf of the General Assembly all arrangements for care of Church Records and for Presbytery Visits.
7. To attend to the general interests of the Church in matters which are not covered by the remit of any other Committee; and to perform such other duties as may be assigned to it by Act or Deliverance of the General Assembly.
8. To deal with urgent issues arising between meetings of the General Assembly or the Commission of Assembly which do not fall within the remit of any Board, provided that
   (a)   it shall not be competent for the Board to take or authorise an action which is

      (i)   of such a nature that it would have been *ultra vires* of the Commission of
            Assembly, or
      (ii) of a legislative or judicial nature, or
      (iii) an order or instruction to any Court or Courts of the Church;
  (b) any action taken in terms of this Clause shall be reported by the Board to the next
       meeting of the General Assembly or the Commission of Assembly, whichever is the
       sooner.

(2) CENTRAL CO-ORDINATING COMMITTEE

MEMBERSHIP
(11 members: seven appointed by the General Assembly, and four *ex officiis* and non-voting,
namely the Principal Clerk, the Solicitor of the Church, the General Treasurer and the Personnel
Manager)
Convener: Mr Leon Marshall CA (2001)
Vice Convener: Mr John Neil OBE

STAFF
Administrative Secretary

REMIT
1.   To be responsible for the proper maintenance and insurance of the Church Offices at
     117–123 George Street, Edinburgh ('the George Street Offices').
2.   To be responsible for matters relating to Health and Safety within the George Street Offices.
3   To be responsible for matters relating to Data Protection within the George Street Offices
     and with respect to the General Assembly Boards and Committees based elsewhere.
4.   To be responsible for the allocation of accommodation within the George Street Offices and
     the annual determination of rental charges to the Boards, Committees and other parties
     accommodated therein.
5.   To oversee the delivery of central services to Departments within the George Street Offices
     and to the General Assembly Boards and Committees based elsewhere, namely:
      •   those facilities directly managed by the Office Manager
      •   information technology (including the provision of support services to Presbytery
         Clerks)
      •   insurance
      •   purchasing and travel
      •   personnel services
      •   financial services (as delivered by the General Treasurer's Department)
      •   legal services (as delivered by the Law Department and subject to such oversight
         not infringing principles of 'client/solicitor' confidentiality).
6.   To provide an internal audit function to the General Assembly Boards, Statutory Corporations
     and Committees (other than the Board of Social Responsibility).

In addition, the Committee shall act as one of the five employing agencies of the Church
and shall act as a consultative and advisory body to the General Assembly Boards, Statutory
Corporations and Committees.

(3) GENERAL TREASURER'S DEPARTMENT

STAFF

General Treasurer:	Mr Donald F. Ross MA CA
Deputy General Treasurers:	Mr Alexander F. Gemmill BAcc CA
	Mr John S. Steven CA
	Mr William J. McKean BAcc CA
Assistant Treasurer:	Mrs Anne Macintosh BA CA
Accountants:	Mr Ross Donaldson
	Mr Derek Cant FCCA

Responsibilities of the General Treasurer's Department include:

- payroll processing for the Board of Ministry, Board of National Mission and Central Co-ordinating Committee
- issuing to congregations their annual requirement figures for Ministry Funds and the Mission and Aid Fund
- receiving payments from congregations towards their central requirements
- making Deed of Covenant tax recoveries on behalf of congregations
- making Gift Aid and Deed of Covenant tax recoveries on behalf of Boards, Committees and Statutory Corporations
- making VAT returns and tax recoveries on behalf of Boards, Committees and Statutory Corporations and providing VAT information to congregations
- providing support, training and advice on financial matters to congregational treasurers
- receiving and discharging legacies and bequests on behalf of Boards, Committees and Statutory Corporations
- providing banking arrangements and operating a central banking system for Boards, Committees and Statutory Corporations
- providing accountancy systems and services for Boards, Committees, Statutory Corporations and the Trustees of the Church's Pension Schemes
- providing Finance Departments for the Boards of World Mission and Parish Education.

(4) INFORMATION TECHNOLOGY DEPARTMENT

STAFF

Information Technology Manager:	Alastair Chalmers
Depute Information Technology Manager:	Veronica Hay

The Department provides computing facilities for Boards and Departments within 121 George Street, Presbytery Clerks, National Mission personnel outwith George Street, the Scottish Churches Parliamentary Office and Pathway Productions. It is also responsible for the telephone services within the George Street Offices.

The facilities provided include:

- the provision and maintenance of networks for both data and voice
- the purchase and installation of hardware and software

- support for problems and guidance on the use of software
- development of in-house software
- maintenance of data within the central databases and finance systems.

(5) THE LAW DEPARTMENT

STAFF

Solicitor of the Church and of the General Trustees:	Mrs J.S. Wilson LLB NP
Depute Solicitor:	Miss M.E. Macleod LLB NP
Assistant Solicitors:	Mr I.K. Johnstone MA LLB
	Mrs E.M. Kemp MA LLB
	Mrs J.M. Hamilton BA NP
	Mrs Elspeth Annan LLB NP
	Miss Susan Killean LLB NP

The Law Department of the Church was created in 1937/38. The Department acts in legal matters for the Church and all of its Courts, Boards, Committees, the Church of Scotland General Trustees, the Church of Scotland Trust and the Church of Scotland Investors Trust. It also acts for individual congregations and is available to give advice on any legal matter arising.

The Department is under the charge of the Solicitor of the Church, a post created at the same time as the formation of the Department and a post which is now customarily held along with the traditional posts of Law Agent of the General Assembly and the Custodier of former United Free Church titles (E-mail: lawdept@cofscotland.org.uk).

(6) OFFICE MANAGER'S DEPARTMENT

STAFF

Office Manager:	Mrs Dorothy Woodhouse (E-mail: dwoodhouse@cofscotland.org.uk)

The responsibilities of the Office Manager's Department include:
- management of a maintenance budget for the upkeep of the Church Offices at 121 George Street, Edinburgh
- responsibility for all aspects of health and safety for staff, visitors and contractors working in the building
- managing a team of staff providing the Offices with security, reception, mail room, print room, switchboard, day-to-day maintenance services and Committee room bookings
- overseeing all sub-contracted services to include catering, cleaning, boiler-room maintenance, intruder alarm, fire alarms and lifts
- maintaining building records in accordance with the requirements of statutory legislation.

(7) THE PERSONNEL DEPARTMENT

STAFF

Personnel Manager:	Mr George B.B. Eadie BA
Deputy Personnel Manager:	Miss Angela Brady MCIPD
Personnel Officer:	Miss Maria Carena
Personnel Assistant:	Mrs Dorothy Menzies

REMIT

The Personnel Committee was set up in 1978 on the Report of the Advisory Board to determine salaries, length of service and conditions generally for Secretaries and Members of Office Staff. In 1991, and again in 1996, the General Assembly made certain minor adjustments to the remit, including a requirement that the Personnel Committee should conduct an annual salary review of those members of staff for which it is the employing agency.

In recognition of the aim that the Personnel Committee may in time operate as the co-ordinating body for the Church in respect of the salaries and conditions of employment of all persons employed by the five employing agencies, the other four employing agencies are required to provide all information on such matters as requested by the Personnel Committee.

This remit passed to the new Central Co-ordinating Committee as from 1 September 2001.

(8) GENERAL TRUSTEES

MEMBERSHIP

(New Trustees are appointed, as required, by the General Assembly, on the recommendation of the General Trustees)

Chairman:	Mr William S. Carswell MA LLB (1999)
Vice Chairman:	Rev. James H. Simpson BD LLB (1999)
Secretary and Clerk:	Mr Alan W. Cowe MA LLB (Tel: 0131-225 5722)
Depute Secretary and Clerk:	Mr T.R.W. Parker LLB

COMMITTEES:

Fabric Committee
Convener: Rev. James H. Simpson BD LLB (1994)

Chairman's Committee
Convener: Mr William S. Carswell MA LLB (1999)

Glebes Committee
Convener: Mr A.S. Chalmers FRICS (1988)

Finance Committee
Convener: Mr R.G. Burnett BComm CA FCMA (1999)

Law Committee
Convener: Professor J. Alistair M. Inglis CBE MA LLB (1999)

STAFF

Secretary and Clerk:	Mr Alan W. Cowe MA LLB
Depute Secretary and Clerk:	Mr T.R.W. Parker LLB
Assistants:	Miss P.M. Burnside LLB NP (Glebes)
	Mr David D. Robertson LLB NP (Ecclesiastical Buildings)
Treasurer:	Mr Donald F. Ross MA CA
Deputy Treasurer:	Mr W.J. McKean BAcc CA

REMIT

The General Trustees are a Property Corporation created and incorporated under the Church of Scotland (General Trustees) Order Confirmation Act 1921. Their duties, powers and responsibilities were greatly extended by the Church of Scotland (Property & Endowments) Acts and Orders 1925 to 1995, and they are also charged with the administration of the Central Fabric Fund (see below) and the Consolidated Fabric Fund and the Consolidated Stipend Fund in which monies held centrally for the benefit of individual congregations are lodged.

The scope of the work of the Trustees is broad, covering all facets of property administration, but particular reference is made to the following matters:

1. **ECCLESIASTICAL BUILDINGS.** The Trustees' Fabric Committee considers proposals for work at buildings, regardless of how they are vested, and plans of new buildings. Details of all such projects should be submitted to the Committee before work is commenced. The Committee also deals with applications for the release of fabric monies held by the General Trustees for individual congregations, and considers applications for assistance from the Central Fabric Fund from which grants and/or loans may be given to assist congregations faced with expenditure on fabric. Application forms relating to consents for work and possible financial assistance from the Central Fabric Fund are available from the Secretary of the Trustees and require to be submitted through Presbytery with its approval. The Committee normally meets on the first or second Tuesday of each month, apart from July, when it meets on the last Tuesday, and August, when there is no meeting.

2. **SALE, PURCHASE AND LETTING OF PROPERTIES.** All sales or lets of properties vested in the General Trustees fall to be carried out by them in consultation with the Financial Board of the congregation concerned, and no steps should be taken towards any sale or let without prior consultation with the Secretary of the Trustees. Where property to be purchased is to be vested in the General Trustees, it is essential that contact be made at the earliest possible stage with the Solicitor to the Trustees, who is responsible for the lodging of offers for such properties and all subsequent legal procedure.

3. **GLEBES.** The Trustees are responsible for the administration of Glebes vested in their ownership. All lets fall to be granted by them in consultation with the minister concerned. It should be noted that neither ministers nor Kirk Sessions may grant lets of Glebe land vested in the General Trustees. As part of their Glebe administration, the Trustees review regularly all Glebe rents.

4. **INSURANCE.** Properties vested in the General Trustees must be insured with the Church of Scotland Insurance Co. Ltd, a company wholly owned by the Church of Scotland whose profits are applied for Church purposes. Insurance enquiries should be sent directly to the Company at 67 George Street, Edinburgh EH2 2JG (Tel: 0131-220 4119; Fax: 0131-220 4120; E-mail: enquiries@cosic.co.uk).

(9) NOMINATION

MEMBERSHIP – NOMINATION COMMITTEE
(44 members)
Convener: Rev. Keith F. Hall BD (2002)
Vice Convener: Rev. Iain D. Cunningham MA BD (2002)
Secretary: The Principal Clerk

REMIT
To bring before the General Assembly names of persons to serve on the Boards and Standing Committees of the General Assembly.

(10) CHURCH OF SCOTLAND INVESTORS TRUST

MEMBERSHIP
(Trustees are appointed by the General Assembly, on the nomination of the Investors Trust)
Chairman: Mr J.B.M. Dick ACIB
Vice Chairman: Mr D.M. Simpson BA FFA
Treasurer: Mr D.F. Ross MA CA
Secretary: Mr Fred Marsh MCIBS

REMIT
The Church of Scotland Investors Trust, established in 1994 by Act of Parliament, offers to Boards, Committees and congregations of the Church a simple and economical medium for the investment of their funds. Investors are at liberty to invest in the Church of Scotland Investors Trust to an unlimited extent, and it is felt that the facilities afforded thereby are preferable to the powers of investment offered by the Trustee Investments Act 1961, with all the attendant restrictions and conditions. The Church of Scotland Investors Trust provides three Funds for Church investors:

1. **THE DEPOSIT FUND** is intended for short-term investment and aims to provide a high rate of interest. Deposits are repayable on demand. Interest is calculated quarterly in arrears and paid gross on 15 May and 15 November. The Fund is invested mainly in short-term loans to Banks, Building Societies and Licensed Deposit-Taking Institutions. The Deposit Fund is professionally managed by Noble Grossart Limited, Edinburgh.

2. **THE GROWTH FUND** is very largely equity-based and is intended for long-term investment. The Fund is operated on a unitised basis and aims to provide capital growth. Units can be purchased or sold monthly. Income is distributed gross on 15 May and 15 November. The Growth Fund is professionally managed by Henderson Global Investors Limited, London.

3. **THE INCOME FUND** is intended for medium-term investment and aims to provide immediate high income. The Fund is invested predominantly in fixed-interest securities and is operated on a unitised basis. Units can be purchased or sold monthly. Income is

distributed gross on 15 March and 15 September. The Income Fund is professionally managed by Baillie Gifford & Company, Edinburgh.

Application Forms for investment and further information may be had from the Secretary of the Church of Scotland Investors Trust, 121 George Street, Edinburgh EH2 4YN.

(11) STEWARDSHIP AND FINANCE

MEMBERSHIP – BOARD OF STEWARDSHIP AND FINANCE
(77 members: 24 appointed by the Assembly, plus Convener and Vice Convener, and 47 Presbytery Representatives who attend three meetings of the Board, at which they have full rights as Board members. The Convener and Secretary of the Co-ordinating Forum, the General Treasurer and the Director of Stewardship are *ex officiis* members of the Board.)

Convener: Rev. J. Colin Caskie BA BD (2001)
Vice Convener: Mrs Vivienne A. Dickson CA (2001)

STAFF
General Treasurer: Mr Donald F. Ross MA CA
Director of Stewardship: Rev. Gordon D. Jamieson MA BD
Administrative Secretary: Mr Fred Marsh MCIBS

BOARD REMIT
1.   To promote teaching and understanding of Christian Stewardship throughout the Church. To provide programmes and training to assist congregations in visiting members, making known the work of the Church, promoting Christian giving and administering congregational finances.
2.   To be responsible for preparing and submitting to the General Assembly a Co-ordinated Budget for the following financial year and a projected Rolling Budget for the next four years.
3.   To be responsible with the Board of Ministry and Presbyteries for allocating among congregations the expenditure contained in the Co-ordinated Budget approved by the General Assembly, and for seeking to ensure that congregations meet their obligations by transmitting contributions towards their allocations regularly throughout the year.
4.   To provide financial, administrative and accounting services and standards for Boards, Committees and Statutory Corporations.

STEWARDSHIP DEPARTMENT
The Stewardship Department is responsible for the promotion of Christian Stewardship throughout the Church (part 1 of the Board Remit). This involves the production of material to assist congregations in developing an understanding of Christian Stewardship and encouraging a higher level of giving of time, talents and money from members of the Church. The staff of the Stewardship Department are regularly involved in meetings with congregations and Presbyteries.

The Stewardship Department is also responsible for processing the allocating of the Mission and Aid Fund among the self-supporting congregations of the Church.

STAFF

Director of Stewardship:	Rev. Gordon D. Jamieson MA BD
Deputy Director:	Mr W. Crawford Conochie
Stewardship Consultants:	Mrs Gillian M. Paterson
	Mr W. John Gray
	Mrs Edith Scott

GIFT AID

As a result of changes to the Gift Aid Scheme which were introduced in April 2000, the £250 minimum for Gift Aid donations has been abolished, so that the scheme now applies to all donations from taxpayers, whether large or small, regular or one-off.

The separate tax relief for payments made under Deed of Covenant has been withdrawn, and relief for such payments is now given under the Gift Aid Scheme.

Gift Aid Certificates have now been replaced by new, simpler and more flexible Gift Aid Declarations, which can be made in advance of the donation, at the time of the donation, or at any time after the donation (subject to the normal six-year limit), and can cover one or more donations.

Donors no longer must pay basic rate income tax – they simply have to pay an amount of income tax or capital gains tax, whether at the basic rate or some other rate, equal to the tax deducted from their donations.

Donors who pay tax at the higher rate will be able to claim further relief in their Self-Assessment tax return against either income tax or capital gains tax.

Companies will no longer be required to deduct tax from their donations to charities.

The new Gift Aid Scheme offers an opportunity for congregations to increase the tax recovered on both regular offerings and one-off donations from taxpayers. In order to meet Inland Revenue requirements, offerings must be received from the donor by cheque, Banker's Order, or cash through Offering Envelopes. Cash put into the Open Plate, which cannot be recorded against the name of the particular person, cannot be treated as Gift Aid donations.

Each congregation is responsible for maintaining proper records, for obtaining Gift Aid Declarations from the donors, and for making repayment claims to the Inland Revenue.

Claims should be submitted on Charity Repayment Claim Form R68 (2000), supported by Schedule R68 (New Gift Aid), to IR (Charities) Scotland, Meldrum House, 15 Drumsheugh Gardens, Edinburgh EH3 7UL (Tel: 0131-777 4040).

GIVING WITH A WILL

Making a will is a sensitive but wise decision. It is also an aspect of good stewardship. The provisions of a will can show our love and concern for our families and friends. They can also provide us with an opportunity to continue supporting the work of the Church of Scotland. The Church acknowledges with gratitude the many legacies it has received over the years and the kind and generous thoughts which have been their inspiration. Such giving is encouraged by the government: gifts of money to the Church are exempt from Inheritance Tax without limit.

The General Treasurer or the Solicitor of the Church of Scotland will always be ready to give information about the work of the Church to members (and their solicitors) interested in providing a legacy.

(12) THE CHURCH OF SCOTLAND PENSION TRUSTEES

Chairman:	Mr W.D.B. Cameron CA
Vice Chairman:	Mr W.J. McCafferty ACII ASFA CIP
Secretary:	Mrs S. Dennison BA

STAFF

Pensions Manager:	Mrs S. Dennison BA
Assistant Pensions Administrators:	Mrs M. Marshall
	Mr M. Hannam

REMIT

The body acts as Trustees for the Church of Scotland's three Pension Schemes:
1. The Church of Scotland Pension Scheme for Ministers and Overseas Missionaries
2. The Church of Scotland Pension Scheme for Staff
3. The Church of Scotland Pension Scheme for Board of National Mission staff.

The Trustees have wide-ranging duties and powers detailed in the Trust Law, Pension Acts and other regulations, but in short the Trustees are responsible for the administration of the Pension Schemes and for the investment of the Scheme Funds. Six Trustees are appointed by the General Assembly, and members nominate up to three Trustees for each Scheme.

The investment of the Funds is delegated to external Investment Managers under the guidelines and investment principles set by the Trustees: Baillie Gifford & Co., Tilney Fund Management and Scottish Value Management.

The benefits provided by the three Pension Schemes differ in detail, but all provide a pension to the Scheme member and dependants on death of the member, and a lump sum death benefit on death in service. Scheme members also have the option to improve their benefits by paying additional voluntary contributions (AVCs) to arrangements set up by the Trustees with leading Insurance Companies.

Further information on any of the Church of Scotland Pension Schemes or on individual benefits can be obtained from the Pensions Manager, Mrs S. Dennison, at the Church of Scotland Offices, 121 George Street, Edinburgh EH2 4YN (Tel: 0131-225 5722 ext. 206; Fax: 0131-240 2220; E-mail: sdennison@cofscotland.org.uk).

---

(13) THE CHURCH OF SCOTLAND GUILD

NATIONAL OFFICE-BEARERS AND EXECUTIVE STAFF

Convener:	Mrs Vivienne Macdonald BSc
Vice Convener:	Miss Moira Alexander RGN SCM RNT MBA
General Secretary:	Mrs Alison Twaddle MA JP
	(E-mail: atwaddle@cofscotland.org.uk)
Information Officer:	Mrs Fiona J. Lange MIPR
	(Tel: 0131-225 5722 ext. 317; 0131-240 2217;
	E-mail: flange@cofscotland.org.uk)

The Church of Scotland Guild is a movement within the Church of Scotland, whose aim is '**to invite and encourage all women to commit their lives to Jesus Christ and to enable them to express their faith in worship, prayer and action**'. Membership of the Guild is open to all who subscribe to that aim. In recent years, men have shown interest in attending meetings and taking a full part in the Guild's activities. The present Constitution is under review and may be amended to include men in its aim.

Groups at congregational level are free to organise themselves under the authority of the Kirk Session, as best suits their own local needs and circumstances. Large groups with frequent meetings and activities continue to operate with a committee or leadership team, while other, smaller groups simply share whatever tasks need to be done among the membership as a whole. Similarly, at Presbyterial Council level, frequency and style of meetings vary according to local needs, as do leadership patterns. Each Council may nominate one person to serve at national level, where six committees made up of these representatives take forward the work of the Guild in accordance with the stated Aim. These Committees are:

- Executive
- Finance and General Purposes
- Projects and Topics
- Programmes and Resources
- Marketing and Publicity
- Matters Relating to Younger Women

There has always been a close relationship between the Boards and Committees of the Church and the Guild, and members welcome the opportunity to contribute to the wider work of the Church through the Project Partnership Scheme.

This scheme affords groups at congregational level the opportunity to select a project, or projects, from a range of up to six, selected by the Projects and Topics Committee from submissions by a wide range of Church Departments and other Church-related bodies. A project partner in each group seeks ways of promoting the project locally, increasing awareness of the issues raised by it, and encouraging support of a financial and practical nature. She is helped in these tasks by the Project Co-ordinator at Council level and by the Information Officer based at the Guild Office.

The Guild is very aware of the importance of good communication in any large organisation, and regularly sends mailings to its groups to pass on information and resources to the members. In addition, the Newsletter, sent to members three times per session, is a useful communication tool. It is a means of sharing both local news and experiences, and of communicating something of the wider interest and influence of the Guild, which is represented on other national bodies such as the Network of Ecumenical Women in Scotland and the Women's National Commission.

Each year, the Guild follows a Theme and produces a resources pack covering worship and study material. In recent years, there has also been a Discussion Topic with supporting material and background information. The theme, topic and projects all relate to a common three-year strategy which, for 2000–3, is '**Strength for Living**'. Each of the six current projects – from National Mission, World Mission, Communication, the Lodging House Mission, the Scottish Bible Society and Mission Aviation Fellowship – reflects some aspect of strength for living. The 2002–3 theme is '**Strength through God's Empowerment**', and Guilds are invited to explore this in a variety of ways. The related discussion topic is '**Check out our Values ... Share God's World**', which addresses issues of globalisation, justice and partnership.

(14) ASSEMBLY COUNCIL

MEMBERSHIP
(12 members appointed by the Assembly)
Convener: Mrs Helen M. McLeod MA, Forfar (1999)
Vice Convener: Rev. David W. Denniston BD (2000)

[The Principal Clerk attends in an advisory capacity, but without the right to vote.]

STAFF
Research and Development Officer: Eleanor Todd BA MPhil
                                     (Tel: 0131-225 5722 ext. 311;
                                     E-mail: etodd@cofscotland.org.uk)
Administrative Secretary: Valerie Smith MA
                                     (Tel: 0131-225 5722 ext. 336;
                                     E-mail: vsmith@cofscotland.org.uk)

REMIT
The revised remit of the Assembly Council, as determined by the General Assembly of 1999, is
as follows:

'In ongoing consultation with *inter alia* Presbyteries, Boards, Committees, congregations,
other denominations and appropriate ecumenical bodies, and in collaboration with the
Co-ordinating Forum, to assess the changing needs, challenges and responsibilities of the
Church, to identify priority areas and tasks, and to make recommendations to the General
Assembly.'

(15) CHURCH AND NATION

MEMBERSHIP – CHURCH AND NATION COMMITTEE
(48 members: 32 appointed by the Assembly; 16 appointed by Presbyteries)
Convener: Rev. Alan D. McDonald LLB BD MTh (2000)
Vice Convener: Ms Morag Ross BA LLB (2001)
Secretary: Rev. David I. Sinclair BSc BD PhD DipSW
                             (E-mail: dsinclair@cofscotland.org.uk)

REMIT
The remit of the Church and Nation Committee as defined by the Assembly is:

'to watch over developments of the Nation's life in which moral and spiritual
considerations specially arise, and to consider what action the Church from time to time may
be advised to take to further the highest interests of the people'.

The committee's work is divided among five groups:
- Holyrood Group
- Westminster Group

- Europe Group
- International Group
- Social Issues Group

---

(16) PANEL ON DOCTRINE

MEMBERSHIP
(20 members: 16 appointed by the Assembly, and four from the four University Faculties/
Departments of Divinity, with the Principal Clerk, the Procurator and the Convener of the Board
of Practice and Procedure *ex officiis*)

Convener:	Rev. John McPake BA BD PhD (1999)
Vice Convener:	Rev. Norma D. Stewart MA MEd BD (2002)

STAFF
Secretary:	Rev. Douglas Galbraith MA BD BMus MPhil ARSCM
	(E-mail: dgalbraith@cofscotland.org.uk)

REMIT
The responsibilities of the Panel on Doctrine include: the fulfilling of remits from the General
Assembly on matters concerning doctrine; drawing the attention of the General Assembly to
matters inside the Church of Scotland or elsewhere which might have significant doctrinal
implications, with recommendations for action; being available for consultation by other
Committees of the General Assembly on any matter which might be of doctrinal significance;
communicating and consulting in an ecumenical context on matters involving doctrine.

---

(17) PANEL ON WORSHIP

MEMBERSHIP
(28 members: all appointed by the Assembly)

Convener:	Very Rev. Gilleasbuig Macmillan CVO MA BD Drhc DD
(1999)	
Vice Convener:	Mr Ian McCrorie BSc (2001)

STAFF
Secretary:	Rev. Douglas Galbraith MA BD BMus MPhil ARSCM
	(E-mail: dgalbraith@cofscotland.org.uk)

REMIT
The Panel on Worship exists to witness to the importance of worship as a primary function of
the Church. It has three major committees:

1. The Liturgical Committee is concerned with the provision of worship materials for public
   use and is responsible, among other things, for the production of *Common Order*.

2. The Prayer and Devotion Committee is responsible for *Pray Now* and for courses and retreats to promote spiritual growth.
3. The Music Committee encourages new developments in church music, the training of musicians and the publication of relevant materials.

The Panel is also engaged in providing materials for worship in Gaelic and is involved in the compilation of new hymn books and supplements. From time to time, it publishes occasional papers on aspects of the practice of Public Worship.

(18) COMMITTEE ON ARTISTIC MATTERS

MEMBERSHIP
(22 members (of whom no fewer than five shall have professional or practical skills and knowledge) appointed by the General Assembly, one appointed from the General Trustees and two appointed from the Committee on New Charge Development, plus up to five co-opted persons with special knowledge)
Convener: Mr Douglas Laird RIBA FRIAS (1999)
Vice Convener: Rev. Richard E. Frazer BA BD DMin (2002)

STAFF
Administrative Secretary: Rev. Douglas Galbraith MA BD BMus MPhil ARSCM
                            (E-mail: dgalbraith@cofscotland.org.uk)
Congregational Liaison: Mrs Alison Robertson MA BMus

REMIT
The Committee advises congregations and Presbyteries regarding the most appropriate way of carrying out renovations, alterations and reordering of interiors, having regard to the architectural quality of Church buildings. It also advises on the installation of stained glass, tapestries, memorials, furniture and furnishings, and keeps a list of accredited artists and craftsworkers.

Any alteration to the exterior or interior of a Church building which affects its appearance must be referred to the Committee for approval, which is given through the General Trustees. Congregations contemplating alterations are urged to consult the Committee at an early stage.

Members of the Committee are prepared, when necessary, to visit churches and meet office-bearers. The Committee's services are given free.

The Committee seeks the conservation of the nation's heritage as expressed in its Church buildings, while at the same time helping to ensure that these buildings continue to serve the worship and witness of the Church in the present day.

In recent years, the General Assembly has conferred these additional duties on the Committee:
1. preparation of reports on the architectural, historical and aesthetic merit of the buildings of congregations involved in questions of readjustment
2. verification of the propriety of repair and renovation work forming the basis of grant applications to Historic Scotland
3. the offering of advice on the maintenance and installation of organs
4. facilitating the transfer of unwanted furnishings and so on from one church to another through the quarterly *Exchange and Transfer*

5.   the compilation of a Register of Churches
6.   the processing of applications from congregations for permission to dispose of surplus communion plate.

---

(19) DEPARTMENT OF MINISTRY
Tel: 0131-225 5722;   Fax: 0131-240 2201
E-mail: ministry@cofscotland.org.uk

BOARD OF MINISTRY
MEMBERSHIP
(91 members: 28 appointed by the Assembly, the Convener and four Vice Conveners, 48 Presbytery Representatives, the Chairperson and Secretary of the Housing and Loan Fund, the Convener and Vice Convener of the Committee on Chaplains to Her Majesty's Forces, the President and Vice President of the Diaconate Council and one member each from the Faculties of Divinity in the Universities of Aberdeen, Edinburgh, Glasgow and St Andrews)

Convener:	Appointment awaited
Vice Conveners:	Rev. R. Douglas Cranston MA BD
	Rev. Alan F.M. Downie MA BD
	Rev. John W. Paterson BSc BD DipEd
	Rev. Ian Taylor BD ThM

REMIT
The Board of Ministry is responsible for all aspects of the recruitment, education, training, in-service training and support of ministers, auxiliary ministers and deacons as well as for making the financial provision for that work. To enable the Board to discharge these responsibilities and fulfil its Remit, the Board shall determine from time to time what Constituent Committees are required. The exceptions to this will be in respect of the Housing and Loan Fund for Retired Ministers and Widows and Widowers of Ministers and the Committee on Chaplains to Her Majesty's Forces, the Trustees and members respectively of which continue to be appointed as at present. They report separately to the General Assembly.

STAFF
General Secretary:	Mrs Ruth Moir BA MA(Ed)
	(Tel: ext. 308; E-mail: rmoir@cofscotland.org.uk)
Senior Pastoral Adviser and Depute General Secretary:	Rev. John P. Chalmers BD
	(Tel: ext. 309; E-mail: jchalmers@cofscotland.org.uk)
Director of Educational Services:	Rev. Nigel J. Robb FCP MA BD ThM MTh
	(Tel: ext. 347; E-mail: nrobb@cofscotland.org.uk)
Senior Vocational Guidance Officer:	Rev. Martin Scott DipMusEd RSAM BD PhD
	(Tel: ext. 389; E-mail: mscott@cofscotland.org.uk)
Accountant:	Mrs Pauline Willder MA PgDipIS
	(Tel: ext. 269; E-mail: pwillder@cofscotland.org.uk)
Finance Officer:	Miss Elizabeth Dailly
	(Tel: ext. 361; E-mail: edailly@cofscotland.org.uk)
Vocational Guidance Officer:	Mrs Elizabeth Chalmers
	(Tel: ext. 348;
	E-mail: echalmers@cofscotland.org.uk)

Education and Development Officers: Rev. Robert S.T. Allan LLB DipLP BD
(Tel: ext. 266; E-mail: rallan@cofscotland.org.uk)
Rev. Angus R. Mathieson MA BD
(Tel: ext. 315;
E-mail: amathieson@cofscotland.org.uk)
Mrs Yvonne Teague DCS
(Tel: ext. 255; E-mail: yteague@cofscotland.org.uk)
Secretary to Housing and Loan Fund: Mr Ronald C. Mather
(Tel: ext. 310; E-mail: rmather@cofscotland.org.uk)

DEPARTMENT OF MINISTRY
Further information about the Board's work and services is obtainable through the Department of Ministry at the Church Offices. Information is available on a wide range of matters including the Consolidated Stipend Fund, Stipend and Aid, Endowment Grants, Travelling and other Expenses, Pulpit Supply, Study Leave, Ministry Development conferences, pastoral care services including occupational health, Enquiry and Assessment, Education and Training and so on.

COMMITTEES
The policy development and implementation of the work of the Board of Ministry is managed under the following committees:

1.   CO-ORDINATING AND RESOURCING COMMITTEE
Convener: Appointment awaited
The Co-ordinating and Resourcing Committee is the Board's executive committee. Its function is to link the Board to the work of its Policy Committees, to ensure the integrated implementation of the Board's strategy and, further, to ensure that the Board's work is contained within agreed budgets. The Co-ordinating and Resourcing Committee also serves as the Board's 'nomination committee'.

2.   MINISTRY SUPPORT AND DEVELOPMENT POLICY COMMITTEE
Convener: Rev. R. Douglas Cranston MA BD
In the light of the *Ministers of the Gospel* report, the Ministry Support and Development Policy Committee is responsible for reviewing and developing policy on all financial, developmental and pastoral matters related to ministry. This includes such matters as Stipend Policy, manses and housing issues, listed expenses, hardship grants, travel expenses, Study Leave provision, Ministerial Review, Child Protection, Ministry Conferences, Manse Family Counselling, Occupational Health, Shetland Arrangements and so on.

The following Implementation Committees work in conjunction with the Ministry Support and Development Policy Committee:

2.1   Ministry Finance Implementation Committee
Convener: Rev. Jeffrey A. McCormick BD
The Ministry Finance Implementation Committee operates with powers to deal with anomalous Vacancy and Revision Schedules, Maintenance Allowances, Hardship Grants and Bursaries, Stipend Advances, management of investments, writing-off shortfalls and the granting of further endowments.

2.2   Ministry Development Implementation Committee
Convener: Rev. Ian Dick MA MSc BD
The Ministry Development Implementation Committee is responsible for running and evaluating the current programme of conferences, the promotion of ministry

development, processing Study Leave applications, continuing to deliver Child Protection training and developing the personal ministerial review process.

2.3   Pastoral Care Implementation Committee
Convener: Rev. Catherine E.E. Collins BA BD

The Pastoral Care Implementation Committee is responsible for the oversight of the Board's concerns in all areas of pastoral care. This includes liaison with the Medical Panel, the integration of Occupational Health with other ministerial support services, the development of the Pastoral Colleague Scheme as well as the telephone and face-to-face counselling services and oversight of the working of Act X 2000 anent the Ill-Health of Ministers.

2.4   Interim Ministry Implementation Committee
Convener: Mrs Fiona B. Cameron

The Interim Ministry Implementation Committee is responsible for maintaining current arrangements, reporting progress on current assignments and reviewing guidelines for the future deployment of interim ministries. It is responsible for the review and investigation of the future development of Interim Ministry within the Church, and, where appropriate, it works in consultation with the Board of National Mission.

3.   VOCATIONAL GUIDANCE EDUCATION AND TRAINING POLICY COMMITTEE
Convener: Rev Ian Taylor BD ThM

In the light of the *Ministers of the Gospel* report, the Vocational Guidance Education and Training Policy Committee is responsible for reviewing and developing policy on the promotion of vocations in the Church, the enquiry and assessment process, the admission and readmission of ministers and the supervision and training of students and Graduate Candidates.

The following Implementation Committees work in conjunction with the Vocational Guidance Education and Training Policy Committee:

3.1   Assessment Scheme Implementation Committee
Convener: Mr Ian Penman

The Assessment Scheme Implementation Committee is responsible for overseeing and reviewing the current enquiry and selection process for Ministers, Auxiliaries and Deacons. The Committee has powers to make final recommendations on suitability for training, hearing appeals, recruiting and training Assessors, Director training and feedback, the recruitment of post-selection counsellors, liaison with presbyteries, running the Selection Conference AGM and liaison with external advisers.

3.2   Candidate Supervision Implementation Committee
Convener: Rev Karen K. Watson BD

The Candidate Supervision Implementation Committee is responsible for the supervision of students and probationers (including deacons), the production of candidates' reports, operating with powers to sustain placements, university liaison, the recruitment and training of Supervisors, arranging placements, delivering the residential and conference programme, liaison with presbyteries, Bible exams and other Church requirements and Auxiliary Ministry training.

4.   TRUSTEES OF HOUSING AND LOAN FUND (11 members)
Chairman: Mr William McVicar RD CA
Secretary: Mr Ronald C. Mather

The Church of Scotland Housing and Loan Fund for Retired Ministers and Widows and Widowers of Ministers endeavours, wherever possible, to assist, with their retirement housing, ministers who are about to retire and surviving widows or widowers of ministers, by way of a house to rent or a house purchase loan. The main source from which the Trustees obtain funds for the purchase of houses or the granting of loans is the levy, at present 2 per cent of stipend, made on all congregations for this specific Fund.

The Trustees may grant the tenancy on advantageous terms of one of their existing houses, or, if necessary, they will purchase a house for renting. Alternatively, the Trustees may grant a house-purchase loan up to a normal maximum of £66,500 or 70 per cent of the house-purchase price, whichever is lower, at favourable rates of interest.

It would be helpful to the Trustees if ministers who wish to be considered for possible help in the future could submit their applications about ten years before their proposed date of retirement so that the Trustees have an indication of their possible future commitment and give the applicant a place on their waiting list.

The Trustees are prepared to consider assisting those who are already housed but who are seeking to move to more suitable accommodation.

Further information may be obtained from the Secretary: Mr Ronald C. Mather, 121 George Street, Edinburgh EH2 4YN (Home Tel: 0131-334 1085).

5.   CHAPLAINS TO HM FORCES (20 members)

Convener:	Professor Herbert Kerrigan QC
Vice Convener:	Rev. Bruce Neill MA BD
Secretary:	Mr Douglas M. Hunter WS
	19 Ainslie Place,
	Edinburgh EH3 6AU.

Recruitment

The Chaplains' Committee is entrusted with the task of recruitment of Chaplains for the Regular, Reserve and Auxiliary Forces. Vacancies occur periodically, and the Committee is happy to receive enquiries from all interested ministers.

Forces Registers

The Committee maintains a Register of all those who have been baptised and/or admitted to Communicant Membership by Service Chaplains.

At the present time, registers are being meticulously prepared and maintained. Parish Ministers are asked to take advantage of the facilities by applying for Certificates from the Secretary of the Committee.

Full information may be obtained from the Honorary Secretary, Mr Douglas M. Hunter WS, 19 Ainslie Place, Edinburgh EH3 6AU (Tel: 0131-226 6881).

A list of Chaplains may be found in List B in Section 6.

---

(20) NATIONAL MISSION

MEMBERSHIP –
BOARD OF NATIONAL MISSION (34 members)

Convener:	Rev. James Gibson TD LTh (2000)
Vice Conveners:	Rev. John C. Matthews MA BD (2001)
	Mrs Fiona M.H. Campbell BA (2000)

PARISH REAPPRAISAL (52 members)
Convener: Rev. Arthur Barrie LTh (1999)
Vice Convener: Rev. David W. Clark MA BD (2002)

NEW CHARGE DEVELOPMENT (23 members)
Convener: Rev. Andrew Ritchie BD DipMin (1999)
Vice Convener: Rev. John Collard MA BD (2001)

PARISH ASSISTANCE (16 members)
Convener: Rev. Stanley A. Brook BD (2000)
Vice Convener: Mrs Alison Henderson (2000)

MISSION AND EVANGELISM RESOURCES (30 members)
Convener: Rev. Colin A.M. Sinclair BA BD (1999)
Vice Conveners: Dr John Berkeley (2001)
                             Rev. Howard G. Taylor BSc BD MTh (2000)

CHAPLAINCIES (25 members)
Convener: Lady Elinor Arbuthnott (2001)
Vice Conveners:
  Church and Industry: Rev. Colin M. Anderson BA BD STM MPhil (2002)
  Hospitals, Healthcare and
    Universities: Rev. Jean W. Gallacher BD (2002)
  Prisons: Rev. William R. Taylor MA BD (1999)

IONA COMMUNITY BOARD
Convener: Rev. Tom Gordon MA BD (2000)

JOINT FAITHS ADVISORY BOARD ON CRIMINAL JUSTICE
Rev. Bruce F. Neill MA BD (2000)

SCOTTISH CHURCHES COMMUNITY TRUST
Church of Scotland representative: Rev. Ian A. Moir MA BD (2000)

STAFF
General Secretary: Rev. Douglas A.O. Nicol MA BD
Secretary Depute: Rev. Alex M. Millar MA BD MBA
Accountant: Miss Elizabeth Orr BSc CA
Property and Safety Manager: Mr Colin Wallace
Chaplaincies Administrator: Mr John K. Thomson
Parish Staffing Administrator: Rev. Frank D. Bardgett MA BD PhD
New Developments Administrator: Appointment awaited
Communications Officer: Mrs Laura Vermeulen

REMIT

1. THE BOARD OF NATIONAL MISSION

Established on 1 January 1990, the Board, with its Constituent Committees, has the responsibility for planning and co-ordinating the Church's strategy and provision for the fulfilment of its mission as the National Church.

The Board's policy is that the most effective missionary strategy for our time is 'the development of strong congregations, adequately resourced, with a missionary concern for the parishes they are called to serve – and all this work at congregational level backed by an interface with strategic areas of Scottish life'.

Subject to the General Assembly, the Board's remit is as follows:

1. **Development of Policy:**
   Aided by reflecting on the deliberations of a regular National Mission Conference, the Board will develop its policy which will be communicated to, and pursued by, the five Constituent Committees: Parish Reappraisal, New Charge Development, Parish Assistance, Mission and Evangelism Resources, and Chaplaincies.

2. **Finance:**
   The agreement of the annual budget and the monitoring of income and expenditure will be the responsibility of the Board.

3. **New Work:**
   Constituent Committees will refer to the Board new work and work which is likely to exceed the budget of the Committee. The Board will consider such referrals and grant permission if agreed.

4. **Property:**
   The Board will have responsibility for the acquisition and disposal of properties and for the proper maintenance of all its properties.

5. **Presbytery Representatives:**
   The Board will have the responsibility of resolving on which Constituent Committees Presbytery representatives would serve.

6. **General Assembly Report:**
   The Board will have the responsibility for the approval of the Report to the General Assembly on the work of the Board and the five Constituent Committees.

Reporting to the General Assembly in association with the Board of National Mission are:

The Iona Community Board
The Joint Faiths Advisory Board on Criminal Justice
The Scottish Churches Community Trust
The Committee on the Parish Development Fund.

In addition, the Board receives reports from the following groups:

1. **Glasgow Lodging House Mission:** This work is based in the Institute in East Campbell Street, Glasgow, and its object is to care for the thousands of homeless in Scotland's industrial capital. Oversight of the work is by a Management Committee appointed by the Presbytery of Glasgow (Tel: 0141-552 0285).

2. **Project Rejoice Group:** This group, which has ecumenical support, produces visual materials for use by congregations in mission related to the key Christian Festivals (E-mail: nmrejoice@uk.uumail.com).

3. **Residential Centres' Executive:** On behalf of the Board, this group manages National Mission's residential centre, the Badenoch Christian Centre. Situated at Kincraig in Strathspey, this Centre offers individuals, families and groups opportunities for enjoying retreats, short breaks and the many outdoor pursuits of the area from a base of Christian fellowship. Opened in 1976, the Centre is mainly self-catering. Full information from the Manager (Tel: 01540 651373; E-mail: badenoch@uk.uumail.com).

2.   THE COMMITTEE ON PARISH REAPPRAISAL

In accordance with the overall policy of the Board, the Committee on Parish Reappraisal

- will undertake full responsibilities and rights in connection with the implementation of Act IV (1984) and Act V (1984) and equivalent subsequent legislation directly to the General Assembly
- will be responsible for dealing with all matters coming from Presbyteries regarding planning and vacancies
- will deal with proposals for the staffing needs of parishes
- will, in consultation with the Presbyteries concerned, and following detailed discussion with the Committee on New Charge Development, determine where new charges shall be established or where, as a result of population growth in an existing charge, an alternative location for the place of worship is deemed desirable
- will be available, when requested, to assist and advise Presbyteries in regard to their own forward and readjustment planning.

The Committee also supports ministry to deaf people and has responsibility for some Community and Associate Ministers and for students employed through the Summer Appointment Scheme.

3.   THE COMMITTEE ON NEW CHARGE DEVELOPMENT

In accordance with the overall policy of the Board of National Mission, the Committee on New Charge Development, without prejudice to any other body (such as the Committee on Parish Reappraisal) which may have prior rights or jurisdiction, will be responsible for the following areas of work:

1.   Following the instructions of the Committee on Parish Reappraisal, to facilitate the creation of new charges. The Committee, in co-operation with other bodies, including Boards, Committees and Presbyteries, will enable the new charge to begin its mission in the new parish area, and will be responsible for
    (a)   the development of the Charge
    (b)   the appointment of the Minister
    (c)   the provision of a suitable building as the place of worship which may be a new church funded and erected by the Committee, or an existing location within a community which would be suitable for the purpose of worship.
2.   In the case of established charges, where significant population growth is being established by the construction of new housing, the Committee on New Charge Development will, on the instruction of the Committee on Parish Reappraisal, enter into discussion with Presbyteries and appropriate Committees to determine the needs of the area with respect to the provision of a place of witness.
3.   Facilitating and supporting the mission of new charges and those not yet in full status, in co-operation with other Committees or Boards as deemed necessary.
4.   (a)   Advising on and, within the limitations of its budget, assisting with major problems and expenditure associated with ongoing necessary maintenance of buildings, where there are building debts outstanding on the part of the congregations concerned, or where the congregation concerned is not yet in full status.
    (b)   The purchase of land and the purchase or erection, maintenance and disposal of buildings pertaining to the work of the Committee on New Charge Development are the express responsibility of the Committee.
5.   To provide arbiters to make the choice of buildings to be retained in a readjustment situation.

The Committee has a responsibility for ten new church developments and nine church extension charges, with a number of other projects at various stages of development.

4. THE COMMITTEE ON PARISH ASSISTANCE

In accordance with the overall policy of the Board and to meet the staffing needs of parishes in regard to National Mission Appointments as determined by Presbytery with the approval of the Committee on Parish Reappraisal, the Committee will
  (a) be responsible for investigating all applications for National Mission Appointments
  (b) be responsible for the Departmental matters relating to the selection, recruitment, training, personal development, employment, deployment and support of National Mission Appointments.
The Committee has responsibility for over 70 Deacons, Parish Assistants and Project Workers, and also for ministers appointed through National Mission Appointments. Posts are advertised, and people are recruited who have the relevant educational standards, expertise and skills and who are called to the work of mission and outreach. Many staff serve in the large housing areas of Scotland's towns and cities where the number of ordained ministers is low in relation to the population.
For more than 30 years, the Board has been providing financial support to **Bridgeton, St Francis-in-the-East Church House,** a centre providing club facilities for young and old who have little or no Church connection. A club leader and assistant are in charge of the work under a Committee of Management whose chair is the minister of the parish (Tel: 0141-554 8045).

5. THE COMMITTEE ON MISSION AND EVANGELISM RESOURCES

In accordance with the overall policy of the Board, the Committee on Mission and Evangelism Resources will be responsible for
* developing vision for the work of mission and evangelism in Scotland
* encouraging mission and evangelism in Presbyteries and parishes through congregations of the Church of Scotland by means of research, development and training
* ensuring that the personnel and Centres under the Committee's direction are serving the missionary and evangelistic purposes of the Church to the best advantage
* identifying, originating and supporting projects which are advancing mission and evangelism in key areas of life in Scotland.
The Committee is responsible for the work of the team of Advisers in Mission and Evangelism who encourage and resource congregations. Mission Contracts are offered to congregations by the Congregational Development Adviser and a team of Contract Enablers. In addition, the team of Advisers supports the networks of Prayer Correspondents and Secretaries, circulates the 'Praying Across Scotland' materials, and runs Schools of Mission and Evangelism. Regional offices are maintained in Glasgow, Inverness, Kirkcaldy and Kirriemuir from which the mission seminar materials, 'Towards Tomorrow', are available. Contact the Senior Adviser (Tel: 01698 428345; E-mail: nmsenioradviser@uk.uumail.com).

A full list of Advisers will be found in List J in Section 6.

The Committee is also responsible for the work of a number of component Committees, projects and centres:

1.   The Apologetics Committee engages in the work of apologetics with key areas of Scottish thought and culture, and produces resources to equip churches in the task of giving a reason for the Christian faith.

2.   The Netherbow: Scottish Storytelling Centre: The integrated facilities of the **Netherbow Theatre** and the **John Knox House Museum**, together with the **Scottish**

Storytelling Centre, are an important cultural and visitor centre on the Royal Mile in Edinburgh and provide advice and assistance nationally in the use of the arts in mission, education and worship. 'Story Source', 'Script Aid' and other resources are available. Contact the Director: The Netherbow, 43–45 High Street, Edinburgh EH1 1SR (Tel: 0131-556 9579/ 2647; Website: http://www.storytellingcentre.org.uk).

3.   The Projects in Evangelism Committee oversees the work of **Mission Projects and 'Impact' Teams**, whereby teams of volunteers are recruited and trained to assist parish-based and High School missions. Youth mission is a priority. Details can be obtained from the Missions Co-ordinator's office at 59 Elmbank Street, Glasgow G2 4PQ (Tel: 0141-352 6946). In addition, the Committee's remit is to identify, originate and support projects in mission and evangelism of a short-term, trial or temporary nature and to liaise with and advise on local or national evangelistic campaigns (Website: http://www.summermission.org.uk).

4.   The Rural Committee maintains an awareness of developments in rural Scottish life on both regional and topical bases and seeks to share good practice in mission and evangelism in rural Scotland through its publication *The Rural Spirit*, local consultations and the Church of Scotland Stand at the Royal Highland Show. Contact the National Mission Kirkcaldy office (Tel: 01592 646406; E-mail: natmisskdy@dial.pipex.com).

5.   The Society, Religion and Technology Project: This unique project, initiated in 1970, studies the impact of new technologies on society and helps the Church to form its response in ways which are practical and prophetic. The Project is a forum for all wishing to shape the Church's response to some of the most pressing issues of our time. A Newssheet, the 'SRT Bulletin', is available. Contact the SRT Director, John Knox House, 45 High Street, Edinburgh EH1 1SR (Tel: 0131-556 2953; E-mail: srtp@srtp.org.uk; Website: http://www.srtp.org.uk).

6.   The Urban Priority Areas Committee oversees the implementation of relevant strategies within Urban Priority Areas and monitors the work of the Church within these areas at both local and national levels. Consultations are held on an annual basis, and a regular publication, 'UPA News', is circulated. Contact the UPA Adviser's office, 59 Elmbank Street, Glasgow G2 4PQ (Tel: 0141-333 1948; E-mail: nmglasgow@uk.uumail.com).

7.   The Well Asian Information and Advice Centre: The Committee provides support and funding for the Presbytery of Glasgow's innovative project that serves the south side of Glasgow by assisting with welfare, housing, immigration, asylum and personal problems. The Well has a strong mission basis on the clear principles that sharing the love of Christ has to include accepting people for who they are and respecting the beliefs of others. A regular prayer letter is available. Contact the Well, 48/50 Albert Road, Glasgow G42 8DN (Tel: 0141-424 4523; Fax: 0141-422 1722; E-mail: info@the-well.clara.co.uk).

8.   Church Pastoral Aid Society: The Board has accredited the work of the Church Pastoral Aid Society, and the CPAS Scotland Consultant, Rev. Richard Higginbottom, encourages local congregations in mission and evangelism through consultancy, preaching, training and resources. Mr Higginbottom can be contacted at: 2 Highfield Place, Bankfoot, Perth PH1 4AX (Tel: 01738 787429; E-mail: rhigginbottom@cpas.org.uk).

6.   THE COMMITTEE ON CHAPLAINCIES

In accordance with the overall policy of the Board, the Committee on Chaplaincies will be responsible, through its subcommittees on Hospitals, Healthcare and Universities, Church and Industry, and Prisons, for the encouragement, development, support and, where appropriate, review of chaplaincies in Hospitals, Healthcare, Universities, Industry and Prisons.

Healthcare Chaplaincies: The Committee administers the scheme by which, under the 1947 National Health Act, ministers and others are appointed as chaplains in all hospitals in Scotland. There are currently well over 30 full-time and around 220 part-time chaplains. Appointments of chaplains are made by the General Secretary of the Board as the 'appointing authority' after consultation with, where appropriate, the Presbytery of the bounds and the relevant Hospital Authority. Presbyteries are responsible for the oversight of part-time chaplains' work. The Committee also employs some full-time and half-time chaplains' assistants.

A list of Hospital Chaplains will be found in List C in Section 6.

Church and Industry: The aim of Industrial Mission is threefold:
1.   to provide pastoral care and witness to the Gospel for men and women in all branches of industry in their place of work
2.   to assess in the interest of the Gospel the nature of the influence which industry exerts both on individuals and on society
3.   to promote the desire for just relationships and understanding at all levels of our industrial society. The work, which is fully ecumenical in character, is now involved in most key industrial sectors. There are about 80 part-time industrial chaplains and seven full-time industrial chaplains. The co-ordinator of Scottish Churches Industrial Mission is the Rev. Erik M. Cramb (Tel: 01382 458764).

A list of Industrial Chaplains will be found in List D in Section 6.

Prison Chaplaincies: The Committee takes an interest in all matters relating to Church of Scotland Chaplains appointed by the Scottish Prison Service. The 2001 General Assembly welcomed discussions between the Board and the Scottish Prison Service on the development of Prison Chaplaincy and care of prisoners, and it is likely that full-time, partnership and support Prison Chaplains will soon be employed directly by the Board.

A list of Church of Scotland Prison Chaplains will be found in List E in Section 6.

Universities: The Committee takes an interest in all matters relating to the appointment and support of Chaplains to Universities.

A list of University Chaplains will be found in List F in Section 6.

7.   BOARDS AND COMMITTEES ASSOCIATED WITH THE BOARD OF NATIONAL MISSION

(a) The Iona Community Board: The Iona Community Board is the body through which the Iona Community reports to the General Assembly. It is made up of Members of the Community and members of the Church appointed by the Assembly. It meets twice yearly, to hear reports of the Community's work both on Iona and Mull and on the mainland, and to assist and guide the Community in its task of seeking 'new ways to touch the hearts of all'.

(b) Joint Faiths Advisory Board on Criminal Justice: The General Assembly of 2000 set up this Board with representatives from the Church of Scotland, the Roman Catholic Church, the Scottish Episcopal Church, Action of Churches Together in Scotland (ACTS) and the Scottish

Interfaith Council. Its principal remit is to contribute to the development of Criminal Justice philosophy, penal reform, and to the rights of offenders, untried persons and their families, and to stimulate the interest and participation of all faiths in ministry within the Criminal Justice System.

(c) **The Scottish Churches Community Trust:** The Scottish Churches Community Trust has been fully operational since January 2001. There are currently eight member churches: Baptist Union, Church of Scotland, Congregational Federation, Roman Catholic Church, Scottish Episcopal Church, Methodist Church, Religious Society of Friends, and United Free Church. Each member church has a nominated representative on the Board of Trustees. Awards totalling £247,817.50 have been made to support projects over the period 2001–4. Support has so far gone to out-of-school care, work with ex-offenders, refugees and rehoused homeless people. Grants are also supplemented by additional training allowances which can be requested for specific purposes.

Office-bearers: Rev. Ian Moir: Chair
Miss E. McQuade: Vice Chair
Mr Gordon Armour: Treasurer
Mr John Dornan: Development Co-ordinator

Applications or offers of support should be made to: Scottish Churches Community Trust, 200 Balmore Road, Glasgow G22 6LJ (Tel/Fax: 0141-336 3766; E-mail: admin@scct.org.uk).

(d) **The Committee on the Parish Development Fund:** A Parish Development Fund was envisaged in the *Report of the Special Commission anent Review and Reform* to the 2001 General Assembly, with the purpose of providing central funding for local mission initiatives. The 2002 Assembly established the Parish Development Fund for a period of five years from 1 January 2003. It was hoped that such central funding by the Church would attract further funding from outside agencies. It was envisaged that projects would primarily be concerned with the employment of people to engage in particular aspects of mission. However, it is also envisaged that the Fund could assist in a minor way with related fabric needs of new projects. In the first instance, information about the Parish Development Fund can be obtained from the General Secretary of the Board of National Mission.

(21) SOCIAL RESPONSIBILITY
Charis House, 47 Milton Road East, Edinburgh EH15 2SR
Tel: 0131-657 2000;   Fax: 0131-657 5000
E-mail: info@charis.org.uk

BOARD OF SOCIAL RESPONSIBILITY
The Board of Social Responsibility engages in social care as part of the Christian witness of the Church to the people of Scotland. In addition, the Board offers guidance to the Church and the media about social, moral and ethical issues.

MEMBERSHIP
(96 members: 44 appointed by the Assembly plus Convener and two Vice Conveners; 47 from Presbyteries; a representative of the Church of Scotland Guild; and a representative from the Committee on Church and Nation. They attend three meetings of the Board per year, in February, June and October, and may be asked to serve on one of the five committees.)

Convener:	Rev. James M. Cowie (2001)
Vice Conveners:	Rev. David L. Court (2001)
	Rev. Gilbert C. Nisbet (2000)

COMMITTEES –
EXECUTIVE
Convener: Rev. James M. Cowie

CENTRAL SERVICES
Convener: Rev. Gilbert C. Nisbet

OPERATIONS
Convener: Rev. Graham T. Dickson

PLANNING AND DEVELOPMENT
Convener: Mr Ronald C. Lavalette

SOCIAL INTERESTS
Convener: Rev. Stephen F. Clipston

STAFF
Director of Social Work:	Mr Ian Manson
Deputy Director (Central Services):	Mr James Maguire
Deputy Director (Operations):	Mr David J. Kellock
Deputy Director (Planning and Development):	Mrs Joyce M. Buchanan

REMIT
The Board of Social Responsibility is Scotland's largest social-work agency in the voluntary sector, employing 2200 full- and part-time staff. The range and breadth of its work is ever-increasing, but the purpose of the Board of Social Responsibility could be broadly defined as follows:
1.   to offer care and help through the varied establishments and projects it operates, and to encourage and enable caring work at parish level
2.   to offer to the Church informed opinion on contemporary social, moral and ethical issues
3.   to encourage balanced judgements on these issues in the light of the Christian faith, and to put forward these judgements at all levels of influence.

DIVISIONAL STRUCTURE
Operationally, the Board's work is split into five geographical areas which cover Scotland. Each of these areas is administered by a Divisional Manager and Assistant Divisional Managers. They are physically located in their own Division, and manage and develop services at a local level. The general administration of the Board, which includes finance, publicity, training and fund-raising, is carried out by staff based at the Board's offices in Charis House, Edinburgh (Tel: 0131-657 2000).

DIVISION 1	**CITY OF GLASGOW, EAST DUNBARTONSHIRE, NORTH LANARKSHIRE**
Divisional Office:	Tom Allan Centre, 23 Elmbank Street, Glasgow G2 4PD (Tel: 0141-243 2897; Fax: 0141-229 0423; E-mail: division1.cos@uk.uumail.com)

Divisional Manager: Paul Robinson
A.D.M. (Planning and Development):   Flora Mackenzie
A.D.M. (Operations):   Marlene Smith

Services for Older People
Baxter House, 8–10 Lowther Terrace, Glasgow G12 0RN
    (Tel: 0141-334 1231; Fax: 0141-334 3965; E-mail: staff@baxter.bosr.org.uk)
Tollcross Mansionhouse, 601–641 Tollcross Road, Glasgow G32 8TF
    (Tel: 0141-778 5406; Fax: 0141-778 5406; E-mail: tollcross.cos@uk.uumail.com)

Drug Dependency
Rainbow House, 1 Belhaven Terrace, Glasgow G12 0TF
    (Tel: 0141-339 2691; Fax: 0141-337 1656; E-mail: staff@rainbow.bosr.org.uk)

Alcohol/Drug Dependency
Victoria View, 21 Westland Drive, Glasgow G14 9NY
    (Tel: 0141-959 1679; Fax: 0141-954 2572; E-mail: victoriaview.cos@uk.uumail.com)

Counselling and Support
Tom Allan Centre, Counselling Service, 23 Elmbank Street, Glasgow G2 4PD
    (Tel: 0141-221 1535; Fax: 0141-248 8452; E-mail: tomallan.cos@uk.uumail.com)

Learning Disabilities
Florentine, 33 Queen Mary Avenue, Glasgow G42 8DS
    (Tel: 0141-423 0279; Fax: 0141-423 0635; E-mail: florentine.cos@uk.uumail.com)
Saltmarket Project, Flat 1/2, 85 Saltmarket, Glasgow G1 5LE
    (Tel: 0141-552 3207; Fax: 0141-552 2407; E-mail: staff@saltmarket.bosr.org.uk)

Learning Disabilities (Children)
Cairnhill Project, 23 Cronberry Quadrant, Crookston, Glasgow G52 3NR
    (Tel: 0141-882 9808; Fax: 0141-810 2930; E-mail: cairnhill.cos@uk.uumail.com)
The Mallard, 100 Morrin Street, Springburn, Glasgow G21 1AW
    (Tel: 0141-558 7575; Fax: 0141-558 3883; E-mail: staff@mallard.bosr.org.uk)

Mental Illness
Allarton, 32 Laurel Street, Glasgow G11 7QR
    (Tel: 0141-339 1383; Fax: 0141-339 1314; E-mail: staff@allarton.bosr.org.uk)

Offenders
Dick Stewart Hostels:
40 Circus Drive, Glasgow G31 2JE
    (Tel: 0141-554 0277; Fax: 0141-554 6646; E-mail: staff@dsp.bosr.org.uk)
2 Westercraigs, Dennistoun, Glasgow G31 2HZ
    (Tel: 0141-554 0212)

Homelessness
Kirkhaven Project, 107 Summerfield Street, Dalmarnock, Glasgow G40 4QT
    (Tel: 0141-550 4889; Fax: 0141-556 2932; E-mail: kirkhaven.cos@uk.uumail.com)

Supported Accommodation
Whiteinch Project, 13 Victoria Park Drive South, Whiteinch, Glasgow G14 9RN
    (Tel: 0141-959 5069; Fax: 0141-950 1991; E-mail: whiteinch.cos@uk.uumail.com)

DIVISION 2   CENTRAL AND SOUTH-WEST SCOTLAND

Divisional Office: Adams House, 136 Auchenlodment Road, Elderslie, Johnstone,
                          Renfrewshire PA5 9NX
                          (Tel: 01505 337303; Fax: 01505 382022;
                          E-mail: division2.cos@uk.uumail.com)

Divisional Manager: Archie Henderson
A.D.M. (Planning and Development):   David Clark
A.D.M. (Operations):   George McNeilly

Epilepsy
Westhaven, 2 Upper Bourtree Drive, High Burnside, Rutherglen G73 4EH
        (Tel: 0141-634 4563; Fax: 0141-634 0599; E-mail: westhaven.cos@uk.uumail.com)

Services for Older People
Auchinlee, Campbeltown, Argyll PA28 6EN
        (Tel: 01586 552568; Fax: 01586 553241; E-mail: staff@auchinlee.bosr.org.uk)
Clyde View, 12 East Montrose Street, Helensburgh G84 7HP
        (Tel: 01436 674529; Fax: 01436 679976; E-mail: clydeview.cos@uk.uumail.com)
Cumnor Hall, 18 Racecourse View, Ayr KA7 2TY
        (Tel: 01292 266450; Fax: 01292 886740; E-mail: cumnor.cos@uk.uumail.com)
Devorgilla House, 33 George Street, Dumfries DG1 1ED
        (Tel: 01387 254007; Fax: 01387 254642; E-mail: staff@dghouse.bosr.org.uk)
Eastwoodhill, 238 Fenwick Road, Giffnock, Glasgow G46 6UU
        (Tel: 0141-638 5127; Fax: 0141-621 4371; E-mail: eastwoodhill.cos@uk.uumail.com)
Invereck, Sandbank, Dunoon, Argyll PA23 8QS
        (Tel: 01369 706231; Fax: 01369 706417; E-mail: invereck.cos@uk.uumail.com)
South Beach House, 7 South Crescent Road, Ardrossan KA22 8DU
        (Tel: 01294 468234; Fax: 01294 604223; E-mail: staff@sbh.bosr.org.uk)
Well Hall, 60 Wellhall Road, Hamilton ML3 9DL
        (Tel: 01698 286151; Fax: 01698 422838; E-mail: staff@wellhall.bosr.org.uk)

Dementia
Adams House, 136 Auchenlodment Road, Elderslie, Johnstone, Renfrewshire PA5 9NX
        (Tel: 01505 337322; Fax: 01505 337872; E-mail: staff@adams.bosr.org.uk)
Williamwood House, Strathtay Avenue, Netherlee, Glasgow G44 3YA
        (Tel: 0141-637 1168; Fax: 0141-637 6398;
        E-mail: staff@williamwood.bosr.org.uk)

Alcohol/Drug Dependency
Ronachan, Clachan, by Tarbet, Argyll PA29 6XW
        (Tel: 01880 740252; Fax: 01880 740616; E-mail: staff@ronachan.bosr.org.uk)

Learning Disabilities
Cornerstone Project, 15 Mill Road, Hamilton ML3 8AA
        (Tel: 01698 282377; Fax: 01698 283122; E-mail: cornerstone.cos@uk.uumail.com)
Kilpatrick House, 3 Bridge Street, Alexandria, Dunbartonshire G83 0TA
        (Tel: 01389 752085; Fax: 01389 751679; E-mail: staff@kilpatrick.bosr.org.uk)
Threshold, Well Hall, 60 Wellhall Road, Hamilton ML3 9DL
        (Tel: 01698 423335; Fax: 01698 423398; E-mail: threshold.cos@uk.uumail.com)

Mental Illness
Morven Day Services, Ardbeg Avenue, Kilmarnock KA3 2AR
    (Tel: 01563 572459; Fax: 01563 571086; E-mail: morven.cos@uk.uumail.com)

Residential Schools
Ballikinrain School, Balfron, Stirlingshire G63 0LL
    (Tel: 01360 440244; Fax: 01360 440946; E-mail: ballikinrain.cos@uk.uumail.com)
Geilsland School, Beith, Ayrshire KA15 1HD
    (Tel: 01505 504044; Fax: 01505 502635; E-mail: geilsland.cos@uk.uumail.com)

DIVISION 3   EDINBURGH AND SOUTH-EAST SCOTLAND

Divisional Office: Gate Lodge, 27 Milton Road East, Edinburgh EH15 2NL
                          (Tel: 0131-669 9576; Fax: 0131-669 5185;
                          E-mail: division3.cos@uk.uumail.com)

Divisional Manager: Jeannette S. Deacon
A.D.M. (Planning and Development):   Graham Lumb
A.D.M. (Operations):   Ruby Rawcliffe

Services for Older People
Morlich House, 11 Church Hill, Edinburgh EH10 4BG
    (Tel: 0131-447 3239; Fax: 0131-447 2512; E-mail: morlich.cos@uk.uumail.com)
Queen's Bay, 49 Milton Road East, Edinburgh EH15 2NN
    (Tel: 0131-669 2828; Fax: 0131-669 6407; E-mail: staff@qbl.bosr.org.uk)
The Elms, 148 Whitehouse Loan, Edinburgh EH9 2EZ
    (Tel: 0131-447 4924; Fax: 0131-447 9051; E-mail: staff@elms.bosr.org.uk)

Alcohol/Drug Dependency
Axis, St Andrew's Centre, 9 Bayswell Road, Dunbar EH42 1AB
    (Tel/Fax: 01368 865351; E-mail: staff@axis.bosr.org.uk)
Malta House, 1 Malta Terrace, Edinburgh EH4 1HR
    (Tel: 0131-332 3217; Fax: 0870 164 2571; E-mail: malta.cos@uk.uumail.com)
Rankeillor Initiative, St Ninian's Centre, 140 The Pleasance, Edinburgh EH8 9RR
    (Tel: 0131-662 0322; Fax: 0131-662 8293; E-mail: rankeillor.cos@uk.uumail.com)

Counselling and Support
Connections Counselling Service, St Andrew's Centre, 9 Bayswell Road, Dunbar EH42 1AB
    (Tel: 01368 865218; Fax: 01368 863066; E-mail: staff@ccs.bosr.org.uk)
National Counselling Service, Wallace House, 3 Boswall Road, Edinburgh EH5 3RJ
    (Tel: 0131-552 8901; Fax: 0131-552 2319; E-mail: ncs.cos@uk.uumail.com)
Number 21 Counselling Service, 21 Rutland Square, Edinburgh EH1 2BB
    (Tel: 0131-221 9377; Fax: 0131-221 9399)
Postnatal Depression Project, Wallace House, 3 Boswell Road, Edinburgh EH5 3RJ
    (Tel: 0131-538 7288; Fax: 0131-552 2319; E-mail: pnd.cos@uk.uumail.com)
Simpson House, Drugs Counselling and Related Services, 52 Queen Street, Edinburgh EH2 3NS
    (Tel: 0131-225 6028; Fax: 0131-220 0064; E-mail: simpson.house@care4free.net)

Learning Disabilities
Dunforth, 46 Park Road, Newhaven, Edinburgh EH6 4LD
    (Tel: 0131-552 3767; Fax: 0131-552 9101; E-mail: staff@dunforth.bosr.org.uk)

Eskmills Project, Clarkston Cottage, 5 South Morton Street, Edinburgh EH15 2NB
    (Tel: 0131-657 3200; Fax: 0131-657 3200; E-mail: eskmills.cos@uk.uumail.com)
Gorgie Park, 21 Gorgie Park Close, Edinburgh EH14 1NQ
    (Tel: 0131-443 6844; Fax: 0131-443 7569;
    E-mail: gorgiepark.cos@uk.uumail.com)
Wolfson House, 95 Milton Road East, Edinburgh EH15 2NL
    (Tel: 0131-669 1216; Fax: 0131-669 1323;
    E-mail: staff@wolfson.bosr.org.uk)

Mental Illness
Tynepark Resource and Day Centre, Poldrate, Haddington EH41 4DA
    (Tel: 01620 822444; Fax: 01620 822977; E-mail: staff@tynepark.bosr.org.uk)

Homelessness
Cunningham House, 205 Cowgate, Edinburgh EH1 1JH
    (Tel: 0131-225 4795; Fax: 0131-220 1354;
    E-mail: staff@cunningham.bosr.org.uk)

DIVISION 4   **FORTH VALLEY AND NORTH-EAST SCOTLAND**

Divisional Office: Kandahar House, 71 Meadowside, Dundee   DD1 1EN
                (Tel: 01382 305920; Fax: 01382 305921
                E-mail: division4.cos@uk.uumail.com)

Divisional Manager: John Wyllie
A.D.M. (Planning and Development):   Clark Bremner
A.D.M. (Operations):   Brenda Fraser

Services for Older People
Ashley Lodge, 253 Great Western Road, Aberdeen AB10 6PP
    (Tel: 01224 585558; Fax: 01224 591429;
    E-mail: staff@ashley.bosr.org.uk)
Balmedie House, Balmedie, Aberdeen AB33 8XU
    (Tel: 01358 742244; Fax: 01358 742382;
    E-mail: staff@balmedie.bosr.org.uk)
Bellfield, 1 Dee Street, Banchory AB31 5XS
    (Tel: 01330 822692; Fax: 01330 822633;
    E-mail: staff@bellfield.bosr.org.uk)
Belmont Castle, Meigle, Perthshire PH12 8TH
    (Tel: 01828 640244; Fax: 01828 640249;
    E-mail: staff@belmont.bosr.org.uk)
Chequers, 12 Atholl Road, Pitlochry PH16 5DH
    (Tel: 01796 472521; Fax: 01796 472381;
    E-mail: chequers.cos@uk.uumail.com)
Clashfarquhar, 23 Robert Street, Stonehaven AB39 2DJ
    (Tel: 01569 762438; Fax: 01569 785785;
    E-mail: staff@clashfarquhar.bosr.org.uk)
Duneaves, 7 Claypotts Road, Broughty Ferry, Dundee DD5 1BX
    (Tel: 01382 738559; Fax: 01382 775728;
    E-mail: staff@duneaves.bosr.org.uk)

Kinloch Day Care and Support Services, 10A Newburgh Road, Auchtermuchty,
Fife KY14 7BS
 (Tel: 01337 827242; Fax: 01337 828515;
 E-mail: staff@kinloch.bosr.org.uk)
Rubislaw Park, Rubislaw Park Road, Aberdeen AB1 8DA
 (Tel: 01224 310641; Fax: 01224 323882;
 E-mail: staff@rubislaw.bosr.org.uk)
Tryst Day Care Centre, Church Road, Pitlochry PH16 5EB
 (Tel: 01796 472160)

Dementia
St Margaret's, St Margaret's Crescent, Polmont, Falkirk FK2 0UP
 (Tel: 01324 716149; Fax: 01324 711841; E-mail: staff@stmargarets.bosr.org.uk)

Counselling and Support
Dundee Women and Children Project, Kandahar House, 71 Meadowside, Dundee DD1 1EN
 (Tel: 01382 201854; Fax: 01382 305921; E-mail: DWCP.cos@uk.uumail.com)

Learning Disabilities (Children)
Keith Lodge, Cameron Street, Stonehaven AB39 2HS
 (Tel: 01569 762213; Fax: 01569 764161; E-mail: staff@keith.bosr.org.uk)
Mental Illness
Gaberston House, 82 Whins Road, Alloa FK10 3SB
 (Tel: 01259 722402; Fax: 01259 725930; E-mail: gaberston.cos@uk.uumail.com)

DIVISION 5   **HIGHLANDS AND ISLANDS**

Divisional Office: Cameron House, Culduthel Road, Inverness IV2 4YG
       (Tel: 01463 236136; Fax: 01463 236247;
       E-mail: division5.cos@uk.uumail.com)

Divisional Manager: Margaret Wilkinson
A.D.M. (Planning and Development): Gerald Robson
A.D.M. (Operations):   Donald MacAskill

Services for Older People
Achvarasdal, Reay, Thurso KW14 7RR
 (Tel: 01847 811226; Fax: 01847 811570;
 E-mail: staff@achvarasdal.bosr.org.uk)
Budhmor House, Portree, Isle of Skye IV51 9DJ
 (Tel: 01478 613387; Fax: 01478 611165; E-mail: budhmor.cos@uk.uumail.com)
The Walter & Joan Gray, Main Street, Scalloway, Shetland ZE1 0XJ
 (Tel: 01595 880691; Fax: 01595 880908;
 E-mail: staff@wandjgray.bosr.org.uk)
Oversteps, Earls Cross Road, Dornoch IV25 3PJ
 (Tel: 01862 810393; Fax: 01862 811559;
 E-mail: staff@oversteps.bosr.org.uk)
Whinnieknowe, Mill Road, Nairn IV12 5EN
 (Tel: 01667 452387; Fax: 01667 451190;
 E-mail: staff@whinnieknowe.bosr.org.uk)

Dementia
Cameron House, Culduthel Road, Inverness IV2 4YG
      (Tel: 01463 243241; Fax: 01463 235808; E-mail: cameron.cos@uk.uumail.com)

Alcohol/Drug Dependency
Beechwood House, 69/71 Old Perth Road, Inverness IV1 3JH
      (Tel: 01463 711335; Fax: 01463 711544;
      E-mail: beechwood.cos@uk.uumail.com)
Lifestyle Centre, Town Hall, Francis Street, Stornoway, Isle of Lewis HS1 2XS
      (Tel: 01851 701010; Fax: 01851 704209;
      E-mail: lifestyle.cos@uk.uumail.com)
Homelessness
Beechwood House, 73/79 Old Perth Road, Inverness IV1 3JH
      (Tel: 01463 711355; Fax: 01463 711544;
      E-mail: beechwood.cos@uk.uumail.com)
Cale House, Flat 1, Millburn Road, Inverness IV1 3PX
      (Tel: 01463 718616; Fax: 01463 229533; E-mail: staff@cale.bosr.org.uk)

Supported Accommodation
Lewis Street Flat 1, 6 Lewis Street, Stornoway, Isle of Lewis HS1 7JF
      (Tel: 01851 706888; Fax: 01851 706888;
      E-mail: lewis-street.cos@uk.uumail.com)

HOME SUPPORT
The Home Support Service is available in some areas of the country. This innovative service is designed to provide whatever kind of help a person might need, from ironing to doing shopping, or even just providing companionship.

Home Support can help anyone, from babies to older people, and is available for as little as an hour, or a whole day or night. For more details about the service, telephone the Home Support Hotline FREE on 0800 389 7557. A video, *Home Support – The Gift of Care*, is available for hire.

SOCIAL INTERESTS
Social Interests Officer: Kristine Gibbs (E-mail: kristine@charis.org.uk)
The remit of the Board of Social Responsibility instructs it 'to study and present essential Christian judgements on social and moral issues arising within the area of its concern'. It does this through Study Groups, which present their findings to the Board of Social Responsibility. The Board then reports to the General Assembly. Some of the recent issues reported upon have been: Euthanasia; Human Sexuality; Human Genetics; Human Fertilisation and Embryology; Decriminalisation of Drugs; Prostitution; Human Cloning; Begging.

MEDIA AND PUBLIC RELATIONS
Communications Officer (Media): Hugh Brown (E-mail: hbrown@charis.org.uk)
The Board takes every opportunity to publicise the caring work of the Church, through *Life & Work*, newspapers, and articles in the press. The Communications Officer (Media) co-ordinates contact with the various media, and is responsible for press statements (in consultation with the Church's Media Relations Unit).

The *Circle of Care* Calendar, which is produced each year, highlights some of the Board's services, and sells 25,000 copies through the channels of the Guild and Church members; 45,000 copies of the *Circle of Care* newspaper are distributed three times a year with the latest news about the Board. Leaflets, brochures and videos are available to explain the Board's work.

Some of the Board's reports to the General Assembly (*The Future of the Family, Euthanasia, Human Genetics, Human Fertilisation and Embryology, Health and Healing*) have been published as books by Saint Andrew Press. There are 'user-friendly' packs on various topics: HIV/AIDS Resource Material, Marriage PLUS – A Study Pack for Couples, and Social Inclusion – A Study Pack for Churches.

CONGREGATIONAL LIAISON
Communications Officer (Congregations): Maggie Chalmers
(E-mail: mchalmers@charis.org.uk)
The post of Communications Officer (Congregations) links the social care managed and developed by the Board of Social Responsibility at a national level with the social work of the Church initiated at parish level. The tasks of the Communications Officer (Congregations) fall into three main categories:
1. to encourage and enable local congregations to identify and meet the needs of local people
2. to ensure and enable local congregations to have knowledge and understanding of the Board's work
3. to maintain a database of projects which can be shared with other congregations wishing support and ideas.

CONGREGATIONAL CONTACTS
Congregational Contacts are the link people between the Board and local churches. Each church should have an appointed Contact who receives mailings three times per year. There are currently over 1000 Congregational Contacts. They undertake work in a variety of ways. They provide current, correct and appropriate information to their Church. They often act as distributors for the *Circle of Care* newspaper and they act as agents for our calendar, Christmas-card and merchandise sales.

Church members are the most important part of the 'Circle of Care' provided by the Church of Scotland. It is the caring work in the communities of Scotland which is our largest area of service provision. Congregational Contacts provide the vital link between the formal services provided by the Board and the community work and prayers of the local churches, and the Board greatly appreciates all the work done by these volunteer champions.

To find out more about how Social Responsibility works with local communities, write, phone or e-mail Maggie Chalmers, Communications Officer (Congregations) with your enquiry.

FINANCIAL DEVELOPMENT
Central Fund-raiser: Maurice Houston (E-mail: mhouston@charis.org.uk)
This post exists to inform people who want to participate in the mission of Social Responsibility and to enable them to help us in our work with some of the most needy people in Scotland. We invite anyone who is interested to pray with us about the day-to-day running of Social Responsibility projects, to volunteer their time to help carry out essential tasks of all kinds and to give money to support our charitable work. If you want to know more, please get in touch with Maurice Houston on 0131-657 2000.

DEPUTATION WORK
Members of staff and of the Board will gladly visit congregations and other Church organisations to speak about the work of the Board. To request a speaker, please write to the Communications Officer (Congregations) at Charis House, 47 Milton Road East, Edinburgh EH15 2SR.

(22) WORLD MISSION
Tel: 0131-225 5722;   Fax: 0131-226 6121
Update: 0131-226 4121;   Answerphone: 0131-240 2231
E-mail: world@cofscotland.org.uk

MEMBERSHIP – BOARD OF WORLD MISSION
(27 members: 12 from Presbyteries, 12 nominated by the General Assembly, Convener and two Vice Conveners)

Convener:	Rev. Alan Greig BSc BD (2002)
Vice Conveners:	Rev. Elisabeth Cranfield MA BD (2000)
	Rev. Andrew F. Anderson MA BD (2002)

DEPARTMENTAL STAFF

General Secretary:	Rev. Prof. Kenneth R. Ross BA BD PhD
Sub-Saharan Africa:	Mr Walter T. Dunlop ARICS
Faithshare: Americas:	
Local Involvement:	Carol Finlay RGN RMN OIPCNE MSc
Finance:	Mrs Anne Macintosh BA CA
	(General Treasurer's Department)
Personnel:	Miss Sheila Ballantyne MA PgDipPM
Europe, Middle East:	Rev. Ian W. Alexander BA BD STM
Asia:	Ms Jill Hughes BA MTh

REMIT
• Give life to the Church of Scotland's understanding that it is part of the Universal Church committed to the advance of the Kingdom of God throughout the world.
• Discern priorities and form policies to guide the Church of Scotland's ongoing worldwide participation in God's transforming mission, through the gospel of Jesus Christ.
• Develop and maintain mutually enriching relationships with partner churches overseas through consultation and the two-way sharing of human and material resources.
• Equip and encourage Church of Scotland members at local, Presbytery and national levels to enjoy being involved in the life of the world church.
• Help the people of Scotland to appreciate the worldwide nature of the Christian faith.

The Board carries on its work through the following constituent committees and groups:

Europe:	Convener: Rev. Gillean Maclean
Israel Centres:	Convener: Rev. Alistair G. Bennett
Overseas Charges:	Convener: Rev. Alastair H. Gray
Local Involvement:	Convener: Rev. Neil Urquhart
Asia:	Convener: Rev. Andrew F. Anderson
Americas:	Convener: Rev. Alastair H. Gray
Faithshare:	Convener: Rev. Norman M. Hutcheson
Budget and Finance:	Convener: Rev. Gavin J. Elliott
Middle East and North Africa:	Convener: Rev. John P. Renton
Personnel:	Convener: Mr Robert Scott
Sub-Saharan Africa:	Convener: Dr Fiona Burnett

STRATEGIC COMMITMENTS: 2001–2010
- Working with partner churches on new initiatives in evangelism
- Working for justice, peace and reconciliation in situations of conflict or threat
- Resourcing the Church to set people free from the oppression of poverty
- Contributing meaningfully to the struggle against the HIV/AIDS epidemic
- Increasing the involvement of Scottish Christians in the world Church.

PARTNERSHIP PRIORITIES

Following a consultation with partner Churches held in St Andrews in September 1999, the Board has identified the following priority areas for partnership in mission:

1. **Theological Education:** developing ministerial and lay training at appropriate levels in all our churches.
2. **Evangelism:** helping one another to create new models and launch new initiatives to take the Gospel to all people.
3. **Holistic Mission:** enabling one another to respond with Christian compassion to human needs in our rapidly changing societies.
4. **Mission in Pluralistic Societies:** strengthening Christian identity in our multi-religious and multi-cultural societies by supporting one another and sharing our experiences.
5. **Prophetic Ministry:** inspiring one another to discern and speak God's Word in relation to critical issues which arise in our times.
6. **Human and Material Resources:** finding new and imaginative ways of sharing our resources at all levels of Church life.

WORLD MISSION AND WORLD RESOURCES

Sharing in the mission of God worldwide requires a continuing commitment to sharing the Church of Scotland's resources of people and money for mission in six continents as contemporary evidence that it is 'labouring for the advancement of the Kingdom of God throughout the world' (First Article Declaratory). Such resource-sharing remains an urgent matter because most of our overseas work is in the so-called 'Third World', or 'South', in nations where the effects of the widening gap between rich and poor is *the* major issue for the Church. Our partner Churches in Africa, most of Asia, in the Caribbean, South and Central America are desperately short of financial and technical resources, which we can to some extent meet with personnel and grants. However, they are more than willing to share the resources of their Christian Faith with us, including things which the Church in the West often lacks: enthusiasm in worship, hospitality and evangelism, and a readiness to suffer and struggle for righteousness, and in many areas a readiness to sink denominational differences. Mutual sharing in the World Church witnesses to its international nature, and has much to offer a divided world, not least in Scotland.

VACANCIES OVERSEAS. The Board welcomes enquiries from men and women interested in serving in the Church overseas. This is usually with indigenous denominations and related organisations with which we are in partnership overseas, in Church of Scotland congregations mostly in Europe, or our work in Israel. Those interested in more information are invited to write to the Assistant Secretary (Personnel) in the first instance.

HIV/AIDS PROJECT. The General Assembly of 2002 adopted an HIV/AIDS Project to be run by the Board of World Mission in 2002–7. The Project aims to raise awareness in congregations about the impact of HIV/AIDS and seeks to channel urgently needed support to partner churches. For further information, contact the Co-ordinator, HIV/AIDS Project, Board of World Mission, 121 George Street, Edinburgh EH2 4YN.

CHRISTIAN AID SCOTLAND. Christian Aid is an official relief development agency of churches in Britain and Ireland. Christian Aid's mandate is to challenge and enable us to fulfil our responsibilities to the poor of the world. Half a million volunteers and collectors and nearly 200 paid staff make this possible, with money given by millions of supporters. The Church of Scotland marks its commitment as a church to this vital part of its mission through an annual grant from the Mission and Aid Fund, transmitted through World Mission, which keeps in close touch with Christian Aid and its work.

Up-to-date information about projects and current emergency relief work can be obtained from the National Secretary, Rev. John Wylie, Christian Aid Scotland, 41 George IV Bridge, Edinburgh EH1 1EL (Tel: 0131-220 1254); the three area co-ordinators, Ms Eildon Dyer and Mrs Ailsa Henderson, Glasgow Office, 759a Argyle Street G3 8DS (Tel: 0141-221 7475), Miss Marjorie Clark, Perth Office, 28 Glasgow Road, Perth PH2 0NX (Tel: 01738 643982); or the Director, Dr Daleep Mukarji, Christian Aid Office, PO Box 100, London SE1 7RT (Tel: 020 7620 4444).

ACCOMMODATION IN ISRAEL. The Church of Scotland has two Christian Guest Houses in Israel which provide comfortable accommodation for pilgrims and visitors to the Holy Land. Further information is available from the St Andrew's Guest House, PO Box 8619, Jerusalem (Tel: 00 972 2 6732401; Fax: 00 972 2 6731711; E-mail: standjer@netvision.net.il), and the St Andrew's Galilee Centre, PO Box 104, Tiberias (Tel: 00 972 6 6721165; Fax: 00 972 6 6790145; E-mail: scottie@rannet.com). The St Andrew's Galilee Centre is presently closed for redevelopment and is expected to reopen in 2003.

A list of Overseas Appointments will be found in List L in Section 6.

A *World Mission Year Book* is available with more details of our partner churches and of people currently serving abroad, including those with ecumenical bodies and para-church bodies.

A list of Retired Missionaries will be found in List M in Section 6.

---

(23) ECUMENICAL RELATIONS

MEMBERSHIP –
COMMITTEE ON ECUMENICAL RELATIONS
(27 members: 12 nominated by the General Assembly, 13 appointed by the main Boards and Committees of the Church, plus five Corresponding Members – the General Secretary of ACTS, one from the Roman Catholic Church in Scotland and three on a rotating basis from the Scottish Episcopal Church, the Synod of the Methodist Church in Scotland, the Salvation Army, the Religious Society of Friends, the United Free Church of Scotland, the United Reformed Church and the Baptist Union of Scotland: Convener and Vice Convener)

Convener:	Rev. Erik M. Cramb LTh (2002)
Secretary:	Rev. Sheilagh M. Kesting BA BD

REMIT
The purpose of the Committee is to enable the Church of Scotland, at local, Presbytery and national levels, increasingly to maximise opportunities and resources for worship, witness and

service together with other churches and related organisations in this country and overseas, working wherever possible through existing Boards and Committees of the Church.
  In fulfilment of this remit, the Committee will
1. be the body within the Church of Scotland through which WCC, ACTS, CTBI and, as appropriate, the other Ecumenical Instruments in Britain and Ireland relate
2. call together for planning, briefing and the exchanging of information, the Church of Scotland's representatives on WCC, ACTS (Central Council, Commissions and Committees), CTBI (the Assembly and the Church Representatives Meetings) and the like
3. bring to the General Assembly for the approval of the General Assembly the names of those who might serve for the following year (or appropriate term) on ACTS, on CTBI and, as appropriate, on Committees, Commissions and the like of these bodies
4. following consultation with the Board of World Mission, bring to the General Assembly for the approval of the General Assembly the names of those who might serve for the following year (or appropriate term) on such bodies as the World Alliance of Reformed Churches, the Conference of European Churches and the World Council of Churches
5. bring to the General Assembly for the approval of the General Assembly the names of those who might be invited to represent the Church of Scotland at the Assemblies or Synods of other Churches in Britain and at Conferences and Gatherings organised on an ecumenical basis at which official Church of Scotland representation is appropriate
6. (a) call for and receive reports from representatives of the Church of Scotland attending the Assemblies or Synods of other Churches and those ecumenical Conferences and Gatherings which are from time to time held
    (b) ensure that appropriate parts of such reports are made available to relevant Boards and Committees
7. (a) be informed of, assist centrally where appropriate, and report to the General Assembly on the Local Ecumenical Partnerships which already exist in Scotland and which may in the future come to exist
    (b) in consultation with the Board of Practice and Procedure (where matters of Church Law and Practice are involved), advise congregations and Presbyteries seeking to establish new Ecumenical Partnerships or to amend existing projects/parishes
8. be the Committee through which reports are submitted to the General Assembly from Groups appointed to take part on behalf of the Church of Scotland in formal conversations and doctrinal dialogues with other Church and ecumenical bodies.

INTER-CHURCH ORGANISATIONS

WORLD COUNCIL OF CHURCHES
The Church of Scotland is a founder member of the World Council of Churches, formed in 1948. As its basis declares, it is 'a fellowship of Churches which confess the Lord Jesus Christ as God and Saviour according to the Scriptures, and therefore seek to fulfil their common calling to the Glory of the one God, Father, Son and Holy Spirit'. Its member Churches, which number over 300, are drawn from all continents and include all the major traditions (except the Roman Catholic) – Eastern and Oriental Orthodox, Reformed, Lutheran, Anglican, Baptist, Disciples, Methodist, Moravian, Friends, Pentecostalist and others. Its Eighth Assembly was held in Harare, Zimbabwe, from 3–14 December 1998. This Assembly marked the 50th Anniversary of the World Council with an act of recommitment by the member Churches. The theme was: 'Turn to God: Rejoice in Hope'. The Council is once again restructuring to form a more flexible working pattern among the staff.
  The General Secretary is Rev. Dr Konrad Raiser, 150 route de Ferney, 1211 Geneva 2, Switzerland (Tel: 00 41 22 791 61 11; Fax: 00 41 22 791 03 61).

WORLD ALLIANCE OF REFORMED CHURCHES

The Church of Scotland is a founder member of the World Alliance of Reformed Churches, which began in 1875 as 'The Alliance of the Reformed Churches Throughout the World Holding the Presbyterian System' and which now includes also Churches of the Congregational tradition. Today it is composed of nearly 200 Churches in nearly 100 countries, with an increasing number in Asia. It brings together, for mutual help and common action, large Churches which enjoy majority status and small minority Churches. It engages in theological dialogue with other Christian traditions – Orthodox, Roman Catholic, Lutheran, Methodist, Baptist and so on. It is organised in three main departments – Co-operation with Witness, Theology, and Partnership.

The General Secretary is Rev. Dr Setri Nyomi, 150 route de Ferney, 1211 Geneva 2, Switzerland (Tel: 00 41 22 791 62 38; Fax: 00 41 22 791 65 05).

CONFERENCE OF EUROPEAN CHURCHES

The Church of Scotland is a founder member of the Conference of European Churches, formed in 1959 and until recently the only body which involved in common membership representatives of every European country (except Albania) from the Atlantic to the Urals. More than 100 Churches, Orthodox and Protestant, are members. Although the Roman Catholic Church is not a member, there is very close co-operation with the Council of European Catholic Bishops' Conferences. With the removal of the long-standing political barriers in Europe, the Conference has now opportunities and responsibilities to assist the Church throughout the continent to offer united witness and service.

Its General Secretary is Rev. Dr Keith Clements, 150 route de Ferney, 1211 Geneva 2, Switzerland (Tel: 00 41 22 791 61 11; Fax: 00 41 22 791 03 61).

CEC: CHURCH AND SOCIETY COMMISSION

The Church of Scotland is a founder member of the European Ecumenical Commission for Church and Society (EECCS). The Commission owes its origins to the Christian concern and vision of a group of ministers and European civil servants about the future of Europe. It was established in 1973 by Churches recognising the importance of this venture. Membership included Churches and ecumenical bodies from the European Union. The process of integration with CEC was completed in 2000, and the name, Church and Society Commission (CSC), established. In Brussels, CSC monitors Community activity, maintains contact with MEPs and promotes dialogue between the Churches and the institutions. It plays an educational role and encourages the Churches' social and ethical responsibility in European affairs. It has a General Secretary, a study secretary and an executive secretary in Brussels and a small office in Strasbourg and Geneva.

The Director is Mr Keith Jenkins, Ecumenical Centre, 174 rue Joseph II, B-1000 Brussels, Belgium (Tel: 00 32 2 230 17 32; Fax: 00 32 2 231 14 13).

CHURCHES TOGETHER IN BRITAIN AND IRELAND (CTBI)
and ACTION OF CHURCHES TOGETHER IN SCOTLAND (ACTS)

In September 1990, Churches throughout Britain and Ireland solemnly committed themselves to one another, promising to one another to do everything possible together. To provide frameworks for this commitment to joint action, the Churches established CTBI for the United Kingdom and Ireland, and for Scotland, ACTS, with sister organisations for Wales and for England.

CTBI has a large Assembly meeting every second year, a Church Representatives Meeting held two or three times a year, and a Steering Committee meeting five times a year. It has commissions on Mission, Racial Justice and Interfaith Relations. It is staffed by a General Secretary and Co-ordinating Secretaries for Church Life, Church and Society, and International Affairs.

The General Secretary of CTBI is Dr David R. Goodbourn, Inter-Church House, 35–41 Lower Marsh, London SE1 7SA (Tel: 020 7523 2121; Fax: 020 7928 0010).

ACTS is in the middle of a review process. The Central Council is to be replaced by a Scottish Churches Forum which will be responsible for the overall agenda of ACTS. Commissions and Committees are to be replaced by Networks – Worshipping Together, Studying Together, Witnessing Together and Serving Together. It has its administrative base at Scottish Churches House, Dunblane.

At local level, there are corresponding Churches Together groups and a continuation of the face-to-face inter-church groups which came into being or were strengthened in the 1980s.

These structures will depend on more regular consultation and more intensive co-operation among those who frame the policies and deploy the resources of the Churches in Scotland and throughout Britain and Ireland; at the same time, they afford greater opportunity for a wide range of members of different Churches to meet in common prayer and study.

The General Secretary of ACTS is Rev. Dr Kevin Franz, Scottish Churches House, Dunblane   FK15 0AJ (Tel: 01786 823588; Fax: 01786 825844; E-mail: acts.ecum@dial.pipex.com).

The Scottish Churches Parliamentary Office: The Scottish Churches Parliamentary Office supports the churches in their relationships with the Scottish Parliament and Executive, providing briefings and updates on Parliamentary activity and advice on contacting MSPs and so on. The Parliamentary Officer is Rev. Dr Graham K. Blount, and the Office is at 14 Johnston Terrace, Edinburgh   EH1 2PW (Tel: 0131-622 2278; Fax: 0131-622 7226; E-mail: gkblount@dial.pipex.com; Website: www.actsparl.org).

---

(24) PARISH EDUCATION
21 Young Street, Edinburgh EH2 4HU
Tel: 08702 415748;   Fax: 0131-260 3120
E-mail: enquiries@parished.org.uk

MEMBERSHIP: BOARD OF PARISH EDUCATION
(Convener, Vice-Convener, 50 members appointed by the General Assembly, one representative from the Church of Scotland Guild)

Convener:	Rev. John C. Christie, Glasgow (2001)
Vice-Convener:	Mrs Lorna Paterson, West Lothian (2000)
Director and General Secretary:	Mr Iain W. Whyte BA DCE DMS
Depute Director:	Mr Steven Mallon MA MSc

STAFF

Child Protection Trainer:	Mr Drew McCannie
Children's and Youth Development Worker:	Mr Iain Campbell
Publications Manager:	Ms Gillian Cloke
National Adviser in Adult Education:	Mr Stewart Cutler
Regional Development Worker (Tayforth):	Rev. Jane Denniston
Regional Development Worker (Highlands):	Ms Shuna Dicks
Glasgow Presbytery Youth Adviser:	Mr Alan Howard
Regional Development Worker (South-west):	Mr Calum Sabey

National Adviser in Children's Ministry:	Mr Doug Swanney
Secretary for the Readership:	Mrs Mary Stobo
National Advisor in Elder Training:	Mrs Sheilah Steven
National Adviser in Child Protection:	Mr Doug Allan
Information, Marketing and PR Officer:	Ms Janet de Vigne
Cowal Education Field Officer:	Mrs Jen Zielinski

SCOC

Principal, SCOC:	Rev. Jayne Scott
Librarian:	Mr Michael Buck
Counselling Course Leader:	Vacant
Associate Counselling Course Leader:	Ms Morag Highet
Learn to Live Programme Director:	Rev. Eric Stoddart
Learn to Live Programme:	Rev. Ian Walker
Learn to Live Programme:	Ms Mairi Munro
Cert. HE Course, SCOC:	Louise Duncan

REMIT

Based at 21 Young Street, Edinburgh, the Board of Parish Education's remit is to oversee the development of an education and leadership training service for the Church of Scotland. A considerable part of the Board's provision is delivered through the Scottish Churches Open College (SCOC), for members of all denominations. The Board's provision covers a wide spectrum of courses and events catering for all ages and abilities, resource material and publications (through Scottish Christian Press – formerly Parish Education Publications). This involves training and resources for children's workers, youth workers, elders and the Readership, and reaches through to degree-level and higher degree-level courses.

COMMITTEES

The Board itself meets twice annually, in February and June, with its committees meeting four or five times annually. The committees are organised to reflect the Board's commitment to learning for all, and to developing the concept of the Faith Community.

ADULT MINISTRIES AND EDUCATION

The remit of the Adult Ministries Section is to support and develop the vast range of adult learning that takes place in the Church. The development of a vibrant and growing congregation rests in two areas – worship and education. For many folk in the Church, Education has historically been a difficulty, but many congregations have at least some form of adult education programme – including discussion groups, Bible study, prayer groups and Lent groups – which they are keen to expand. The Adult Education Advisor's role is to assist in this development and to help congregations examine new areas of development. In particular, we are piloting a congregational renewal programme based on the *Church Without Walls* report, study material and an evaluation package to help congregations identify where they can develop and how they can go about taking the necessary steps to achieve their goals.

CHILDREN'S AND YOUTH MINISTRY

Children's and Youth Ministry is based around the principles of education, empowerment and creating best practice for the whole Church. The Board is involved in training children's and youth leaders through a number of courses, as well as working with children and young people themselves. The Year of the Child project, which was launched in December 2001 and runs throughout 2002, has been a landmark in the experience of children in the Church.

Through this project, children's forums have been able to contribute their opinions on the life of the Church. This work is supported locally by a number of Children's Ministry Advisers who deliver training through the National Training Course in Children's Ministry. Support is also offered to churches through a number of training packs for children's workers.

The Board is also responsible for both the National Youth Assembly and the Youth Representatives to the General Assembly. The Youth Assembly is an annual event attracting young adults from all over the UK, centring around debate, fellowship, worship and community.

As well as events at home, the Board organises and participates in ecumenical events and trips abroad; it also resources youth groups by providing training for youth leaders and supplying educational material. The Board is a major contributor to the Crossover Festival, a weekend event of worship, speakers, debates, fun and reflection.

CHILD PROTECTION

It has long been the vision of the Board that integrating the principles of protection and safety with the nurture and education of our young people is essential in the Church. The Child Protection Section puts this ideal into practice, regularly organising training throughout the country for children's and youth workers, ensuring the highest standards and best practice. This section also has responsibility for implementing the Church's policy on Child Protection through the network of Child Protection Co-ordinators. It has produced a handbook on good practice within this area which will be regularly updated, and a policy statement for the protection of children within the Church. In addition, the General Assembly of 2002 gave this section responsibility for administering the criminal records checks required by legislation.

ELDERSHIP

Being an elder is a demanding but rewarding role, and is an important part of the Church of Scotland in its team ministry. The Eldership Working Party supports this crucial leadership role within the Church, working with a network of Elder Trainers; at present there are 39 in 26 Presbyteries, with four more in training. Elder Trainers are regularly impressed by the commitment of time and talent to the Church shown by the elders with whom they come in contact, and the Team supports this by holding regular conferences and training days for elders and session clerks, and providing a variety of study material on eldership, including books and videos. Interest in eldership is increasing, especially in the comparatively new fields of leading worship and youth eldership; and enquiries are always welcome.

READERSHIP

The Board of Parish Education and SCOC support the Readership Committee in providing training opportunities and services to maintain this important component of the Church's team ministry. Readers are members of the Kirk set apart by their Presbyteries for 'duties principally concerned with the Ministry of the Word and the conduct of public worship'. Recently, their role has developed: while still associated primarily with worship and preaching, there are new opportunities for the fully trained Reader. Further information for those interested in Readership is available on request from the Board.

REGIONAL SERVICES

The Board has made a conscious decision to use more of its resources locally rather than having everything happen from the central offices. To date, we have appointed three Regional Development Workers – for the South-west region based in Dumfries, for the Tayforth region based in Perth and for the Highland region based in Inverness. Each member of the Regional Services staff is committed to providing quality educational resources and experiences for local churches.

SCOTTISH CHRISTIAN PRESS

The Scottish Christian Press (formerly Parish Education Publications, or PEP) is the publishing and information wing of the Board of Parish Education, publicising the work of the Board and publishing a wide variety of resources produced from within the Church. The unit produces an annual catalogue listing SCP's own publications in the field of Christian education, developed from ongoing work in the field by the Board's own staff. It also offers resources available from other bodies within the Church and some of the best available material from other denominations, as well as co-publishing ventures and material from educational publishers worldwide. SCP also produces a regular online newsletter, *Online Parish Education News* (OPEN), with a circulation of around 7,000; for information, or to receive this, contact SCP through the Edinburgh office or the general enquiry line.

SCOC

The Scottish Churches Open College is an ecumenical initiative of the churches in Scotland. It offers a wide range of dispersed learning courses under the motto 'Live to learn – learn to live'. Modular courses on offer range from diploma to certificate and BA degrees, in subjects as diverse as counselling and community care. These are validated by Napier University (for further information, e-mail education@scoc.ac.uk).

---

(25) EDUCATION COMMITTEE

MEMBERSHIP:

(20 members together with Convener and Vice Convener)
Convener: Rev. John J. Laidlaw MA (1999)
Vice Convener: Mr David Alexander (2002)

STAFF

Secretary: Ms Susan Leslie

REMIT

The Education Committee is the oldest continuing Committee of the General Assembly (formed in 1825) and has a long and historic connection with Scottish Education. The key aspects of the Committee's remit are:

1. to represent the Church on matters of state education at every level
2. to support the Church Representatives whom it appoints on behalf of the General Assembly to deal with education on each of Scotland's 32 Local Authorities
3. to co-operate with Presbyteries and Local Authorities in undertaking the support and training of chaplains in schools and in Further Education Colleges
4. to promote good learning and teaching in the curriculum and ensure the place of Religious and Moral Education
5. to commission and produce resources to ensure that Scottish Christianity and the life and work of the Church of Scotland can be properly represented in the curriculum
6. to co-operate with other Churches and faith groups working to enhance Scottish Education.

The Committee responds to consultation documents from the Scottish Executive and seeks to develop and maintain links with Education Ministers, with Members of the Scottish Parliament and with the relevant Committees.

It participates in the work of the Scottish Joint Committee on Religious and Moral Education and is represented on the Religious Education Movement (Scotland) and the Association for the Teaching of Religious Education in Scotland (ATRES).

It has established useful and practical links with the Roman Catholic Church through its Education Commission, and it has a good record of liaison with the Educational Institute of Scotland and other unions in the educational field. It nominates one person to represent the Church on the General Teaching Council.

(26) COMMUNICATION

MEMBERSHIP
BOARD OF COMMUNICATION
(18 members, appointed by the Assembly)

Convener:	Rev. Jean B. Montgomerie (1999)
Vice Convener:	Rev. Iain F. Paton (2002)
Secretary:	Mr Brian McGlynn

STAFF

Secretary and Director:	Mr Brian McGlynn
Management Accountant:	Mr Steve Murray
Media Relations Unit:	Mrs Pat Holdgate, Head of Media Relations
Design Services:	Mr Peter J.F. Forrest, Head of Design Services
Life & Work:	Ms Lynne Robertson, Editor
Saint Andrew Press:	Mrs Ann Crawford, Head of Publishing
Pathway Productions:	Mr Laurence P. Wareing, Director
Ministers' Forum:	Rev. John A. Ferguson, Editor
Year Book:	Rev. Ronald S. Blakey, Editor

REMIT
Under a revised constitution approved by the General Assembly in 1995, the Board is responsible for providing the Church with professional communication services as well as promoting effective communication within the Church and to the outside world. The Board's services are as follows:

DIRECTOR
Mr Brian McGlynn   direct line 0131-240 2236
                          (E-mail: brianmcglynn@dial.pipex.com)

Marketing and Publicity Officer
Alison Fleming   0131-225 5722 ext. 239
                          (E-mail: afleming@cofscotland.org.uk)

1.   MEDIA RELATIONS UNIT

Head of Media Relations:	Pat Holdgate	0131-240 2243
Senior Media Relations Officer:	Brian McGuire	0131-240 2204
Internet/Media Relations Officer:	Post vacant	0131-240 2202
Website Editor:	Post vacant	0131-225 5722 ext. 244

(E-mail: cofsmedia@dial.pipex.com)

The Media Relations Unit is the link between the media and the Church, and is the first point of contact for journalists seeking information on the work and views of the Church's Boards and Committees. The Unit issues regular press releases on matters of interest and provides an audio release service to independent local radio. The Unit develops and maintains the Church's website (www.churchofscotland.org.uk). Unit staff maintain close links with a large network of media contacts and are happy to facilitate interviews with key personnel within the Church. The Unit also supports parish ministers and Church members by promoting local news and events on their behalf and offering advice on local media work.

2.   DESIGN SERVICES
(Tel: 0131-225 5722/0131-240 2224; Fax: 0131-220 5407; E-mail: cofs.design@dial.pipex.com) This part of the Board's work is concerned with the design and production of a wide range of promotional literature, display materials and exhibitions. Members of staff are pleased to advise congregations and Presbyteries on their particular communications needs.

A mailing list is maintained to provide parish magazine editors with suitable material and resources for their publications. Anyone wishing to be added to this list should provide their name and address to the Department.

3.   PATHWAY PRODUCTIONS – the Church's audio-visual production unit
(Tel: 0131-225 5722; Fax: 0131-240 2236; E-mail: pathway@cofscotland.org.uk) From its premises at 123 George Street, Edinburgh EH2 4YN, the Unit produces and markets videos, tape-slide sets and audio cassettes. One of the Unit's key initiatives is developing webcasting as a new means of communication. Short training courses in television, radio and video are also held here. The Unit has pioneered Church production and use of video as a means of Christian communication. It also produces occasional programmes for broadcast television. In conjunction with the Media Relations Unit, Pathway supports religious output on Independent Local Radio.

Videos and audio cassettes may be hired or bought from Wesley Owen Bookshops in Scotland or bought through Pathway's distributor, Saint Andrew Press.

4.   LIFE & WORK
(Tel: 0131-225 5722; Fax: 0131-240 2207; E-mail: lifework@dial.pipex.com) *Life & Work* is the Church of Scotland's monthly magazine. Its purpose is to keep the Church informed about events in church life at home and abroad and to provide a forum for Christian opinion and debate on a variety of topics. It has an independent editorial policy. Contributions which are relevant to any aspect of the Christian faith are welcome.

The price of *Life & Work* this year is £1.00. With a circulation of around 47,000, it also offers advertisers a first-class opportunity to reach a discerning readership in all parts of Scotland.

5.   SAINT ANDREW PRESS
(Tel: 0131-240 2253; Fax: 0131-220 3113; E-mail rallen@cofscotland.org.uk) Saint Andrew Press is the Church of Scotland's publishing house. Since its creation in 1954, it has published many titles that have made a major contribution to Christian literature. The much-loved series of New Testament commentaries by the late Professor William Barclay is world-renowned. The series is currently being sensitively updated for a 21st-century readership and is published as the *New Daily Study Bible* series in 17 volumes. Other best-sellers include the *Glasgow Gospel* by Jamie Stuart, and now *Outside Verdict* by Harry Reid, a headline-grabbing, Scottish top-10 book that probes the very heart of the Church of Scotland and makes a series of radical, inspiring proposals. Saint Andrew Press has also published on behalf of the Church of Scotland Panel on Worship the critically acclaimed *Common Order* and the ecumenical songbook *Common Ground*.

Saint Andrew Press also acts as distributor for Wild Goose Publications, Pathway Productions and Church of Scotland stationery.

All proposals for new publications should be sent to the Head of Publishing in the form of a two-page description of the book and its readership together with one sample chapter. Saint Andrew Press staff are always willing to offer professional help and advice.

LOCAL BROADCASTING

The Board of Communication encourages the work of a number of ecumenical groups assisting local radio stations with their religious broadcasting. Enquiries about local religious broadcasting should be made to the Media Relations Unit (see above).

CHURCHES ADVISORY COUNCIL FOR LOCAL BROADCASTING (CACLB)

CACLB was formed in 1967 to provide an advisory body to the Churches and to the broadcasters. Membership of the Council is drawn from members of ACTS, the Roman Catholic Church and the Evangelical Alliance, with representatives of the BBC and ILR, together with three members co-opted from the Association of Christians in Broadcasting (see below).

Present Officers
President: Baroness Nicholson of Winterbourne MEP
Chairman: Rt Rev. Dr Tom Butler
Director: Peter Blackman, PO Box 6613, South Woodham Ferrers,
                    Essex CM3 5DY
                    (Tel: 01245 322158; Fax: 01245 321957;
                    E-mail: office@caclb.org.uk; Website: www.caclb.org.uk)

ASSOCIATION OF CHRISTIANS IN BROADCASTING (ACB)

ACB was formed at a CACLB Conference in 1980 to meet the evident need for an association to provide 'mutual support, help and comfort' for Christians involved in local radio, in whatever role. Membership is also open to those who, though not directly involved in local radio, appreciate its importance and wish to keep in touch with its problems and development.

For further information about membership, contact Peter Blackman, PO Box 6613, South Woodham Ferrers, Essex CM3 5DY (Tel: 01245 322158; Fax: 01245 321957; E-mail: office@caclb.org.uk; Website: www.caclb.org.uk).

---

(27) CHURCH OF SCOTLAND TRUST

MEMBERSHIP

(Members are appointed by the General Assembly, on the Nomination of the Trust)
Chairman: Mr J.M. Hodge WS
Vice Chairman: Mr C.N. Mackay WS
Treasurer: Mr D.F. Ross MA CA
Secretary and Clerk: Mrs J.M. Hamilton BA

REMIT

The Church of Scotland Trust was established by Act of Parliament in 1932. The Trust's function since 1 January 1995 has been to hold properties outwith Scotland and to act as Trustee in a number of third-party trusts.

Further information can be obtained from the Secretary and Clerk of the Church of Scotland Trust, 121 George Street, Edinburgh EH2 4YN (Tel: 0131-240 2222; E-mail: jhamilton@ cofscotland.org.uk).

SECTION 2

General Information

(1) OTHER CHURCHES IN THE UNITED KINGDOM

ASSOCIATED PRESBYTERIAN CHURCHES
Clerk of Presbytery: Rev. Dr M. McInnes, PO Box 2, Gairloch IV21 2YA (Tel: 01463 223983).

THE REFORMED PRESBYTERIAN CHURCH OF SCOTLAND
Stated Clerk: Rev. G.M. Milligan, RP Manse, 1 Albert Terrace, London Road, Stranraer DG9 8AB.

THE FREE CHURCH OF SCOTLAND
Principal Clerk: Rev. James MacIver, The Mound, Edinburgh EH1 2LS (Tel: 0131-226 4978/5286;
   E-mail: freechurch@compuserve.com).

THE FREE PRESBYTERIAN CHURCH OF SCOTLAND
Rev. John Macleod, 16 Matheson Road, Stornoway HS1 2LA (Tel: 01851 702755).

THE UNITED FREE CHURCH OF SCOTLAND
General Secretary: Rev. John Fulton BSc BD, United Free Church Offices, 11 Newton Place,
   Glasgow G3 7PR (Tel: 0141-332 3435; E-mail: ufcos@charis.co.uk).

THE PRESBYTERIAN CHURCH IN IRELAND
Clerk of the General Assembly and General Secretary: Very Rev. Dr Samuel Hutchinson BA
   BD MTH DD, Church House, Fisherwick Place, Belfast BT1 6DW (Tel: 02890 322284;
   E-mail: clerk@presbyterianireland.org).

THE PRESBYTERIAN CHURCHES OF WALES
General Secretary: Rev. Gareth Edwards BA BD, 53 Richmond Road, Cardiff CF24 3WJ (Tel:
   02920 494913; Fax: 02920 464293; E-mail: ebcpcw@aol.com).

THE UNITED REFORMED CHURCH
General Secretary: Rev. David Cormick, 86 Tavistock Place, London WC1H 9RT (Tel: 020
   7916 2020; Fax: 020 7916 2021).

UNITED REFORMED CHURCH SCOTLAND SYNOD
Synod Clerk: Rev. Kenneth M. Forbes BA BD, Church House, PO Box 189, Glasgow G1
   2BX (Tel: 0141-332 7667; E-mail: scotland@urc.org.uk).

BAPTIST UNION OF SCOTLAND
General Secretary: Rev. William G. Slack, 14 Aytoun Road, Glasgow G41 5RT (Tel: 0141-423
   6169; E-mail: admin@scottishbaptist.org.uk).

CONGREGATIONAL FEDERATION IN SCOTLAND
Area Secretary: Mr John B. Fulton, 21 Victoria Road, Burnside, Rutherglen, Glasgow G73
   3QF (Tel: 0141-647 5296).

RELIGIOUS SOCIETY OF FRIENDS (QUAKERS)
Clerk to the General Meeting of Scotland: Margaret Peacock, 16 Drumlin Drive, Milngavie,
   Glasgow G62 6LN (Tel: 0141-956 1183; E-mail: nmjpeacock@yahoo.co.uk).

ROMAN CATHOLIC CHURCH
The Rt Rev. Mgr Henry Docherty, General Secretariat, Bishops' Conference for Scotland, 64
   Aitken Street, Airdrie ML6 6LT (Tel: 01236 764061; Fax: 01236 762489; E-mail:
   gensec@bpsconfscot.com).

THE SALVATION ARMY
Scotland Secretary: Colonel John Flett, Scotland Secretariat, 30 Rutland Square, Edinburgh
EH1 2BW (Tel: 0131-221 9699; E-mail: scotland@salvationarmy.org.uk).

SCOTTISH EPISCOPAL CHURCH
General Secretary: Mr John F. Stuart, 21 Grosvenor Crescent, Edinburgh EH12 5EL (Tel: 0131-
225 6357; E-mail: secgen@scotland.anglican.org).

THE SYNOD OF METHODIST CHURCH IN SCOTLAND
Secretary: Rev. David Cooper, Methodist Central Hall, West Tollcross, Edinburgh EH3 9BP (Tel:
0131-221 9029; E-mail: edinmethodistmission@talk21.com).

GENERAL SYNOD OF THE CHURCH OF ENGLAND
Secretary General: Church House, Great Smith Street, London SW1P 3NZ
(Tel: 020 7898 1000).

---

(2) OVERSEAS CHURCHES

PRESBYTERIAN CHURCH IN AMERICA
Stated Clerk: 1700 North Brown Road, Suite 105, Lawrenceville, GA 30043, USA (E-mail:
ac@pcanet.org; Website: http://www. pcanet.org).

PRESBYTERIAN CHURCH IN CANADA
Clerk of Assembly: 50 Wynford Drive, North York, Ontario M3C 1J7, Canada (E-mail:
pccadmin@presbycan.ca; Website: http://www.presbycan.ca).

UNITED CHURCH OF CANADA
General Secretary: Suite 300, 3250 Bloor Street West, Toronto, Ontario M8X 2Y4, Canada
(Website: http://www.united-church.ca).

PRESBYTERIAN CHURCH (USA)
Stated Clerk: 100 Witherspoon Street, Louisville, KY 40202-1396, USA (E-mail:
presbytel@pcusa.org; Website: http://www.pcusa.org).

REFORMED PRESBYTERIAN CHURCH IN NORTH AMERICA
Stated Clerk: 7408 Penn Avenue, Pittsburgh, PA15208, USA
(Website: http://www.reformedpresbyterian.org).

CUMBERLAND PRESBYTERIAN CHURCH
General Secretary: 1978 Union Avenue, Memphis, TN 38104, USA (E-mail: gac@
cumberland.org; Website: http://www.cumberland.org).

REFORMED CHURCH IN AMERICA
General Secretary: 475 Riverside Drive, NY 10115, USA (E-mail: rcamail@rca.org).

UNITED CHURCH OF CHRIST
General Minister: 700 Prospect Avenue, Cleveland, Ohio 44115, USA
Website: (http://www.ucc.org).

UNITING CHURCH IN AUSTRALIA
General Secretary: PO Box A2266, Sydney South, New South Wales 1235, Australia (E-mail:
enquiries@nat.uca.org.au).

PRESBYTERIAN CHURCH OF AUSTRALIA
Clerk of Assembly: 168 Chalmers Street, Surry Hills, NSW 2010, Australia (E-mail: general@ pcnsw.org.au).

PRESBYTERIAN CHURCH OF AOTEAROA, NEW ZEALAND
Executive Secretary: PO Box 9049, 100 Tory Street, Wellington, New Zealand (E-mail: aes@pccnz.org.nz; Website: http://www.presbyterian.org.nz).

EVANGELICAL PRESBYTERIAN CHURCH, GHANA
Synod Clerk: PO Box 18, Ho, Volta Region, Ghana.

PRESBYTERIAN CHURCH OF GHANA
Synod Clerk: PO Box 1800, Accra, Ghana.

PRESBYTERIAN CHURCH OF EAST AFRICA
Secretary General: PO Box 48268, Nairobi, Kenya.

CHURCH OF CENTRAL AFRICA PRESBYTERIAN
Senior Clerk, General Synod, PO Box 30398, Lilongwe, Malawi.
General Secretary, Blantyre Synod, PO Box 413, Blantyre, Malawi.
General Secretary, Livingstonia Synod, PO Box 112, Mzuzu, Malawi.
General Secretary, Nkhoma Synod, PO Box 45, Nkhoma, Malawi.

IGREJA EVANGELICA DE CRISTO EM MOÇAMBIQUE (EVANGELICAL CHURCH OF CHRIST IN MOZAMBIQUE)
(Nampula) General Secretary: Cx. Postale 284, Nampula 70100, Mozambique.
(Zambezia) General Secretary: Cx. Postale 280, Zambezia, Quelimane, Mozambique.

PRESBYTERIAN CHURCH OF NIGERIA
Principal Clerk: PO Box 2635, Aba, Abia State, Nigeria.

UNITING PRESBYTERIAN CHURCH IN SOUTHERN AFRICA (SOUTH AFRICA)
General Secretary: PO Box 96188, Brixton 2019, South Africa.

UNITING PRESBYTERIAN CHURCH IN SOUTHERN AFRICA (ZIMBABWE)
Synod Clerk: PO Box 389, Masvingo, Zimbabwe.

PRESBYTERIAN CHURCH OF SUDAN (A)
General Secretary: PO Box 66168, Nairobi, Kenya.

PRESBYTERIAN CHURCH OF SUDAN (M)
General Secretary: PO Box 3421, Khartoum, Sudan.

UNITED CHURCH OF ZAMBIA
General Secretary: PO Box 20122, 15101 Ridgeway, Lusaka, Zambia.

CHURCH OF BANGLADESH
Moderator: Synod Office, 54 Johnson Road, Dhaka 1100, Bangladesh.

CHURCH OF NORTH INDIA
General Secretary: Synod Office, 16 Pandit Pant Marg, New Delhi, 110 001, India.

CHURCH OF SOUTH INDIA
General Secretary: Synod Office, 5 White's Road, Royapettah, Chennai 600 114, India.

PRESBYTERIAN CHURCH OF KOREA
General Secretary: CPO Box 1125, Seoul 110 611, Korea.

PRESBYTERIAN CHURCH IN THE REPUBLIC OF KOREA
General Secretary: 1501 The Korean Ecumenical Building, 136–156 Yunchi-Dong, Chongno-Ku, Seoul, Korea.

THE UNITED MISSION TO NEPAL
Executive Director: PO Box 126, Kathmandu, Nepal.

CHURCH OF PAKISTAN
General Secretary: Mission Compound, Daska, Distr Sialkot, Punjab, Pakistan.

PRESBYTERY OF LANKA
Moderator: 127/1 D S Senanayake Veedyan, Kandy, Sri Lanka.

PRESBYTERIAN CHURCH IN TAIWAN
General Secretary: 3 Lane 269 Roosevelt Road, Sec. 3, Taipei, Taiwan 10763, ROC.

CHURCH OF CHRIST IN THAILAND
General Secretary: 109 CCT (13th Floor), Surawong Road, Khet Bangrak, Bangkok 10500, Thailand.

PRESBYTERY OF GUYANA
Moderator: 81 Croal Street, PO Box 10151, Georgetown, Guyana.

NATIONAL PRESBYTERIAN CHURCH OF GUATEMALA
Executive Secretary: Av. Simeon Canas 7–13, Zona 2, Aptdo 655, Guatemala City, Guatemala (E-mail: ienpg@terra.com.gt).

UNITED CHURCH IN JAMAICA AND THE CAYMAN ISLANDS
General Secretary: 12 Carlton Crescent, PO Box 359, Kingston 10, Jamaica (E-mail: unitedchurch@colis.com).

PRESBYTERIAN CHURCH IN TRINIDAD AND TOBAGO
General Secretary: Box 92, Paradise Hill, San Fernando, Trinidad (E-mail: pctt@tstt.net.tt).

BELGIAN PROTESTANT CHURCH
Rue de Champ de Mars 5, B-1050 Bruxelles, Belgium.

REFORMED CHRISTIAN CHURCH IN CROATIA
Bishop's Office: Vladimira Nazora 31, HR-32100 Vinkovci, Croatia.

EVANGELICAL CHURCH OF THE CZECH BRETHREN
Moderator: Jungmannova 9, PO Box 466, CZ-11121 Praha 1, Czech Republic (E-mail: srcce@srcce.cz; Website: http://www.srcce.cz).

EGLISE REFORMEE DE FRANCE
General Secretary: 47 rue de Clichy, F-75311 Paris, France (E-mail: coordinations@unacerf.org; Website: http://www.eglise-reformee-fr.org).

HUNGARIAN REFORMED CHURCH
General Secretary: H-1440 Budapest, PO 5, Hungary (E-mail: zsinatko@matavnet.hu; Website: http://www.reformatus.hu).

WALDENSIAN CHURCH
Moderator: Via Firenze 38, 00184, Rome, Italy (E-mail: tvmode@tin.it; Website: http://www.chiesavaldese.org).

NETHERLANDS REFORMED CHURCH
Landelijk Dienstcentrum Samen op Weg-Kerken, Postbus 8504, NL-3503 RM Utrecht (Website: http://www.ngk.nl).

REFORMED CHURCH IN ROMANIA
Bishop's Office: Str IC Bratianu No. 51, R-3400, Cluj-Napoca, Romania (E-mail: office@reformatus.ro).

REFORMED CHRISTIAN CHURCH IN YUGOSLAVIA
Bishop's Office: YU-24323 Feketic, Bratstva 26, Yugoslavia.

SYNOD OF THE NILE OF THE EVANGELICAL CHURCH
General Secretary: Synod of the Nile of the Evangelical Church, PO Box 1248, Cairo, Egypt (E-mail: pcegypt@link.net).

DIOCESE OF THE EPISCOPAL CHURCH IN JERUSALEM AND THE MIDDLE EAST
Bishop's Office: PO Box 19122, Jerusalem 91191, via Israel (E-mail: ediosces@netvision.net.il; Website: http://www.jerusalem.anglican.org).

NATIONAL EVANGELICAL SYNOD OF SYRIA AND LEBANON
General Secretary: PO Box 70890, Antelias, Lebanon (E-mail: nessl@minero.net).

[Full information on Churches overseas may be obtained from the Board of World Mission.]

---

(3) SCOTTISH DIVINITY FACULTIES
[*denotes a Minister of the Church of Scotland]
[(R) Reader   (SL) Senior Lecturer   (L) Lecturer]

ABERDEEN
(University Faculty of Arts and Divinity and Christ's College)
King's College, Old Aberdeen AB24 3UB
(Tel: 01224 272380;   Fax: 01224 273750;
E-mail: divinity@abdn.ac.uk)

Master of Christ's College: Rev. Prof. I.R. Torrance* TD MA BD DPhil
Head of School
   of Divinity and
   Religious Studies: S. Kunin BA PhD

Professors: Rev. I.R. Torrance* TD MA BD DPhil
   (Patristics and Christian Ethics)
   F.B. Watson BA DPhil (New Testament)

Lecturers:
K.T. Aitken BD PhD (Hebrew)
A.D. Clarke BA MA PhD (SL) (New Testament)
Rev. J.W. Drane MA PhD (SL) (Practical Theology)
S. Gathercole BA MA PhD (New Testament)
S. Kunin BA PhD (SL) (Anthropology of Religion)
Ian A. McFarland BA MDiv ThM MPhil PhD (Systematic Theology)
M.A. Mills MA PhD (Anthropology of Religion)
F.A. Murphy BA MA PhD (R) (Systematic Theology)
Rev. J. Swinton* BD PhD RNM (SL) (Practical Theology)
N.J. Thompson BA MA MTh PhD (Church History)
Rev. Karla Wubbenhorst BA MDiv (Doctrine and Ethics)

ST ANDREWS
(University College of St Mary)
St Mary's College, St Andrews, Fife KY16 9JU
(Tel: 01334 462850/1;   Fax: 01334 462852)

Head of School and Principal: T.A. Hart BA PhD
Dean of Faculty: Appointment awaited

Chairs: R.J. Bauckham BA MA PhD FBA (New Testament Studies)
P.F. Esler BA LLB LLM DPhil (Biblical Criticism)
M.D. Hampson* BA DPhil ThM ThD MA (Divinity)
T.A. Hart BA PhD (Divinity)
B. Lang DipTheol Dr Theol Dr Theol Habil (Old Testament)
R.A. Piper BA BD PhD (Christian Origins)
C.R. Seitz AB MTS MA MPhil PhD
  (Old Testament and Theological Studies)
A.J. Torrance* MA BD DrTheol (Systematic Theology)

Readerships, Senior Lectureships, Lectureships:

M.I. Aguilar BA MA STB PhD (SL) (Religion and Contextual Theology)
J.S. Begbie BA BD PhD LRAM ARCM (Institute of Theology, Imagination and the Arts)
I.C. Bradley* BA MA BD DPhil (SL) (Practical Theology)
J.R. Davila BA MA PhD (Early Jewish Studies)
B.W. Longenecker BA MRel PhD (New Testament)
E.D. Reed BA PhD (Theology and Ethics)

Teaching Fellows and Research Fellows

M. Bredin Mtheol PhD (TF) (New Testament and Hebrew)
S.R. Guthrie BMus BD PhD (RF) (Institute of Theology, Imagination and the Arts)
L.J. Lawrence BA MA (TF) (New Testament)
N. MacDonald MA MPhil (TF) (Old Testament and Hebrew)

EDINBURGH
(Faculty of Divinity and New College)
New College, Mound Place, Edinburgh EH1 2LX
(Tel: 0131-650 8900; Fax: 0131-650 6579; E-mail: divinity.faculty@ed.ac.uk)

Dean of Faculty: Prof. Stewart J. Brown BA MA PhD FRHistS
Vice Dean and
   Head of Department: Prof. Larry W. Hurtado BA MA PhD
Principal of New College: Rev. A. Graeme Auld* MA BD PhD DLitt FSAScot

Chairs: Rev. A. Graeme Auld* MA BD PhD DLitt FSAScot
                                       (Hebrew Bible)
                                    Stewart J. Brown BA MA PhD FRHistS
                                       (Ecclesiastical History)
                                    Rev. David A.S. Fergusson* MA BD DPhil (Divinity)
                                    Larry W. Hurtado BA MA PhD
                                       (New Testament Language, Literature and Theology)
                                    David Kerr MA BA DPhil
                                       (Christianity in the Non-Western World)
                                    Rev. William F. Storrar* MA BD PhD
                                       (Christian Ethics and Practical Theology)
                                    David F. Wright MA FRHistS DD
                                       (Patristics and Reformed Christianity)
                                    Nicolas Wyatt BA BD MTh PhD
                                       (Ancient Near Eastern Religions)

Readers, Senior Lecturers and Lecturers:
Hebrew and Old Testament: A. Peter Hayman BA PhD (SL)
                                Timothy Lim BA MPhil DPhil (R)
                                David J. Reimer BTh BA MA MA (L)

New Testament Language, Literature and Theology:
                                Helen K. Bond MTheol PhD (L)
                                David L. Mealand MA MLitt PhD (SL)

Christian Ethics and Practical Theology:
                                Marcella Althaus Reid BTh PhD (SL)
                                Jolyon Mitchell BA MA (SL)
                                Michael S. Northcott MA PhD (R)
                                Murray Chalmers* MA (Part-time) (L)
                                Ewan Kelly* MB ChB BD (Part-time) (L)

Ecclesiastical History: Jane E.A. Dawson BA PhD DipEd (SL)
                                Jack Thompson BA PhD (SL)
                                Susan Hardman Moore MA PhD (L)

Systematic Theology: Nicholas S. Adams BA PhD (L)
                                John C. McDowell BD PhD (L)
                                Michael Purcell MA PhD PhL PhB (L)

Religious Studies: James L. Cox BA MDiv PhD (R)
                            Jeanne Openshaw BA MA PhD (L)

World Christianity: Elizabeth Kopping MA PhD DipSocSci MTh

Fulton Lecturer in Speech and Communication:
                            Richard Ellis BSc MEd LGSM

GLASGOW
(Faculty of Divinity and Trinity College)
4 The Square, University of Glasgow, Glasgow G12 8QQ
(Tel: 0141-330 6526; Fax: 0141-330 4943; E-mail: m.macmillan@arts.gla.ac.uk)

Dean of Faculty: Rev. Professor David Jasper MA PhD BD
Principal of Trinity College: Rev. Prof. George M. Newlands* MA BD PhD

Chairs: John M.G. Barclay MA PhD (New Testament and Christian Origins)
                 Joseph Houston MA BD DPhil (Philosophical Theology)
                 Rev. David Jasper MA PhD BD (Literature and Theology)
                 Rev. Donald Macleod MA (Visiting Hon. Professor)
                 Rev. George M. Newlands* MA BD PhD (Divinity)
                 Rev. John K. Riches MA (Divinity and Biblical Criticism)
                 Perry Schmidt-Leukel Dipl theol MA Dr theol Dr theol habil (Munich)
                     (Systematic Theology and Religious Studies)
Reader: W. Ian P. Hazlett BA BD Drtheol (Ecclesiastical History)

Senior Lecturers and Lecturers: Theology and Religious Studies:
                 Julie P. Clague BSc PGCE PGDip MTh (L)
                 Rev. Alastair G. Hunter* MSc BD PhD (SL)
                 Rev. Jeffrey F. Keuss BA MDiv (L)
                 Lesley Orr Macdonald MA BD PhD (L)
                 Sarah Nicholson MTheol PhD (L)
                 Lloyd V.J. Ridgeon BA MA PhD (L)
                 Yvonne M. Sherwood BA PhD DipJS (SL)
                 Mona Siddiqui MA MLL PhD (L)
                 Kyoshi Tsuchiya MA PhD (L)
                 Heather E. Walton BA MA(Econ) PhD (L)

Centre for Study of Literature, Theology and the Arts:
Director: Rev. Professor George M. Newlands* MA BD PhD
Assistant Director: Kyoshi Tsuchiya MA PhD

(4) SOCIETIES AND ASSOCIATIONS

The undernoted list shows the name of the Association, along with the name and address of the Secretary.

INTER-CHURCH ASSOCIATIONS

THE FELLOWSHIP OF ST ANDREW: Mr Peter Desmond, 4 Ballengeich Road, Stirling FK8 1TN (Tel: 01786 479875).

THE FELLOWSHIP OF ST THOMAS: An ecumenical association formed to promote informed interest in and learn from the experience of Churches in South Asia (India, Pakistan, Bangladesh, Nepal, Sri Lanka). Secretary: Rev. Margaret S. MacGregor MA BD DipEd, 16 Learmonth Court, Edinburgh EH4 1PB (Tel: 0131-332 1089).

THE SCOTTISH ORDER OF CHRISTIAN UNITY: Secretary: Rev. William D. Brown MA, 121 Dalkeith Road, Edinburgh EH16 5AJ (Tel/Fax: 0131-667 1124; E-mail: wdbrown@conventus.co.uk).

CHURCH PASTORAL AID SOCIETY (CPAS): Consultant for Scotland: Rev. Richard W. Higginbottom, 2 Highfield Place, Bankfoot, Perth PH1 4AX (Tel: 01738 787429). A home mission agency working cross-denominationally through consultancy training and resources to encourage churches in local evangelism: accredited officially to the Board of National Mission.

FRONTIER YOUTH TRUST: Encourages and resources those engaged in youth work, particularly with disadvantaged young people. Co-ordinator: Feri Salvesen, c/o Anderson/ Kelvingrove Church, 759b Argyle Street, Glasgow G3 8DS (Tel: 0141-204 4800).

IONA COMMUNITY: Leader: Rev. Kathy Galloway, Fourth Floor, Savoy House, 140 Sauchiehall Street, Glasgow G2 3DH (Tel: 0141-332 6343; Fax: 0141-332 1090); Warden: Ms Jan Sutch Pickard, Iona Abbey, Isle of Iona, Argyll PA76 6SN (Tel: 01681 700404; E-mail: ionacomm@gla.iona.org.uk; Website: http://www.iona.org.uk).

SCOTTISH CHRISTIAN YOUTH ASSEMBLY: Chairperson: Mr Eric Whitten, 41 Kingston Avenue, Glasgow G14 0EB.

SCOTTISH CHURCHES HOUSING AGENCY: Provides the Churches with information, education, advice and support concerning homelessness. Co-ordinator: Alastair Cameron, 28 Albany Street, Edinburgh EH1 3QH (Tel: 0131-477 4500; Fax: 0131-477 2710; E-mail: scotchho@ednet.co.uk; Website: www.scotchho.org.uk).

SCOTTISH CHURCHES WORLD EXCHANGE: Arranges overseas placements for 40–50 volunteers annually. Placements are for periods of up to two years, mainly in Africa, Asia, Latin America and the Middle East. Chief Executive: Rev. Robert S. Anderson, St Colm's International House, 23 Inverleith Terrace, Edinburgh EH3 5NS (Tel: 0131-315 4444; Website: www.worldexchange.org.uk).

ST COLM'S INTERNATIONAL HOUSE: English-language and Capacity Building Courses for community leaders from the developing world. A place to meet in the heart of the Capital on the perimeter of the Royal Botanic Gardens (Tel: 0131-315 4444).

SCOTTISH JOINT COMMITTEE ON RELIGIOUS AND MORAL EDUCATION: Ms Susan Leslie and Mr Lachlan Bradley, 6 Clairmont Gardens, Glasgow G3 7LW (Tel: 0141-353 3595).

SCOTTISH NATIONAL COUNCIL OF YMCAs: National General Secretary: Mr Peter Crory, 11 Rutland Street, Edinburgh EH1 2AE (Tel: 0131-228 1464).

SCOTTISH SUNDAY SCHOOL UNION FOR CHRISTIAN EDUCATION: Offers financial assistance by way of grant or loan to help fund training and provide resources in the promotion of Christian Education for children in Scotland. General Secretary: Mrs Lynne Collingham, 2 Fraser Avenue, Newton Mearns, Glasgow G77 6HW (Tel: 0141-571 7359).

INTERSERVE SCOTLAND: Interserve is an evangelical and interdenominational mission agency with roots stretching back 150 years to India. Currently, the International Fellowship of Interserve is active in 26 countries in the Middle East and Asia, where nearly 600 missionary partners serve, 30 of whom are from Scotland. Director: Mr John M. Jackson, 12 Elm Avenue, Lenzie, Glasgow G66 4HJ (Tel: 0141-578 0207; Fax: 0141-578 0208; E-mail: info@isscot.prestel.co.uk; Website: www.interserve.org).

SCRIPTURE UNION SCOTLAND: 9 Canal Street, Glasgow G4 0AB (Tel: 0141-332 1162; Fax: 0141-352 7600; E-mail: postmaster@scriptureunionscotland.org.uk; Website: http://www.suscotland.org.uk).

STUDENT CHRISTIAN MOVEMENT: Mr Nick Davies, 1 Bristo Square, Edinburgh EH8 9AL (Tel: 0131-667 4321).

UNIVERSITIES AND COLLEGES CHRISTIAN FELLOWSHIP: Alan Hewerdine, 38 De Montfort Street, Leicester LE1 7GP (Tel: 0116-255 1700; E-mail: agh@uccf.org.uk).

WORLD DAY OF PRAYER: SCOTTISH COMMITTEE: Convener: Col. Ruth Flett; Secretary: Mrs Margaret Broster, St Columba's Manse, Dipple Road, Kilbirnie, Ayrshire KA25 7JU (Tel: 01505 682098; Fax 01505 684024; E-mail: sec@wdpscotland.org.uk; Website: http://www.wdpscotland.org.uk).

CHURCH OF SCOTLAND SOCIETIES

ASSOCIATION OF GENERAL ASSEMBLY AND PRESBYTERY CLERKS: Rev. R.A. Baigrie MA, 32 Inchcolm Terrace, South Queensferry EH30 9NA (Tel: 0131-331 4311).

AROS (Association of Returned Staff of the Church of Scotland Board of World Mission): Secretary: Miss Mary S. Ritchie, 1 Afton Bridgend, New Cumnock KA18 4AX (Tel: 01290 338218).

SCOTTISH CHURCH SOCIETY: Secretary: Rev. Matthew Z. Ross LLB BD FSAScot, The Manse, Ceres, Cupar, Fife KY15 5NQ (Tel: 01334 828233).

SCOTTISH CHURCH THEOLOGY SOCIETY: Rev. William D. Brown MA, 121 Dalkeith Road, Edinburgh EH16 5AJ (Tel: 0131-667 1124).

SOCIETY OF FRIENDS OF ST ANDREW'S JERUSALEM: Hon. Secretary: Major D.J. McMicking LVO, Board of World Mission, 121 George Street, Edinburgh EH2 4YN. Hon. Treasurer Mr Donald Ross, General Treasurer, The Church of Scotland, 121 George Street, Edinburgh EH2 4YN (Tel: 0131-225 5722).

THE CHURCH OF SCOTLAND CHAPLAINS' ASSOCIATION: Hon. Secretary: Rev. Donald M. Stephen TD MA BD ThM, 10 Hawkhead Crescent, Edinburgh EH16 6LR (Tel: 0131-658 1216).

THE CHURCH OF SCOTLAND RETIRED MINISTERS' ASSOCIATION: Hon. Secretary: Rev. Elspeth G. Dougall MA BD, 60B Craigmillar Park, Edinburgh EH16 SPU (Tel: 0131-668 1342).

THE CHURCH SERVICE SOCIETY: Secretary: Rev. Rachel J.W. Dobie, The Manse, Broughton, Biggar ML12 6HQ (Tel: 01899 830331; E-mail: revracheldobie@aol.com).

THE IRISH MINISTERS' FRATERNAL: Secretary: Rev. Colin R. Williamson LLB BD, Manse of Aberdalgie, Perth PH2 0QD (Tel: 01738 625854).

THE NATIONAL CHURCH ASSOCIATION: Membership Secretary: Miss Margaret P. Milne, 10 Balfron Crescent, Hamilton ML3 9UH.

BIBLE SOCIETIES

THE SCOTTISH BIBLE SOCIETY: Executive Director: Rev. M. Douglas Campbell BA MDiv, 7 Hampton Terrace, Edinburgh EH12 5XU (Tel: 0131-337 9701).

WEST OF SCOTLAND BIBLE SOCIETY: Rev. Alexander Macdonald MA BD, Manse of Neilston, Glasgow G78 3NP (Tel: 0141-881 1958).

GENERAL

THE BOYS' BRIGADE: Scottish Headquarters, Carronvale House, Carronvale Road, Larbert FK5 3LH (Tel: 01324 562008; Fax: 01324 552323; E-mail: carronvale@boys-brigade.org.uk).

THE GIRLS' BRIGADE: Scottish Headquarters, Paxton House, 11 Woodside Crescent, Charing Cross, Glasgow G3 7UL (Tel: 0141-332 1765).

THE GUIDE ASSOCIATION SCOTLAND: 16 Coates Crescent, Edinburgh EH3 7AH (Tel: 0131-226 4511; Fax: 0131-220 4828; E-mail: administrator@scottishguides.org.uk).

THE SCOUT ASSOCIATION: Scottish Headquarters, Fordell Firs, Hillend, Dunfermline KY11 7HQ (Tel: 01383 419073; E-mail: shq@scouts-scotland.org.uk).

BOYS' AND GIRLS' CLUBS OF SCOTLAND: 88 Giles Street, Edinburgh EH6 6BZ (Tel: 0131-555 1729; E-mail: bgcs@freezone.co.uk).

YOUTH SCOTLAND: Balfour House, 19 Bonnington Grove, Edinburgh EH6 4BL (Tel: 0131-554 2561; fax: 0131-454 3438; E-mail: office@youthscotland.org.uk).

CHRISTIAN AID SCOTLAND: National Secretary: Rev. John Wylie, 41 George IV Bridge, Edinburgh EH1 1EL (Tel: 0131-220 1254; Fax: 0131-225 8861).

FEED THE MINDS: Scottish Secretary, Mr Stanley Bonthron, 41 George IV Bridge, Edinburgh EH1 1EL (Tel: 0131-226 5254; Fax: 0131-225 8861; E-mail: ftm@churchuk.net).

LADIES' GAELIC SCHOOLS AND HIGHLAND BURSARY ASSOCIATION: Mr Donald J. Macdonald, 9 Hatton Place, Edinburgh EH9 1UD (Tel: 0131-667 1740).

COUPLE COUNSELLING SCOTLAND: Director: Mrs Frances Love, 40 North Castle Street, Edinburgh EH2 3BN (E-mail: enquiries@couplecounselling.org.uk; Website: couplecounselling.org).

RUTHERFORD HOUSE: Warden: Rev. David C. Searle MA, 17 Claremont Park, Edinburgh EH6 7PJ (Tel: 0131-554 1206; Fax: 0131-555 1002).

SCOTTISH CHURCH HISTORY SOCIETY: Rev. Peter H. Donald MA PhD BD, 39 Southside Road, Inverness IV2 4XA (Tel: 01463 231140; Fax: 01463 230537).

SCOTTISH EVANGELICAL THEOLOGY SOCIETY: Secretary: Rev. Canon Peter Cook, Bel Abri, Leadgate, Alston, Cumbria CA9 3EL (Tel: 01434 381873).

CHRISTIAN ENDEAVOUR IN SCOTLAND: Winning, Teaching and Training Youngsters for Christ and the Church: The Murray Library, 8 Shore Street, Anstruther, Fife KY10 3EA (Tel: 01333 310345).

TEARFUND: 100 Church Road, Teddington TW11 8QE (Tel: 020 8977 9144). Manager: Peter Chirnside, Tearfund Scotland, Challenge House, Canal Street, Glasgow G4 0AD (Tel: 0141-332 3621).

THE AFRICA EVANGELICAL FELLOWSHIP: Mr David Brown, 287 Crofthill Road, Croftfoot, Glasgow G44 5NL (Tel: 0141-634 5540; E-mail: simscot@compuserve.com).

THE LEPROSY MISSION: 89 Barnton Street, Stirling FK8 1HJ (Tel: 01786 449266; Fax 01786 449766). Executive Director: Miss Linda Todd. Scottish Meetings Co-ordinator: Rev. J.G. McConnell, 7 Henderson Court, East Calder EH53 0RQ (Tel: 01506 881125).

THE LORD'S DAY OBSERVANCE SOCIETY: Rev. A. Hanna, 2 The Gallolee, Edinburgh EH13 9QJ (Tel: 0131-441 3116).

THE MONTHLY VISITOR TRACT SOCIETY: 122 Thirlestane Road, Edinburgh EH9 1AN.

THE SCOTTISH REFORMATION SOCIETY: The Society, The Magdalene Chapel, 41 Cowgate, Edinburgh EH1 1JR (Tel: 0131-220 1450).

THE SOCIETY IN SCOTLAND FOR PROPAGATING CHRISTIAN KNOWLEDGE: David McLetchie Esq., Tods Murray WS, 66 Queen Street, Edinburgh EH2 4NE (Tel: 0131-226 4771).

THE WALDENSIAN MISSIONS AID SOCIETY FOR WORK IN ITALY: David A. Lamb SSC, 36 Liberton Drive, Edinburgh EH16 6NN (Tel: 0131-664 3059; E-mail: dlamb@dial.pipex.com.uk).

YWCA SCOTLAND: Chief Executive: Elaine Samson, 7B Randolph Crescent, Edinburgh EH3 7TH (Tel: 0131-225 7592; Website: info@ywcascotland.org).

(5) TRUSTS AND FUNDS

THE SOCIETY FOR THE BENEFIT OF THE SONS AND DAUGHTERS OF THE CLERGY OF THE CHURCH OF SCOTLAND

Chairman:	Dr Douglas Grant
Secretary and Treasurer:	R. Graeme Thom FCA
	17 Melville Street
	Edinburgh EH3 7PH (Tel: 0131-473 3500)

Annual grants are made to assist in the education of the children (normally between the ages of 12 and 25 years) of ministers of the Church of Scotland. The Society also gives grants to aged and infirm daughters of ministers and ministers' unmarried daughters and sisters who are in need. Applications are to be lodged by 31 May in each year.

THE GLASGOW SOCIETY OF THE SONS AND DAUGHTERS OF MINISTERS OF THE CHURCH OF SCOTLAND

President:	Rev. John P. Cubie
Secretary and Treasurer:	R. Graeme Thom FCA
	17 Melville Street
	Edinburgh EH3 7PH (Tel: 0131-473 3500)

The Society's primary purpose is to grant financial assistance to children (no matter what age) of deceased ministers of the Church of Scotland. Applications are to be submitted by 1 February in each year. To the extent that funds are available, grants are also given for the children of ministers or retired ministers, although such grants are normally restricted to students. These latter grants are considered in conjunction with the Edinburgh-based Society. Limited funds are also available for individual application for special needs or projects. Applications are to be submitted by 31 May in each year. Emergency applications can be dealt with at any time when need arises. Application forms may be obtained from the Secretary.

HOLIDAYS FOR MINISTERS

The undernoted hotels provide special terms for ministers and their families. Fuller information may be obtained from the establishments:

CRIEFF HYDRO HOTEL and MURRAYPARK HOTEL: The William Meikle Trust Fund and Paton Fund make provision whereby active ministers and their spouses, members of the Diaconate and other full-time Church workers may enjoy the accommodation and leisure facilities. Facilities available are Leisure Centre, Lagoon, Cinema and many others both indoor and out. Self-catering Chalets are also available. Enquiries to the Accommodation Sales Team, Crieff Hydro Hotel, Crieff PH7 3LQ (Tel: 01764 651670; E-mail enquiries@crieffhydro.com).

THE CINTRA BEQUEST: The Trust provides financial assistance towards the cost of accommodation in Scotland for missionaries on leave, or for ministers on temporary holiday, or on rest. Applications should be made to Mrs J.S. Wilson, Solicitor, 121 George Street, Edinburgh EH2 4YN.

THE LYALL BEQUEST: For the benefit of Ministers of the Church of Scotland, the Bequest makes available the following benefits:
1. A payment towards the cost of holiday accommodation at any hotel or boarding house in St Andrews will be paid to any minister and to his wife at the rate of £10 per day each for a minimum stay of three days and a maximum stay of one week. Due to the number of

applications which the Trustees now receive, an applicant will not be considered to be eligible if he or she has received a grant from the Bequest during the three years prior to the holiday for which application is made. Applications, prior to the holiday, should be made to the Secretaries.

2. Grants towards costs of sickness and convalescence so far as not covered by the National Health Service or otherwise may be available to applicants, who should apply to the Secretaries giving relevant details.

All communications should be addressed to Messrs Pagan Osborne, Solicitors, Secretaries to the Lyall Bequest, 106 South Street, St Andrews KY16 9QD (Tel: 01334 475001).

MARGARET AND JOHN ROSS TRAVELLING FUND: Offers grants to ministers and their spouses for travelling and other expenses for trips to the Holy Land where the purpose is recuperation or relaxation. Applications should be made to the Secretary and Clerk, Church of Scotland Trust, 121 George Street, Edinburgh EH2 4YN (Tel: 0131-240 2222; E-mail: jhamilton@cofscotland.org.uk).

The undernoted represents a list of the more important trusts available for ministers, students and congregations. A brief indication is given of the trust purposes, but application should be made in each case to the person named for full particulars and forms of application.

THE ABERNETHY TRUST: Offers residential accommodation and outdoor activities for Youth Fellowships, Church family weekends, Bible Classes and so on at four outdoor centres in Scotland. Further details from the Executive Director, Abernethy Trust, Nethybridge PH25 3ED (Tel/Fax: 01479 821279).

THE ARROL TRUST: The object of the Trust is 'to promote the benefit and advance the education of young people between the ages of 16 and 25 years of age who are physically or mentally disadvantaged or are in necessitous circumstances by assisting such persons to gain experience through education and training for their future careers through travel within or without the United Kingdom'. Further details and forms of application can be obtained from C.S. Kennedy WS, Lindsays WS, 11 Atholl Crescent, Edinburgh EH3 8HE (Tel: 0131-229 1212).

THE BAIRD TRUST: Assists in the building and repair of churches and halls, endows Parishes and generally assists the work of the Church of Scotland. Apply to Ronald D. Oakes CA ACMA, 182 Bath Street, Glasgow G2 4HG (Tel: 0141-332 0476; Fax: 0141-331 0874).

THE REV. ALEXANDER BARCLAY BEQUEST: Assists mother, daughter, sister or niece of deceased minister of the Church of Scotland who at the time of his death was acting as his housekeeper and who is in needy circumstances. Apply to Robert Hugh Allan LLB DipLP NP, Pomphreys, 79 Quarry Street, Hamilton ML3 7AG (Tel: 01698 891616).

BELLAHOUSTON BEQUEST FUND: Gives grants to Protestant evangelical denominations in the City of Glasgow and certain areas within five miles of the city boundary for building and repairing churches and halls and the promotion of religion. Apply to Mr John A.M. Cuthbert, Mitchells Roberton, 36 North Hanover Street, Glasgow G1 2AD.

BEQUEST FUND FOR MINISTERS: Assists ministers in outlying districts with manse furnishings, pastoral efficiency aids, educational or medical costs. Apply to A. Linda Parkhill CA, 60 Wellington Street, Glasgow G2 6HJ.

CARNEGIE TRUST: In cases of hardship, the Carnegie Trust is prepared to consider applications by students of Scottish birth or extraction (at least one parent born in Scotland), or who have had at least two years' education at a secondary school in Scotland, for financial assistance with the payment of their fees for a first degree. For further details, students should apply to the Secretary, Carnegie Trust for the Universities of Scotland, Cameron House, Abbey Park Place, Dunfermline, Fife KY12 7PZ (Tel: 01383 622148; E-mail: jgray@carnegie-trust.org; Website: www.carnegie-trust.org).

CHURCH OF SCOTLAND INSURANCE CO. LTD: Undertakes insurance of Church property and pays surplus profits to Church schemes. The company can also arrange household insurance for members and adherents of the Church of Scotland. At 67 George Street, Edinburgh EH2 2JG (Tel: 0131-220 4119; Fax: 0131-220 4120; E-mail: enquiries@cosic.co.uk).

CHURCH OF SCOTLAND MINISTRY BENEVOLENT FUND: Makes grants to retired men and women who have been ordained or commissioned for the ministry of the Church of Scotland and to widows, widowers, orphans, spouses or children of such, who are in need. Apply to the General Secretary, Board of Ministry, 121 George Street, Edinburgh EH2 4YN (Tel: 0131-225 5722).

CLARK BURSARY: Awarded to accepted candidate(s) for the ministry of the Church of Scotland whose studies for the ministry are pursued at the University of Aberdeen. Applications or recommendations for the Bursary to the Clerk to the Presbytery of Aberdeen, Mastrick Church, Greenfern Road, Aberdeen AB16 6TR by 16 October annually.

THE REV. JOHN CLARK FUND: Provides annuities (1) for blind persons and (2) for orphan or fatherless children of ministers or missionaries of the Church of Scotland. Apply to Fyfe Ireland WS, Orchard Brae House, 30 Queensferry Road, Edinburgh EH4 2HG.

CRAIGCROOK MORTIFICATION:
Chairman: G.A. Henry WS
Clerk and Factor: R. Graeme Thom FCA
                             17 Melville Street
                             Edinburgh EH3 7PH (Tel: 0131-473 3500)
Pensions are paid to poor men and women over 60 years old, born in Scotland or who have resided in Scotland for not less than 10 years. At present, pensions amount to £600 p.a.
    Ministers are invited to notify the Clerk and Factor of deserving persons and should be prepared to act as a referee on the application form.

THE ALASTAIR CRERAR TRUST FOR SINGLE POOR: Provides Churches, Christian Organisations and individual Christians with grants to help single adults and groups of single people, who live on low incomes and have little capital, to improve their quality of life. Apply to the Secretary, Michael I.D. Sturrock, 58 Frederick Street, Edinburgh EH2 1LS (Tel: 0131-200 1200).

CROMBIE SCHOLARSHIP: Provides grants annually on the nomination of the Deans of Faculty of Divinity of the Universities of St Andrews, Glasgow, Aberdeen and Edinburgh, who each nominate one matriculated student who has taken a University course in Greek (Classical or Hellenistic) and Hebrew. Award by recommendation only.

THE DRUMMOND TRUST: Makes grants towards the cost of publication of books of 'sound Christian doctrine and outreach'. The Trustees are willing to receive grant requests towards the cost of audio-visual programme material, but not equipment. Requests for application forms should be made to the Secretaries, Hill and Robb, 3 Pitt Terrace, Stirling FK8 2EY (Tel: 01786 450985; E-mail: douglaswhyte@hillandrobb.co.uk). Manuscripts should *not* be sent.

THE DUNCAN TRUST: Makes grants annually to students for the ministry in the Faculties of Arts and Divinity. Preference is given to those born or educated within the bounds of the former Presbytery of Arbroath. Applications not later than 31 October to G.J.M. Dunlop, Brothockbank House, Arbroath DD11 1NJ (Tel: 01241 872683), or to Rev. Matthew S. Bicket, 8 Arbroath Road, Carnoustie DD7 6BL (Tel: 01241 854478).

ESDAILE TRUST:
Chairman: Dr Douglas Grant
Clerk and Treasurer: R. Graeme Thom FCA
                                 17 Melville Street
                                 Edinburgh EH3 7PH (Tel: 0131-473 3500)
Assists education and advancement of daughters of ministers, missionaries and widowed deaconesses of the Church of Scotland between 12 and 25 years of age. Applications are to be lodged by 31 May in each year.

FERGUSON BEQUEST FUND: For the maintenance and promotion of religious ordinances and education and missionary operations in the first instance in the Counties of Ayr, Kirkcudbright, Wigtown, Lanark, Renfrew and Dunbarton. Apply to Ronald D. Oakes CA ACMA, 182 Bath Street, Glasgow G2 4HG (Tel: 0141-332 0476; Fax: 0141-331 0874).

GEIKIE BEQUEST: Makes small grants to students for the ministry, including students studying for entry to the University, preference being given to those not eligible for SAAS awards. Apply to the General Secretary, Board of Ministry, 121 George Street, Edinburgh EH2 4YN.

JAMES GILLAN'S BURSARY FUND: Bursaries are available for students for the ministry who were born or whose parents or parent have resided and had their home for not less than three years continually in the old counties (not Districts) of Moray or Nairn. Apply to R. and R. Urquhart, 121 High Street, Forres IV36 0AB.

HALDANE TRUST FUND: Provides grants to ministers of the Church of Scotland on their first induction, towards the purchase of theological books. Apply to Bennett and Robertson Solicitors, 25 George IV Bridge, Edinburgh EH1 1EP (Tel: 0131-226 2011).

HAMILTON BURSARY TRUST: Awarded, subject to the intention to serve overseas under the Church of Scotland Board of World Mission or to serve with some other Overseas Mission Agency approved by the Committee, to a student at the University of Aberdeen. Preference given to a student born or residing in (1) Parish of Skene, (2) Parish of Echt, (3) the Presbytery of Aberdeen, Kincardine and Deeside, or Gordon; failing which to Accepted Candidate(s) for the Ministry of the Church of Scotland whose studies for the Minstry are pursued at Aberdeen University. Applications or recommendations for the Bursary to the Clerk to the Presbytery of Aberdeen by 16 October annually.

MARTIN HARCUS BEQUEST: Makes annual grants to candidates for the ministry resident within the City of Edinburgh. Applications to the Clerk to the Presbytery of Edinburgh, 10 Palmerston Place, Edinburgh EH12 5AA by 15 October.

THE HOGARTH FUND: Provides annuities to orphan or fatherless children of ministers and missionaries of the Church of Scotland. Apply to Fyfe Ireland WS, Orchard Brae House, 30 Queensferry Road, Edinburgh EH4 2HG.

THE HOPE TRUST: Gives some support to organisations involved in combating drink and drugs, and has as its main purpose the promotion of the Reformed Faith throughout the world.

There is also a Scholarship programme for Postgraduate Theology Study in Scotland. Apply to Miss Carole Hope LLB, 31 Moray Place, Edinburgh EH3 6BY (Tel: 0131-226 5151).

GILLIAN MACLAINE BURSARY FUND: Open to candidates for the ministry of the Church of Scotland of Scottish or Canadian nationality. Preference is given to Gaelic-speakers. Bursaries are awarded after an examination which is held annually in November. Information and application forms from Rev. Jeffrey A. McCormick BD, The Manse, Ardchattan, Connel, Argyll PA37 1QZ (Tel: 01631 710364; E-mail: akph64@uk.uumail.com).

THE MISSES ANN AND MARGARET McMILLAN'S BEQUEST: Makes grants to ministers of the Free and United Free Churches, and of the Church of Scotland, in charges within the Synod of Argyll, with income not exceeding the minimum stipend of the Church of Scotland. Apply by 30 June in each year to Business Manager, Royal Bank of Scotland, 37 Victoria Street, Rothesay, Isle of Bute PA20 0AP.

THE MANSE AUXILIARY: Convener: Mrs Jean Baigrie, 32 Inchcolm Terrace, South Queensferry EH30 9NA (Tel: 0131-331 4311). Assists with clothing and household linen to parish ministers, missionaries, ministers' widows and others, especially those in remote areas. Enquiries to the Convener or to the Secretary, Miss Joan McNeel-Caird, 2/26 Goldenacre Terrace, Edinburgh EH3 5RD (Tel: 0131-551 2720).

MORGAN BURSARY FUND: Makes grants to students for the ministry in Arts and Divinity at the University of Glasgow. Apply to Rev. David W. Lunan MA BD, 260 Bath Street, Glasgow G2 4JP (Tel/Fax: 0141-332 6606).

NOVUM TRUST: Provides small short-term grants to initiate projects in Christian research and action which cannot readily be financed from other sources. Special consideration is given to proposals aimed at the welfare of young people, the training of lay people, and new ways of communicating the faith. Applications to Rev. Alex M. Millar, 121 George Street, Edinburgh EH2 4YN (E-mail: amillar@cofscotland.org.uk).

PATON TRUST: Assists ministers in ill health to have a recuperative holiday outwith, and free from the cares of, their parishes. Apply to Iain A.T. Mowat CA, Alexander Sloan, Chartered Accountants, 144 West George Street, Glasgow G2 2HG (Tel: 0141-354 0354; Fax: 0141-354 0355; E-mail iatm@alexandersloan.co.uk).

RENFIELD STREET TRUST: Assists in the building and repair of churches and halls. Apply to Ronald D. Oakes CA ACMA, 182 Bath Street, Glasgow G2 4HG (Tel: 0141-332 0476; Fax 0141-331 0874).

SCOTTISH CHURCHES ARCHITECTURAL HERITAGE TRUST: Assists congregations of any denomination in the preservation of churches regularly used for public worship and of architectural value and historic interest. Apply to the Secretary, 15 North Bank Street, The Mound, Edinburgh EH1 2LP (Tel/Fax: 0131-225 8644).

SMIETON FUND: Enables a few ministers to have a holiday at Crieff. Applications to the General Secretary, Board of Ministry, 121 George Street, Edinburgh EH2 4YN.

MARY DAVIDSON SMITH CLERICAL AND EDUCATIONAL FUND FOR ABERDEENSHIRE: Assists ministers who have been ordained for five years or over and are in full charge of a congregation in Aberdeen, Aberdeenshire and the north, to purchase books, or to travel for educational purposes, and assists their children with scholarships for further education or vocational training. Apply to Alan J. Innes MA LLB, 100 Union Street, Aberdeen AB10 1QR.

THE NAN STEVENSON CHARITABLE TRUST FOR RETIRED MINISTERS: Provides houses, or loans to purchase houses, for retired ministers or missionaries on similar terms to the Housing and Loan Fund, with preference given to those with a North Ayrshire connection. Secretary: Rev. David Broster, Manse of St Columba's, Kilbirnie KA25 7JU.

SYNOD OF ARGYLL BURSARY FUND: Provides book grants for candidates for the ministry of the Church of Scotland who are native to or have strong connections within the bounds of the former Synod of Argyll (i.e. the Presbyteries of Dunoon, Lorn and Mull and South Argyll). Applications should be made by 31 October to Rev. Jeffrey A. McCormick BD, The Manse, Ardchattan, Connel, Argyll PA37 1QZ (Tel: 01631 710364; E-mail: akph64@uk.uumail.com).

SYNOD OF GRAMPIAN CHILDREN OF THE CLERGY FUND: Makes annual grants to children of deceased ministers. Apply to Rev. Iain U. Thomson, Clerk and Treasurer, The Manse, Skene, Westhill AB32 6LX.

SYNOD OF GRAMPIAN WIDOWS FUND: Makes annual grants (currently £225 p.a.) to widows of deceased ministers who have served in a charge in the former Synod. Apply to Rev. Iain U. Thomson, Clerk and Treasurer, The Manse, Skene, Westhill AB32 6LX.

YOUNG MINISTERS' FURNISHING LOAN FUND: Makes loans (of £1000) to young ministers in their first charge to assist with furnishing the manse. Apply to the General Secretary, Board of Ministry, 121 George Street, Edinburgh EH2 4YN.

(6) RECENT LORD HIGH COMMISSIONERS
TO THE GENERAL ASSEMBLY

1965/66	The Hon. Lord Birsay CBE QC TD
1967/68	The Rt Hon. Lord Reith of Stonehaven GCVO GBE CB TD
1969	Her Majesty the Queen attended in person
1970	The Rt Hon. Margaret Herbison PC
1971/72	The Rt Hon. Lord Clydesmuir of Braidwood CB MBE TD
1973/74	The Rt Hon. Lord Ballantrae of Auchairne and the Bay of Islands GCMG GCVO DSO OBE
1975/76	Sir Hector MacLennan KT FRCPGLAS FRCOG
1977	Francis David Charteris, Earl of Wemyss and March KT LLD
1978/79	The Rt Hon. William Ross MBE LLD
1980/81	Andrew Douglas Alexander Thomas Bruce, Earl of Elgin and Kincardine KT DL JP
1982/83	Colonel Sir John Edward Gilmour BT DSO TD
1984/85	Charles Hector Fitzroy Maclean, Baron Maclean of Duart and Morvern KT GCVO KBE
1986/87	John Campbell Arbuthnott, Viscount of Arbuthnott CBE DSC FRSE FRSA
1988/89	Sir Iain Mark Tennant KT FRSA
1990/91	The Rt Hon. Donald MacArthur Ross FRSE
1992/93	The Rt Hon. Lord Macfarlane of Bearsden

1994/95	Lady Marion Fraser
1996	Her Royal Highness the Princess Royal LG GCVO
1997	The Rt Hon. Lord Macfarlane of Bearsden
1998/99	The Rt Hon. Lord Hogg of Cumbernauld
2000	His Royal Highness the Prince Charles, Duke of Rothesay
2001/02	The Rt Hon. Viscount Younger of Leckie

(7) RECENT MODERATORS
OF THE GENERAL ASSEMBLY

1965	Archibald Watt STM DD, Edzell and Lethnot
1966	R. Leonard Small OBE DD, Edinburgh St Cuthbert's
1967	W. Roy Sanderson DD, Stenton with Whittingehame
1968	J.B. Longmuir TD DD, Principal Clerk of Assembly
1969	T.M. Murchison MA DD, Glasgow St Columba Summertown
1970	Hugh O. Douglas CBE DD LLD, Dundee St Mary's
1971	Andrew Herron MA BD LLB, Clerk to the Presbytery of Glasgow
1972	R.W.V. Selby Wright JP CVO TD DD FRSE, Edinburgh Canongate
1973	George T.H. Reid MC MA BD DD, Aberdeen Langstane
1974	David Steel MA BD DD, Linlithgow St Michael's
1975	James G. Matheson MA BD DD, Portree
1976	Thomas F. Torrance MBE DLitt DD FRSE, University of Edinburgh
1977	John R. Gray VRD MA BD ThM, Dunblane Cathedral
1978	Peter P. Brodie MA BD LLB DD, Alloa St Mungo's
1979	Robert A.S. Barbour MA BD STM DD, University of Aberdeen
1980	William B. Johnston MA BD DD, Edinburgh Colinton
1981	Andrew B. Doig BD STM DD, National Bible Society of Scotland
1982	John McIntyre CVO DD DLitt FRSE, University of Edinburgh
1983	J. Fraser McLuskey MC DD, London St Columba's
1984	John M.K. Paterson MA ACII BD, Milngavie St Paul's
1985	David M.B.A. Smith MA BD DUniv, Logie
1986	Robert Craig CBE DLitt LLD DD, Emeritus of Jerusalem
1987	Duncan Shaw *Bundesverdienstkreuz* JP PhD ThDr, Edinburgh Craigentinny St Christopher's
1988	James A. Whyte MA LLD, University of St Andrews
1989	William J.G. McDonald MA BD DD, Edinburgh Mayfield
1990	Robert Davidson MA BD DD FRSE, University of Glasgow
1991	William B.R. Macmillan MA BD LLD DD, Dundee St Mary's
1992	Hugh R. Wyllie MA MCIBS DD, Hamilton Old Parish Church
1993	James L. Weatherhead CBE MA LLB DD, Principal Clerk of Assembly
1994	James A. Simpson BSc BD STM DD, Dornoch Cathedral
1995	James Harkness CB OBE MA DD, Chaplain General (Emeritus)
1996	John H. McIndoe MA BD STM DD, London: St Columba's linked with Newcastle: St Andrew's
1997	Alexander McDonald BA CMIWSc DUniv, General Secretary, Department of Ministry
1998	Alan Main TD MA BD STM PhD, Professor of Practical Theology at Christ's College, University of Aberdeen
1999	John B. Cairns LTh LLB, Dumbarton Riverside

2000	Andrew R.C. McLellan MA BD STM DD, Edinburgh St Andrew's and St George's
2001	John D. Miller BA BD DD, Glasgow Castlemilk East
2002	Finlay A.J. Macdonald MA BD PhD DD, Principal Clerk of Assembly

MATTER OF PRECEDENCE

The Lord High Commissioner to the General Assembly of the Church of Scotland (while the Assembly is sitting) ranks next to the Sovereign and the Duke of Edinburgh and before the rest of the Royal Family.

The Moderator of the General Assembly of the Church of Scotland ranks next to the Lord Chancellor of Great Britain and before the Prime Minister and the Dukes.

(8) HER MAJESTY'S HOUSEHOLD IN SCOTLAND
ECCLESIASTICAL

Dean of the Chapel Royal: Very Rev. James Harkness CB OBE MA DD

Dean of the Order of the Thistle: Very Rev. Gilleasbuig Macmillan
CVO MA BD Drhc DD

Domestic Chaplain: Rev. Robert P. Sloan MA BD

Chaplains in Ordinary: Very Rev. Gilleasbuig Macmillan
CVO MA BD Drhc DD
Rev. Charles Robertson MA JP
Very Rev. James A. Simpson BSc STM DD
Rev. Norman W. Drummond MA BD
Rev. John L. Paterson MA BD STM
Rev. Alastair H. Symington MA BD
Very Rev. John B. Cairns LTh LLB
Rev. Prof. Iain R. Torrance TD MA BD DPhil
Right Rev. Finlay A.J. Macdonald
MA BD PhD DD

Extra Chaplains: Very Rev. W. Roy Sanderson DD
Very Rev. Prof. John McIntyre
CVO DD DLitt Drhc FRSE
Rev. H.W.M. Cant MA BD STM
Rev. Kenneth MacVicar MBE DFC TD MA
Very Rev. Prof. Robert A.S. Barbour
KCVO MC BD STM DD
Rev. Alwyn Macfarlane MA
Very Rev. William B. Johnston
MA BD DD DLitt
Rev. Colin Forrester-Paton MA BD
Rev. Mary I. Levison BA BD DD
Very Rev. William J. Morris KCVO PhD LLD DD JP
Rev. John MacLeod MA
Rev. A. Stewart Todd MA BD DD

Very Rev. William B.R. Macmillan
MA BD LLD DD
Very Rev. James L. Weatherhead CBE MA LLB DD
Rev. Maxwell D. Craig MA BD ThM

(9) LONG SERVICE CERTIFICATES

Long Service Certificates, signed by the Moderator, are available for presentation to elders and others in respect of not less than 30 years of service. It should be noted that the period is years of *service*, not (for example) years of ordination in the case of an elder.

In the case of Sunday School teachers and Bible Class leaders, the qualifying period is 21 years of service.

Certificates are not issued posthumously, nor is it possible to make exceptions to the rules, for example by recognising quality of service in order to reduce the qualifying period, or by reducing the qualifying period on compassionate grounds, such as serious illness.

A Certificate will be issued only once to any particular individual.

Applications for Long Service Certificates should be made in writing to the Principal Clerk at 121 George Street, Edinburgh EH2 4YN by the parish minister, or by the session clerk on behalf of the Kirk Session. Certificates are not issued from this office to the individual recipients, nor should individuals make application themselves.

(10) LIBRARIES OF THE CHURCH

GENERAL ASSEMBLY LIBRARY AND RECORD ROOM
Most of the books contained in the General Assembly Library have been transferred to the New College Library. Records of the General Assembly, Synods, Presbyteries and Kirk Sessions are now in HM Register House, Edinburgh. All records more than 50 years old and not in current use should be sent to the Principal Clerk.

CHURCH MUSIC
The Library of New College contains a selection of works on Church music.

(11) RECORDS OF THE CHURCH OF SCOTLAND

Church records more than 50 years old, unless still in use, should be sent or delivered to the Principal Clerk for onward transmission to the Scottish Record Office. Where ministers or session clerks are approached by a local repository seeking a transfer of their records, they should inform the Principal Clerk, who will take the matter up with the National Archives of Scotland.

Where a temporary retransmission of records is sought, it is extremely helpful if notice can be given three months in advance so that appropriate procedures can be carried out satisfactorily.

SECTION 3

Church Procedure

(1) THE MINISTER AND BAPTISM

The administration of Baptism to infants is governed by Act V (2000). The Statement on the Doctrine of Baptism may be found in the 1991 'Blue Book', page 224.

The Act itself is as follows:

3 (1)   Baptism may be administered to an unbaptised person upon personal profession of faith. The minister shall judge whether the individual is of sufficient maturity to make personal profession of faith.

3 (2)   Baptism may be administered to a child:
   (a)   whose parents, one or both, have themselves been baptised, are in full communion with the Church, and undertake the Christian upbringing of the child;
   (b)   whose parents, one or both, having been baptised, but not in full communion, are such that the Kirk Session is satisfied that he or she is an adherent permanently connected with the congregation and supporting the work and worship of the Church and will undertake the Christian upbringing of the child;
   (c)   whose parents, one or both, have themselves been baptised, profess the Christian faith, undertake to ensure that such child grows up in the life and worship of the Church and express the desire to seek admission to full membership of the Church. In such cases the Kirk Session shall appoint the elder of the district in which the parents reside, or some other person, to shepherd them into full communion and to exercise pastoral care of the child concerned;
   (d)   who, being of unknown parentage, or otherwise separated from his or her parents, is in the view of the Kirk Session under Christian care and guardianship.

4.   Baptism may be administered only by ministers authorised by the General Assembly to dispense the Sacrament of the Lord's Supper.

5.   Baptism may be administered only after the parents or guardians have received such instruction in its meaning as the minister shall deem necessary.

6.   No minister shall baptise a child resident outwith his or her own parish, whose parents are not members or adherents of his or her congregation, without consent of the minister of that parish or of the Presbytery.

7.   Without the consent of the Presbytery, no minister may administer Baptism in a case where to his or her knowledge another minister has declined to do so.

8.   Baptism shall normally be administered at a diet of public worship of the congregation of which the parents or guardians are members or adherents, or of the congregation of the parish in which they normally reside. In exceptional circumstances, Baptism may be administered elsewhere (e.g. at home, in hospitals or institutions). In every case, an entry shall be made in the Register of Baptism kept by the Kirk Session of the congregation of which the parents or guardians are members or adherents, or in that of the parish in which they normally reside, as the case may be.

9.   Baptism shall be administered in the Name of the Father, and of the Son, and of the Holy Ghost, with water, by sprinkling, pouring, or immersion. Other elements may not be used.

10.   In all cases, a Certificate of Baptism shall be given by the minister.

11.   Nothing in this Act shall be taken to mean that the Church of Scotland rejects Baptism in the name of the Father and of the Son and of the Holy Ghost duly administered in accordance with the law and discipline of other Churches.

(2) THE MINISTER AND MARRIAGE

1. BACKGROUND

Prior to 1939, every marriage in Scotland fell into one or other of two classes: regular or irregular. The former was marriage by a minister of religion after due notice of intention had been given; the latter could be effected in one of three ways: (1) declaration *de presenti*, (2) by promise *subsequente copula*, or (3) by habit and repute.

The Marriage (Scotland) Act of 1939 put an end to (1) and (2) and provided for a new classification of marriage as either religious or civil.

The law of marriage as it was thus established in 1939 had two important limitations to the celebration of marriage: (1) certain preliminaries had to be observed; and (2) in respect of religious marriage, the service had to be conducted according to the forms of either the Christian or the Jewish faith.

2. THE MARRIAGE (SCOTLAND) ACT 1977

These two conditions were radically altered by the Marriage (Scotland) Act 1977.

Since 1 January 1978, in conformity with the demands of a multi-racial society, the benefits of religious marriage have been extended to adherents of other faiths, the only requirements being the observance of monogamy and the satisfaction of the authorities with the forms of the vows imposed.

Since 1978, the calling of banns has also been discontinued. The couple themselves must each complete a Marriage Notice form and return this to the District Registrar for the area in which they are to be married, irrespective of where they live, at least 15 days before the ceremony is due to take place. The form details the documents which require to be produced with it.

If everything is in order, the District Registrar will issue, not more than seven days before the date of the ceremony, a Marriage Schedule. This must be in the hands of the minister officiating at the marriage ceremony before the service begins. Under no circumstances must the minister deviate from this rule. To do so is an offence under the Act.

Ministers should note the advice given by the Procurator of the Church in 1962, that they should not officiate at any marriage until at least one day after the 16th birthday of the younger party.

3. THE MARRIAGE (SCOTLAND) ACT 2002

Although there have never been any limitations as to the place where a religious marriage can be celebrated, civil marriage can take place only in the Office of a Registrar. The Marriage (Scotland) Act 2002, when it comes into effect, will, however, permit the solemnisation of civil marriages at places approved by Local Authorities. Regulations are to be made to specify the kinds of place which may be 'approved' with a view to ensuring that the places approved will not compromise the solemnity and dignity of civil marriage and will have no recent or continuing connection with any religion so as to undermine the distinction between religious and civil ceremonies.

4. PROCLAMATION OF BANNS

Proclamation of banns is no longer required in Scotland; but, in the Church of England, marriage is governed by the provisions of the Marriage Act 1949, which requires that the parties' intention to marry has to have been proclaimed and which provides that in the case of a party residing in Scotland a Certificate of Proclamation given according to the law or custom prevailing in Scotland shall be sufficient for the purpose. In the event that a minister is asked to call banns for a person resident within the registration district where his or her church is situated, the proclamation needs only to be made on one Sunday if the parties are known to the minister. If they are not, it should be made on two Sundays. In all cases, the Minister should, of course, have no reason to believe that there is any impediment to the marriage.

Proclamation should be made at the principal service of worship in this form:

> There is a purpose of marriage between AB (Bachelor/Widower/Divorced), residing at .... in this Registration District, and CD (Spinster/Widow/Divorced), residing at .... in the Registration District of ...., of which proclamation is hereby made for the first and only (second and last) time.

Immediately after the second reading, or not less than 48 hours after the first and only reading, a Certificate of Proclamation signed by either the minister or the Session Clerk should be issued in the following terms:

> At .... the ...... day of ...... 20 ....
> It is hereby certified that AB, residing at ...., and CD, residing at ...., have been duly proclaimed in order to marriage in the Church of .... according to the custom of the Church of Scotland, and that no objections have been offered.
> Signed .... minister or
> Signed .... Session Clerk

5. MARRIAGE OF FOREIGNERS

Marriages in Scotland of foreigners, or of foreigners with British subjects, are, if they satisfy the requirements of Scots Law, valid within the United Kingdom and the various British overseas territories; but they will not necessarily be valid in the country to which the foreigner belongs. This will be so only if the requirements of the law of his or her country have also been complied with. It is therefore most important that, before the marriage, steps should be taken to obtain from the Consul, or other diplomatic representative of the country concerned, a satisfactory assurance that the marriage will be accepted as valid in the country concerned.

6. REMARRIAGE OF DIVORCED PERSONS

By virtue of Act XXVI (1959), a minister of the Church of Scotland may lawfully solemnise the marriage of a person whose former marriage has been dissolved by divorce and whose former spouse is still alive. The minister, however, must carefully adhere to the requirements of the Act which, as slightly altered in 1985, are briefly as follows:

1. The minister should not accede as a matter of routine to a request to solemnise such a marriage. To enable a decision to be made, he or she should take all reasonable steps to obtain relevant information, which should normally include the following:
   (a) Adequate information concerning the life and character of the parties. The Act enjoins the greatest caution in cases where no pastoral relationship exists between the minister and either or both of the parties concerned.
   (b) The grounds and circumstances of the divorce case.
   (c) Facts bearing upon the future well-being of any children concerned.
   (d) Whether any other minister has declined to solemnise the proposed marriage.
   (e) The denomination to which the parties belong. The Act enjoins that special care should be taken where one or more parties belong to a denomination whose discipline in this matter may differ from that of the Church of Scotland.
2. The minister should consider whether there is danger of scandal arising if he or she should solemnise the remarriage, at the same time taking into careful consideration before refusing to do so the moral and spiritual effect of a refusal on the parties concerned.

3.   As a determinative factor, the minister should do all he or she can to be assured that there has been sincere repentance where guilt has existed on the part of any divorced person seeking remarriage. He or she should also give instruction, where needed, in the nature and requirements of a Christian marriage.
4.   A minister is not required to solemnise a remarriage against his or her conscience. Every Presbytery is required to appoint certain individuals with one of whom ministers in doubt as to the correct course of action may consult if they so desire. The final decision, however, rests with the minister who has been asked to officiate.

(3) CONDUCT OF MARRIAGE SERVICES
(CODE OF GOOD PRACTICE)

The code which follows was submitted to the General Assembly in 1997. It appears, on page 1/10, in the Volume of Assembly Reports for that year within the Report of the Board of Practice and Procedure.

1.   *Marriage in the Church of Scotland is solemnised by an ordained minister in a religious ceremony wherein, before God, and in the presence of the minister and at least two competent witnesses, the parties covenant together to take each other as husband and wife as long as they both shall live, and the minister declares the parties to be husband and wife. Before solemnising a marriage, a minister must be assured that the necessary legal requirements are being complied with and that the parties know of no legal impediment to their marriage, and he or she must afterwards ensure that the Marriage Schedule is duly completed.* (Act I 1977)
2.   Any ordained minister of the Church of Scotland who is a member of Presbytery or who holds a current Ministerial Certificate may officiate at a marriage service (see Act II 1987).
3.   While the marriage service should normally take place in church, a minister may, at his or her discretion, officiate at a marriage service outwith church premises. Wherever conducted, the ceremony will be such as to reflect appropriately both the joy and the solemnity of the occasion. In particular, a minister shall ensure that nothing is done which would bring the Church and its teaching into disrepute.
4.   A minister agreeing to conduct a wedding should endeavour to establish a pastoral relationship with the couple within which adequate pre-marriage preparation and subsequent pastoral care may be given.
5.   'A minister should not refuse to perform ministerial functions for a person who is resident in his or her parish without sufficient reason' (Cox, *Practice and Procedure in the Church of Scotland*, sixth edition, page 55). Where either party to the proposed marriage has been divorced and the former spouse is still alive, the minister invited to officiate may solemnise such a marriage, having regard to the guidelines in the Act anent the Remarriage of Divorced Persons (Act XXVI 1959 as amended by Act II 1985).
6.   A minister is acting as an agent of the National Church which is committed to bringing the ordinances of religion to the people of Scotland through a territorial ministry. As such, he or she shall not be entitled to charge a fee or allow a fee to be charged for conducting a marriage service. When a gift is spontaneously offered to a minister as a token of appreciation, the above consideration should not be taken to mean that he or she should not accept such an unsolicited gift. The Financial Board of a congregation is at liberty to

set fees to cover such costs as heat and light, and in addition Organists and Church Officers are entitled to a fee in respect of their services at weddings.

7. A minister should not allow his or her name to be associated with any commercial enterprise that provides facilities for weddings.

8. A minister is not at liberty to enter the bounds of another minister's parish to perform ministerial functions without the previous consent of the minister of that parish. In terms of Act VIII 1933, a minister may 'officiate at a marriage or funeral by private invitation', but, for the avoidance of doubt, an invitation conveyed through a commercial enterprise shall not be regarded as a 'private invitation' within the meaning of that Act.

9. A minister invited to officiate at a Marriage Service where neither party is a member of his or her congregation or is resident within his or her own parish or has any connection with the parish within which the service is to take place should observe the following courtesies:
   (a) he or she should ascertain from the parties whether either of them has a Church of Scotland connection or has approached the appropriate parish minister(s);
   (b) if it transpires that a ministerial colleague has declined to officiate, then he or she (the invited minister) should ascertain the reasons therefor and shall take these and all other relevant factors into account in deciding whether or not to officiate.

(4) THE MINISTER AND WILLS

The Requirements of Writing (Scotland) Act of 1995, which came into force on 1 August 1995, has removed the power of a minister to execute wills notarially. Further clarification, if required, may be obtained from the Solicitor of the Church.

SECTION 4

The
General Assembly
of 2002

(1) OFFICIALS OF THE GENERAL ASSEMBLY

The Lord High Commissioner: The Rt Hon. Viscount Younger of Leckie

Moderator: Right Rev. Finlay A.J. Macdonald
          MA BD PhD DD

Chaplains to the Moderator: Rev. Rolf H. Billes
          Rev. Jennifer Macrae

Acting Principal Clerk: Rev. Marjory A. MacLean

Acting Depute Clerk: Rev. Matthew Z. Ross

Procurator: Mr Patrick S. Hodge QC

Law Agent: Mrs Janette S. Wilson

Convener of the Business Committee: Rev. David W. Lacy

Vice-Convener of the Business Committee: Rev. William C. Hewitt

Precentor: Rev. Douglas Galbraith

Assembly Officer: Mr David McColl

Assistant Assembly Officer   Mr Craig Marshall

---

(2) THE MODERATOR

The Right Reverend Finlay A.J. Macdonald MA BD PhD DD

Finlay Macdonald was born on 1 July 1945, the son of a Church of Scotland minister. He grew up in Dundee, where his father was minister of Lochee Old Parish Church. He was educated at Dundee High School, where he gained the Dux Medal in Music. He gained an MA in Philosophy and a BD from St Andrews University, and during his time there he served for a year as President of the Students' Representative Council, the last incumbent to do so without a sabbatical year. He also served a term as a Vice President of the then Scottish Union of Students.

He served as assistant minister at Bo'ness Old Kirk before being called to his first charge at Menstrie in Clackmannanshire in 1971. During his time there, Finlay became involved in the administration of the Presbytery, serving for four years as Junior Clerk and Treasurer.

In 1977, he was called as minister to Jordanhill in the west end of Glasgow. In this vibrant parish, he was to remain until his appointment as Principal Clerk in 1996. In Jordanhill, his ministry reached far beyond the walls of the church. He built on an existing strong chaplaincy link with the then Jordanhill College School. When the school's existence was threatened in the mid-1980s, Finlay accepted an invitation to chair the PTA Action Committee which campaigned successfully for the school's survival as the local primary and secondary within the public sector. He subsequently served as a Governor of Jordanhill College of Education, and was involved in the discussions which led to the College becoming the Education Faculty of

Strathclyde University. From 1993 to 1996, he was a lay member of Strathclyde University Court.

It was during his ministry at Jordanhill that Finlay became involved in the work of the General Assembly. Constitutional matters have always fascinated him, perhaps reflecting his original intention to study law. In 1983, he was awarded a PhD, again from St Andrews University. His thesis explored the constitutional, as distinct from the theological, significance of the Westminster Confession of Faith for the Church of Scotland. He served from 1988 to 1992 as Convener of the General Assembly's Board of Practice and Procedure and of the Assembly's Business Committee. For the final three years of his ministry at Jordanhill, Finlay combined that with the role of Depute Clerk to the General Assembly.

Finlay has always had a keen interest in ecumenical matters, and has been involved in ACTS (Action of Churches Together in Scotland), CTBI (Churches Together in Britain and Ireland) and EECCS (European Ecumenical Commission on Church and Society). In his time as Principal Clerk, his commitment to people working together has led him to foster an increasing measure of co-operation among the boards and committees which form the Church's central administration.

In December 2001, he was appointed a Chaplain to the Queen in Scotland.

Finlay is married to Elma who is a primary-school teacher, and they have two sons. Stephen is a doctor in Perth, Western Australia, and Philip is an architect in Edinburgh.

(From information supplied by the Media Relations Unit)

Finlay Macdonald brings to the role of Moderator of the 2002 General Assembly a wealth of experience in all aspects of the Church. He is a familiar face to commissioners, for he has occupied the seat of Principal Clerk for the last six Assemblies. He is steeped in the procedure of the Assembly, yet has always brought to his role a sensitivity and diplomacy which have been in no small way responsible for the smooth running of proceedings each year. These qualities are among the many that he now brings to the Moderatorial Chair.

His time as Principal Clerk has allowed Finlay to fulfil many of the interests he developed as a student: politics, the diplomatic service, law and the ministry. It has also been a time when he has been able to observe the picture of the wider church that has been so much a part of his life. Before becoming Principal Clerk, he worked for 25 years in the parish, and he has not lost sight of what life there can entail. His vision has always been of a church in which all people can offer their individual gifts for ministry, and he has great skills in enabling even the more timid to do so. He believes strongly in working alongside people, and is skilled in helping them to develop their own particular gifts. Both his chaplains have over the years benefited greatly from his wisdom and experience. Perhaps it was the recognition of such gifts that led to the almost constant presence of student or probationer ministers working with Finlay in Jordanhill.

As he takes on the role of Moderator, there is for Finlay the constant challenge of where the church is going in the 21st century. He recognises certain key issues in this, particularly inter-faith relations. Yet at the core of his ministry is an understanding of the church as one holy, catholic and apostolic institution, not one which began in 1560, but one which goes right back through the saints and apostles to Jesus Christ. His Assembly worship, based on the 'I am' sayings of Jesus from John's gospel, reflects this belief. As well as that sense of the historical, there is a geographical understanding, and Finlay is keen to further the valuable links we already have with partner churches throughout the world. His Moderatorial travels also reflect the key issues, with a significant visit being planned to the predominantly Muslim countries of Egypt, Syria and Lebanon. The Board of World Mission has also asked that Finlay and his wife, Elma, should travel to south-east Asia, including visits to Sri Lanka and Singapore. In his Presbytery visits, he will have the opportunity to experience the Church here in Scotland in a variety of settings and cultures.

It is a source of great delight to Finlay and Elma that the Assembly Week brought an opportunity for their family to be reunited. Their younger son, Philip, is based in Edinburgh, but his older brother, Stephen, came from Perth, Australia, so that both of them could be part of the first days of Finlay's Moderatorial year. Their support and encouragement, along with that of their wider family and many friends, have meant a great deal to Finlay and Elma as they undertake this new venture in the journey of seeking to advance Christ's kingdom in all the world.

(Jennifer Macrae and Rolf Billes)

(3) DIGEST OF ASSEMBLY DECISIONS

Those who turn to, or chance upon, this section of the *Year Book* are not likely to be those who know or want to know all the complex workings of the Church of Scotland in fine detail. They will know, or will quickly discover, that the full text of the Reports, Acts and Deliverances of the General Assembly can be obtained from the Principal Clerk. What follows, therefore, is a brief indication of those decisions of the Assembly of 2002 which, in the personal opinion of the Editor, are likely to be of interest to both the committed Church member and the more casual observer of our Church's doings. The Assembly took many decisions, a number of which may turn out to have far-reaching implications for the future life, work and structures of our Church. A year or two down the line, it may be all too clear that the Editor was here guilty of a number of glaring sins of omission. As things stand, however, the following seem to him likely to catch the interest of those who, for whatever reason, stray into these particular pages.

ASSEMBLY COUNCIL
The Council and the Board of Practice and Procedure will consider whether elders might moderate Kirk Sessions.

BOARD OF COMMUNICATION
The Assembly encouraged the continuing development of a single integrated website for the Boards and Committees of the Church, with the Board of Communication acting as lead Board in co-ordinating this service.

BOARD OF MINISTRY
The Assembly approved the new stipend scheme proposed by the Board, authorised its implementation from 2004–6 and instructed the Board to work with the Board of Stewardship and Finance in providing information to presbyteries and congregations on its implementation.
    The Assembly instructed the Board, in consultation with presbyteries, to ascertain the pastoral and preaching needs of the Gaelic-speaking congregations and to take steps to make provision for such needs through candidate training and study-leave programmes.
    In consultation with the General Trustees and the Board of Stewardship and Finance, the Board was instructed to investigate some means of maintaining manses to an agreed national standard and to report to the General Assembly of 2003.

BOARD OF NATIONAL MISSION
The Assembly endorsed the immediate steps taken by the Board to control its mounting deficits.
    The Board was instructed to establish a task force for change, involving the Board of Ministry and other Boards and Committees, to develop a coherent strategy for Ministry and Mission, with subsequent implications for funding. A report is to be given to the General Assembly by 2004.

The attention of congregations was drawn to the availability of funds from the Scottish Churches Community Trust for inter-church projects aimed at the relief of poverty.

BOARD OF PARISH EDUCATION
The Assembly welcomed the appointment of regional staff as an indication of the Board's desire to deliver its services more locally. (Three members of staff had thus far been appointed, based in Inverness, Tayside and the South-west; they were working closely with local groups to develop educational strategies and to raise awareness of the value of education and training for the congregations in their areas.)

BOARD OF PRACTICE AND PROCEDURE
In relation to sexual harassment, and subject to approval by the Assembly of 2003:
(a) the Central Co-ordinating Committee, in consultation with other agencies, was instructed to devise a written and enforceable code for application to employees of the Committee and of these agencies
(b) the Board of Ministry was instructed to devise a written and enforceable code for ministers. The Board of Parish Education was instructed to keep awareness of sexual harassment and sexual misconduct before the whole Church in its gender-related work.

BOARD OF SOCIAL RESPONSIBILITY
The Assembly noted the Board's approach to sex-selection which included the following:
(a) the appeal to society as a whole not to place prospective parents under pressure to have a child of a particular sex
(b) the recognition that sex-selection may be acceptable when done in order to preclude serious sex-linked disease; the rejection of it when done to give parents a child of their preferred sex.

BOARD OF STEWARDSHIP AND FINANCE
For a pilot period of five years, a Parish Development Fund, to provide all or part-funding for local mission projects initiated by congregations, was established. Over the five-year period, £3 million will be provided by grants from the Mission and Aid Fund.

BOARD OF WORLD MISSION
The Assembly adopted the HIV/AIDS Project outlined in the Board's Report as a response from the whole Church to the challenges posed by the pandemic, instructed the Board to implement the Project forthwith and encouraged all congregations and church members to play their part in it.
In respect of the Tiberias Development (St Andrew's Galilee), the Assembly supported the Board's decision to complete meantime only those buildings on which work had already started. (This decision had the agreement of both the Board of Stewardship and Finance and of the Church of Scotland Trust.)

CHURCH OF SCOTLAND GUILD
The Assembly recognised the need for the Churches to increase their understanding of the issues underlying domestic violence and to respond to them. There was a welcome for the Guild's involvement in, and support of, forthcoming ecumenical initiatives on this issue. The Church and Nation Committee, having consulted with appropriate Boards and Committees of the Church, was instructed to bring a report on this subject to the Assembly of 2003, with recommendations for further action.
In receiving the Report, the Assembly noted that the Guild was reviewing its Constitution to see whether further amendments were necessary to improve the Guild's smooth running. Specific mention was made of pleas that the Guild should be more inclusive in its language: the Guild's aim was still expressed in terms of women, even though the presence of men at Guild meetings was no longer the 'startling oddity' that it once was.

CHURCH OF SCOTLAND PENSION TRUSTEES

The Assembly noted that the Church had arranged two Stakeholder Pension Schemes through Standard Life to provide access to a Stakeholder Pension as necessary for any employee who was not eligible to join any of the three Pension Schemes. It was further noted that existing Scheme Members could contribute to these Stakeholder Pensions as an alternative or in addition to paying Additional Voluntary Contributions.

COMMITTEE ON CHAPLAINS TO HM FORCES

The Assembly encouraged the Committee to explore imaginatively the possibilities of increased co-operation between chaplains and the local church wherever possible.

COMMITTEE ON CHURCH AND NATION

The Assembly warmly congratulated local congregations on their efforts in offering support to refugees and asylum-seekers, and encouraged others to develop awareness of these issues.

The Assembly commended to the Church inter-faith dialogue and acts of solidarity which seek to overcome religious or racial intolerance.

Recognising that sectarianism was not someone else's problem, the Assembly encouraged congregations to set up local working groups to look at this issue within their own communities, expressed regret for any part the Church of Scotland had played in sectarianism in the past and affirmed support for future moves towards a more tolerant society.

COMMITTEE ON ECUMENICAL RELATIONS

Congregations were encouraged to use the Charta Oecumenica imaginatively to promote better ecumenical relations in their area. (The Charta Oecumenica, prepared by the Conference of European Churches and the Council of European Catholic Bishops' Conference, offers guidelines for the growing co-operation among the Churches in Europe.)

The Committee was instructed to try to set up friendly talks with fellow Presbyterians in Scotland.

COMMITTEE ON EDUCATION

The Youth Assembly was invited to consider the remit of the Review Group on Religious Observance in Scottish Schools and to offer views to the Committee.

COMMITTEE TO REVISE THE HYMNARY

The Assembly received the draft of the new hymn book and authorised its use throughout the Church, subject to such alteration as might be agreed by the Committee. The intention was that the book would be published in 2003.

GENERAL TRUSTEES

The Assembly urged the Scottish Ministers to make available to Historic Scotland significantly increased funding for the provision of grants towards the cost of maintenance of buildings listed as being of special architectural or historic interest.

Presbyteries were instructed to ensure that manses are inspected at least once a year by congregational Fabric Committees and that any necessary remedial works are timeously undertaken.

JOINT COMMITTEE ON THE PROTECTION OF CHILDREN AND YOUNG PEOPLE IN THE CHURCH

The Joint Boards Group was authorised to revise the Church of Scotland Code of Good Practice for the Protection of Children and Young People and to issue it to all congregations for implementation.

The Child Protection Unit was instructed to provide advice, guidance and information to congregations and agencies of the Church to assist in the implementation of policies regarding Scottish Criminal Record Office checks.

PANEL ON DOCTRINE

The Panel intends to produce for a future Assembly a report on the nature of Church membership and a statement on the Doctrine of Baptism.

PANEL ON WORSHIP

The Panel's Report contained an Appendix dealing helpfully and in some detail with issues raised by, and relating to, All-Age Worship. In receiving it, the Assembly welcomed the intended provision of printed material to give guidance in the planning of worship for all ages.

The Church of Scotland

HOUSING & LOAN FUND
FOR MINISTERS AND WIDOWS AND WIDOWERS OF MINISTERS

Many Ministers and their widows(er)s need help to secure a home for their retirement. They live in manses during their years of service, but as these are tied houses, the manse families must move and down new roots.

The Church of Scotland Housing and Loan Fund owns and acquires houses for renting, or give loans, which make it possible for the manse family to secure retirement housing.

The Fund can also assist Retired Ministers and their widow(er)s by helping them move to more suitable accommodation.

Over the years, these services on favourable terms have been greatly valued. Ministers and others remember our fund in their wills and gifts enable our work to continue into the future and are welcome at any time.

Donations, Gift Aids and Legacies will be gratefully received by The Secretary, Ronald C. Mather, The Church of Scotland Housing and Loan Fund for Retired Ministers and Widows and Widowers of Ministers, 121 George Street, Edinburgh EH2 4YN; to whom also applications for assistance should be directed.

THE CHURCH OF SCOTLAND

CHARITY No. Sc 015273

SECTION 5

Presbytery Lists

SECTION 5 – PRESBYTERY LISTS

In each Presbytery list, the congregations are listed in alphabetical order. In a linked charge, the names appear under the first named congregation. Under the name of the congregation will be found the name of the minister and, where applicable, that of an associate minister, auxiliary minister and member of the Diaconate. The years indicated after a minister's name in the congregational section of each Presbytery list are the year of ordination (column 1) and the year of current appointment (column 2). Where only one date is given, it is both the year of ordination and the year of appointment.

In the second part of each Presbytery list, those named are listed alphabetically. The first date is the year of ordination, and the following date is the year of appointment or retirement. If the person concerned is retired, then the appointment last held will be shown in brackets.

KEY TO ABBREVIATIONS

(E)   Indicates a Church Extension charge. New Charge Developments are separately indicated.
(GD) Indicates a charge where it is desirable that the minister should have a knowledge of Gaelic.
(GE) Indicates a charge where public worship must be regularly conducted in Gaelic.
(H)   Indicates that a Hearing Aid Loop system has been installed. In Linked charges, the (H) is placed beside the appropriate building as far as possible.
(L)   Indicates that a Chair Lift has been installed.
(T)   Indicates that the minister has been appointed on the basis of Terminable Tenure.

PRESBYTERY NUMBERS

1	Edinburgh	18	Dumbarton
2	West Lothian	19	South Argyll
3	Lothian	20	Dunoon
4	Melrose and Peebles	21	Lorn and Mull
5	Duns	22	Falkirk
6	Jedburgh	23	Stirling
7	Annandale and Eskdale	24	Dunfermline
8	Dumfries and Kirkcudbright	25	Kirkcaldy
9	Wigtown and Stranraer	26	St Andrews
10	Ayr	27	Dunkeld and Meigle
11	Irvine and Kilmarnock	28	Perth
12	Ardrossan	29	Dundee
13	Lanark	30	Angus
14	Paisley	31	Aberdeen
15	Greenock	32	Kincardine and Deeside
16	Glasgow	33	Gordon
17	Hamilton	34	Buchan

35	Moray
36	Abernethy
37	Inverness
38	Lochaber
39	Ross
40	Sutherland
41	Caithness
42	Lochcarron–Skye
43	Uist
44	Lewis
45	Orkney
46	Shetland
47	England
48	Europe
49	Jerusalem

(1) EDINBURGH

Meets at Palmerston Place Church, Edinburgh, on the first Tuesday of October, November, December, February, April and May and on the second Tuesday in September and on the last Tuesday of June. When the first Tuesday of April falls in Holy Week, the meeting is on the second Tuesday.

| Clerk: | REV. W. PETER GRAHAM MA BD | 10 Palmerston Place, Edinburgh EH12 5AA
[E-mail: akph50@uk.uumail.com] | 0131-225 9137 |

1 Edinburgh: Albany Deaf Church of Edinburgh (H) (0131-556 3128)

| Alistair F. Kelly BL (Locum) | 1961 | 19 Avon Place, Edinburgh EH4 6RE | |

2 Edinburgh: Balerno (H)

| Jared W. Hay BA MTh DipMin | 1987 | 2001 | 3 Johnsburn Road, Balerno EH14 7DN
[E-mail: jared.hay@blueyonder.co.uk] | 0131-449 3830 |
| Charles W.H. Barrington MA BD (Assoc) | 1997 | | 3 Newmills Road, Balerno EH14 5AG
[E-mail: charles.barrington@classicfm.net] | 0131-449 4249 |

3 Edinburgh: Barclay (0131-229 6810)

| D. Graham Leitch MA BD | 1974 | 1980 | 38 Cluny Gardens, Edinburgh EH10 6BN
[E-mail: revdgl@blueyonder.co.uk] | 0131-447 8702 |

4 Edinburgh: Blackhall St Columba (0131-332 4431)

| Alexander B. Douglas BD | 1979 | 1991 | 5 Blinkbonny Crescent, Edinburgh EH4 3NB | 0131-343 3708 |

5 Edinburgh: Bristo Memorial Craigmillar

| Angus L. Bayne LTh BEd MTh | 1969 | 1994 | 72 Blackchapel Close, Edinburgh EH15 3SL
[E-mail: baynez@aol.com] | 0131-657 3266 |
| Agnes M. Rennie (Miss) DCS | | | 3/1 Craigmillar Court, Edinburgh EH16 4AD | 0131-661 8475 |

6 Edinburgh: Broughton St Mary's (H) (0131-556 4786)

| I. Alasdair Elders MA BD | 1964 | 1973 | 103 East Claremont Street, Edinburgh EH7 4JA
[E-mail: alelders@hotmail.com] | 0131-556 7313 (Tel)
0131-558 7313 (Fax) |

7 Edinburgh: Canongate (H)

| Charles Robertson MA | 1965 | 1978 | Manse of Canongate, Edinburgh EH8 8BN
[E-mail: canongate1@aol.com] | 0131-556 3515 |

8 Edinburgh: Carrick Knowe (H) (0131-334 1505)

| Fiona M. Mathieson (Mrs) BEd BD | 1988 | 2001 | 21 Traquair Park West, Edinburgh EH12 7AN
[E-mail: fiona.mathieson@ukgateway.net] | 0131-334 9774 |

9 Edinburgh: Cluny (H) (0131-447 6745)

| Derek Browning MA BD DMin | 1987 | 2001 | 20 Braidburn Crescent, Edinburgh EH10 6EN
[E-mail: Derek.Browning@btinternet.com] | 0131-447 1617 (Tel/Fax)
07050 133876 (Mbl) |

10	**Edinburgh: Colinton (H) (0131-441 2232)**				
	George J. Whyte BSc BD	1981	1992	The Manse, Colinton, Edinburgh EH13 0JR	0131-441 2315
				[E-mail: georgewhyte@vestry.fisnet.co.uk]	
	Mark Evans DCS			13 East Drylaw Drive, Edinburgh EH4 2QA	0131-343 3089
11	**Edinburgh: Colinton Mains (H)**				
	Ian A. McQuarrie BD	1993		17 Swanston Green, Edinburgh EH10 7EW	0131-445 3451
				[E-mail: ian.mcquarrie@talk21.com]	
12	**Edinburgh: Corstorphine Craigsbank (H) (0131-334 6365)**				
	W. John Harvey BA BD (Interim Minister)	1965	2001	22 Belgrave Road, Edinburgh EH12 6NF	0131-334 3557
13	**Edinburgh: Corstorphine Old (H) (0131-334 7864)**				
	James Bain BD DipMin	1996	2002	23 Manse Road, Edinburgh EH12 7SW	0131-334 5425
14	**Edinburgh: Corstorphine St Anne's (0131-316 4740)**				
	Maryann M. Rennie BD MTh	1998	2002	23 Belgrave Road, Edinburgh EH12 6NG	0131-334 3188
15	**Edinburgh: Corstorphine St Ninian's (H)**				
	Alexander T. Stewart MA BD	1975	1995	17 Templeland Road, Edinburgh EH12 8RZ	0131-334 2978
	Margaret Gordon (Mrs) DCS			92 Lanark Road West, Currie EH14 5LA	0131-449 2554
16	**Edinburgh: Craigentinny St Christopher's**				
	Lilly C. Easton (Mrs)	1999		61 Milton Crescent, Edinburgh EH15 3PQ	0131-669 2429
17	**Edinburgh: Craiglockhart (H)**				
	Andrew Ritchie BD DipMin	1984	1991	202 Colinton Road, Edinburgh EH14 1BP	0131-443 2020
				[E-mail: arit202@aol.com]	
18	**Edinburgh: Craigmillar Park (T) (H) (0131-667 5862)**				
	Sarah E.C. Nicol (Mrs) BSc BD	1985	1994	14 Hallhead Road, Edinburgh EH16 5QJ	0131-667 1623
				[E-mail: sneditions@easynet.co.uk]	
19	**Edinburgh: Cramond (H)**				
	G. Russell Barr BA BD MTh DMin	1979	1993	Manse of Cramond, Edinburgh EH4 6NS	0131-336 2036
				[E-mail: rev.r.barr@cwcom.net]	
20	**Edinburgh: Currie (H) (0131-451 5141) (E-mail: currie.kirk@btinternet.com)**				
	Keith W. Ross MA BD	1984	2000	43 Lanark Road West, Currie EH14 5JX	0131-449 4719
	Paul Middleton BMus BD	2000	2001	11/13 Caledonian Crescent, Edinburgh EH11 2AN	0131-478 3467
21	**Edinburgh: Dalmeny**				
	Vacant			Dalmeny, South Queensferry EH30 9TT	0131-331 1869

22	**Edinburgh: Davidson's Mains (H) (0131-312 6282) (E-mail: dmains_parish_church@talk21.com)**		
	Jeremy R.H. Middleton LLB BD	1981 1988	1 Hillpark Terrace, Edinburgh EH4 7SX	0131-336 3078
23	**Edinburgh: Dean (H)**		
	Mark M. Foster BSc BD	1998	1 Ravelston Terrace, Edinburgh EH4 3EF [E-mail: markmfoster@mac.com]	0131-332 5736
24	**Edinburgh: Drylaw (0131-343 6643)**		
	I. Maxwell Homewood MSc BD	1997 2001	5 Essex Brae, Edinburgh EH4 6LN [E-mail: max.homewood@btinternet.com]	0131-339 3554
25	**Edinburgh: Duddingston**		
	James A.P. Jack DMin BSc BArch BD	1989 2001	Manse of Duddingston, Old Church Lane, Edinburgh EH15 3PX [E-mail: jamesapjack@aol.com]	0131-661 4240
26	**Edinburgh: Fairmilehead (H) (0131-445 2374)**		
	John R. Munro BD	1976	73 Dundas Street, Edinburgh EH3 6RS	0131-556 3012
27	**Edinburgh: Gilmerton (H)**		
	Vacant		43 Ravenscroft Street, Edinburgh EH17 8QJ	0131-664 2147
28	**Edinburgh: Gorgie (H) (0131-337 7936)**		
	Peter I. Barber MA BD	1984 1995	90 Myreside Road, Edinburgh EH10 5BZ [E-mail: pibarber@supanet.com]	0131-337 2284
29	**Edinburgh: Granton (H) (0131-552 3033)**		
	F. Lynne MacMurchie (Miss) LLB BD	1998	8 Wardie Crescent, Edinburgh EH5 1AG [E-mail: lynnemac@fish.co.uk]	0131-551 2159
	Marilynn Steele (Mrs) DCS		2 Northfield Gardens, Prestonpans EH32 9LQ	01875 811497
30	**Edinburgh: Greenbank (H) (0131-447 9969)**		
	Ian G. Scott BSc BD STM	1965 1983	112 Greenbank Crescent, Edinburgh EH10 5SZ [E-mail: igscott@blueyonder.co.uk]	0131-447 4032
31	**Edinburgh: Greenside (H) (0131-556 5588)**		
	Andrew F. Anderson MA BD	1981	80 Pilrig Street, Edinburgh EH6 5AS [E-mail: afanderson@compuserve.com]	0131-554 3277 (Tel/Fax)
32	**Edinburgh: Greyfriars Tolbooth and Highland Kirk (GE) (H) (0131-225 1900)**		
	Vacant		12 Tantallon Place, Edinburgh EH9 1NZ	0131-667 8671
33	**Edinburgh: High (St Giles') (0131-225 4363)**		
	Gilleasbuig Macmillan CVO MA BD Drhc DD	1969 1973	St Giles' Cathedral, Edinburgh EH1 1RE [E-mail: theminister@stgilescathedral.org.uk minister.stgiles@btconnect.com]	0131-225 4363

34	**Edinburgh: Holyrood Abbey (H) (0131-661 4883)**			
	Philip R. Hair BD	1980	100 Willowbrae Avenue, Edinburgh EH8 7HU	0131-652 0640
35	**Edinburgh: Holy Trinity (H) (0131-442 3304)**			
	Stanley A. Brook BD MTh	1977	16 Thorburn Road, Edinburgh EH13 0BQ	0131-441 7167
	Michael S. Dawson BTech BD (Assoc)	1979	12 Sighthill Crescent, Edinburgh EH11 4QE	0131-453 6279
	Joyce Mitchell (Mrs) DCS		16/4 Murrayburn Place, Edinburgh EH14 2RR	0131-453 6548
36	**Edinburgh: Inverleith (H)**			
	D. Hugh Davidson MA	1965	43 Inverleith Gardens, Edinburgh EH3 5PR [E-mail: hdavidson@freeuk.com]	0131-552 3874
37	**Edinburgh: Juniper Green (H)**			
	James S. Dewar MA BD	1983 2000	476 Lanark Road, Juniper Green, Edinburgh EH14 5BQ [E-mail: jsdewar@supanet.com]	0131-453 3494
38	**Edinburgh: Kaimes Lockhart Memorial**			
	Iain D. Penman BD	1977 1995	76 Lasswade Road, Edinburgh EH16 6SF	0131-664 2287
39	**Edinburgh: Kirkliston**			
	Glenda J. Keating (Mrs) MTh	1996	43 Main Street, Kirkliston EH29 9AF [E-mail: kirkglen@aol.com]	0131-333 3298
40	**Edinburgh: Kirk o' Field (T) (H)**			
	Ian D. Maxwell MA BD PhD	1977 1996	31 Hatton Place, Edinburgh EH9 1UA [E-mail: i.d.maxwell@quista.net]	0131-667 7954
41	**Edinburgh: Leith North (H) (0131-553 7378)**			
	Alistair G.C. McGregor QC BD	1987	22 Primrose Bank Road, Edinburgh EH5 3JG	0131-551 2802
42	**Edinburgh: Leith St Andrew's (H)**			
	John Cook MA BD	1967	13 Claremont Park, Edinburgh EH6 7PJ	0131-554 7695
43	**Edinburgh: Leith St Serf's (T) (H)**			
	Sara R. Embleton (Mrs) BA BD	1977 1999	20 Wilton Road, Edinburgh EH16 5NX [E-mail: sara.embleton@which.net]	0131-478 1624
44	**Edinburgh: Leith St Thomas' Junction Road (T)**			
	Vacant		28 Summerside Street, Edinburgh EH6 4NU	0131-554 5039
45	**Edinburgh: Leith South (H) (0131-554 2578) (E-mail: slpc@dial.pipex.com)**			
	Ian Y. Gilmour BD	1985 1995	37 Claremont Road, Edinburgh EH6 7NN [E-mail: ianyg@aol.com]	0131-554 3062
	Jennifer Booth (Mrs) BD (Assoc)	1996	39 Lilyhill Terrace, Edinburgh EH8 7DR	0131-661 3813

46 **Edinburgh: Leith Wardie (H) (0131-551 3847)**
    Brian C. Hilsley LLB BD   1990
    35 Lomond Road, Edinburgh EH5 3JN
    [E-mail: brian@wardie10.freeserve.co.uk]
    0131-552 3328

47 **Edinburgh: Liberton (H)**
    John N. Young MA BD PhD   1996
    7 Kirk Park, Edinburgh EH16 6HZ
    [E-mail: john@nicolyoung.freeserve.co.uk]
    0131-664 3067

48 **Edinburgh: Liberton Northfield (H) (0131-551 3847)**
    John M. McPake LTh   2000
    9 Claverhouse Drive, Edinburgh EH16 6BR
    0131-658 1754

49 **Edinburgh: London Road (H) (0131-661 1149)**
    William L. Armitage BSc BD   1976 1991
    26 Inchview Terrace, Edinburgh EH7 6TQ
    [E-mail: billarm@blueyonder.co.uk]
    0131-669 5311

50 **Edinburgh: Marchmont St Giles' (H) (0131-447 4359)**
    Karen K. Watson (Mrs) BD   1997 2002
    19 Hope Terrace, Edinburgh EH9 2AP
    0131-447 2834

51 **Edinburgh: Mayfield Salisbury (0131-667 1522)**
    Scott S. McKenna BA BD   1994 2000
    26 Seton Place, Edinburgh EH9 2JT
    [E-mail: scottsmckenna@aol.com]
    0131-667 1286

52 **Edinburgh: Morningside Braid (0131-447 9430)**
    John R. Wells BD DipMin   1991
    5 Cluny Avenue, Edinburgh EH10 4RN
    0131-447 4647

53 **Edinburgh: Morningside United (H) (0131-447 3152)**
    John R. Smith MA BD   1973 1998
    1 Midmar Avenue, Edinburgh EH10 6BS
    [E-mail: ministermuc@aol.com]
    0131-447 8724

54 **Edinburgh: Muirhouse St Andrew's (E)**
    Frederick D.F. Shewan MA BD   1970 1980
    35 Silverknowes Road, Edinburgh EH4 5LL
    0131-336 4546

55 **Edinburgh: Murrayfield (H) (0131-337 1091) (E-mail: murrayfield@parish-church.fsnet.co.uk)**
    William D. Brown BD CQSW   1987 2001
    45 Murrayfield Gardens, Edinburgh EH12 6DH
    0131-337 5431

56 **Edinburgh: Newhaven (H)**
    Grant MacLaughlan BA BD   1998
    11 Laverockbank Terrace, Edinburgh EH5 3BL
    0131-552 8906

57 **Edinburgh: New Restalrig (H) (0131-661 5676)**
    David L. Court BSc BD   1989 2000
    19 Abercorn Road, Edinburgh EH8 7DP
    [E-mail: david@lamont-court.freeserve.co.uk]
    0131-661 4045

58 **Edinburgh: Old Kirk (H)**
    Vacant
    24 Pennywell Road, Edinburgh EH4 4HD
    0131-332 4354

59 **Edinburgh: Palmerston Place (H) (0131-220 1690)**
    Colin A.M. Sinclair BA BD   1981 1996
    30B Cluny Gardens, Edinburgh EH10 6BJ
    [E-mail: colins@globalnet.co.uk]
    0131-447 9598
    0131-225 3312 (Fax)

No.	Congregation / Minister	Year	Year	Address	Tel
60	**Edinburgh: Pilrig St Paul's (0131-553 1876)** John M. Tait BSc BD	1985	1999	78 Pilrig Street, Edinburgh EH6 5AS [E-mail: john.m.tait@btinternet.com]	0131-554 1842
61	**Edinburgh: Polwarth (H) (0131-346 2711)** John K.S. McMahon MA BD	1998		6 Trotter Haugh, The Grange, Edinburgh EH9 2GZ [E-mail: j.k.s.mcmahon@virgin.net]	0131-667 4055
62	**Edinburgh: Portobello Old (H)** Neil Buchanan BD	1991		6 Hamilton Terrace, Edinburgh EH15 1NB	0131-669 5312
63	**Edinburgh: Portobello St James' (H)** Peter Webster BD	1977	2002	34 Brighton Place, Edinburgh EH15 1LT	0131-669 1767
64	**Edinburgh: Portobello St Philip's Joppa (H) (0131-669 3641)** John Weir Cook MA BD	1962	1988	6 St Mary's Place, Edinburgh EH15 2QF [E-mail: jwc@freeuk.com]	0131-669 2410
65	**Edinburgh: Priestfield (H) (0131-667 5644)** Thomas N. Johnston LTh	1972	1990	13 Lady Road, Edinburgh EH16 5PA [E-mail: tomjohnston@blueyonder.co.uk]	0131-668 1620
66	**Edinburgh: Queensferry (H)** John G. Carrie BSc BD	1971		1 Station Road, South Queensferry EH30 9HY [E-mail: john.carrie@virgin.net]	0131-331 1100
67	**Edinburgh: Ratho** Ian J. Wells BD	1999		Ratho, Newbridge EH28 8NP [E-mail: ian@rathomanse.fsnet.co.uk]	0131-333 1346
68	**Edinburgh: Reid Memorial (H) (0131-662 1203)** Brian M. Embleton BD	1976	1985	20 Wilton Road, Edinburgh EH16 5NX [E-mail: brian.embleton@which.net]	0131-667 3981
69	**Edinburgh: Richmond Craigmillar (H) (0131-661 6561)** Elizabeth M. Henderson (Miss) MA BD MTh	1985	1997	13 Wisp Green, Edinburgh EH15 3QX [E-mail: lizhende@aol.com]	0131-669 1133
70	**Edinburgh: St Andrew's and St George's (H) (0131-225 3847)** Andrew R.C. McLellan MA BD STM DD	1970	1986	25 Comely Bank, Edinburgh EH4 1AJ [E-mail: beano@pandles.freeserve.co.uk]	0131-332 5324

71 **Edinburgh: St Andrew's Clermiston**   1989
Alistair H. Keil BD DipMin
87 Drum Brae South, Edinburgh EH12 8TD
[E-mail: alistair.h.keil@talk21.com]
0131-339 4149

72 **Edinburgh: St Catherine's Argyle (H) (0131-667 7220)**
Victor W.N. Laidlaw BD   1975
5 Palmerston Road, Edinburgh EH9 1TL
[E-mail: vandslaidlaw@supanet.com]
0131-667 9344

73 **Edinburgh: St Colm's (T)(H)**
Stewart M. McPherson BD CertMin   1991
1 Merchiston Gardens, Edinburgh EH10 5DD
[E-mail: stewart@merchis.abel.co.uk]
0131-337 1107

Mary Gargrave (Mrs) DCS
229/2 Calder Road, Edinburgh EH11 4RG
0131-476 3493

74 **Edinburgh: St Cuthbert's (H) (0131-229 1142)**
Tom C. Cuthell MA BD MTh   1965
34A Murrayfield Road, Edinburgh EH12 6ER
0131-337 6637
Peter Neilson MA BD MTh (Assoc)   1975   1997
12 Strathalmond Court, Edinburgh EH4 8AE
0131-339 4536

75 **Edinburgh: St David's Broomhouse (H) (0131-443 9851)**
Neil J. Dougall BD   1991
33 Traquair Park West, Edinburgh EH12 7AN
[E-mail: neild3344@aol.com]
0131-334 1730

76 **Edinburgh: St George's West (H) (0131-225 7001)**
Peter J. Macdonald BD DipMin   1986   1998
6 Wardie Avenue, Edinburgh EH5 2AB
[E-mail: pjmacdon@aol.com]
0131-552 4333

77 **Edinburgh: St John's Oxgangs**
Vacant
2 Caiystane Terrace, Edinburgh EH10 6SR
0131-445 1688

78 **Edinburgh: St Margaret's (H) (0131-554 7400)**
Ewan R. Aitken BA BD   1992   1995
43 Moira Terrace, Edinburgh EH7 6TD
[E-mail: ewanaitken@compuserve.com]
0131-669 7329

Marion Buchanan (Mrs) DCS
6 Hamilton Terrace, Edinburgh EH15 1NB
0131-669 5312

79 **Edinburgh: St Martin's**
Elizabeth J.B. Ross (Ms) BD   1996   1999
5 Duddingston Crescent, Edinburgh EH15 3AS
[E-mail: elizabethross@ugenie.co.uk]
0131-657 9894

Liz Crocker (Mrs) DCS
77C Craigcrook Road, Edinburgh EH4 3PH
0131-332 0227

80 **Edinburgh: St Michael's (H)**
Margaret R. Forrester (Mrs) MA BD   1974   1980
25 Kingsburgh Road, Edinburgh EH12 6DZ
[E-mail: margaret@theforresters.fsnet.co.uk]
0131-337 5646

81 **Edinburgh: St Nicholas' Sighthill**
Kenneth J. Mackay MA BD   1971   1976
122 Sighthill Loan, Edinburgh EH11 4NT
0131-453 6921

82 **Edinburgh: St Stephen's Comely Bank (0131-315 4616)**
Graham T. Dickson MA BD   1985   1996
8 Blinkbonny Crescent, Edinburgh EH4 3NB
[E-mail: mail@dickson22.fsnet.co.uk]
0131-332 3364 (Tel/Fax)

83 Edinburgh: Slateford Longstone
Gordon R. Palmer MA BD STM 1986 1994 50 Kingsknowe Road South, Edinburgh EH14 2JW [E-mail: gkrspalmer@blueyonder.co.uk] 0131-443 2960

84 Edinburgh: Stenhouse St Aidan's
Colin A. Strong BSc BD 1989 2001 65 Balgreen Road, Edinburgh EH12 5UA [E-mail: cstrong@bigfoot.com] 0131-337 7711
Mary Gargrave (Mrs) DCS 229/3 Calder Road, Edinburgh EH11 4RG 0131-476 3493

85 Edinburgh: Stockbridge (H) (0131-332 0122)
Anne T. Logan (Mrs) MA BD MTh 1981 1993 19 Eildon Street, Edinburgh EH3 5JU [E-mail: anne@logan68.freeserve.co.uk] 0131-557 6052

86 Edinburgh: Tron Moredun
Stephen Manners MA BD 1989 467 Gilmerton Road, Edinburgh EH17 7JG [E-mail: sk.manners@btinternet.com] 0131-666 2584

87 Edinburgh: Viewforth (T) (H) (0131-229 1917)
Anthony P. Thornthwaite MTh 1995 91 Morningside Drive, Edinburgh EH10 5NN [E-mail: tony.thornthwaite@blueyonder.co.uk] 0131-447 6684

Aitken, Alexander R. MA 1965 1997 (Newhaven) 36 King's Meadow, Edinburgh EH16 5JW 0131-667 1404
Alexander, Ian W. BA BD STM 1990 1995 Board of World Mission c/o 121 George Street, Edinburgh EH2 4YN 0131-225 5722
Anderson, Hugh MA BD PhD DD 1951 1985 (University of Edinburgh) 23/13 Maxwell Street, Edinburgh EH10 5HT 0131-447 1401
Anderson, Robert S. BD 1988 1997 Scottish Churches World Exchange St Colm's International House, 23 Inverleith Terrace, Edinburgh EH3 5NS 0131-315 4444

Auld, A. Graeme MA BD PhD DLitt FSAScot 1973 1973 University of Edinburgh Nether Swanshiel, Hobkirk, Bonchester Bridge, Hawick TD9 8JU

Baigrie, R.A. MA 1945 1985 (Kirkurd with Newlands) 32 Inchcolm Terrace, South Queensferry EH30 9NA 0131-331 4311
Bardgett, Frank D. MA BD PhD 1987 2001 Board of National Mission 6 Inchcolm Drive, North Queensferry, Inverkeithing KY11 1LD 01383 416863
Baxter, Richard F. OBE MA BD 1954 1990 (Assistant at St Andrew's and St George's)

Beckett, David M. BA BD 1964 2002 (Greyfriars, Tolbooth and Highland Kirk) 138 Braid Road, Edinburgh EH10 6JB 0131-447 7735
1F1, 31 Sciennes Road, Edinburgh EH9 1NT [E-mail: davidbeckett3@aol.com] 0131-667 2672

Blakey, Ronald S. MA BD MTh 1962 2000 Editor: The Year Book 61 Orchard Brae Avenue, Edinburgh EH4 2UR 0131-343 6039
Brady, Ian D. BSc ARCST BD 1967 2001 (Edinburgh: Corstorphine Old) 28 Frankfield Crescent, Dalgety Bay, Dunfermline KY11 9LW 01383 825104
Brown, William D. MA 1963 1989 (Wishaw Thornlie) 121 Dalkeith Road, Edinburgh EH16 5AJ 0131-667 1124
Bruce, Lilian M. (Miss) BD MTh 1971 2001 (Daviot and Dunlichity with Moy, Dalarossie and Tomatin) 3 Fountainhall Court, 3 Fountainhall Road, Edinburgh EH9 2NL 0131-667 4261

Cameron, G. Gordon MA BD STM 1957 1997 (Juniper Green) 4 Ladywell Grove, Clackmannan FK10 4JQ 01259 723769
Cameron, John W.M. MA BD 1957 1996 (Liberton) 10 Plewlands Gardens, Edinburgh EH10 5JP 0131-447 1277
Cattanach, William D. DD 1951 1990 (Geneva) 145 Craigleith Road, Edinburgh EH4 2ED 0131-332 4503

Name			Position / Church	Address	Telephone
Chalmers, John P. BD	1979	1995	Department of Ministry	10 Liggars Place, Dunfermline KY12 7XZ	01383 739130
Chalmers, Murray MA	1965	1991	Hospital Chaplain	25 Greenbank Road, Edinburgh EH10 5RX	0131-447 3387
Cheyne, Alexander C. MA BD BLitt DLitt	1958	1986	(University of Edinburgh)	12 Crossland Crescent, Peebles EH45 8LF	01721 722288
Clinkenbeard, William W. BSc BD STM	1966	2000	(Edinburgh: Carrick Knowe)	4 Aline Court, Dalgety Bay, Dunfermline KY11 5GP [E-mail: bjclinks@compuserve.com]	01383 824011
Cobain, Alan R. BD	2000		Army Chaplain	54 Cowan Road, Edinburgh EH11 1RJ	0131-337 4529
Cross, Brian F. MA	1961	1998	(Coalburn)	23 Broomlee Court, Broomlee Crescent, West Linton EH46 7EY	01968 660705
Currie, David E.P. BSc BD	1983	2000	Adviser in Evangelism	21 Rosa Burn Avenue, Lindsayfield, East Kilbride G75 9DE	01355 248510
Davidson, Ian M.P. MBE MA BD	1957	1994	(Stirling: Allan Park South with Church of the Holy Rude)	13/8 Craigend Park, Edinburgh EH16 5XX	0131-664 0074
Dilbey, Mary D. (Miss) BD	1997	2002	(West Kirk of Calder)	41 Bonaly Rise, Edinburgh EH13 0QU	0131-441 6867
Dougall, Elspeth G. (Mrs) MA BD	1989	2001	(Edinburgh: Marchmont St Giles')	60B Craigmillar Park, Edinburgh EH16 5PU	0131-668 1342
Doyle, Ian B. MA BD PhD	1946	1991	(Department of National Mission)	21 Lygon Road, Edinburgh EH16 5QD	0131-667 2697
Drummond, R. Hugh	1953	1991	(Balmaclellan with Kells)	19 Winton Park, Edinburgh EH10 7EX	0131-445 3634
Drummond, Rhoda (Miss) DCS			(Deaconess)	Flat K, 23 Grange Loan, Edinburgh EH9 2ER	0131-668 3631
Dunn, W. Iain C. DA LTh	1983	1998	(Pilrig and Dalmeny Street)	10 Fox Covert Avenue, Edinburgh EH12 6UQ	0131-334 1665
Elliot, George MA BD STM	1958	1989	(Board of Stewardship and Finance)	28 Pentland Gardens, Edinburgh EH10 6NW	0131-447 4017
Faulds, Norman L. MA BD FSAScot	1968	2000	(Aberlady with Gullane)	Wellwood, 8 Juniper Place, Juniper Green, Edinburgh EH14 5TX	0131-453 4984
Fergusson, David A.S. MA BD DPhil	1984	2000	University of Edinburgh	23 Riselaw Crescent, Edinburgh EH10 6HN	0131-447 4022
Finlayson, J. Clarence MA	1930	1972	(Grange)	52 Falcon Avenue, Edinburgh EH10 4AW	0131-447 6550
Forrester, Duncan B. MA BD DPhil DD	1962	1978	(University of Edinburgh)	25 Kingsburgh Road, Edinburgh EH12 6DZ	0131-337 5646
Fraser, Shirley A. (Miss) MA BD	1992	2001	Edinburgh Team Leader: Friends International		
Galbraith, Douglas MA BD BMus MPhil ARSCM	1965	1995	Office for Worship, Doctrine and Artistic Matters	30 Parkhead Avenue, Edinburgh EH11 4SJ c/o 121 George Street, Edinburgh EH2 4YN [E-mail: dgalbraith@cofscotland.org.uk]	0131-443 7268 0131-240 2233
Gibson, John C.L. MA BD DPhil	1959	1994	(University of Edinburgh)	Cairnbank, Morton Street South, Edinburgh EH15 2NB	0131-669 3635
Gillon, J. Blair MA	1935	1980	(Borthwick with Heriot)	12A Craigmillar Park, Edinburgh EH16 5PS	0131-667 0004
Glass, Irene (Miss) DCS			(Deaconess)	3E Falcon Road West, Edinburgh EH10 4AA	0131-447 6554
Gordon, Tom MA BD	1974	1994	Chaplain: Fairmile Marie Curie Centre	22 Gosford Road, Port Seton, Prestonpans EH32 0HF	01875 812262
Graham, W. Peter MA BD	1967	1993	Presbytery Clerk	23/6 East Comiston, Edinburgh EH10 6RZ [E-mail: akph50@uk.uumail.com]	0131-445 5763
Grubb, George D.W. BA BD BPhil DMin	1962	2001	(Edinburgh: Corstorphine Craigsbank)	10 Wellhead Close, South Queensferry EH30 9WA	0131-331 2072
Hardy, Basil G. MA BD	1946	1984	(Dundee Meadowside St Paul's)	14 Elliot Place, Edinburgh EH14 1DR	0131-441 3449
Harkness, James CB OBE QHC MA LLB DD	1961	1995	(Chaplain General: Army)	13 Saxe Coburg Place, Edinburgh EH3 5BR	0131-343 1297
Hepburn, James L. MA BD	1950	1991	(Ardoch with Blackford)	16 Marchmont Road, Edinburgh EH9 1HZ	0131-229 6170
Hill, J. William BA BD	1967	2001	(Corstorphine St Anne's)	33/9 Murrayfield Road, Edinburgh EH12 6EP	
Hutchison, Maureen (Mrs) DCS			(Deaconess)	23 Drylaw Crescent, Edinburgh EH4 2AU	0131-332 8020
Jamieson, Gordon D. MA BD	1974	2000	Director of Stewardship	41 Goldpark Place, Livingston EH54 6LW	01506 412020
Jeffrey, Eric W.S. JP MA	1954	1994	(Edinburgh Bristo Memorial)	18 Gillespie Crescent, Edinburgh EH10 4HT	0131-229 7815
Johnston, William B. MA BD DD DLitt	1945	1991	(Colinton)	15 Elliot Road, Edinburgh EH14 1DU	0131-441 3387
Kant, Everard FVCM MTh	1953	1988	(Kinghorn)	38 Redford Loan, Edinburgh EH13 0AX	0131-441 3853

Name			Position	Address	Telephone
Kelly, Alastair F. BL	1961		Board of National Mission	34/1 Shore Road, South Queensferry EH30 9SG	0131-319 1841
Kelly, Ewan R. MB ChB BD	1994	1998	Edinburgh University	29 Buckstone Crescent, Edinburgh EH10 6RJ	
Kesting, Sheilagh M. (Miss) BA BD	1980	1993	Ecumenical Relations	12 Glenview Drive, Falkirk FK1 5JU	01324 671489
Lamont, A. Donald BSc BD	1941	1975	(Nakuru)	36 St Clair Terrace, Edinburgh EH10 5PS	0131-447 4267
Lawson, Kenneth C. MA BD	1963	1999	(Adviser in Adult Education)	56 Easter Drylaw View, Edinburgh EH4 2QP	0131-539 3311
Lyall, David BSc BD STM PhD	1965	1990	University of Edinburgh	1 North Meggetland, Edinburgh EH14 1XG	0131-443 7640
Lyon, D.H.S. MA BD STM	1952	1986	(Board of World Mission and Unity)	30 Mansfield Road, Balerno EH14 7JZ	0131-449 5031
Macdonald, Finlay A.J. MA BD PhD	1971	1996	Principal Clerk	c/o 121 George Street, Edinburgh EH2 4YN	0131-225 5722
McDonald, James I.H. MA BD MTh PhD	1958	1998	(University of Edinburgh)	23 Ravelston House Road, Edinburgh EH4 3LP	0131-332 2172
Macdonald, William J. BD	1976	1999	(Board of National Mission: New Charge Development)	1/13 North Werber Park, Edinburgh EH4 1SY	0131-332 0254
McDonald, William J.G. DD	1953	1992	(Mayfield)	7 Blacket Place, Edinburgh EH9 1RN	0131-667 2100
McDowell, Brian		1999	Chaplain: Fettes College	6 West Woods, Fettes College, Edinburgh EH4 1RA	0131-332 9510
McGillivray, A. Gordon MA BD STM	1951	1993	(Presbytery Clerk)	7 Greenfield Crescent, Balerno EH14 7HD	0131-449 4747
MacGregor, Margaret S. (Miss) MA BD DipEd	1985	1994	(Calcutta)	16 Learmonth Court, Edinburgh EH4 1PB	0131-332 1089
McGregor, T. Stewart MBE MA BD	1957	1998	(Chaplain: Edinburgh Royal Infirmary)	19 Lonsdale Terrace, Edinburgh EH3 9HL [E-mail: cetsm@dircon.uk]	0131-229 5332
McIntosh, Hamish MC MA BD	1943	1983	(Auchterarder St Andrew's and West)	St Raphael's Nursing Home, 2 South Oswald Road, Edinburgh EH9 2HQ	
McIntyre, John CVO DLitt DD Drhc FRSE	1941	1986	(University of Edinburgh)	27/317 West Savile Terrace, Edinburgh EH9 3DT	0131-667 1203
Mackie, Steven G. MA BD	1956	1994	(University of St Andrews)	38 Grange Loan, Edinburgh EH9 2NR	0131-667 9532
Maclean, Ailsa G. (Mrs) BD DipCE	1979	1988	Chaplain: George Heriot's School	28 Swan Spring Avenue, Edinburgh EH10 6NJ	0131-445 1320
MacLean, Marjory A. (Miss) LLB BD	1991	1998	Board of Practice and Procedure	c/o 121 George Street, Edinburgh EH2 4YN	0131-225 5722
McLeod, Roderick MA BD	1951	1990	(Lochwinnoch)	2 East Savile Road, Edinburgh EH16 5ND	0131-667 1475
Macmillan, W.B.R. LLD DD	1954	1993	(Dundee: St Mary's)	3/5 Craigend Park, Edinburgh EH16 5XY	0131-672 1832
McPheat, Elspeth DCS			Deaconess: Social Responsibility	11/5 New Orchardfield, Edinburgh EH6 5ET	0131-554 4143
McPhee, Duncan C. MA BD	1953	1993	(Department of National Mission)	8 Belvedere Park, Edinburgh EH6 4LR	0131-552 6784
Macpherson, Allan S. MA	1967	1993	Chaplain: Merchiston Castle School	The Fairway, Merchiston Castle School, Edinburgh EH13 0PU	
Macpherson, Colin C.R. MA BD	1958	1996	(Dunfermline St Margaret's)	7 Eva Place, Edinburgh EH9 3ET	0131-667 1456
Mathieson, Angus R. MA BD	1988	1998	Department of Ministry	21 Traquair Park West, Edinburgh EH12 7AN [E-mail: angus.mathieson@which.net]	0131-334 9774
Moir, Ian A. MA BD	1962	2000	(Adviser for Urban Priority Areas)	28/6 Comely Bank Avenue, Edinburgh EH4 1EL	0131-332 2748
Morrice, William G. MA BD STM PhD	1957	1991	(St John's College Durham)	Flat 37, The Cedars, 2 Manse Road, Edinburgh EH12 7SN [E-mail: w.g.morrice@btinternet.com]	0131-316 4845
Morrison, Mary B. (Mrs) MA BD DipEd	1978	2000	(Edinburgh: Stenhouse St Aidan's)	14 Eildon Terrace, Edinburgh EH3 5LU	0131-556 1962
Morton, Andrew R. MA BD DD	1956	1994	(Board of World Mission and Unity)	11 Oxford Terrace, Edinburgh EH4 1PX	0131-332 6592
Morton, R. Colin BA BD	1960	1998	(Jerusalem)	313 Lanark Road West, Currie EH14 5RS	0131-449 7359
Moyes, Sheila A. (Miss) DCS			(Deaconess)	158 Pilton Avenue, Edinburgh EH5 2JZ	0131-551 1731
Mulligan, Anne (Miss) DCS			Deaconess: Hospital Chaplain's Assistant	27A Craigour Avenue, Edinburgh EH17 1NH	0131-664 3426
Munro, George A.M.	1968	2000	(Edinburgh: Cluny)	108 Caiyside, Edinburgh EH10 7HR	0131-445 5829

Name	Ord	Ind	Position / Charge	Address	Tel
Murison, William G.	1951	1990	(Department of World Mission and Unity)	21 Hailes Gardens, Edinburgh EH13 0IL	0131-441 2460
Murrie, John BD	1953	1996	(Kirkliston)	31 Nicol Road, The Whins, Broxburn EH52 6JJ	01506 852464
Newell, Alison M. (Mrs) BD	1986	2000	Director: Ecumenical Spirituality Prog.	1A Inverleith Terrace, Edinburgh EH3 5NS	
Newell, J. Philip	1982	2000	Scholar in Spirituality: St Giles'	1A Inverleith Terrace, Edinburgh EH3 5NS	
Nicol, Douglas A.O. MA BD	1974	1991	National Mission Secretary	24 Corbiehill Avenue, Edinburgh EH4 5DR	0131-336 1965
O'Neill, John C. BA BD PhD	1960	1996	(University of Edinburgh)	9 Lonsdale Terrace, Edinburgh EH3 9HN	0131-229 6070
Page, Ruth MA BD DPhil	1976	2000	(University of Edinburgh)	7 Seton Place, Edinburgh EH9 2TT	0131-662 4564
Paterson, Ian M. MA	1947	1985	(Eccles with Greenlaw)	45/15 Maidencraig Crescent, Edinburgh EH4 2UU	0131-332 9735
Paterson, J.M.K. MA ACII BD DD	1964	1987	(Milngavie St Paul's)	58 Orchard Drive, Edinburgh EH4 2DZ	0131-332 5876
Paterson, John M.	1976	1987	(Blackbraes and Shieldhill)	28/21 Roseburn Place, Edinburgh EH12 5NX	0131-337 0095
Philip, James MA	1948	1997	(Holyrood Abbey)	3 Ferguson Gardens, Musselburgh EH21 6XF	0131-653 2310
Philp, Connie (Miss) BD	1980	1995	(Arbuthnott with Bervie)	22/5 South Elixa Place, Baronscourt View, Edinburgh EH8 7PG	0131-661 3124
Plate, Maria A.G. (Miss) LTh BA	1983	2000	(South Ronaldsay and Burray)	Flat 29, 77 Barnton Park View, Edinburgh EH4 6EL	0131-339 8539
Porteous, Norman W. DD	1929	1968	(University of Edinburgh)	3 Hermitage Gardens, Edinburgh EH10 6DL	0131-447 4632
Potts, Jean (Miss) DCS			(Deaconess)	28B East Claremont Street, Edinburgh EH7 4JP	0131-557 2144
Rae, David L.	1955	1990	(Kolhapur)	29 Falcon Avenue, Edinburgh EH10 4AL	0131-447 3158
Reid, W. Scott BD MA DipPS PhD	1950	1990	(London Road)	14/37 Ethel Terrace, Edinburgh EH10 5NA	0131-447 7642
Renton, Ian P.	1958	1990	(St Colm's)	98 Homeross House, Strathearn Road, Edinburgh EH9 2QY	0131-447 0601
Ridland, Alistair K. MA BD	1982	2001	Chaplain: Western General Hospital	13 Stewart Place, Kirkliston EH29 0BQ	0131-333 2711
Ronald, Norma A. (Miss) MBE DCS			(Deaconess)	43/26 Gillespie Crescent, Edinburgh EH10 4HY	0131-228 1008
Ross, Andrew C. MA BD STM PhD	1958	1998	(University of Edinburgh)	27 Colinton Road, Edinburgh EH10 5DR	0131-447 5987
Ross, Kenneth R. BA BD PhD	1982	1999	General Secretary, Board of World Mission	c/o 121 George Street, Edinburgh EH2 4YN	0131-225 5722
Sandilands, Ian S.	1986	1999	(Black Mount)	51 Little Road, Edinburgh EH16 6SH	0131-664 6924
Schofield, Melville F. MA	1960	2000	(Chaplain: Western General Hospitals)	25 Rowantree Grove, Currie EH14 5AT	0131-449 4745
Scott, Martin DipMus RSAM BD PhD	1986	2000	Department of Ministry	7/4 Blandfield, Edinburgh EH7 4QJ	0131-477 9584
Searle, David C. MA DipTh	1965	1993	Warden: Rutherford House	38 Rosslyn Crescent, Edinburgh EH6 5AX	0131-554 5713
Sim, John G. MA	1946	1987	(Kirkcaldy Old)	7 Grosvenor Crescent, Edinburgh EH12 5EP	0131-226 3190
Skinner, Donald M. MBE JP FIES	1962	2000	(Edinburgh: Gilmerton)	12 Sraid a Cnoc, Clynder, Helensburgh G84 0QX	
Sloan, Elma C. (Miss) DCS			(Deaconess)		
Steel, David MA BD DD LLD	1936	1976	(Linlithgow St Michael's)	The Elms, 148 Whitehouse Loan, Edinburgh EH9 2EZ	0131-446 6207
Stephen, Donald M. TD MA BD ThM	1962	2001	(Edinburgh: Marchmont St Giles')	10 Hawkhead Crescent, Edinburgh EH16 6LR	0131-658 1216
Stevenson, John MA BD	1963	2001	(Department of Education)	12 Swanston Gardens, Edinburgh EH10 7DL	0131-445 3960
Stiven, Iain K. MA BD	1960	1997	(Strachur and Strathlachlan)	3 Gloucester Place, Edinburgh EH3 6EE	0131-225 8177
Storrar, William F. MA BD PhD	1984	2000	University of Edinburgh	35 Strathalmond Park, Edinburgh EH4 8AH	
Taylor, Howard G. BSc BD MTh	1971	1998	Chaplain: Heriot Watt University	The Chaplaincy, Heriot Watt University, Riccarton, Currie EH14 4AS	0131-449 5111 (ext 4508)
Teague, Yvonne (Mrs) DCS	1978	2001	Board of Ministry	46 Craigcrook Avenue, Edinburgh EH4 3PX	0131-336 3113
Telfer, Iain J. BD DPS	1951	1981	Chaplain: Royal Infirmary	32 Alnwickhill Park, Edinburgh EH16 6UH	0131-536 3084
Thom, Helen (Miss) DCS			(Deaconess)	84 Great King Street, Edinburgh EH3 6QU	0131-556 5687
Thomson, J.G.S.S. MA BD BA PhD	1954	1989	(Wigtown)	4 Drum Brae South, Edinburgh EH12 8SJ	0131-334 6035
Torrance, James B. MA BD	1940	1979	(University of Aberdeen)	3 Greenbank Crescent, Edinburgh EH10 5TE	0131-447 3230
Torrance, Thomas F. MBE DLitt DD DSc DrTheol DrTheol FBA FRSE	1941	1981	(University of Edinburgh)	37 Braid Farm Road, Edinburgh EH10 6LE	
Walker, R.W. MB ChB			(Lesmahagow Abbeygreen)	39/22 Blackford Avenue, Edinburgh EH9 3HN	0131-667 0578

Name	Years	Role	Address	Phone
Whyte, Iain A. BA BD STM	1968 2001	Community Mental Health Chaplain	41 George IV Bridge, Edinburgh EH1 1EL	0131-220 5150
Wigglesworth, J. Christopher MBE BSc PhD BD	1967 1999	(St Andrew's College, Selly Oak)	12 Leven Terrace, Edinburgh EH3 9LW	0131-228 6335
Wilkie, James L. MA BD	1959 1998	(Board of World Mission)	7 Comely Bank Avenue, Edinburgh EH4 1EW [E-mail: jl.wilkie@btinternet.com]	0131-343 1552
Wilkinson, John BD MD FRCP DTM&H	1946 1975	(Kikuyu)	70 Craigleith Hill Gardens, Edinburgh EH4 2JH	0131-332 2994
Williams, Jenny M. (Miss) BSc CQSW BD	1996 1997	Christian Fellowship of Healing	16 Blantyre Terrace, Edinburgh EH10 5AE	0131-447 0050
Wilson, John M. MA	1964 1995	(Adviser in Religious Education)	27 Bellfield Street, Edinburgh EH15 2BR	0131-669 5257
Young, Alexander W. BD DipMin	1988 1999	Chaplain: Western General Hospitals	19B Craigour Drive, Edinburgh EH17 7NY	0131-664 0388

EDINBURGH ADDRESSES

Church	Address
Albany	Albany Street
Balerno	Johnsburn Road, Balerno
Barclay	Barclay Place
Blackhall St Columba	Queensferry Road
Bristo Memorial	Peffermill Road, Craigmillar
Broughton St Mary's	Bellevue Crescent
Canongate	Canongate
Carrick Knowe	North Saughton Road
Cluny	Cluny Gardens
Colinton	Dell Road
Colinton Mains	Oxgangs Road North
Corstorphine	
Craigsbank	Craig's Crescent
Old	Kirk Loan
St Anne's	Kaimes Road
St Ninian's	St John's Road
Craigentinny	
St Christopher's	Craigentinny Road
Craiglockhart	Craiglockhart Avenue
Craigmillar Park	Craigmillar Park
Cramond	Cramond Glebe Road
Currie	Kirkgate, Currie
Davidson's Mains	Quality Street
Dean	Dean Path
Drylaw	Groathill Road North
Duddingston	Old Church Lane, Duddingston
Fairmilehead	Frogston Road West, Fairmilehead
Gilmerton	Ravenscroft Street
Gorgie	Gorgie Road
Granton	Boswall Parkway
Greenbank	Braidburn Terrace
Greenside	Royal Terrace
Greyfriars Tolbooth and Highland Kirk	Greyfriars Place
High (St Giles')	High Street
Holyrood Abbey	Dalziel Place x London Road
Holy Trinity	Hailesland Place, Wester Hailes
Inverleith	Inverleith Gardens
Juniper Green	Lanark Road, Juniper Green
Kaimes Lockhart Memorial	Gracemount Drive
Kirkliston	The Square, Kirkliston
Kirk o' Field	Pleasance
Leith	
North	Madeira Street off Ferry Road
St Andrew's	Easter Road
St Serf's	Ferry Road
St Thomas' Junction Road	
Junction Road	Great Junction Street
South	Kirkgate, Leith
Wardie	Primrosebank Road
Liberton	Kirkgate, Liberton
Northfield	Gilmerton Road, Liberton
London Road	London Road
Marchmont St Giles'	Kilgraston Road
Mayfield Salisbury	Mayfield Road x West Mayfield
Morningside Braid	Nile Grove
Morningside United	Bruntsfield Place x Chamberlain Road
Muirhouse St Andrew's	Pennywell Gardens
Murrayfield	Abinger Gardens
Newhaven	Craighall Road
New Restalrig	Willowbrae Road
Old Kirk	Pennywell Road
Palmerston Place	Palmerston Place
Pilrig St Paul's	Pilrig Street
Polwarth	Polwarth Terrace x Harrison Road
Portobello	
Old	Bellfield Street
St James'	Rosefield Place
St Philip's, Joppa	Abercorn Terrace
Priestfield	Dalkeith Road x Marchhall Place
Queensferry	The Loan, South Queensferry
Ratho	Baird Road, Ratho
Reid Memorial	West Savile Terrace
Richmond Craigmillar	Niddrie Mains Road
St Andrew's and St George's	George Street
St Andrew's Clermiston	Clermiston View
St Catherine's Argyle	Grange Road x Chalmers Crescent
St Colm's	Dalry Road x Cathcart Place
St Cuthbert's	Lothian Road
St David's Broomhouse	Broomhouse Crescent
St George's West	Shandwick Place
St John's Oxgangs	Oxgangs Road
St Margaret's	Restalrig Road South
St Martin's	Magdalene Drive
St Michael's	Slateford Road
St Nicholas' Sighthill	Calder Road
St Stephen's Comely Bank	Comely Bank
Slateford Longstone	Kingsknowe Road North
Stenhouse St Aidan's	Chesser Avenue
Stockbridge	Saxe Coburg Street
Tron Kirk Moredun	Ferniside Drive
Viewforth	Gilmore Place

(2) WEST LOTHIAN

Meets in St John's Church Hall, Bathgate, on the first Tuesday of every month, except December, when the meeting is on the second Tuesday, and January, July and August, when there is no meeting.

Clerk: REV. DUNCAN SHAW BD MTh   St John's Manse, Mid Street, Bathgate EH48 1QD   01506 653146
[E-mail: aksph78@uk.uumail.com]

Abercorn linked with Pardovan, Kingscavil and Winchburgh
A. Scott Marshall DipComm BD   1984   1998   The Manse, Winchburgh, Broxburn EH52 6TT   01506 890919
[E-mail: pkwla@aol.com]

Armadale (H)
Vacant
Glenda Wilson (Mrs) DCS   2000   70 Mount Pleasant, Armadale EH48 3HB   01501 730358
118 Old Rows, Seafield, West Lothian EH47 7AW   01506 655298

Avonbridge linked with Torphichen
Clifford R. Acklam BD MTh   1997   2000   Manse Road, Torphichen, Bathgate EH48 4LT   01506 652794
[E-mail: cracklam@waitrose.com]

Bathgate: Boghall (H)
John McLean MA BD   1967   1 Manse Place, Ash Grove, Bathgate EH48 1NJ   01506 652940

Bathgate: High (H)
Ronald G. Greig MA BD   1987   1998   19 Hunter Grove, Bathgate EH48 1NN   01506 652654
[E-mail: ron.greig@care4free.net]

Bathgate: St David's
Elliot G.S. Wardlaw BA BD DipMin   1984   70 Marjoribanks Street, Bathgate EH48 1AH   01506 653177
[E-mail: elliot@stdavidschurch.fsnet.co.uk]

Bathgate: St John's (H)
Duncan Shaw BD MTh   1975   1978   St John's Manse, Mid Street, Bathgate EH48 1QD   01506 653146
[E-mail: duncanshaw@uk.uumail.com]

Blackburn and Seafield
Robert A. Anderson MA BD DPhil   1980   1998   Blackburn, Bathgate EH47 7QR   01506 652825
[E-mail: robertaland@supanet.com]

Blackridge linked with Harthill St Andrew's
H. Warner Hardie BD   1979   East Main Street, Harthill, Shotts ML7 5QW   01501 751239
[E-mail: warner@hardies55.freeserve.co.uk]

Breich Valley
Thomas Preston BD   1978   2001   Stoneyburn, Bathgate EH47 8AU   01501 762018

Broxburn (H)
Richard T. Corbett BSc MSc PhD BD   1992   2 Church Street, Broxburn EH52 5EL
[E-mail: revcorbett@pgen.net]   01506 852825

Fauldhouse: St Andrew's
Elizabeth Smith (Mrs) BD   1996   2000   7 Glebe Court, Fauldhouse, Bathgate EH47 9DX
[E-mail: smithrevb@aol.com]   01501 771190

Harthill St Andrew's See Blackridge

Kirknewton and East Calder
Ann M. Ballentine (Miss) MA BD   1981   1993   8 Manse Court, East Calder EH53 0HF   01506 880802

Kirk of Calder (H)
John M. Povey MA BD   1981   19 Maryfield Park, Mid Calder EH53 0SB
[E-mail: revjpovey@aol.com]   01506 882495

Linlithgow: St Michael's (H)
John L. Paterson MA BD STM   1964   1977   St Michael's Manse, Kirkgate, Linlithgow EH49 7AL
[E-mail: stmichaels@connectfree.co.uk]   01506 842195

Thomas S. Riddell BSc (Aux)   1993   1994   4 The Maltings, Linlithgow EH49 6DS
[E-mail: tsriddell@blueyonder.co.uk]   01506 843251

Linlithgow: St Ninian's Craigmailen (H)
Iain C. Morrison BA BD   1990   29 Philip Avenue, Linlithgow EH49 7BH
[E-mail: cmo2@dial.pipex.com]   01506 845535

Livingston Ecumenical Parish
Incorporating the Worship Centres at:
Carmondean and Craigshill (St Columba's)
Gillean P. Maclean (Mrs) BD   1994   2000   53 Garry Walk, Craigshill, Livingston EH54 5AS
[E-mail: gmaclean@fish.co.uk]   01506 434536

Knightsridge and Ladywell (St Paul's)
Colin R. Douglas MA BD STM   1969   1987   27 Heatherbank, Ladywell, Livingston EH54 6EE
[E-mail: colindouglas@callnetuk.com]   01506 432326

Dedridge (The Lanthorn)
Marion Keston MB ChB MTh   12B Carrick Gardens, Murieston, Livingston EH54 9ET
(Scottish Episcopal Church)   [E-mail: mkeston@fish.co.uk]   01506 410668

Livingston: Old (H)
Graham W. Smith BA BD FSAScot   1995   Manse of Livingston, Charlesfield Lane, Livingston EH54 7AJ   01506 420227

Pardovan, Kingscavil and Winchburgh See Abercorn

Polbeth Harwood linked with West Kirk of Calder (H)
Vacant   27 Learmonth Crescent, West Calder EH55 8AF   01506 870460

Strathbrock
David W. Black BSc BD   1968   Manse Park, Uphall, Broxburn EH52 6NX   01506 852550

Torphichen See Avonbridge

Uphall South (H)
Margaret Steele (Miss) BSc BD   2000   8 Fernlea, Uphall, Broxburn EH52 6DF   01506 852788
[E-mail: msteele@beeb.net]

West Kirk of Calder (H) See Polbeth Harwood

Whitburn: Brucefield (H)
Vacant   Brucefield Drive, Whitburn, Bathgate EH47 8NU   01501 740263

Whitburn: South (H)
Vacant   5 Mansewood Crescent, Whitburn EH47 8HA   01501 740333

Name			Address	Phone
Brough, Robin BA	1968	2002	(Whitburn: Brucefield)	'Kildavanan', 10 Printers Lea, Lennoxtown, Glasgow G66 7GF	01360 310223
Cameron, Ian MA BD	1953	1981	(Kilbrandon and Kilchattan)	37 Burghmuir Court, Linlithgow EH49 7LJ	01506 847987
Crichton, Thomas JP ChStJ MA	1965	1989	Hospital Chaplain	18 Carlton Terrace, Edinburgh EH7 5DD	0131-557 0009
Dickson, A. Stuart	1963	1995	(Glasgow: Govan Old – Assoc)	74 Netherwood Park, Deans, Livingston EH54 8RW	01506 420167
Dundas, Thomas B.S. LTh	1969	1996	(West Kirk of Calder)	35 Coolkill, Sandyford, Dublin 18, Republic of Ireland	00353 12953061
Manson, Robert L. MA DPS	1956	1991	(Chaplain: Royal Edinburgh Hospital)	4 Murieston Drive, Livingston EH54 9AU	01506 434746
Moore, J.W. MA	1950	1983	(Daviot with Rayne)	31 Lennox Gardens, Linlithgow EH49 7PZ	01506 842534
Morrice, Charles S. MA BD PhD	1959	1997	(Kenya)	104 Baron's Hill Avenue, Linlithgow EH49 7JG	01506 847167
Moyes, Andrew	1959	1992	(Broxburn)	5 Grange Road, Broxburn EH52 5HL	01506 858203
Murray, Ronald N.G. MA	1946	1986	(Pardovan and Kingscavil with Winchburgh)	42 Lennox Gardens, Linlithgow EH49 7QA	01506 845680
Nelson, Georgina (Mrs) MA BD PhD DipEd	1990	1995	Hospital Chaplain	6 Pentland Park, Craigshill, Livingston EH54 5NR	01506 434874
Robertson, Emmanuel ThM ThD	1953	1993	(Armadale)	39 Drumcross Road, Bathgate EH48 4HF	01506 654766
Russell, Archibald MA	1949	1991	(Duror with Glencoe)	4 Bonnytoun Avenue, Linlithgow EH49 7JS	01506 842530
Smith, W. Ewing BSc	1962	1994	(Livingston: Old)	8 Hardy Gardens, Bathgate EH48 1NH	01506 652028
Stirling, A. Douglas BSc	1956	1994	(Rhu and Shandon)	162 Avontoun Park, Linlithgow EH49 6QH	01506 845021
				[E-mail: douglas@stirling162.fsnet.co.uk]	
Trimble, Robert DCS			(Deacon)	5 Temple Rise, Dedridge, Livingston EH54 6PJ	01506 412504
Walker, Ian BD MEd DipMS	1943	1984	Parish Education	92 Carse Knowe, Linlithgow EH49 7LG	01506 844412

(3) LOTHIAN

Meets at Musselburgh: St Andrew's High Parish Church on the last Thursday of January and June and the first Thursday of March, April, May, Sepember, October, November and December.

Clerk: MR JOHN D. McCULLOCH DL   Auchindinny House, Penicuik EH26 8PE   01968 676300 (Tel/Fax)
[E-mail: akph65@uk.uumail.com]

Aberlady (H) linked with Gullane (H)
John B. Cairns LTh LLB   1974 2001   Hummel Road, Gullane EH31 2BG   01620 843192

Athelstaneford linked with Whitekirk and Tyninghame
Kenneth D.F. Walker MA BD PhD   1976   The Manse, Athelstaneford, North Berwick EH39 5BE   01620 880378
[E-mail: kandv-walker@connectfree.co.uk]

Belhaven (H) linked with Spott
Laurence H. Twaddle MA BD MTh   1977 1978   Belhaven Road, Dunbar EH42 1NH   01368 863098
[E-mail: revtwaddle@aol.com]

Bolton and Saltoun linked with Humbie linked with Yester (H) (http://www.lbes.demon.co.uk)
Donald Pirie LTh   1975 1999   Tweeddale Avenue, Gifford, Haddington EH41 4QN   01620 810515

Bonnyrigg (H)
John Mitchell LTh CMin   1991   9 Viewbank View, Bonnyrigg EH19 2HU   0131-663 8287 (Tel/Fax)
[E-mail: rev.jmitchell@tiscali.co.uk]

Borthwick (H) linked with Newtongrange (H)
Vacant   7 Maesterton Place, Newtongrange, Dalkeith EH22 4UF   01875 822772

Cockenzie and Port Seton: Chalmers Memorial (H)
Robert L. Glover BMus BD ARCO   1971 1997   Braemar Villa, 2 Links Road, Port Seton, Prestonpans EH32 0HA   01875 812481
[E-mail: rlglover@btinternet.com]

Cockenzie and Port Seton: Old (H)
Vacant   1 Links Road, Port Seton, Prestonpans EH32 0HA   01875 812310

Cockpen and Carrington (H) linked with Lasswade (H) linked with Rosewell (H)
Wendy F. Drake (Mrs) BD   1978 1992   11 Pendreich Terrace, Bonnyrigg EH19 2DT   0131-663 6884

Cranstoun, Crichton and Ford (H) linked with Fala and Soutra (H)
Vacant   Cranstoun Cottage, Ford, Pathhead EH37 5RE   01875 320314

Dalkeith: St John's and King's Park (H)
Keith L. Mack BD MTh DPS | 2002 | 13 Weir Crescent, Dalkeith EH22 3JN [E-mail: kthmacker@aol.com] | 0131-454 0206

Dalkeith: St Nicholas' Buccleuch (H)
Vacant | | 116 Bonnyrigg Road, Dalkeith EH22 3HZ | 0131-663 3036

Dirleton (H) (E-mail: dirletonkirk@hotmail.com) linked with North Berwick: Abbey (H) (01620 890110) (E-mail: abbeychurch@hotmail.com)
David J. Graham BSc BD PhD | 1982 1998 | 20 Westgate, North Berwick EH39 4AF [E-mail: davidjohn@grahams.fsbusiness.co.uk] | 01620 892410

Dunbar (H)
Eric W. Foggitt MA BSc BD | 1991 2000 | The Manse, Bayswell Road, Dunbar EH42 1AB [E-mail: ericleric3@btopenworld.com] | 01368 863749 (Tel/Fax)

Dunglass
Anne R. Lithgow (Mrs) MA BD | 1992 1994 | The Manse, Cockburnspath TD13 5XZ [E-mail: anne.lithgow@btinternet.com] | 01368 830713

Fala and Soutra See Cranstoun, Crichton and Ford

Garvald and Morham linked with Haddington: West (H)
Cameron Mackenzie BD | 1997 | 15 West Road, Haddington EH41 3RD | 01620 822213

Gladsmuir linked with Longniddry (H)
A. Graham Black MA | 1964 1973 | The Manse, Elcho Road, Longniddry EH32 0LB [E-mail: grablack@aol.com] | 01875 853195

Florence A. Underwood (Mrs) BD (Assist) | 1992 | The Shieling, Main Street, Stenton, Dunbar EH42 1TE | 01368 850629

Glencorse (H) linked with Roslin (H)
James A. Manson LTh | 1981 | 38 Penicuik Road, Roslin EH25 9LH [E-mail: jamanson@supanet.com] | 0131-440 2012

Gorebridge (H)
Mark S. Nicholas MA BD | 1999 | 100 Hunterfield Road, Gorebridge EH23 4TT [E-mail: mark.nicholas@fish.co.uk] | 01875 820387

Gullane See Aberlady

Haddington: St Mary's (H) (http://ourworld/compuserve.com/homepages/Russell-Darling)
James M. Cowie BD | 1977 2002 | 21 Sidegate, Haddington EH41 4BZ [E-mail: jim@jimcowie.demon.co.uk] | 01620 823109

Haddington: West See Garvald and Morham

Howgate (H) linked with Penicuik: South (H)
Frank Ribbons MA BD DipEd   1985   18 Broomhill Avenue, Penicuik EH26 9EG   01968 674692

Humbie See Bolton and Saltoun
Lasswade See Cockpen and Carrington

Loanhead
Graham L. Duffin BSc BD DipEd   1989 2001   120 The Loan, Loanhead EH20 9AJ   0131-448 2459
[E-mail: gduffin@xalt.co.uk]

Longniddry See Gladsmuir

Musselburgh: Northesk (H)
Alison P. Matheson MA BD   1991 1998   16 New Street, Musselburgh EH21 6JP   0131-665 2128
[E-mail: alison.matheson@btinternet.com]

Musselburgh: St Andrew's High (H) (0131-665 7239)
Ian Andrew MA BD   2001   8 Ferguson Drive, Musselburgh EH21 6XA   0131-665 5583
[E-mail: sahmin@fish.co.uk]

Musselburgh: St Clement's and St Ninian's
Moira McDonald MA BD   1997   Wallyford Loan Road, Wallyford, Musselburgh EH21 8BU   0131-653 6588
[E-mail: moira.mc@tesco.net]
Gordon R. Steven BD DCS   51 Nantwich Drive, Edinburgh EH7 6RB   0131-669 2054

Musselburgh: St Michael's Inveresk
Andrew B. Dick BD DipMin   1986 1999   8 Hope Place, Musselburgh EH21 7QE   0131-665 0545
[E-mail: dixbit@aol.com]

Newbattle (H) (http://freespace.virgin.net/newbattle.focus)
Vacant   70 Newbattle Abbey Crescent, Dalkeith EH22 3LW   0131-663 3245

Newton
Jan E. Gillies (Mrs) BD   1998 2001   The Manse, Newton, Dalkeith EH22 1SR   0131-663 3845
[E-mail: jgillies@fish.co.uk]

Newtongrange See Borthwick
North Berwick: Abbey See Dirleton

North Berwick: St Andrew Blackadder (H) (http://www.users.zetnet.co.uk/st-andrew-blackadder)
Vacant   7 Marine Parade, North Berwick EH39 4LD   01620 892132

Ormiston linked with Pencaitland
Mark Malcolm MA BD   1999   Pencaitland Manse, Pencaitland, Tranent EH34 5DL   01875 340208
[E-mail: mark.minister@virgin.net]

Pencaitland See Ormiston

Penicuik: North (H)
John W. Fraser MA BD   1974   1982   93 John Street, Penicuik EH26 8AG   01968 672213
[E-mail: john1946@fish.co.uk]

Penicuik: St Mungo's (H)
William D. Irving LTh   1985   31a Kirkhill Road, Penicuik EH26 8JB   01968 672916
[E-mail: wdi@freeuk.com]

Penicuik: South See Howgate

Prestonpans: Prestongrange
Robert R. Simpson BA BD   1994   East Loan, Prestonpans EH32 9ED   01875 810308
[E-mail: robert@pansmanse.co.uk]

Christine A.Y. Ritchie (Mrs) BD (Aux)   2002   Through-Gate, 78 High Street, Dunbar EH42 1JH   01368 863141
[E-mail: critchie@fish.co.uk]

Rosewell See Cockpen and Carrington
Roslin See Glencorse
Spott See Belhaven

Tranent
Thomas M. Hogg BD   1986   244 Church Street, Tranent EH33 1BW   01875 610210
[E-mail: tom@hoggtran.freeserve.co.uk]

Traprain
Howard J. Haslett BA BD   1972   2000   Preston Road, East Linton EH40 3DS   01620 860227 (Tel/Fax)
[E-mail: howard.haslett@btopenworld.com]

Whitekirk and Tyninghame See Athelstaneford
Yester See Bolton and Saltoun

Name				Address	Tel
Adamson, T. Sidney S. MA BD	1937	1985	(Musselburgh: St Michael's Inveresk)	48 Hailes Gardens, Edinburgh EH13 0JH	0131-441 2471
Brown, Ronald H.	1974	1998	(Musselburgh: Northesk)	6 Monktonhall Farm Cottages, Musselburgh EH21 6RZ	0131-653 2531
Brown, William BD	1972	1997	(Edinburgh: Polwarth)	13 Thornyhall, Dalkeith EH22 2ND	(Tel/Fax) 0131-654 0929
Chalmers, William R. MA BD STM	1953	1992	(Dunbar)	18 Forest Road, Burghead, Elgin IV30 5XL	01343 835674
Day, Colin T. MA	1947	1984	(Warden, Carberry Tower)	20 Hadfast Road, Cousland, Dalkeith EH22 2NU	0131-660 5777
Donaldson, Colin V.	1982	1998	(Ormiston with Pencaitland)	3A Playfair Terrace, St Andrews KY16 9HX	01334 472889
Fraser, John W. BEM MA BD PhD	1950	1983	(Farnell)	12 Quarryfoot Green, Bonnyrigg EH19 2EJ	0131-663 8037
Gilfillan, James LTh	1968	1997	(East Kilbride: Old)	15 Long Cram, Haddington EH41 4NS	01620 824843
Hill, Arthur T.	1940	1981	(Ormiston with Prestonpans: Grange)	8A Hamilton Road, North Berwick EH39 4NA	01620 893961
Hutchison, Alan E.W.			(Deacon)	132 Lochbridge Road, North Berwick EH39 4DR	01620 894077
Levison, L. David MA BD	1943	1982	(Ormiston with Pencaitland)	Westdene Conservatory Flat, 506 Perth Road, Dundee DD2 1LS	01382 630460
Macdonell, Alasdair W. MA BD	1955	1992	(Haddington: St Mary's)	St Andrews Cottage, Duns Road, Gifford, Haddington EH41 4QW	01620 810341

Name			Place	Address	Tel
Macrae, Norman C. MA DipEd	1942	1985	(Loanhead)	49 Lixmount Avenue, Edinburgh EH5 3EW [E-mail: nandc.macrae@btopenworld.com]	0131-552 2428
Maule-Brown, Robert MA	1949	1985	(Strathy and Halladale)	5 Acredales Walk, Haddington EH41 4RR	01620 824959
Ritchie, James McL. MA BD	1950	1985	(Coalsnaughton)	46 St James's Gardens, Penicuik EH26 9DU [E-mail: ritchjm@aol.com]	01968 676123
Robertson, James LTh	1970	2000	(Newton)	11 Southfield Square, Edinburgh EH15 1QS	
Sanderson, W. Roy DD	1933	1973	(Stenton with Whittinghame)	20 Craigleith View, Station Road, North Berwick EH39 4BF	01620 892780
Sawers, E.A.H. VRD	1950	1989	(Cranstoun Crichton and Ford with Fala and Soutra)		
Swan, Andrew F. BD	1983	2000	(Loanhead)	18 Lydgait Gardens, Haddington EH41 3DB	01620 825830
Thomson, William H.	1964	1999	(Edinburgh: Liberton Northfield)	3 Mackenzie Gardens, Dolphinton, West Linton EH46 7HS	01968 682247
				3 Baird's Way, Bonnyrigg EH19 3NS [E-mail: w.h.thomson@tesco.net]	0131-654 9799
Torrance, David W. MA BD	1955	1991	(Earlston)	38 Forth Street, North Berwick EH39 4JQ [E-mail:dwtmet@connectfree.co.uk]	(Tel/Fax) 01620 895109
Underwood, Geoffrey H. BD DipTh FPhS	1964	1992	(Cockenzie and Port Seton: Chalmers Memorial)	The Shieling, Main Street, Stenton, Dunbar EH42 1TE	01368 850629
Whiteford, David H. CBE MA BD PhD	1943	1985	(Gullane)	3 Old Dean Road, Longniddry EH32 0QY	01875 852980

(4) MELROSE AND PEEBLES

Meets at Innerleithen, on the first Tuesday of February, March, May, October, November, December, and on the fourth Tuesday of June, and in places to be appointed on the first Tuesday of September.

Clerk: REV. ALASDAIR J. MORTON   8 Ormiston Grove, Melrose TD6 9SR   **01896 822033**
MA BD DipEd FEIS   [E-mail: akph66@uk.uumail.com]

Ashkirk linked with Selkirk (H)
James W. Campbell BD   1995   1 Loanside, Selkirk TD7 4DJ   01750 22833
[E-mail: revjimashkirk@aol.com]

Bowden (H) linked with Newtown
Joseph F. Crawford BA   1970 2000   The Manse, Newtown St Boswells, Melrose TD6 0PL   01835 822106

Broughton, Glenholm and Kilbucho (H) linked with Skirling linked with Stobo and Drumelzier linked with Tweedsmuir (H)
Rachel J.W. Dobie (Mrs) LTh   1991 1996   The Manse, Broughton, Biggar ML12 6HQ   01899 830331
[E-mail: revracheldobie@aol.com]

Caddonfoot (H) linked with Galashiels St Ninian's (H)
Hilary W. Smith (Miss) BD DipMin MTh PhD 1999   Mossilee Road, Galashiels TD1 1NF   01896 752058

Carlops linked with Kirkurd and Newlands (H) linked with West Linton St Andrew's (H)
Thomas W. Burt BD   1982 1985   The Manse, West Linton, Peeblesshire EH46 7EN   01968 660221

Channelkirk linked with Lauder: Old
John M. Shields MBE LTh   1972 1997   Brownsmuir Park, Lauder, Berwickshire TD2 6QD   01578 722320

Earlston
Michael D. Scouler MBE BSc BD   1988 1992   The Manse, High Street, Earlston, Berwickshire TD4 6DE
[E-mail: michaelscouler@talk21.com]   01896 849236

Eddleston (H) linked with Peebles Old (H)
Malcolm M. Macdougall BD   1981 2001   The Old Manse, Innerleithen Road, Peebles EH45 8BD
[E-mail: calum.macdougall@lineone.net]   01721 720568

Ettrick and Yarrow
Vacant   Yarrow Manse, Yarrow, Selkirk TD7 5LA   01750 82219

Galashiels: Old and St Paul's (H)
Leslie M. Steele MA BD   1973 1988   Barr Road, Galashiels TD1 3HX
[E-mail: lms@stpauls.worldonline.co.uk]   01896 752320

Galashiels: St Aidan's (H)
Vacant   High Road, Galashiels TD1 2BD   01896 752420

Galashiels: St John's (H)
Stephen F. Clipston MA BD   1982   Hawthorn Road, Galashiels TD1 2JZ
[E-mail: steve.clipston@btinternet.com]   01896 752573 (Tel)
01896 758561 (Fax)

Galashiels: St Ninian's See Caddonfoot

Innerleithen (H), Traquair and Walkerburn
Janice M. Faris (Mrs) BSc BD   1991 2001   The Manse, 1 Millwell Park, Innerleithen, Peebles EH44 6JF   01896 830309

Kirkurd and Newlands See Carlops
Lauder: Old See Channelkirk

Lyne and Manor
Nancy M. Norman (Miss) BA MDiv MTh   1988 1998   25 March Street, Peebles EH45 8EP   01721 721699

Maxton and Mertoun linked with St Boswells
Bruce F. Neill MA BD   1966 1996   St Modans Manse, Main Street, St Boswells, Melrose TD6 0BB
[E-mail: bneill@fish.co.uk]   01835 822255

Melrose (H)
Alistair G. Bennett BSc BD   1978 1984   Tweedmount Road, Melrose, Roxburghshire TD6 9ST
[E-mail: agbennettmelrose@aol.com]   01896 822217

Newtown See Bowden
Peebles: Old See Eddleston

Peebles: St Andrew's Leckie (H)
James H. Wallace MA BD   1973   1983   Mansefield, Innerleithen Road, Peebles EH45 8BE   01721 721749 (Tel/Fax)
[E-mail: jimwallace10@freeuk.com]

St Boswells See Maxton and Mertoun
Selkirk See Ashkirk
Skirling See Broughton, Glenholm and Kilbucho
Stobo and Drumelzier See Broughton, Glenholm and Kilbucho

Stow: St Mary of Wedale and Heriot
Catherine Buchan (Mrs) MA MDiv   2002   The Manse, 209 Galashiels Road, Stow, Galashiels TD1 2RE   01578 730237

Tweedsmuir See Broughton, Glenholm and Kilbucho
West Linton St Andrew's See Carlops

Name			Charge	Address	Tel
Brown, Robert BSc	1962	1997	(Kilbrandon and Kilchattan)	11 Thornfield Terrace, Selkirk TD7 4DU [E-mail: thornfield@ukgateway.net]	01750 20311
Cashman, P. Hamilton BSc	1985	1998	(Dirleton with North Berwick: Abbey)	38 Abbotsford Road, Galashiels TD1 3HR	01896 752711
Devenny, Robert P.	2002		Borders Health Board	Blakeburn Cottage, Wester Housebyres, Melrose TD6 9BW	01896 822350
Dick, J. Ronald BD	1973	1996	Hospital Chaplain	5 Georgefield Farm Cottages, Earlston TD4 6BH	01896 848956
Donald, Thomas W. LTh CA	1977	1987	(Bowden with Lilliesleaf)	The Quest, Huntly Road, Melrose TD6 9SB	01896 822345
Duncan, Charles A. MA	1956	1992	(Heriot with Stow St Mary of Wedale)	10 Elm Grove, Galashiels TD1 3JA	01896 753261
Kellet, John M. MA	1962	1995	(Leith: South)	4 High Cottages, Walkerburn, Peeblesshire EH43 6QW	01896 870351
Kennon, Stanley BA BD	1992	2000	Chaplain: Navy	1 Anson Way, Helston, Cornwall TR13 8BS	
Laing, William F. DSC VRD MA	1952	1986	(Selkirk: St Mary's West)	10 The Glebe, Selkirk TD7 5AB	01750 21210
McCann, George McD. BSc ATI	1994		Auxiliary Minister	Rosbeg, Parsonage Road, Galashiels TD1 3HS	01896 752055
MacFarlane, David C. MA	1957	1997	(Eddleston with Peebles Old)	61 Viewlands Road, Perth PH1 1ND	01738 624996
Moore, W. Haisley MA	1966	1996	(Secretary: The Boys' Brigade)	26 Tweedbank Avenue, Tweedbank, Galashiels TD1 3SP	01896 668577
Morton, Alasdair J. MA BD DipEd FEIS	1960	2000	(Bowden with Newtown)	8 Ormiston Grove, Melrose TD6 9SR [E-mail: alasgilmor@compuserve.com]	01896 822033
Morton, Gillian M. (Mrs) MA BD PGCE	1983	1996	(Hospital Chaplain)	8 Ormiston Grove, Melrose TD6 9SR	01896 822033
Rae, Andrew W.	1951	1987	(Anman: St Andrew's Greenknowe Erskine)	Roseneuk, Tweedside Road, Newtown St Boswells TD6 0PQ	01835 823783
Slack, J.W.	1968	1985	(Ashkirk with Selkirk Lawson Memorial)	17 Grenville Avenue, St Anne's-on-Sea, Fylde FY8 2RR	01253 728863
Taverner, Glyn R. MA BD	1957	1995	(Maxton and Mertoun with St Boswells)	Woodcot Cottage, Waverley Road, Innerleithen EH44 6QW	01896 830156
Thomson, G.F.M. MA	1956	1988	(Dollar Associate)	49 High Cross Avenue, Melrose TD6 9SX	01896 823112

(5) DUNS

Meets at Duns, in the Old Parish Church Hall, normally on the first Tuesday of February, March, April, May, October, November, December, on the last Tuesday in June, and in places to be appointed on the first Tuesday of September.

Clerk: REV. JAMES S.H. CUTLER BD CEng MIStructE   The Manse, Duns Road, Coldstream TD12 4DP   **01890 882537**
[E-mail: akph49@uk.uumail.com]

Ayton (H) and Burnmouth linked with Grantshouse and Houndwood and Reston
Vacant   Grey Gables, Beanburn, Ayton, Eyemouth TD14 5QY   01890 781333

Berwick-upon-Tweed: St Andrew's Wallace Green (H) and Lowick
Vacant   1999   3 Meadow Grange, Berwick-upon-Tweed TD15 1NW   01289 303304

Bonkyl and Preston linked with Chirnside (H) linked with Edrom Allanton (H)
Celia G. Kenny (Mrs) BA MTh   1995 2002   Parish Church Manse, Chirnside, Duns TD11 3XL   01890 818911

Chirnside See Bonkyl and Preston

Coldingham and St Abb's linked with Eyemouth
Daniel G. Lindsay BD   1978 1979   Victoria Road, Eyemouth TD14 5JD   01890 750327

Coldstream (H) linked with Eccles
James S.H. Cutler BD CEng MIStructE   1986 1995   Duns Road, Coldstream TD12 4DP   01890 882537
[E-mail: akph49@uk.uumail.com]

Duns (H)
Andrew A. Morrice MA BD   1999   The Manse, Duns, Berwickshire TD11 3DP   01361 883755
[E-mail: andrew.morrice@ntlworld.com]

Eccles See Coldstream
Edrom Allanton See Bonkyl and Preston
Eyemouth See Coldingham and St Abb's

Fogo and Swinton linked with Ladykirk linked with Leitholm linked with Whitsome (H)
Alan C.D. Cartwright BSc BD   1976   Swinton, Duns TD11 3JJ   01890 860228

Foulden and Mordington linked with Hutton and Fishwick and Paxton
Geraldine H. Hope (Mrs) MA BD   1986   Hutton, Berwick upon Tweed TD15 1TS   01289 386396
[E-mail: geraldine.hope@virgin.net]

Gordon: St Michael's linked with Greenlaw (H) linked with Legerwood linked with Westruther
Thomas S. Nicholson BD DPS   1982 1995   The Manse, Todholes, Greenlaw, Berwickshire TD10 6XD   01361 810316

Grantshouse and Houndwood and Reston See Ayton and Burnmouth
Greenlaw See Gordon St Michael's
Hutton and Fishwick and Paxton See Foulden and Mordington

Kirk of Lammermuir linked with Langton and Polwarth
Vacant   The Manse, Cranshaws, Duns TD11 3SJ   01361 890289

Ladykirk See Fogo and Swinton
Langton and Polwarth See Kirk of Lammermuir
Legerwood See Gordon St Michael's
Leitholm See Fogo and Swinton
Westruther See Gordon St Michael's
Whitsome See Fogo and Swinton

Name				Address	Phone
Gaddes, Donald R.	1961	1994	(Kelso North and Ednam)	35 Winterfield Gardens, Duns TD11 3EZ [E-mail: doruga@winterfield.fslife.co.uk]	01361 883172
Gale, Ronald A.A. LTh	1982	1995	(Dunoon Old and St Cuthbert's)	55 Lennel Mount, Coldstream TD12 4NS	01890 883699
Hay, Bruce J L.	1957	1997	(Makerstoun and Smailholm with Stichill, Hume and Nenthorn)	Tweed House, Tweed Street, Berwick-upon-Tweed TD15 1NG	01289 303171
Higham, Robert D. BD	1985	2002	(Tiree)	36 Low Greens, Berwick-upon-Tweed TD15 1LZ	01289 302329
Jackson, John MA	1958	1990	(Bonnybridge)	2 Milne Graden West, Coldstream TD12 4HE	01890 883435
Kerr, Andrew MA BLitt	1948	1991	(Kilbarchan West)	Meikle Harelaw, Westruther, Gordon, Berwickshire TD10 6XT	01578 740263
Macleod, Allan M. MA	1945	1985	(Gordon St Michael's with Legerwood with Westruther)	Silverlea, Machrihanish, Argyll PA28 6PZ	
Paterson, William BD	1977	2001	(Bonkyl and Preston with Chirnside with Edrom Allanton)	Benachie, Gavinton, Duns TD11 3QT	01361 882727
Slorach, Alexander CA BD	1970	2002	(Kirk of Lammermuir with Langton and Polwarth)	61 Inverleith Row, Edinburgh EH3 5PX	

(6) JEDBURGH

Meets at Jedburgh on the first Wednesday of February, March, May, October, November and December and on the last Wednesday of June. Meets in the Moderator's church on the first Wednesday of September.

Clerk   REV. ALAN D. REID MA BD   23 Langholm Street, Newcastleton TD9 0QX   01387 375242
    [E-mail: akph56@uk.uumail.com]
    [E-mail: jedburghpresbytery@uk.uumail.com]

Ancrum linked with Crailing and Eckford with Lilliesleaf (T)
W. Frank Campbell BA BD   1989 1991   22 The Glebe, Ancrum, Jedburgh TD8 6UX   01835 830318

Bedrule linked with Denholm (H) linked with Minto linked with Hobkirk and Southdean
Vacant   Denholm, Hawick TD9 8NB   01450 870268

Cavers and Kirkton linked with Hawick St Mary's and Old
William R. Taylor MA BD   1983   1998   Braid Road, Hawick TD9 9LZ   01450 377865
                                                                            [E-mail: revwrt@aol.com]

Crailing and Eckford See Ancrum
Denholm See Bedrule

Hawick: Burnfoot
Charles J. Finnie LTh DPS   1991   1997   29 Wilton Hill, Hawick TD9 8BA   01450 373181
                                                                            [E-mail: charles@finnierev.freeserve.co.uk]
Ronald M. Mackinnon DCS   70 Eildon Road, Hawick TD9 8ES   01450 374816 (Tel)
                                                                                                                                 07808 117538 (Mbl)

Hawick: Teviot (H) and Roberton
Neil R. Combe BSc MSc BD   1984   Buccleuch Road, Hawick TD9 0EL   01450 372150
                                                                            [E-mail: neil.combe@btinternet.com]

Hawick: St Mary's and Old (H) See Cavers and Kirkton

Hawick: Trinity (H)
E.P. Lindsay Thomson MA   1964   1972   Fenwick Park, Hawick TD9 9PA   01450 372705

Hawick: Wilton linked with Teviothead
Vacant   4 Wilton Hill Terrace, Hawick TD9 8BE   01450 370744

Hobkirk and Southdean See Bedrule

Jedburgh: Old and Edgerston
Bruce McNicol JP BL BD   1967   1992   Honeyfield Drive, Jedburgh TD8 6LQ   01835 863417

Jedburgh: Trinity
John A. Riddell MA BD   1967   42 High Street, Jedburgh TD8 6DQ   01835 863223

Kelso: North (H) and Ednam (H) (01573 224154)
Tom McDonald BD   1994   20 Forestfield, Kelso TD5 7BX   01573 224677
                                                                            [E-mail: revtom@20thepearlygates.fsnet.co.uk]

Kelso: Old (H) and Sprouston
Marion E. Dodd MA BD LRAM   1988   1989   Glebe Lane, Kelso, Roxburghshire TD5 7AU   01573 226254
                                                                            [E-mail: mariondodd@macunlimited.net]

Liddesdale (H)
Alan D. Reid MA BD   1989   23 Langholm Street, Newcastleton TD9 0QX   01387 375242
                                                                            [E-mail: liddesdale@uk.uumail.com]

Lilliesleaf See Ancrum

Linton linked with Morebattle and Hownam linked with Yetholm (H)
Robin D. McHaffie BD   1979   1991   Kirk Yetholm, Kelso TD5 8RD   01573 420308
[E-mail: robin.mchaffie@virgin.net]

Makerstoun and Smailholm linked with Roxburgh linked with Stichill, Hume and Nenthorn
Valerie G.C. Watson (Ms) MA BD STM   1987 2001   The Manse, 1 The Meadow, Stichill, Kelso TD5 7TG   01573 470607
[E-mail: vwatson@tiscali.co.uk]

Minto See Bedrule
Morebattle and Hownam See Linton

Oxnam
Continued Vacancy

Roxburgh See Makerstoun and Smailholm
Stitchill, Hume and Nenthorn See Makerstoun and Smailholm
Teviothead See Hawick: Wilton
Yetholm See Linton

Name			Charge	Address	Phone
Bowie, Adam McC.	1976	1996	(Cavers and Kirkton with Hobkirk and Southdean)	Glenbield, Redpath, Earlston TD4 6AD	01896 848173
Brown, Joseph MA	1954	1991	(Linton with Hownam and Morebattle with Yetholm)	The Orchard, Hermitage Lane, Shedden Park Road, Kelso TD5 7AN	01573 223481
Fox, G. Dudley A.	1972	1988	(Kelso Old)	14 Pinnacle Hill Farm, Kelso TD5 8HD	01573 223335
Hamilton, Robert MA BD	1938	1979	(Kelso Old)	Ridge Cottage, 391 Totnes Road, Collaton St Mary, Paignton TQ4 7PW	01803 526440
Longmuir, William LTh	1984	2001	(Bedrule with Denholm with Minto)	112 Weensland Road, Hawick TD9 9PH	01450 379460
McConnell, Robert	1959	1983	(Hawick St Margaret's and Wilton South with Roberton)	Flat 9, Queensfort Court, Carryduff, Belfast BT8 8NF	
Ritchie, Garden W.M.	1961	1995	(Ardersier with Petty)	23 Croft Road, Kelso TD5 7EP	01573 224419
Thompson, W.M.D. MA	1950	1997	(Crailing and Eckford with Oxnam with Roxburgh)	The Old Manse, Oxnam, Jedburgh TD8 6RD	01835 862492

HAWICK ADDRESSES

Burnfoot	Fraser Avenue
St Mary's and Old	Kirk Wynd
Teviot	off Buccleuch Road
Trinity	Central Square
Wilton	Princes Street

(7) ANNANDALE AND ESKDALE

Meets on the first Tuesday of February, May, September and December, and the third Tuesday of March, June and October, in a venue to be determined by Presbytery.

Clerk:	REV. C. BRYAN HASTON LTh	The Manse, Gretna Green DG16 5DU [E-mail: akph37@uk.uumail.com] [E-mail: cbhaston@uk.uumail.com]	01461 338313 (Tel) 08701 640119 (Fax)

Annan: Old (H)
Vacant
12 Plumdon Park Avenue, Annan DG12 6EY
01461 201405

Annan: St Andrew's (H)
George K. Lind BD MCIBS   1998
1 Annerley Road, Annan DG12 6HE
[E-mail: gklind@bosinternet.com]
01461 202626

Applegarth and Sibbaldbie (H) linked with Johnstone linked with Lochmaben (H)
Jack M. Brown BSc BD   1977   2002
Lochmaben, Lockerbie DG11 1QF
01387 810590

Brydekirk linked with Hoddam
S. Edwin P. Beveridge BA   1959   1993
Ecclefechan, Lockerbie DG11 3BU
01576 300357

Canonbie (H)
Vacant
9 Watchhill Park, Canonbie DG11 0TD
01387 371200

Carlisle: Chapel Street linked with Longtown: St Andrew's
David J. Thom BD   2000   2002
30 Dunmail Drive, Carlisle CA2 6DF
[E-mail: david@kirkscotland.org.uk]
01228 819832

Dalton linked with Hightae linked with St Mungo
Alexander C. Stoddart BD   2001
Hightae, Lockerbie DG11 1JL
[E-mail: sandystoddart@netscapeonline.co.uk]
01387 811499

Dornock
Ronald S. Seaman MA   1967
Dornock, Annan DG12 6NR
01461 40268

Eskdalemuir linked with Hutton and Corrie linked with Tundergarth
Vacant
Hutton Manse, Boreland, Lockerbie DG11 2PB
01576 610213

Gretna: Old (H), Gretna: St Andrew's and Half Morton and Kirkpatrick Fleming
C. Bryan Haston LTh   1975
The Manse, Gretna Green DG16 5DU
[E-mail: cbhaston@cofs.demon.co.uk]
01461 338313 (Tel)
08701 640119 (Fax)

Hightae See Dalton
Hoddam See Brydekirk
Hutton and Corrie See Eskdalemuir

Johnstone See Applegarth and Sibbaldbie

Kirkpatrick Juxta linked with Moffat St Andrew's (H) linked with Wamphray
David M. McKay MA BD   1979   2001   The Manse, 1 Meadowbank, Moffat DG10 9LR   01683 220128 (Tel)
01683 220758 (Fax)

Kirtle-Eaglesfield linked with Middlebie linked with Waterbeck
Trevor C. Williams LTh   1990   1999   Kirtlebridge, Lockerbie DG11 3LY   01461 500378
[E-mail: revwill@tinyworld.co.uk]

Langholm, Ewes and Westerkirk
Robert B. Milne BTh   1999   1999   Langholm DG13 0BL   01387 380252
[E-mail: rbmilne@aol.com]   01387 381399 (Fax)

Lochmaben See Applegarth and Sibbaldbie

Lockerbie: Dryfesdale
David M. Almond BD   1996   The Manse, 5 Carlisle Road, Lockerbie DG11 2DW   01576 202361

Longtown: St Andrew's See Carlisle: Chapel Street
Middlebie See Kirtle-Eaglesfield

Moffat St Andrew's (H) linked with Wamphray See Kirkpatrick Juxta

St Mungo See Dalton
Tundergarth See Eskdalemuir
Wamphray See Moffat St Andrew's
Waterbeck See Kirtle-Eaglesfield

Name				Address	Telephone
Annand, James M. MA BD	1955	1995	(Lockerbie Dryfesdale)	48 Main Street, Newstead, Melrose TD6 9DX	01461 201486
Baillie, David R.	1979	1990	(Crawford with Lowther)	1 Preston Court, Annan DG12 5HS [E-mail: annan@baillie.abel.co.uk]	
Byers, Alan J.	1959	1992	(Gamrie with King Edward)	Meadowbank, Plumdon Road, Annan DG12 6SJ	01461 206512
Byers, Mairi (Mrs) BTh CPS	1992	1998	(Jura)	Meadowbank, Plumdon Road, Annan DG12 6SJ	01461 206512
Fisher, D. Noel MA BD	1939	1979	(Glasgow Sherbrooke St Gilbert's)	Sheraig Cottage, Killochries Fold, Kilmacolm PA13 4TE	
Kirk, W. Logan MA BD MTh	1988	2000	(Dalton with Hightae with St Mungo)	2 Firpark Cottages, Lockerbie DG11 1BL	01576 204653

McLean, Margaret G. BD	1978 1991	(Community Minister: Annandale and Eskdale)	84 Union Road, Gretna DG16 5JT	01461 338491
MacMillan, William M. LTh	1980 1998	(Kilmory with Lamlash)	Balskia, 61 Queen Street, Lochmaben DG11 1PP	01387 811528
Macpherson, Duncan J. BSc BD	1993 2002	Chaplain: Army		
Owen, John J.C. LTh	1967 2001	(Applegarth and Sibbaldbie with Lochmaben)	5 Galla Avenue, Dalbeattie DG5 4Z [E-mail: jjowen@macunlimited.net]	01556 612125
Rennie, John D. MA	1962 1996	(Broughton, Glenholm and Kilbucho with Skirling with Stobo and Drumelzier with Tweedsmuir)	Dundoran, Ballplay Road, Moffat DG10 9JX [E-mail: rennies@dundoran96.freeserve.co.uk]	01683 220223
Ross, Alan C. CA BD	1988 1997	(Annan: St Andrew's Greenknowe)	Yarra, Ettrickbridge, Selkirk TD7 5JN [E-mail: alkaross@aol.com]	01750 52324 (Tel/Fax)
Swinburne, Norman BA	1960 1993	(Sauchie)	Damerosehay, Birch Hill Lane, Kirkbride, Wigton CA7 5HZ	01697 351497

(8) DUMFRIES AND KIRKCUDBRIGHT

Meets at Dumfries, on the first Wednesday of February, March, April, May, September, October, November, December, and the last Wednesday of June.

Clerk:	REV. GORDON M.A. SAVAGE MA BD		11 Laurieknowe, Dumfries DG2 7AH [E-mail: akph44@uk.uumail.com]	01387 252929
Depute Clerk:	REV. WILLIAM T. HOGG MA BD		The Manse, Glasgow Road, Sanquhar DG4 6BS [E-mail: tervit@btopenworld.com]	01659 50247

Anwoth and Girthon linked with Borgue

Valerie J. Ott (Mrs) BA BD	2002	Gatehouse of Fleet, Castle Douglas DG7 2EQ [E-mail: dandvott@aol.com]	01557 814233

Auchencairn and Rerrick linked with Buittle and Kelton

James H. Sinclair MA BD	1966 1992	Auchencairn, Castle Douglas DG7 1QS	01556 640288

Balmaclellan and Kells (H) linked with Carsphairn (H) linked with Dalry (H)

David S. Bartholomew BSc MSc PhD BD	1994	Dalry, Castle Douglas DG7 3PJ [E-mail: dhbart@care4free.net]	01644 430380

Balmaghie linked with Tarff and Twynholm (H)

Christopher Wallace BD DipMin	1988	Twynholm, Kirkcudbright DG6 4NY [E-mail: c.wallace3@ntlworld.com]	01557 860381

Borgue See Anwoth and Girthon
Buittle and Kelton See Auchencairn and Rerrick

Caerlaverock

Elizabeth A. Mack (Miss) DipPEd (Aux)	1994 2001	24 Roberts Crescent, Dumfries DG2 7RS	01387 264847

Carsphairn See Balmaclellan and Kells

Castle Douglas (H)
Robert J. Malloch BD   1987 2001   1 Castle View, Castle Douglas DG7 1BG   01556 502171
[E-mail: robert@scotnish.freeserve.co.uk]

Closeburn linked with Durisdeer
James W. Scott MA CDA   1952 1953   Durisdeer, Thornhill, Dumfriesshire DG3 5BJ   01848 500231

Colvend, Southwick and Kirkbean
Vacant   Colvend, Dalbeattie DG5 4QN   01556 630255

Corsock and Kirkpatrick Durham linked with Crossmichael and Parton
James A. Guthrie   1969 1999   Knockdrocket, Clarebrand, Castle Douglas DG7 3AH   01556 503645

Crossmichael and Parton See Corsock and Kirkpatrick Durham

Cummertrees linked with Mouswald linked with Ruthwell (H)
James Williamson BA BD   1986 1991   Ruthwell, Dumfries DG1 4NP   01387 870217
[E-mail: jimwill@rcmkirk.freeserve.co.uk]

Dalbeattie (H) linked with Urr (H)
Norman M. Hutcheson MA BD   1973 1988   36 Mill Street, Dalbeattie DG5 4HE   01556 610029
[E-mail: norman.hutcheson@virgin.net]

Dalry See Balmaclellan

Dumfries: Greyfriars (T) (H)
W.C. Campbell-Jack BD MTh PhD   1979 1999   4 Georgetown Crescent, Dumfries DG1 4EQ   01387 257045
[E-mail: c-j@fish.co.uk]

Dumfries: Lincluden linked with Holywood (T)
Vacant   96 Glasgow Road, Dumfries DG2 9DE   01387 264298

Dumfries: Lochside
Thomas M. Bryson BD   1997   27 St Anne's Road, Dumfries DG2 9HZ   01387 252912
[E-mail: t-m-bryson@talk21.com]

Dumfries: Maxwelltown West (H)
Gordon M.A. Savage MA BD   1977 1984   Maxwelltown West Manse, 11 Laurieknowe, Dumfries DG2 7AH   01387 252929
[E-mail: gordonsavage@uk.uumail.com]

Dumfries: St George's (H)
Donald Campbell BD   1997   9 Nunholm Park, Dumfries DG1 1JP   01387 252965
[E-mail: donald@campbell3.freeserve.co.uk]

Charge / Minister	Ordained	Inducted	Address	Tel
Dumfries: St Mary's (H) Vacant			47 Moffat Road, Dumfries DG1 1NN	01387 254873
Dumfries: St Michael's and South Maurice S. Bond MTh BA DipEd PhD	1981	1999	39 Cardoness Street, Dumfries DG1 3AL	01387 253849
Dumfries: Troqueer (H) William W. Kelly BSc BD	1994		Troqueer Road, Dumfries DG2 7DF [E-mail: wwkelly@ntlworld.com]	01387 253043
Dunscore linked with Glencairn and Moniaive Christine Sime (Miss) BSc BD	1994		Wallaceton, Auldgirth, Dumfries DG2 0TJ [E-mail: revsime@aol.com]	01387 820245
Durisdeer See Closeburn **Glencairn and Moniaive** See Dunscore **Holywood** See Dumfries: Lincluden				
Irongray, Lochrutton and Terregles David J. Taylor MA BD	1982	2002	Shawhead Road, Dumfries DG2 9SJ [E-mail: david@bunessan.f9.co.uk]	01387 730287
Kirkconnel (H) David Deas Melville BD	1989	1999	Kingsway, Kirkconnel, Sanquhar DG4 6PN [E-mail: ddm@kirkconn.freeserve.co.uk]	01659 67241
Kirkcudbright (H) Douglas R. Irving LLB BD WS	1984	1998	6 Bourtree Avenue, Kirkcudbright DG6 4AU [E-mail: douglasirving@kirkcudbright99.freeserve.co.uk]	01557 330489
Kirkgunzeon Continued Vacancy				
Kirkmahoe Dennis S. Rose LTh	1996		Kirkmahoe, Dumfries DG1 1ST [E-mail: dennros@aol.com]	01387 710572
Kirkmichael, Tinwald and Torthorwald Louis C. Bezuidenhout MA DD	1978	2000	Manse of Tinwald, Tinwald, Dumfries DG1 3PL [E-mail: macbez@btinternet.com]	01387 710246
Lochend linked with New Abbey William Holland MA	1967	1971	New Abbey, Dumfries DG2 8BY [E-mail: bilholland@aol.com]	01387 850232
Mouswald See Cummertrees				

New Abbey See Lochend

Penpont, Keir and Tynron See Thornhill

Ruthwell (H) See Cummertrees

Sanquhar: St Bride's (H)
William T. Hogg MA BD   1979   2000   Glasgow Road, Sanquhar DG4 6BS   01659 50247
[E-mail: tervit@btopenworld.com]

Tarff and Twynholm See Balmaghie

Thornhill (H) linked with Penpont, Keir and Tynron
Vacant   Thornhill, Dumfriesshire DG3 5ER   01848 331191

Urr See Dalbeattie

Name			Charge	Address	Phone
Bennett, David K.P. BA	1974	2000	(Kirkpatrick Irongray with Lochrutton with Terregles)	53 Anne Arundel Court, Heathhall, Dumfries DG1 3SL	01387 257755
Calderwood, Walter M. MA BD	1934	1974	(Leven Forman)	Flat 10, Daar Lodge, 6 St Mary Street, Kirkcudbright DG6 4AQ	01557 330330
Craig, N. Douglas MA BD	1947	1987	(Dalbeattie Craignair with Urr)	33 Albert Road, Dumfries DG2 9DN	01387 252187
Elder, Albert B. MA	1960	1998	(Dumfries: St Michael's & South)	87 Glasgow Street, Dumfries DG2 9AG	01387 249811
Geddes, Alexander J. MA BD	1960	1998	(Stewarton: St Columba's)	166 Georgetown Road, Dumfries DG1 4DT	01387 252287
Gillespie, Ann M. (Miss) DCS			(Deaconess)	Barlochan House, Palnackie, Castle Douglas DG7 1PF	01556 600378
Grant, James BA	1961	1987	(Penpont Keir and Tynron)	147A Drumlanrig Street, Thornhill DG3 5LJ	01848 330829
Greer, A. David C. LLB DMin DipAdultEd	1956	1996	(Barra)	10 Watling Street, Dumfries DG1 1HF	01387 256113
Hamill, Robert BA	1956	1989	(Castle Douglas St Ringan's)	11 St Andrew Drive, Castle Douglas DG7 1EW	01556 502962
Hutchison, Mary L. (Mrs) BD	1982	1995	(Dumfries Lincluden with Holywood)	Monzie, 25 Twiname Way, Heathhall, Dumfries DG1 3ST	01387 250610
Johnston, John MA BD	1963	1999	(Hospital Chaplain)	Near Bye, Amisfield, Dumfries DG1 3LN	01387 710254
Leishman, James S LTh BD MA(Div)	1969	1999	(Kirkmichael with Tinwald with Torthorwald)	11 Hunter Avenue, Heathhall, Dumfries DG1 3UX	01387 249241
Mackay, Donald MBE FCP FSAScot	1951	1986	(Ardrossan: St John's)	8 Urquhart Crescent, Dumfries DG1 8XF	01387 259132
McKenzie, William M. DA	1958	1993	(Dumfries: Troqueer)	41 Kingholm Road, Dumfries DG1 4SR [E-mail: mckenzie.dumfries@virgin.net]	01387 253688
Miller, John R. MA BD	1958	1992	(Carsphairn with Dalry)	4 Fairgreen Court, Rhonehouse, Castle Douglas DG7 1SA	01556 680428
Morrison, James G. MBE MA	1942	1980	(Rotterdam)	Auchenshiel, Rhonehouse, Castle Douglas DG7 1SA	01556 680526
Robertson, Ian W. MA BD	1956	1995	(Colvend, Southwick and Kirkbean)	10 Marjoriebanks, Lochmaben, Lockerbie DG11 1QH	01387 810541
Robertson, Thomas R. MA BD	1934	1976	(Broughton, Glenholm and Kilbucho with Skirling)	1 Church Row, Kirkcudbright DG6 4AP	01557 330795
Smith, Richmond OBE MA BD	1952	1983	(World Alliance of Reformed Churches)	Aignish, Merse Way, Kippford, Dalbeattie DG5 4LH	01556 620624
Strachan, Alexander E. MA BD	1974	1999	(Dumfries Health Care Chaplain)	2 Leafield Road, Dumfries DG1 2DS [E-mail: aestrachan@aol.com]	01387 279460
Vincent, C. Raymond MA FSAScot	1952	1992	(Stonehouse)	Rosebank, Newton Stewart Road, New Galloway, Castle Douglas DG7 3RT	01644 420451

Wilkie, James R. MA MTh	1957 1993	(Penpont, Keir and Tynron)	31 West Morton Street, Thornhill DG3 5NF	01848 331028
Wotherspoon, Robert C. LTh	1976 1998	(Corsock and Kirkpatrick Durham with Crossmichael and Parton) (Airdrie: Broomknoll)	7 Hillowton Drive, Castle Douglas DG7 1LL	01556 502267
Young, John MTh DipMin	1963 1999		Craigview, North Street, Moniaive, Thornhill DG3 4HR	01848 200318

DUMFRIES ADDRESSES

Greyfriars	Church Crescent	Maxwelltown West	Laurieknowe	St Michael's and South	St Michael's Street
Lincluden	Stewartry Road	St George's	George Street	Troqueer	Troqueer Road
Lochside	Lochside Road	St Mary's	St Mary's Street		

(9) WIGTOWN AND STRANRAER

Meets at Glenluce, in Old Luce Parish Church, on the first Tuesday of each month, except January, April, July and August, when there is no meeting, June, when it meets on the fourth Tuesday, and October, when it meets in the Moderator's Church.

Clerk: REV. D.W. DUTTON BA   High Kirk Manse, Leswalt High Road, Stranraer DG9 0AA   **01776 703268**
[E-mail: akph79@uk.uumail.com]

Ervie Kirkcolm linked with Leswalt
Michael J. Sheppard BD   1997   Ervie Manse, Stranraer DG9 0QZ   01776 854225
[E-mail: michael@erviecos.freeserve.co.uk]

Glasserton and Isle of Whithorn linked with Whithorn: St Ninian's Priory
Alexander I. Currie BD CPS   1990   Whithorn, Newton Stewart DG8 8PY   01988 500267

Inch linked with Stranraer: St Andrew's (H)
John H. Burns BSc BD   1985 1988   Bay View Road, Stranraer DG9 8BE   01776 702383

Kirkcowan (H) linked with Wigtown (H)
Martin Thomson BSc DipEd BD   1988   Harbour Road, Wigtown, Newton Stewart DG8 9AL   01988 402242
[E-mail: martin@thomsonm40.freeserve.co.uk]

Kirkinner linked with Sorbie (H)
Jeffrey M. Mead BD   1978 1986   Kirkinner, Newton Stewart DG8 9AL   01988 840643

Kirkmabreck linked with Monigaff (H)
Hugh D. Steele LTh DipMin   1994   Cree Bridge, Newton Stewart DG8 6NR   01671 403361

Kirkmaiden (H) linked with Stoneykirk
Ian McIlroy BSS BD   1996   Church Street, Sandhead, Stranraer DG9 9JJ   01776 830337
Mary Munro (Mrs) BA (Aux)   1993   High Barbeth, Leswalt DG9 0QS   01776 870250

Leswalt See See Ervie Kirkcolm

Mochrum (H)
Roger A.F. Dean LTh   1983 1995   Port William, Newton Stewart DG8 9QP   01988 700257

Monigaff (H) See Kirkmabreck

New Luce (H) linked with Old Luce (H)
Thomas M. McWhirter MA MSc BD   1992 1997   Glenluce, Newton Stewart DG8 0PU   01581 300319

Old Luce See New Luce

Penninghame (H)
Neil G. Campbell BA BD   1988 1989   The Manse, Newton Stewart DG8 6HH   01671 402259
[E-mail: neilcampbell@yahoo.com]

Portpatrick linked with Stranraer: St Ninian's (H)
Gordon Kennedy BSc BD   1993 2000   London Road, Stranraer DG9 9AB   01776 702443
[E-mail: gordon.kennedy1@btinternet.com]

Sorbie See Kirkinner
Stoneykirk See Kirkmaiden

Stranraer: High Kirk (H)
David W. Dutton BA   1973 1986   Leswalt High Road, Stranraer DG9 0AA   01776 703268
[E-mail: akph79@uk.uumail.com]

Stranraer: Old (H)
Samuel McC. Harris BA BD   1974 1990   Linden, Leswalt High Road, Stranraer DG9 0AA   01776 706387

Stranraer St Andrew's See Inch
Stranraer St Ninian's See Portpatrick
Whithorn: St Ninian's Priory See Glasserton and Isle of Whithorn
Wigtown See Kirkcowan

Cairns, Alexander B. MA	1957	1997	(Ervie Kirkcolm with Leswalt)	Beechwood, Main Street, Sandhead, Stranraer DG9 9JG	01776 830389
Cordiner, John	1950	1986	(Portpatrick)	Tara, Fellview Road, Stranraer DG9 8BK	01776 704720
Harkes, George	1962	1988	(Cumbernauld Old)	11 Main Street, Sorbie, Newton Stewart DG8 8EG	01988 850255
McCreadie, David W.	1961	1995	(Kirkmabreck)	77 St John Street, Creetown, Newton Stewart DG8 7JB	01671 820390
McGill, Thomas W.	1972	1990	(Portpatrick with Stranraer St Ninian's)	Ravenstone Moor, Dramrae, Whithorn, Newton Stewart DG8 8DS	01988 700449
Ogilvy, Oliver M.	1959	1985	(Leswalt)	8 Dale Crescent, Stranraer DG9 0HG	01776 706285

(10) AYR

Meets on the first Tuesday of every month from September to May, excluding January, and on the fourth Tuesday of June. The June meeting will be held in the Moderator's Church. One meeting will be held in a venue to be determined by the Business Committee. Other meetings will be held in Alloway Church Hall.

Clerk:	REV. JAMES CRICHTON MA BD MTh			30 Garden Street, Dalrymple KA6 6DG [E-mail: akph39@uk.uumail.com] [E-mail: akph40@uk.uumail.com]	01292 560263 01292 560574 (Fax)
				Presbytery Office	
Alloway (H) Neil A. McNaught BD MA		1987	1999	1A Parkview, Alloway, Ayr KA7 4QG [E-mail: neilmcnaught@ukgateway.net]	01292 441252
Ambank (H) linked with Tarbolton Mary C. McLauchlan (Mrs) LTh		1997	2001	1 Kirkport, Tarbolton, Mauchline, Ayrshire KA5 5QJ [E-mail: mary.shaw@ntlworld.com]	01292 541236
Arnsheen Barrhill linked with Colmonell John S. Lochrie BSc BD MTh PhD		1967	1999	Manse Road, Colmonell, Girvan KA26 0SA	01465 881224
Auchinleck (H) linked with Catrine James Sloan BA MD		1987	2002	28 Mauchline Road, Auchinleck KA18 2BN	01290 421108
Ayr: Auld Kirk of Ayr (St John the Baptist) (H) David R. Gemmell MA BD		1991	1999	58 Monument Road, Ayr KA7 2UB [E-mail: drgemmell@aol.com]	01292 262580 (Tel/Fax)
Ayr: Castlehill (H) Vacant				3 Old Hillfoot Road, Ayr KA7 3LF	01292 267332
Ayr: Newton on Ayr (H) G. Stewart Birse CA BD BSc		1980	1989	9 Nursery Grove, Ayr KA7 3PH	01292 264251
Ayr: St Andrew's (H) Harry B. Mealyea BArch BD		1984	2000	31 Bellevue Crescent, Ayr KA7 2DP [E-mail: harrybellmealyea@netscapeonline.co.uk]	01292 261126
Ayr: St Columba (H) Fraser R. Aitken MA BD		1978	1991	2 Hazelwood Road, Ayr KA7 2PY [E-mail: fraser.aitken@columba92.fsnet.co.uk]	01292 284177

Ayr: St James'
Gillian Weighton (Mrs) BD STM | 1992 | 1 Prestwick Road, Ayr KA8 8LD
[E-mail: gillweighton@aol.com] | 01292 262420

Ayr: St Leonard's (H)
Robert Lynn MA BD | 1984 | 1989 | 7 Shawfield Avenue, Ayr KA7 4RE
[E-mail: robert@shawfield200.fsnet.co.uk] | 01292 442109

Ayr: St Quivox (H)
David T. Ness LTh | 1972 | 1988 | 11 Springfield Avenue, Prestwick KA9 2HA | 01292 478306

Ayr: Wallacetown (H)
Vacant | | | 87 Forehill Road, Ayr KA7 3JR | 01292 269161

Ballantrae (H)
Robert P. Bell BSc | 1968 | 1998 | Ballantrae, Girvan KA26 0NH
[E-mail: revbobbell@aol.com] | 01465 831252 (Tel)
01465 831260 (Fax)

Barr linked with Dailly linked with Girvan South
Ian K. McLachlan MA BD | 1999 | 30 Henrietta Street, Girvan KA26 9AL
[E-mail: iankmclachlan@yetiville.freeserve.co.uk] | 01465 713370

Catrine See Auchinleck
Colmonell See Arnsheen Barrhill

Coylton linked with Drongan: The Schaw Kirk
Paul R. Russell MA BD | 1984 | 1991 | 4 Hamilton Place, Coylton, Ayr KA6 6JQ
[E-mail: russellpr@btinternet.com] | 01292 570272

Craigie linked with Symington
Alastair M. Sanderson BA LTh | 1971 | 2000 | 16 Kerrix Road, Symington, Kilmarnock KA1 5QD
[E-mail: alel@sanderson29.fsnet.co.uk] | 01563 830205

Crosshill linked with Dalrymple
James Crichton MA BD MTh | 1969 | 30 Garden Street, Dalrymple KA6 6DG
[E-mail: akph39@uk.uumail.com] | 01292 560263 (Tel)
01292 560574 (Fax)

Dailly See Barr

Dalmellington
Kenneth B. Yorke BD DipEd | 1982 | 1999 | 4 Carsphairn Road, Dalmellington, Ayr KA6 7RE
[E-mail: k.yorke@zoom.co.uk] | 01292 550353

Dalrymple See Crosshill
Drongan: The Schaw Kirk See Coylton

Dundonald (H) Robert Mayes BD	1982	1988	Dundonald, Kilmarnock KA2 9HG	01563 850243
Fisherton (H) linked with Maybole: West Thomas C. Bogle BD	1983	1996	West Manse, 22 Coral Glen, Maybole KA19 7EB	01655 883102
Girvan: North (Old and St Andrew's) (H) Douglas G. McNab BA BD	1999		38 The Avenue, Girvan KA26 9DS	01465 713203
Girvan: South: See Barr linked with Dailly				
Kirkmichael linked with Straiton: St Cuthbert's W. Gerald Jones MA BD MTh	1984	1985	Patna Road, Kirkmichael, Maybole KA19 7PJ [E-mail: revgerald@jonesg99.freeserve.co.uk]	01655 750286
Kirkoswald (H) Arrick D. Wilkinson BSc BD	2000	2000	Kirkoswald, Maybole KA19 8JA [E-mail: arrick@clergy.net]	01655 760210
Lugar linked with Old Cumnock: Old (H) John W. Paterson BSc BD DipEd	1994		33 Barrhill Road, Cumnock KA18 1PJ [E-mail: ocochurchwow@hotmail.com]	01290 420769
Mauchline (H) Alan B. Telfer BA BD	1983	1991	4 Westside Gardens, Mauchline KA5 5DJ [E-mail: abtelfer@btinternet.com]	01290 550386
Maybole: Old David Whiteman BD	1998		64 Culzean Road, Maybole KA19 8AH [E-mail: davesoo@aol.com]	01655 889456
Maybole: West See Fisherton				
Monkton and Prestwick: North (H) Arthur A. Christie BD	1997	2000	40 Monkton Road, Prestwick KA9 1AR [E-mail: revaac@compuserve.com]	01292 477499
Muirkirk (H) linked with Sorn Vacant			2 Smallburn Road, Muirkirk, Cumnock KA18 3RF	01290 661157
New Cumnock (H) Rona M. Young (Mrs) BD DipEd	1991	2001	New Cumnock, Cumnock KA18 4AG	01290 338296

Ochiltree linked with Stair
Carolyn M. Baker (Mrs) BD   1997   10 Mauchline Road, Ochiltree, Cumnock KA18 2PZ   01290 700365
[E-mail: carolynmbaker2001@yahoo.co.uk]

Old Cumnock: Crichton West and St Ninian's
J. Edward Andrews MA BD DipCG   1985 2002   46 Ayr Road, Cumnock KA18 1DW   01290 422145

Old Cumnock: Old See Lugar

Patna Waterside
Vacant
Muriel Wilson (Ms) DCS   23 Jellieston Terrace, Patna, Ayr KA6 7JZ   01292 532492

Prestwick: Kingcase (H) (E-mail: office@kingcase.freeserve.co.uk)
T. David Watson BSc BD   1988 1997   15 Bellrock Avenue, Prestwick KA9 1SQ   01292 479571
[E-mail: tdwatson@tesco.net]

Prestwick: St Nicholas' (H)
George R. Fiddes BD   1979 1985   3 Bellevue Road, Prestwick KA9 1NW   01292 477613
[E-mail: george@gfiddes.freeserve.co.uk]

Prestwick: South (H)
Kenneth C. Elliott BD CertMin   1989   68 St Quivox Road, Prestwick KA9 1JF   01292 478788
[E-mail: kenneth@revelliott.freeserve.co.uk]

Sorn See Muirkirk
Stair See Ochiltree
Straiton St Cuthbert's See Kirkmichael
Symington See Craigie

Tarbolton See Annbank

Troon: Old (H)
Alastair H. Symington MA BD   1972 1998   85 Bentinck Drive, Troon KA10 6HZ   01292 313644
[E-mail: revahs@care4free.net]

Troon: Portland (H)
Ronald M.H. Boyd BD DipTh   1995 1999   89 South Beach, Troon KA10 6EQ   01292 313285

Troon: St Meddan's (H) (E-mail: st.meddan@virgin.net)
David L. Harper BSc BD   1972 1979   27 Bentinck Drive, Troon KA10 6HX   01292 311784
[E-mail: d.l.harper@btinternet.com]

Name			Description	Address	Phone
Andrew, R.J.M. MA	1955	1994	(Uddingston Old)	6A Ronaldshaw Park, Ayr KA7 2TS	01292 263430
Banks, John BD	1968	2001	(Hospital Chaplain)	19 Victoria Drive, Troon KA10 6JF	01292 317758
Barr, John BSc PhD BD	1958	1979	(Kilmacolm Old)	7 Kilbrandon Way, Doonfoot, Ayr KA7 4JY	01292 445631
Bird, John W.	1965	1997	(Bathgate High)	14 Springfield Avenue, Prestwick KA9 2HA	01292 476037
Blyth, James G.S. BSc BD	1963	1986	(Glenmuick)	40 Robsland Avenue, Ayr KA7 2RW	01292 261276
Campbell, Effie C. (Mrs) BD	1981	1991	(Old Cumnock Crichton West with St Ninian's)		
Cranston, George BD	1976	2001	(Rutherglen: Wardlawhill)	7 Lansdowne Road, Ayr KA8 8LS	01292 264282
Dickie, Michael M. BSc	1955	1994	(Ayr Castlehill)	20 Capperview, Prestwick KA9 1BH	01292 476627
Garrity, T. Alan W. BSc BD MTh	1969	1999	Christ Church, Warwick, Bermuda	8 Noltmire Road, Ayr KA8 9ES / PO Box PG88, Paget PG BX, Bermuda	
Glencross, William M. LTh	1968	1999	(Bellshill: Macdonald Memorial)	1 Lochay Place, Troon KA10 7HH	01292 317097
Grant, J. Gordon MA BD	1957	1997	(Edinburgh: Dean)	33 Fullarton Drive, Troon KA10 6LE	01292 311852
Hannah, William BD MCAM MIPR	1987	2001	(Muirkirk)	8 Dovecot View, Kirkintilloch, Glasgow G66 3HY	01387 259255
Helon, Roger G. BA BD	1984	2000	(Barr linked with Dailly)	9 Park Road, Maxwelltown, Dumfries DG2 7PW	01292 500273
Hollins, Roger M. BSc DipEd FEIS	1957	1988	(Lecturer in Religious Education)	Smithy Cottage, Dunure, Ayr KA7 4LH	01292 471980
Johnston, Kenneth L. BA LTh	1969	2001	(Annbank)	2 Rylands, Prestwick KA9 2DX	01386 421562
Kent, Arthur F.S.	1966	1999	(Monkton and Prestwick: North)	17 St David's Drive, Evesham, Worcs WR11 6AS	01292 283085
Macdonald, Ian U.	1960	1997	(Tarbolton)	18 Belmont Road, Ayr KA7 2PF	01292 442554
McNidder, Roderick H. BD	1987	1997	Chaplain, South Ayrshire Hospitals Trust	6 Hollow Park, Alloway KA7 4SR	01292 282108
McPhail, Andrew M. BA	1968	2002	(Ayr: Wallacetown)	25 Maybole Road, Ayr KA7 2QA	01292 610556
Mitchell, Sheila M. (Miss) BD MTh	1995	2002	Chaplain: Ayrshire and Arran Primary Care Trust	Ailsa Hospital, Ayr	
Robertson, Daniel M. MA	1960	2000	(Auchinleck)	14 Corrie Place, Drongan, Ayr KA6 7DU	01292 590150
Saunders, Campbell M. MA BD	1952	1989	(Ayr St Leonard's)	42 Marle Park, Ayr KA7 4RN	01292 441673
Stirling, Ian R. BSc BD	1990	2002	Chaplain: The Ayrshire Hospice		
Sutherland, Alexander S.	1952	1987	(Symington with Craigie)	8 Phillips Avenue, Largs KA30 9EP	01475 674846

AYR ADDRESSES

Ayr

Auld Kirk	Kirkport (116 High Street)
Castlehill	Castlehill Road x Hillfoot Road
Lochside	Lochside Road x Murray Street
Newton-on-Ayr	Main Street
St Andrew's	Park Circus
St Columba	Midton Road x Carrick Park
St James'	Prestwick Road x Falkland Park Road
St Leonard's	St Leonard's Road x Monument Road
Wallacetown	John Street x Church Street

Girvan

North	Montgomerie Street
South	Stair Park

Maybole

Old	Centre of Cassillis Road
West	Foot of Coral Glen

Prestwick

Kingcase	Waterloo Road
Monkton and Prestwick North	Monkton Road
St Nicholas	Main Street
South	Main Street

Troon

Old	Ayr Street
Portland	St Meddan's Street
St Meddan's	St Meddan's Street

(11) IRVINE AND KILMARNOCK

The Presbytery meets ordinarily at 6.30 pm in the Hall of Howard St Andrew's Church, Kilmarnock, on the first Tuesday of each month from September to May, (except January when it meets on the second Tuesday for the celebration of Holy Communion and in conference or socially) and on the fourth Tuesday in June.

Clerk:	REV. COLIN G.F. BROCKIE BSc(Eng) BD		51 Portland Road Kilmarnock KA1 2EQ [E-mail: akph57@uk.uumail.comm]	01563 525311
Depute Clerk:	I. STEUART DEY LLB NP		72 Dundonald Road, Kilmarnock KA1 1RZ [E-mail: steuartdey@netscapeonline.co.uk]	01563 521686
Treasurer:	JAMES McINTOSH BA CA		15 Dundonald Rd, Kilmarnock KA1 1RU	01563 523552

Crosshouse
Vacant

27 Kilmarnock Road, Crosshouse, Kilmarnock KA2 0EZ — 01563 521035

Darvel
Charles M. Cameron BA BD PhD — 1980 — 2001

46 West Main Street, Darvel KA17 0AQ — 01560 322924

Dreghorn and Springside
Gary E. Horsburgh BA — 1976 — 1983

96A Townfoot, Dreghorn, Irvine KA11 4EZ — 01294 217770

Dunlop
Maureen M. Duncan (Mrs) BD — 1996

4 Dampark, Dunlop, Kilmarnock KA3 4BZ — 01560 484083

Fenwick (H)
Geoffrey Redmayne BSc BD MPhil — 2000

2 Kirkton Place, Fenwick, Kilmarnock KA3 6DW [E-mail: geoff@gredmayne.fsnet.co.uk] — 01560 600217

Galston (H)
T.J. Loudon Blair MA BD — 1965 — 1980

60 Brewland Street, Galston KA4 8DX [E-mail: loudon.blair@virgin.net] — 01563 820246

John H.B. Taylor MA BD DipEd FEIS (Assoc) — 1952 — 1990

62 Woodlands Grove, Kilmarnock KA3 1TZ — 01563 526698

Hurlford (H)
James D. McCulloch BD MIOP — 1996

12 Main Road, Crookedholm, Kilmarnock KA3 6JT — 01563 535673

Irvine: Fullarton
Neil Urquhart BD DipMin — 1989

48 Waterside, Irvine KA12 8QJ [E-mail: neilurquhart@beeb.net] — 01294 279909

Charge / Minister	Year(s)	Address	Telephone
Irvine: Girdle Toll (E) (H) Clare B. Sutcliffe BSc BD	2000	2 Littlestane Rise, Irvine KA11 2BJ	01294 213565
Irvine: Mure (H) Hugh M. Adamson BD	1976	West Road, Irvine KA12 8RE	01294 279916
Irvine: Old (H) (01294 273503) Robert Travers BA BD	1993 1999	22 Kirk Vennel, Irvine, Ayrshire KA12 0DQ [E-mail: robert@travers46.freeserve.co.uk]	01294 279265
Irvine: Relief Bourtreehill (H) Vacant		4 Kames Court, Irvine KA11 1RT	01294 216939
Irvine: St Andrew's (H) (01294 276051) Morag A. Dawson BD	1999	206 Bank Street, Irvine KA12 0YD	01294 211403
Kilmarnock: Grange (H) (01563 534490) Colin G.F. Brockie BSc(Eng) BD	1967 1978	51 Portland Road, Kilmarnock KA1 2EQ [E-mail: revcol@revcol.demon.co.uk]	01563 525311
Kilmarnock: Henderson (H) (01563 541302) David W. Lacy BA BD	1976 1989	52 London Road, Kilmarnock KA3 7AJ [E-mail: thelacys@tinyworld.co.uk]	01563 523113 (Tel/Fax)
Kilmarnock: Howard St Andrew's (H) Malcolm MacLeod BA BD	1979 1989	1 Evelyn Villas, Holehouse Road, Kilmarnock KA3 7AX [E-mail: cal.macleod@ntlworld.com]	01563 522278
Kilmarnock: Laigh West High (H) David S. Cameron BD	2001	1 Holmes Farm Road, Kilmarnock KA1 1TP	01563 525416
Kilmarnock: Old High Kirk (H) William M. Hall BD	1972 1979	107 Dundonald Road, Kilmarnock KA1 1UP	01563 525608
Kilmarnock: Riccarton (H) Thomas W. Jarvie BD	1953 1968	2 Jasmine Road, Kilmarnock KA1 2HD	01563 525694
Kilmarnock: St Andrew's Glencairn Robert A.K. Martin MA	1957 1970	19 Holehouse Road, Kilmarnock KA3 7AU	01563 525023
Kilmarnock: St John's Onthank (H) Susan M. Anderson (Mrs)	1997	84 Wardneuk Drive, Kilmarnock KA3 2EX [E-mail: stjohnthank@yahoo.co.uk]	01563 521815
Catherine A.M. Shaw MA (Aux)	1998	40 Merrygreen Place, Stewarton, Kilmarnock KA3 5EP [E-mail: catherine.shaw@tesco.net]	01560 483352

Kilmarnock: St Kentigern's
S. Grant Barclay LLB BD   1995   1 Thirdpart Place, Kilmarnock KA1 1UL   01563 571280
[E-mail: grant.barclay@bigfoot.com]

Kilmarnock: St Marnock's (H) (01563 541337)
James McNaughtan BD DipMin   1983   1989   35 South Gargieston Drive, Kilmarnock KA1 1TB   01563 521665
[E-mail: jmcnaughtan@cwcom.net]

Kilmarnock: St Ninian's Bellfield (T) (01563 524705) linked with Kilmarnock: Shortlees (T)
Vacant   186 Whatriggs Road, Kilmarnock KA1 3TJ   01563 525480

Kilmarnock: Shortlees (T) See Kilmarnock: St Ninian's Bellfield

Kilmaurs: St Maur's Glencairn (H)
John A. Urquhart BD   1993   9 Standalane, Kilmaurs, Kilmarnock KA3 2NB   01563 538289

Newmilns: Loudoun (H)
John Macleod MA BD   2000   116A Loudoun Road, Newmilns KA16 9HH   01560 320174

Stewarton: John Knox
Samuel Hosain BD MTh PhD   1979   1993   27 Avenue Street, Stewarton, Kilmarnock KA3 5AP   01560 482418

Stewarton: St Columba's (H)
Elizabeth A. Waddell (Mrs) BD   1999   1 Kirk Glebe, Stewarton, Kilmarnock KA3 5BJ   01560 482453

Ayrshire Mission to the Deaf
S. Grant Barclay LLB BD (Chaplain)   1991   1998   89 Mure Avenue, Kilmarnock KA3 1TT   01563 571280
[E-mail: grant.barclay@bigfoot.com]

Name				Phone
Boath, Gibson K. BA	1951	1989	(Kilmarnock Howard St Andrew's)	6 Woodlands Place, Kilmarnock KA3 1UA	01563 571170
Campbell, George H.	1957	1992	(Stewarton: John Knox)	20 Woodlands Grove, Kilmarnock KA3 1TZ	01563 536365
Campbell, John A. JP FIEM	1984	1998	(Irvine St Andrew's)	Flowerdale, Balmoral Lane, Blairgowrie PH10 7AF	01250 872795
Christie, Robert S. MA BD ThM	1964	2001	(Kilmarnock: West High)	69 Dundonald Road, Kilmarnock KA1 1TJ	01563 525302
Crawford, Robert MA	1933	1972	(Annan Erskine)	Dunselma Residential Home, 55 Main Street, Fenwick, Kilmarnock KA3 6DR	
Downie, Andrew A. BD BSc DipEd DipMin ThB	1994	1999	Prison Chaplain	HMP Bowhouse, Mauchline Road, Kilmarnock KA1 5AA	01563 548928
Goudie, Stuart M. MA BD	1951	1988	(Perceton and Dreghorn)	6 Charles Drive, Troon KA10 7AG	01292 311610
Hare, Malcolm M.W. BA BD	1956	1994	(Kilmarnock St Kentigern's)	21 Raith Road, Fenwick, Kilmarnock KA3 6DB	01560 600388
Hay, W.J.R. MA BD	1959	1995	(Buchanan with Drymen)	18 Jamieson Place, Stewarton, Kilmarnock KA3 3AY	01560 482799
Huggett, Judith A. (Miss) BA BD	1990	1998	Hospital Chaplain	4 Westmoor Crescent, Kilmarnock KA1 1TX	
Jamieson, Robert C. MA	1943	1980	(Galston Old)	20 Brewland Street, Galston KA4 8DR	01563 820304

Name			Charge	Address	Tel
Kelly, Thomas A. Davidson MA BD FSAScot	1975	2002	(Glasgow: Govan Old)	2 Springhill Stables, Portland Road, Kilmarnock KA1 2EJ	
Lane, Christina M. BD	1983	1999	(Irvine: Girdle Toll)	5 Carters Place, Irvine KA12 0BU	01563 525254
MacDonald, James M.	1964	1987	(Kilmarnock St John's Onthank)	29 Carmel Place, Kilmarnock, Kilmarnock KA3 2QU	01294 271257
McGarva, Sarah (Miss) DCS			(Deaconess)	87 Hunter Drive, Irvine KA12 9BS	01563 544447
Patience, Donald MA	1954	1993	(Kilmaurs)	Kirkhill, 42 Fenwick Road, Kilmaurs, Kilmarnock KA3 2TD	01560 482185
Roy, James BA	1967	1982	(Irvine Girdle Toll)	23 Bowes Rigg, Stewarton, Kilmarnock KA3 5EL [E-mail: jroy@dougyr.globalnet.co.uk]	
Scott, Thomas T.	1968	1989	(Kilmarnock St Marnock's)	6 North Hamilton Place, Kilmarnock KA1 2QN [E-mail: 101725.216@compuserve.com]	01563 531415
Urquhart, Barbara (Mrs) DCS			Deaconess, Part-time Hospital Chaplain and Presbytery S.S. Adviser	9 Standalane, Kilmaurs, Kilmarnock KA3 2NB	01563 538289

IRVINE and KILMARNOCK ADDRESSES

Irvine

Church	Address
Dreghorn and Springside	Townfoot x Station Brae
Fullarton	Marress Road x Church Street
Girdle Toll	Bryce Knox Court
Mure	West Road
Old Parish	Kirkgate
Relief	Crofthead, Bourtreehill
St Andrew's	Caldon Road x Oaklands Ave

Kilmarnock

Church	Address	Church	Address
Ayrshire Mission to the Deaf		Riccarton	Old Street
Grange	10 Clark Street	St Andrew's	St Andrew's Street
Henderson	Woodstock Street	Glencairn	84 Wardneuk Street
Howard	London Road	St John's Onthank	St Marnock's Street
Laigh	5 Portland Road	St Marnock's	Whatriggs Road
Old High	John Dickie Street	St Ninian's Bellfield	Central Avenue
	Church Street x Soulis Street	Shortlees	Portland Street
		West High	

(12) ARDROSSAN

Meets at Saltcoats, New Trinity, on the first Tuesday of February, March, April, May, September, October, November and December, and on the second Tuesday of January and June.

Clerk: REV. DAVID BROSTER BA DipTh CPS Manse of St Columba's, Kilbirnie KA25 7JU 01505 683342 (Tel) / 01505 684024 (Fax) / 07836 380383 (Mbl)
[E-mail: akph38@uk.uumail.com]

Ardrossan: Barony St John's (H) (01294 465009)
Colin Alexander Sutherland LTh 1995 1999 10 Seafield Drive, Ardrossan KA22 8NU 01294 463868
[E-mail: colin@csutherland.fsnet.co.uk]

Ardrossan: Park (01294 463711)
William R. Johnston BD 1998 35 Ardneil Court, Ardrossan KA22 7NQ 01294 471808
Marion L.K. Howie (Mrs) MA ACRS (Aux) 1992 51 High Road, Stevenston KA20 3DY 01294 466571
[E-mail: marion.howie@ndirect.co.uk]

Beith: High (H) (01505 502686) linked with Beith: Trinity (H)

Andrew R. Black BD	1987	1998	2 Glebe Court, Beith KA15 1ET	01505 503858

[E-mail: rev_black@lineone.net]

Fiona C. Ross (Miss) BD DipMin (Assoc)	1996	16 Spiers Avenue, Beith KA15 1JD	01505 502131

[E-mail: fionaross@calvin78.freeserve.co.uk]

Beith: Trinity (H) See Beith: High

Brodick linked with Corrie

Ian MacLeod LTh BA MTh PhD	1969	1974	4 Manse Crescent, Brodick, Isle of Arran KA27 8AS	01770 302334

Corrie See Brodick

Cumbrae

Marjory H. Mackay (Mrs) BD DipEd CCE	1998	Marine Parade, Millport, Isle of Cumbrae KA28 0ED	01475 530416

Dalry: St Margaret's
Vacant   Bridgend, Dalry KA24 4DA   01294 832234

Dalry: Trinity (H)

David I.M. Grant MA BD	1969	West Kilbride Road, Dalry KA24 5DX	01294 832363

Fairlie (H)

Robert J. Thorburn BD	1978	1980	14 Fairlieburne Gardens, Fairlie, Largs KA29 0ER	01475 568342

[E-mail: rjthorburn@aol.com]

Fergushill linked with Kilwinning Erskine
Vacant   14 McLuckie Drive, Kilwinning KA13 6DL   01294 551565

Kilbirnie: Auld Kirk (H)

Ian W. Benzie BD	1999	49 Holmhead, Kilbirnie KA25 6BS	01505 682348

[E-mail: revian@ibenzie.freeserve.co.uk]

Kilbirnie: St Columba's (H) (01505 685239)

David Broster BA DipTh CPS	1969	1983	Manse of St Columba's, Kilbirnie KA25 7JU	01505 683342 (Tel)
				01505 684024 (Fax)
				07836 380383 (Mbl)

[E-mail: pres@broster.org]

Kilmory
Vacant

Kilwinning: Abbey (H)

Gordon A. McCracken BD CertMin	1988	2002	54 Dalry Road, Kilwinning KA13 7HE	01294 552606

[E-mail: gordonangus@btopenworld.com]

Kilwinning: Erskine (01294 552188) See Fergushill

Kilwinning: Mansefield Trinity (E) (01294 550746)
Douglas S. Paterson MA BD — 1976 — 27 Treesbank, Kilwinning KA13 6LY — 01294 552453

Lamlash linked with Lochranza and Pirnmill linked with Shiskine (H)
Barry Knight BD — 1991 2002 — Shiskine, Brodick, Isle of Arran KA27 8EP — 01770 860380

Largs: Clark Memorial (H) (01475 675186)
Stephen J. Smith BSc BD — 1993 1998 — 31 Douglas Street, Largs KA30 8PT
[E-mail: stephenrevsteve@aol.com] — 01475 672370

Largs: St Columba's (01475 686212)
Roderick J. Grahame BD CPS — 1991 2002 — 17 Beachway, Largs KA30 8QH
[E-mail: rjgrahame@supanet.com] — 01475 673107

Largs: St John's (H) (01475 674468)
Andrew F. McGurk BD — 1983 1993 — 1 Newhaven Grove, Largs KA30 8NS
[E-mail: afmcg.largs@talk21.com] — 01475 676123

Lochranza and Pirnmill See Lamlash

Saltcoats: New Trinity (H) (01294 472001)
Alexander D. McCallum BD — 1987 1994 — 1 Montgomerie Crescent, Saltcoats KA21 5BX
[E-mail: sandy@newtrinity.co.uk] — 01294 461143

Saltcoats: North (01294 464679)
Vacant — 25 Longfield Avenue, Saltcoats KA21 6DR — 01294 604923

Saltcoats: St Cuthbert's (H)
Brian H. Oxburgh BSc BD — 1980 1988 — 10 Kennedy Road, Saltcoats KA21 5SF
[E-mail: boxburgh@aol.com] — 01294 602674

Shiskine See Lamlash

Stevenston: Ardeer linked with Stevenston: Livingstone (H)
John M.M. Lafferty BD — 1999 — 32 High Road, Stevenston KA20 3DR — 01294 464180
Alexander T. McAspurren BD MTh CPS — 2002 — Ardeer Manse, 40 Shore Road, Stevenston KA20 3LA — 01294 463814
(Assist)

Stevenston: High (H)
M. Scott Cameron MA BD — 2002 — Glencairn Street, Stevenston KA20 3DL
[E-mail: scottie.cameron@ukonline.co.uk] — 01294 463356

Stevenston: Livingstone (H) See Stevenston: Ardeer

West Kilbride: Overton (H)
Norman Cruickshank BA BD   1983   Goldenberry Avenue, West Kilbride KA23 9LJ   01294 823186

West Kilbride: St Andrew's (H) (01294 829902)
D. Ross Mitchell BA BD   1972 1980   7 Overton Drive, West Kilbride KA23 9LQ   01294 823142
[E-mail: ross.mitchell@virgin.net]

Whiting Bay and Kildonan
Elizabeth R.L. Watson (Miss) BA BD   1981 1982   Whiting Bay, Brodick, Isle of Arran KA27 8RE   01770 700289
[E-mail: elizabeth@rlwatson.freeserve.co.uk]

Name	Dates	Position	Address	Tel
Dailly, J.R. BD DipPS	1979 1979	Staff Chaplain: Army	DACG, HQ 42 (NW) Bde, Fulwood Barracks, Preston PR2 8AA	
Downie, Alexander S.	1975 1997	(Ardrossan: Park)	14 Korsankel Wynd, Saltcoats KA21 6HY	01294 464097
Ewing, James MA BD	1948 1987	(Ardrossan: Barony)	8 Semple Crescent, Fairlie, Largs KA29 0EN	01475 568115
Fisher, Kenneth H.	1969 1994	(Stronsay with Eday)	33 Halfway Street, West Kilbride KA23 9EQ	01294 829973
Gordon, David C.	1953 1988	(Gigha and Cara)	16 Braeside Avenue, Largs KA30 8HD	
Harbison, David J.H.	1958 1998	(Beith: High with Beith: Trinity)	42 Mill Park, Dalry KA24 5BB [E-mail: djh@harbi.fsnet.co.uk]	01294 834092
Hebenton, David J. MA BD	1958 2002	(Ayton and Burnmouth linked with Grantshouse and Houndwood and Reston)	22B Faulds Wynd, Seamill, West Kilbride KA23 9FA	
Kirkwood, Hugh BA BD	1942 1981	(Saltcoats Erskine)	2 Alton Way, West Kilbride KA23 9JJ	01294 823932
Lamb, A. Douglas MA	1964 2002	(Dalry: St Margaret's)	130 Denstrath Road, Edzell Woods, Brechin DD9 7XF [E-mail: a.d.lamb@lamb.junglelink.co.uk]	01356 648139
McCance, Andrew M. BSc	1986 1995	(Coatbridge: Middle)	15 The Crescent, Skelmorlie PA17 5DX	
McKay, Johnston R. MA BA	1969 1987	Religious Broadcasting (BBC)	27 Stanlane Place, Largs KA30 8DD [E-mail: evelyn.mckay@virgin.net]	01475 672960
Maclagan, David W. MA ThD	1965 1991	(Largs: St John's)	Flat C, 1 Greenock Road, Largs KA30 8PQ	01475 673258
Paterson, John H. BD	1977 2000	(Kirkintilloch: St David's Memorial Park)	Creag Bhan, Golf Course Road, Whiting Bay, Arran KA27 8QT	01770 700569
Risby, Lesley P. (Mrs) BD	1994 2000	(Aberdeen: Denburn)	Portnahaven, Corrie, Brodick, Isle of Arran KA27 8JP	01770 810272
Roy, Iain M. MA BD	1960 1997	(Stevenston: Livingstone)	2 The Fieldings, Dunlop, Kilmarnock KA3 4AU	01560 483072
Selfridge, John BTh BREd	1969 1991	(Eddrachillis)	Strathclyde House, Apt 1, Shore Road, Skelmorlie PA17 5AN	01475 529514
Taylor, Andrew S. BTh FPhS	1959 1992	(Greenock Union)	9 Raillies Avenue, Largs KA30 8QY	01475 674709
Thomson, Margaret (Mrs)	1988 1993	(Saltcoats: Erskine)	72 Knockrivoch Place, Ardrossan KA22 7PZ	01294 468685
Walker, David S. MA	1939 1978	(Markerstoun with Smailholm with Stichill, Hume and Nenthorn)	6 Stairlie Crescent, West Kilbride KA23 9BT	01294 823061

(13) LANARK

Meets at Lanark on the first Tuesday of February, March, April, May, September, October, November and December, and on the third Tuesday of June.

Clerk: REV. GAVIN J. ELLIOTT MA BD — The Manse, 61 High Street, Biggar ML12 6DA — 01899 220227 (Tel/Fax)
[E-mail: akph60@uk.uumail.com]
[E-mail: lanarkpresbytery@uk.uumail.com]
[http://www.biggar.net.co.uk/lanark]

Biggar (H)
Gavin J. Elliott MA BD — 1976 1995 — 61 High Street, Biggar ML12 6DA — 01899 220227 (Tel/Fax)
[E-mail: biggarkirk@biggar-net.co.uk]

Black Mount linked with Culter linked with Libberton and Quothquan
Stephen A. Pacitti MA — 1963 1997 — 17 Mercat Loan, Biggar ML12 6DG — 01899 220625

Cairngryffe linked with Symington
Graham R. Houston BSc BD MTh PhD — 1978 2001 — 16 Abington Road, Symington, Biggar ML12 6JX — 01899 308838
[E-mail: gandihouston@aol.com]

Carluke: Kirkton (H) (01555 750778)
Iain D. Cunningham MA BD — 1979 1987 — 9 Station Road, Carluke ML8 5AA — 01555 771262 (Tel/Fax)
[E-mail: iaindc@fish.co.uk]

Carluke: St Andrew's (H)
Helen E. Jamieson (Mrs) BD DipED — 1989 — 120 Clyde Street, Carluke ML8 5BG — 01555 771218
[E-mail: helenj@icscotland.net]

Carluke: St John's (H)
Michael W. Frew BSc BD — 1978 1991 — 18 Old Bridgend, Carluke ML8 4HN — 01555 772259
[E-mail: mwfrew@aol.com]

Carnwath (H)
Beverly G.D.D. Gauld MA BD — 1972 1978 — The Manse, Carnwath, Lanark ML11 8JY — 01555 840259

(Auchengray Tarbrax and Woolfords)

Carstairs linked with Carstairs Junction
J. Melvyn Coogan LTh — 1992 1996 — 80 Lanark Road, Carstairs ML11 8QH — 01555 870250

Carstairs Junction See Carstairs

Coalburn linked with Lesmahagow: Old
Vacant — Calsay Cottage, 103 New Trows Road, Lesmahagow ML11 0ER — 01555 892425

Crossford linked with Kirkfieldbank
Steven Reid BAcc CA BD — 1989 1997 — The Manse, Crossford, Carluke ML8 5RE [E-mail: stevenreid@v21mail.co.uk] — 01555 860415

Cutter linked with Libberton and Quothquan See Black Mount

Douglas: St Bride's linked with Douglas Water and Rigside
Bryan Kerr BA BD — 2002 — The Manse, Douglas, Lanark ML11 0RB [E-mail: bryan@fish.co.uk] — 01555 851213

Forth: St Paul's (H)
Vacant — 22 Lea-Rig, Forth, Lanark ML11 8EA — 01555 811748

Glencaple linked with Lowther
Margaret A. Muir (Miss) MA LLB BD — 1989 2001 — 66 Carlisle Road, Crawford, Biggar ML12 6TW — 01864 502625

Kirkfieldbank See Crossford

Kirkmuirhill (H)
David A. Young — 1972 1974 — The Manse, 2 Lanark Road, Kirkmuirhill, Lanark ML11 9RB [E-mail: davidkcs@aol.com] — 01555 892409 (Tel/Fax)

Lanark: Greyfriars
Catherine E.E. Collins (Mrs) MA BD — 1993 — 2 Friarsdene, Lanark ML11 9EJ [E-mail: greyfriars@webartz.com] — 01555 663363
David A. Collins BSc BD — 1993

Lanark: St Nicholas'
Alison A. Meikle (Mrs) BD — 1999 2002 — 32 Braxfield Road, Lanark ML11 9BS — 01555 662600 (Tel) / 01555 665905 (Fax)

Law
Vacant

Lesmahagow: Abbeygreen
David S. Carmichael — 1982 — Abbeygreen Manse, Lesmahagow, Lanark ML11 0DB — 01555 893384

Lesmahagow: Old (H) See Coalburn
Libberton and Quothquan See Black Mount
Lowther See Glencaple
Symington See Cairngryffe

Cowell, Susan G. (Miss) BA BD	1986	1998	(Budapest)	39 Main Street, Symington, Lanarkshire ML12 6LL	01899 308257
Craig, William BA LTh	1974	1997	(Cambusbarron: The Bruce Memorial)	31 Heathfield Drive, Blackwood, Lanark ML11 9SR	01555 893710
Jones, Philip H.	1968	1987	(Bishopbriggs Kenmure)	81 Vere Road, Kirkmuirhill, Lanark ML11 9RP	01555 894326
McCormick, W. Cadzow MA BD	1943	1983	(Glasgow Maryhill Old)	82 Main Street, Symington, Biggar ML12 6LJ	01899 308221
McMahon, Robert J. BD	1959	1997	(Crossford with Kirkfieldbank)	7 Ridgepark Drive, Lanark ML11 9PG	01555 663844
Seath, Thomas J.G.	1980	1992	(Motherwell: Manse Road)	1 Allan Avenue, Carluke ML8 5UA	01555 771644
Stewart, John M. MA BD	1964	2001	(Johnstone with Kirkpatrick Juxta)	5 Rathmor Road, Biggar ML12 6QG	01899 220398
Thomson, John S. MA	1934	1972	(Covington and Thankerton with Libberton and Quothquan)	20 Whitehouse Loan, Edinburgh EH9 2EZ	0131-447 9455

(14) PAISLEY

Meets at Paisley, in St James' Church Hall, on the second Tuesday of each month, except January, July and August.

Clerk: REV. DAVID KAY BA BD MTh   6 Southfield Avenue, Paisley PA2 8BY   0141-884 3600 (Tel/Fax)
[E-mail: akph69@uk.uumail.com]

Barrhead: Arthurlie (H) (0141-881 8442)
James S.A. Cowan BD DipMin   1986   1998   10 Arthurlie Avenue, Barrhead, Glasgow G78 2BU   0141-881 3457
[E-mail: jim_cowan@ntlworld.com]

Barrhead: Bourock (H) (0141-881 9813)
Maureen Leitch (Mrs) BA BD   1995   14 Maxton Avenue, Barrhead, Glasgow G78 1DY   0141-881 1462
[E-mail: bourockmanse@compuserve.com]

Barrhead: South and Levern (H) (0141-881 7825)
R.M. Hetherington MA BD   1966   1977   3 Colinbar Circle, Barrhead, Glasgow G78 2BE   0141-571 4059
[E-mail: rmhmanse@freeserveuk.com]

Bishopton (H)
Gaye J.A. Taylor (Mrs) BD   1999   The Manse, Newton Road, Bishopton PA7 5JP   01505 862161

Bridge of Weir: Freeland (H) (01505 612610)
Kenneth N. Gray BA BD   1988   15 Lawmarnock Crescent, Bridge of Weir PA11 3AS   01505 690919

Bridge of Weir: St Machar's Ranfurly (01505 614364)
Suzanne Dunleavy (Miss) BD DipEd   1990   1992   9 Glen Brae, Bridge of Weir PA11 3BH   01505 612975

Charge / Minister			Address	Tel
Caldwell John Campbell MA BA BSc	1973	2000	The Manse of Caldwell, Uplawmoor, Glasgow G78 4AL [E-mail: johncampbell@minister.com]	01505 850215
Elderslie Kirk (H) (01505 323348) David N. McLachlan BD	1985	1994	282 Main Road, Elderslie, Johnstone PA5 9EF	01505 321767
Erskine (0141-812 4620) Ian W. Bell LTh Morag Erskine (Miss) DCS	1990	1998	7 Leven Place, Linburn, Erskine PA8 6AS 111 Main Drive, Erskine PA8 7JJ	0141-581 0955 0141-812 6096
Houston and Killellan (H) Georgina M. Baxendale (Mrs) BD	1981	1989	The Manse of Houston, Main Street, Houston, Johnstone PA6 7EL	01505 612569
Howwood David Stewart MA DipEd BD MTh	1977	2001	The Manse, Beith Road, Howwood, Johnstone PA9 1AS [E-mail: revdavidst@aol.com]	01505 703678
Inchinnan (H) (0141-812 1263) Marilyn MacLaine (Mrs) LTh	1995		The Manse, Inchinnan, Renfrew PA4 9PH	0141-812 1688
Johnstone: High (H) (01505 336303) Ann C. McCool (Mrs) BD DSD IPA ALCM	1989	2001	76 North Road, Johnstone PA5 8NF	01505 320006
Johnstone: St Andrew's Trinity Vacant				
Johnstone: St Paul's (H) (01505 321632) James A.S. Boag BD	1992		61 Auchenlodment Road, Elderslie, Johnstone PA5 9PA [E-mail: j.boag@ntlworld.com]	01505 320060
Kilbarchan: East Vacant			Church Street, Kilbarchan, Johnstone PA10 2JQ	01505 702621
Kilbarchan: West Arthur Sherratt BD	1994		West Manse, Shuttle Street, Kilbarchan, Johnstone PA10 2JR [E-mail: arthur.sherratt@ntlworld.com]	01505 342930
Linwood (H) (01505 328802) T. Edward Marshall BD	1987		The Manse, Bridge Street, Linwood, Paisley PA3 3DL [E-mail: marshall@manse.fslife.co.uk]	01505 325131

Lochwinnoch (T)				
Robin N. Allison BD DipMin	1994	1999	1 Station Rise, Lochwinnoch PA12 4NA [E-mail: robin@mansemob.org]	01505 843484
Neilston (0141-881 9445)				
Alexander Macdonald MA BD	1966	1984	The Manse, Neilston Road, Neilston, Glasgow G78 3NP [E-mail: macdonaldal@supanet.com]	0141-881 1958
Paisley: Abbey (H) (Tel: 0141-889 7654; Fax: 0141-887 3929)				
Alan D. Birss MA BD	1979	1988	15 Main Road, Castlehead, Paisley PA2 6AJ [E-mail: alan.birss@virgin.net]	0141-889 3587
Paisley: Castlehead				
Esther J. Ninian MA BD	1993	1998	28 Fulbar Crescent, Paisley PA2 9AS	01505 812304
Paisley: Glenburn (0141-884 2602)				
George C. MacKay BD CertMin	1994		10 Hawick Avenue, Paisley PA2 9LD	0141-884 4903
Paisley: Laigh Kirk (H) (0141-889 7700)				
Thomas M. Cant MA BD	1964	1972	18 Oldhall Road, Paisley PA1 3HL	0141-882 2277
Paisley: Lylesland (H) (0141-561 7139)				
Andrew W. Bradley BD	1975	1998	36 Potterhill Avenue, Paisley PA2 8BA	0141-884 2882
Greta Gray (Miss) DCS			67 Crags Avenue, Paisley PA3 6SG	0141-884 6178
Paisley: Martyrs' (0141-889 6603)				
Alison Davidge (Mrs) MA BD	1990	1997	12 Low Road, Paisley PA2 6AG	0141-889 2182
Paisley: Oakshaw Trinity (H) (Tel: 0141-887 4647; Fax: 0141-848 5139; E-mail: iancurrie@ntlworld.com)				
Ian S. Currie MBE BD	1975	1980	9 Hawkhead Road, Paisley PA1 3ND	0141-887 0884
Paisley: St Columba Foxbar (H) (01505 812377)				
Anthony J.R. Fowler BSc BD	1982	1985	13 Corsebar Drive, Paisley PA2 9QD [E-mail: ajr.fowler@virgin.net]	0141-889 9988
Mary Johnston (Miss) DCS			19 Lounsdale Drive, Paisley PA2 9ED	0141-849 1615
Paisley: St James' (0141-889 2422)				
Eleanor J. McMahon (Miss) BEd BD	1994		38 Woodland Avenue, Paisley PA2 8BH [E-mail: eleanor.mcmahon@ukgateway.net]	0141-884 3246
Paisley: St Luke's (H)				
D. Ritchie M. Gillon BD DipMin	1994		31 Southfield Avenue, Paisley PA2 8BX [E-mail: revgillon@hotmail.com]	0141-884 6215

Paisley: St Mark's Oldhall (H) (0141-882 2755)
Alistair H. Morrison BTh DipYCS   1985   1989   36 Newtyle Road, Paisley PA1 3JX   0141-889 4279
                                                             [E-mail: alistairmorrison@supanet.com]

Paisley: St Ninian's Ferguslie (E) (0141-887 9436) (New charge development)
James G. Redpath BD DipPTh   1988   2001   10 Stanely Drive, Paisley PA2 6HE   0141-884 4177
                                                             [E-mail: james.g.redpath@btinternet.com]

Paisley: Sandyford (Thread Street) (0141-889 5078)
David Kay BA BD MTh   1974   6 Southfield Avenue, Paisley PA2 8BY   0141-884 3600
                                                             [E-mail: revdkay@hotmail.com]

Paisley: Sherwood Greenlaw (H) (0141-889 7060)
Alasdair F. Cameron BD CA   1986   1993   5 Greenlaw Drive, Paisley PA1 3RX   0141-889 3057
                                                             [E-mail: alcamron@lineone.net]
May Bell (Mrs) (Assistant)   1998   7 Leven Place, Linburn, Erskine PA8 6AS   0141-581 0955

Paisley: Wallneuk North (Tel: 0141-889 9265; Fax: 0141-887 6670)
Thomas Macintyre MA BD   1972   1988   27 Mansionhouse Road, Paisley PA1 3RG   0141-581 1505

Renfrew: North (0141-885 2154)
E. Lorna Hood (Mrs) MA BD   1978   1979   1 Alexandra Drive, Renfrew PA4 8UB   0141-886 2074
                                                             [E-mail: lorna.hood@ntlworld.com]

Renfrew: Old
Alexander C. Wark MA BD STM   1982   1998   31 Gibson Road, Renfrew PA4 0RH   0141-886 2005
                                                             [E-mail: alecwark@yahoo.co.uk]

Renfrew: Trinity (H) (0141-885 2129)
Stuart C. Steell BD CertMin   1992   25 Paisley Road, Renfrew PA4 8JH   0141-886 2131
                                                             [E-mail: scsren@tinyonline.co.uk]

Abeledo, Benjamin J.A. BTh DipTh PTh	1991	2000	Army Chaplain	4 Redford Place, Colinton, Edinburgh EH13 0AL	0131-441 5199
Alexander, Douglas N. MA BD	1961	1999	(Bishopton)	West Morningside, Main Road, Langbank, Port Glasgow PA4 6XP	01475 540249
Cameron, Margaret (Miss) DCS			(Deaconess)	2 Rowans Gate, Paisley PA2 6RD	0141-840 2479
Cubie, John P. MA BD	1961	1999	(Caldwell)	36 Winram Place, St Andrews KY16 8XH	01334 474708
Lowe, Edwin MA BD	1950	1988	(Caldwell)	45 Duncarnock Crescent, Neilston, Glasgow G78 3HH	0141-580 5726
McBain, Margaret (Miss) DCS				33 Quarry Road, Paisley PA2 7RD	0141-884 2920
MacColl, James C. BSc BD	1966	2002	(Johnstone: St Andrew's Trinity)	Greenways, Winton, Kirkby Stephen, Cumbria CA17 4HL	01768 372290
MacColl, John BD DipMin	1989	2001	Teacher: Religious Education	1 Birch Avenue, Johnstone PA5 0DD	01505 326506
McDonald, Alexander BA CMIWSC DUniv	1968	1988	Department of Ministry	36 Alloway Grove, Paisley PA2 7DQ	0141-560 1937

McLachlan, Duncan MA BD ThM	1955 1992	(Paisley: Sherwood)	27 Penilee Road, Paisley PA1 3EU	0141-882 6353
Marr, E.R. MA	1933 1977	(Buittle)	Abbey Care Centre, Lonend, Paisley	
Mathers, J. Allan C.	1950 1989	(Inchinnan)	19 Braemar Road, Inchinnan PA4 9QB	0141-561 2870
Moffet, James R. BA	1942 1979	(Paisley: St Matthew's)	Flat 49, Strathclyde House, 31 Shore Road, Skelmorlie PA17 5AN	
O'Leary, Thomas BD	1983 1998	(Lochwinnoch)	1 Carters Place, Irvine KA12 0BU	01505 615280
Palmer, S.W. BD	1980 1991	(Kilbarchan: East)	4 Bream Place, Houston PA6 7ZJ	0141-842 1585
Prentice, George BA BTh	1964 1997	(Paisley: Martyrs)	46 Victoria Gardens, Corsebar Road, Paisley PA2 9AQ	0141-886 2896
Rule, James A.	1952 1991	(Renfrew: Moorpark)	6 St Andrew's Road, Renfrew PA4 0SN	0141-889 9512
Steele, Jean (Miss) DCS		(Deaconess)	93 George Street, Paisley PA1 2JX	

PAISLEY ADDRESSES

Abbey	Town Centre	Oakshaw: Trinity	Churchill
Castlehead	Canal Street	St Columba Foxbar	Amochrie Road, Foxbar
Glenburn	Nethercraigs Drive off Glenburn Road	St James'	Underwood Road
Laigh	Causeyside Street	St Luke's	Neilston Road
Lylesland	Rowan Street off Neilston Road	St Mark's Oldhall	Glasgow Road, Ralston
Martyrs'	Broomlands	St Ninian's Ferguslie	Blackstoun Road
		Sandyford (Thread St)	Gallowhill
		Sherwood Greenlaw	Glasgow Road
		Wallneuk North	off Renfrew Road

(15) GREENOCK

Meets at Greenock, in Ardgowan Parish Church Hall, on the second Tuesday of December, February and May, on the fourth Tuesday of October and March, on the third Tuesday of June, and in the Moderator's Church on the second Tuesday of September.

Clerk: REV. DAVID MILL KGSJ MA BD   105 Newark Street, Greenock PA16 7TW   01475 639602
[E-mail: akph53@uk.uumail.com]
[E-mail: greenockpresbytery@uk.uumail.com]

Gourock: Old Gourock and Ashton (H)
Frank J. Gardner MA   1966 1979   90 Albert Road, Gourock PA19 1NN   01475 631516
[E-mail: frankgardner@oldgourockashton.freeserve.co.uk]

Gourock: St John's (H)
P. Jill Clancy (Mrs) BD   2000   6 Barrhill Road, Gourock PA19 1JX   01475 632143
[E-mail: jgibson@totalise.co.uk]

Greenock: Ardgowan
Alan H. Ward MA BD   1978 2002   72 Forsyth Street, Greenock PA16 8SX   01475 790849
[E-mail: alanward@ntlworld.com]

Greenock: Cartsdyke Vacant			84 Forsyth Street, Greenock PA16 8QY	01475 721439
Greenock: Finnart St Paul's (H) David Mill KGSJ MA BD	1978	1979	105 Newark Street, Greenock PA16 7TW [E-mail: david.mill@uk.uumail.com]	01475 639602
Greenock: Mount Kirk James H. Simpson BD LLB	1964	1965	76 Finnart Street, Greenock PA16 8HJ	01475 722338
Greenock: Old West Kirk C. Ian W. Johnson MA BD	1997		39 Fox Street, Greenock PA16 8PD [E-mail: ian_ciw_johnson@tesco.net]	01475 888277
Eileen Manson (Mrs) DipCE (Aux)	1994		1 Cambridge Avenue, Gourock PA19 1XT [E-mail: jrmanson@btinternet.com]	01475 632401
Greenock: St George's North W. Douglas Hamilton BD	1975	1986	67 Forsyth Street, Greenock PA16 8SX	01475 724003
Greenock: St Luke's (H) William C. Hewitt BD DipPS	1977	1994	50 Ardgowan Street, Greenock PA16 8EP [E-mail: william.hewitt@ntlworld.com]	01475 721048
Greenock: St Margaret's (01475 781953) Isobel J.M. Kelly (Miss) MA BD DipEd	1974	1998	105 Finnart Street, Greenock PA16 8HN	01475 786590
Greenock: St Ninian's Allan G. McIntyre BD	1985		5 Auchmead Road, Greenock PA16 0PY [E-mail: agmcintyre@lineone.net]	01475 631878
Greenock: Wellpark Mid Kirk Alan K. Sorensen BD MTh DipMin FSAScot	1983	2000	101 Brisbane Street, Greenock PA16 8PA [E-mail: alansorensen@beeb.net]	01475 721741
Inverkip (H) Elizabeth A. Crumlish (Mrs) BD	1995	2002	The Manse, Longhouse Road, Inverkip, Greenock PA16 0BJ [E-mail: lizcrumlish@aol.com]	01475 521207
Kilmacolm: Old (H) Gordon D. Irving BD	1994	1998	Glencairn Road, Kilmacolm PA13 4NJ [E-mail: g.irving@oldkirkmanse3.freeserve.co.uk]	01505 873174
Kilmacolm: St Columba (H) R. Douglas Cranston MA BD	1986	1992	6 Churchill Road, Kilmacolm PA13 4LH [E-mail: robert.cranston@lineone.net]	01505 873271

Langbank (T)
Anna S. Rodwell (Mrs) BD DipMin — 1998 — Langbank, Port Glasgow PA14 6XB — 01475 540252

Port Glasgow: Hamilton Bardrainney
James A. Munro BD DMS — 1979   2002 — 80 Bardrainney Avenue, Port Glasgow PA14 6HD — 01475 701213

Port Glasgow: St Andrew's (H)
Andrew T. MacLean BA BD — 1980   1993 — Barr's Brae, Port Glasgow PA14 5QA [E-mail: a.maclean@dial.pipex.com] — 01475 741486

Port Glasgow: St Martin's
John G. Miller BEd BD MTh — 1983   1998 — Clunebraehead, Clune Brae, Port Glasgow PA14 5SL — 01475 704115

Skelmorlie and Wemyss Bay
William R. Armstrong BD — 1979 — 3A Montgomerie Terrace, Skelmorlie PA17 5TD [E-mail: william@warmst.freeserve.co.uk] — 01475 520703

Name	Years	Charge	Address	Tel
Bruce, A. William MA	1942 1981	(Fortingall and Glenlyon)	75 Union Street, Greenock PA16 8BG	01475 787534
Chestnut, Alexander MBE BA	1948 1987	(Greenock St Mark's Greenbank)	5 Douglas Street, Largs KA30 8PS	01475 674168
Copland, Agnes M. (Mrs) MBE DCS		(Deacon)	3 Craigmuschat Road, Gourock PA19 1SE	01475 631870
McCully, M. Isobel (Miss) DCS		(Deacon)	10 Broadstone Avenue, Port Glasgow PA14 5BB [E-mail: i.mccully@tesco.net]	01475 742240
McLachlan, Fergus C. BD	1982 2002	Hospital Chaplain: Inverclyde Royal	46 Queen Square, Glasgow G41 2AZ	0141-423 3830
MacQuien, Duncan DCS		(Deacon)	2 Manor Crescent, Gourock PA19 1UY	01475 633407
Marshall, Fred J. BA	1946 1992	(Bermuda)	Flat 4, Varrich House, 7 Church Hill, Edinburgh EH10 4BG	0131-446 0205
Montgomery, Robert A. MA	1955 1992	(Quarrier's Village: Mount Zion)	11 Myreton Avenue, Kilmacolm PA13 4LJ	01505 872028
Nicol, Joyce M. (Mrs) DCS		(Deacon)	93 Brisbane Street, Greenock PA16 8NY	01475 723235
Porteous, Alexander MA BD	1965 1987	(Greenock: Mid Kirk)	Strathmore, Golf Road, Millport, Isle of Cumbrae KA28 0HB	01475 530460
Pyper, J. Stewart BA	1951 1986	(Greenock: St George's North)	39 Brisbane Street, Greenock PA16 8NR	01475 793234
Scott, Ernest M. MA	1959 1992	(Port Glasgow: St Andrew's)	17 Brueacre Road, Wemyss Bay PA18 6ER [E-mail: ernie.scott@ernest70.fsnet.co.uk]	01475 522267
Stone, W. Vernon MA BD	1949 1985	(Langbank)	36 Woodrow Court, Port Glasgow Road, Kilmacolm KA13 4QA	01505 872644
Whyte, John H. MA	1946 1986	(Gourock: Ashton)	6 Castle Levan Manor, Cloch Road, Gourock PA19 1AY	01475 636788

GREENOCK ADDRESSES

Gourock
Old Gourock and Ashton — 41 Royal Street
St John's — Bath Street x St John's Road

Greenock
Ardgowan — 31 Union Street
Cartsdyke — 14 Crescent Street
Finnart St Paul's — Newark Street x Bentinck Street
Mount Kirk — Dempster Sreet at Murdieston Park
Old West Kirk — Esplanade x Campbell Street
St George's North — George Square
St Luke's — 9 Nelson Street
St Margaret's — Finch Road x Kestrel Crescent
St Ninian's — Warwick Road, Larkfield
Wellpark Mid Kirk — Cathcart Square

Port Glasgow
Hamilton
Bardrainney — Bardrainney Avenue x Auchenbothie Road
St Andrew's — Princes Street
St Martin's — Mansion Avenue

(16) GLASGOW

Meets at New Govan Church, Govan Cross, Glasgow, on the second Tuesday of each month, except June when the meeting takes place on the third Tuesday. In January, July and August there is no meeting.

Clerk: REV. DAVID W. LUNAN MA BD   **260 Bath Street, Glasgow G2 4JP**   **0141-332 6606 (Tel/Fax)**
                                                              [E-mail: akph84@uk.uumail.com]
                                                              [E-mail: cofs-glasgow.presbytery@uk.uumail.com]
Hon. Treasurer: COPELAND KNIGHT Esq   [E-mail: glasgowpres@yahoo.co.uk]

1 **Banton linked with Twechar**
   Vacant   Manse of Banton, Kilsyth, Glasgow G65 0QL   01236 826129

2 **Bishopbriggs: Kenmure**
   Iain A. Laing MA BD   1971   1992   5 Marchfield, Bishopbriggs, Glasgow G64 3PP   0141-772 1468

3 **Bishopbriggs: Springfield**
   William Ewart BSc BD   1972   1978   39 Springfield Road, Bishopbriggs, Glasgow G64 1PL   0141-772 1540

4 **Blairbeth Rodger Memorial (T)**
   Vacant   4 Milrig Road, Rutherglen, Glasgow G73 2NH   0141-647 6762

5 **Broom (0141-639 3528)**
   James Whyte BD   1981   1987   3 Laigh Road, Newton Mearns, Glasgow G77 5EX   0141-639 2916
                                                                                                                  0141-639 3528 (Fax)
   Margaret McLelland (Mrs) DCS   18 Broom Road East, Newton Mearns, Glasgow G77 5SD   0141-639 6853

6 **Burnside (0141-634 4130)**
   David J.C. Easton MA BD   1965   1977   59 Blairbeth Road, Burnside, Glasgow G73 4JD   0141-634 1233 (Tel)
                                                              [E-mail: theoffice@burnsideparishchurch.org.uk]   0141-634 7383 (Fax)

7 **Busby (0141-644 2073)**
   Jeremy C. Eve BSc BD   1998   17A Carmunnock Road, Busby, Glasgow G76 8SZ   0141-644 3670
                                                              [E-mail: jerry.eve@btinternet.com]

8 **Cadder (0141-772 7436)**
   Graham S. Finch MA BD   1977   1999   6 Balmuildy Road, Bishopbriggs, Glasgow G64 3BS   0141-772 1363

9 **Cambuslang: Flemington Hallside**
   R. David Currie BSc BD   1984   103 Overton Road, Cambuslang, Glasgow G72 7XA   0141-641 2097

10   Cambuslang: Old
Vacant
74 Stewarton Drive, Cambuslang, Glasgow   G72 8DG   0141-641 3261

11   Cambuslang: St Andrew's
John Stevenson LTh   1998   37 Brownside Road, Cambuslang, Glasgow   G72 8NH   0141-641 3847 (Tel)
[E-mail: john@stevensonj.fsnet.co.uk]   0141-641 0773 (Fax)
James Birch PGDip FRSA FIOC (Aux)   2001   1 Kirkhill Grove, Cambuslang, Glasgow   G72 8EH   0141-583 1722

12   Cambuslang: Trinity St Paul's
William Jackson BD CertMin   1994   4 Glasgow Road, Cambuslang, Glasgow   G72 7BW   0141-641 3414
[E-mail: wiljackson4@aol.com]

13   Campsie (01360 310939)
David J. Torrance BD DipMin   1993   19 Redhills View, Lennoxtown, Glasgow   G66 7BL   01360   312527

14   Chryston (H)
Martin A.W. Allen MA BD ThM   1977   Main Street, Chryston, Glasgow   G69 9LA   0141-779 1436
David J. McAdam BSc BD (Assoc)   1990   12 Dunellan Crescent, Moodiesburn, Glasgow   G69 0GE   01236 870472
[E-mail: dmca29@aol.com]

15   Eaglesham (01355 302047)
W. Douglas Lindsay BD CPS   1978   The Manse, East Kilbride Road, Eaglesham, Glasgow   G76 0NS   01355   303495

16   Fernhill and Cathkin
Vacant
82 Blairbeth Road, Rutherglen, Glasgow   G73 4JA   0141-634 1508

17   Gartcosh (H) (01236 873770) linked with Glenboig (01236 875625)
Alexander M. Fraser BD DipMin   1985   26 Inchknock Avenue, Gartcosh, Glasgow   G69 8EA   01236 872274
[E-mail: sandy@revfraser.freeserve.co.uk]

18   Giffnock: Orchardhill (0141-638 3604)
John M. Spiers LTh MTh   1972   58 Woodlands Road, Thornliebank, Glasgow   G46 7JQ   0141-638 0632 (Tel/Fax)
[E-mail: john.spiers@ntlworld.com]

19   Giffnock: South (0141-638 2599)
Edward V. Simpson BSc BD   1972   5 Langtree Avenue, Whitecraigs, Glasgow   G46 7LN   0141-638 8767 (Tel)
0141-620 0605 (Fax)

20   Giffnock: The Park
Calum D. Macdonald BD   1993   41 Rouken Glen Road, Thornliebank, Glasgow   G46 7JD   0141-638 3023

21   Glenboig See Gartcosh

22   Greenbank (H) (0141-644 1891)
Vacant
Greenbank Manse, Clarkston, Glasgow   G76 7DJ   0141-644 1395 (Tel)
0141-644 4804 (Fax)

No.	Congregation / Minister			Address	Telephone
23	**Kilsyth: Anderson** Charles M. MacKinnon BD	1989	1999	Anderson Manse, Kingston Road, Kilsyth, Glasgow G65 0HR	01236 822345
24	**Kilsyth: Burns and Old** Thomas A. McLachlan BSc	1972	1983	The Grange, Glasgow Road, Kilsyth, Glasgow G65 9AE	01236 823116
25	**Kirkintilloch: Hillhead** Lily F. McKinnon (Mrs) MA BD	1993	2000	64 Waverley Park, Kensington Gate, Kirkintilloch, Glasgow G66 2BP	0141-776 6270
26	**Kirkintilloch: St Columba's (H)** David M. White BA BD	1988	1992	14 Crossdykes, Kirkintilloch, Glasgow G66 3EU	0141-578 4357
27	**Kirkintilloch: St David's Memorial Park (H)** Bryce Calder MA BD	1995	2001	2 Roman Road, Kirkintilloch, Glasgow G66 1EA	0141-776 1434
28	**Kirkintilloch: St Mary's** Mark E. Johnstone MA BD	1993	2001	The Manse, Union Road, Kirkintilloch, Glasgow G66 1DH [E-mail: mark.johnstone@ntlworld.com]	0141-776 1252
29	**Lenzie: Old (H)** Douglas W. Clark LTh	1993	2000	41 Kirkintilloch Road, Lenzie, Glasgow G66 4LB	0141-776 2184
30	**Lenzie: Union (H)** James B. Ferguson LTh	1972	1984	1 Larch Avenue, Lenzie, Glasgow G66 4HX [E-mail: jasbferguson@lineone.net]	0141-776 3831
31	**Maxwell Mearns Castle (Tel/Fax: 0141-639 5169)** David C. Cameron BD CertMin	1993		122 Broomfield Avenue, Newton Mearns, Glasgow G77 5JR [E-mail: office@maxwellmearns.com]	0141-616 0642
32	**Mearns (H) (0141-639 6555)** Joseph A. Kavanagh BD DipPTh MTh Anne M. MacFadyen (Mrs) BSc BD (Aux)	1992 1995	1998 2000	Manse of Mearns, Newton Mearns, Glasgow G77 5BU 295 Mearns Road, Newton Mearns, Glasgow G77 5LT	0141-616 2410 (Tel/Fax) 0141-639 3605
33	**Milton of Campsie (H)** Diane E. Stewart BD	1988		33 Birdstone Road, Milton of Campsie, Glasgow G66 8BX	01360 310548 (Tel/Fax)
34	**Netherlee (H)** Thomas Nelson BSc BD	1992	2002	25 Ormonde Avenue, Glasgow G44 3QY	0141-585 7502 (Tel/Fax)

35	**Newton Mearns (H) (0141-639 7373)**				
	Angus Kerr BD CertMin ThM	1983	1994	28 Waterside Avenue, Newton Mearns, Glasgow G77 6TJ	0141-616 2079
				[E-mail: anguskerr@newtonmearns.ndo.co.uk]	
36	**Rutherglen: Old (H)**				
	Alexander Thomson BSc BD MPhil PhD	1973	1985	31 Highburgh Drive, Rutherglen, Glasgow G73 3RR	0141-647 6178
37	**Rutherglen: Stonelaw (0141-647 5113)**				
	Alastair S. May	2002		80 Blairbeth Road, Rutherglen, Glasgow G73 4JA	0141-583 0157
38	**Rutherglen: Wardlawhill**				
	Vacant			26 Parkhill Drive, Rutherglen, Glasgow G73 2PW	0141-563 9590
39	**Rutherglen: West**				
	John W. Drummond MA BD	1971	1986	12 Albert Drive, Rutherglen, Glasgow G73 3RT	0141-569 8547
40	**Stamperland (0141-637 4999) (H)**				
	Alastair J. Cherry BA BD	1982	1987	109 Ormonde Avenue, Glasgow G44 3SN	0141-637 4976 (Tel/Fax)
				[E-mail: a.j.cherry@btinternet.com]	
41	**Stepps (H)**				
	Kenneth S. Baird	1998		2 Lenzie Road, Stepps, Glasgow G33 6DX	0141-779 9556
	MSc PhD BD CEng MIMarE				
42	**Thornliebank (H)**				
	Robert M. Silver BA BD	1995		19 Arthurlie Drive, Giffnock, Glasgow G46 6UR	0141-620 2133
43	**Torrance (T) (01360 620970)**				
	Nigel L. Barge BSc BD	1991		27 Campbell Place, Meadow Rise, Torrance, Glasgow G64 4HR	01360 622379
				[E-mail: nigel@nbarge.freeserve.co.uk]	
44	**Twechar** See Banton				
45	**Williamwood**				
	G. Hutton B. Steel MA BD	1982	1990	125 Greenwood Road, Clarkston, Glasgow G76 7LL	0141-571 7949
46	**Glasgow: Anderston Kelvingrove (0141-221 9408)**				
	Vacant			16 Royal Terrace, Glasgow G3 7NY	0141-332 3136
47	**Glasgow: Baillieston Mure Memorial (0141-773 1216)**				
	Allan S. Vint BSc BD	1989	1996	28 Beech Avenue, Baillieston, Glasgow G69 6LF	0141-771 1217
				[E-mail: allan@vint.co.uk]	
48	**Glasgow: Baillieston St Andrew's (0141-771 6629)**				
	Robert Gehrke BSc BD CEng MIEE	1994	2001	12 Oakhill Avenue, Baillieston, Glasgow G69 7ES	0141-771 1791

49	**Glasgow: Balshagray Victoria Park**				
	Campbell Mackinnon BSc BD	1982		20 St Kilda Drive, Glasgow G14 9JN	0141-954 9780
50	**Glasgow: Barlanark Greyfriars**				
	David I.W. Locke MA MSc BD		2000	4 Rhindmuir Grove, Glasgow G69 6NE	0141-771 1240
				[E-mail: davidlocke@ukgateway.net]	
51	**Glasgow: Battlefield East (H) (0141-632 4206)**				
	Alan C. Raeburn MA BD	1971	1977	110 Mount Annan Drive, Glasgow G44 4RZ	0141-632 1514
52	**Glasgow: Blawarthill**				
	Ian M.S. McInnes BD DipMin	1995	1997	46 Earlbank Avenue, Glasgow G14 9HL	0141-579 6521
53	**Glasgow: Bridgeton St Francis in the East (H) (L) (Church House: Tel: 0141-554 8045)**				
	Howard R. Hudson MA BD	1982	1984	10 Albany Drive, Rutherglen, Glasgow G73 3QN	0141-587 8667
				[E-mail: howard.hudson@ntlworld.com]	
	Margaret S. Beaton (Miss) DCS			64 Gardenside Grove, Fernlee Meadows, Carmyle, Glasgow G32 8EZ	0141-646 2297
54	**Glasgow: Broomhill (0141-334 2540)**				
	William B. Ferguson BA BD	1971	1987	27 St Kilda Drive, Glasgow G14 9LN	0141-959 3204
55	**Glasgow: Calton Parkhead (0141-554 3866)**				
	Ronald Anderson BD DipTh	1992		98 Drumover Drive, Glasgow G31 5RP	0141-556 2520
				[E-mail: ron@anderson296.freeserve.co.uk]	
56	**Glasgow: Cardonald (0141-882 6264)**				
	Eric McLachlan BD MTh	1978	1983	133 Newtyle Road, Paisley PA1 3LB	0141-561 1891
				[E-mail: eric.mclachlan@ntlworld.com]	
57	**Glasgow: Carmunnock**				
	G. Gray Fletcher BSc BD	1989	2001	The Manse, 161 Waterside Road, Carmunnock, Glasgow G76 9AJ	0141-644 1578 (Tel/Fax)
58	**Glasgow: Carmyle linked with Kenmuir Mount Vernon**				
	Murdo Maclean BD CertMin	1997	1999	3 Meryon Road, Glasgow G32 9NW	0141-778 2625
59	**Glasgow: Carntyne Old linked with Eastbank**				
	Ronald A.S. Craig BACC BD	1983		211 Sandyhills Road, Glasgow G32 9NB	0141-778 1286
60	**Glasgow: Carnwadric (E)**				
	Graeme K. Bell BA BD	1983		62 Loganswell Road, Glasgow G46 8AX	0141-638 5884
	Christine M. McVean (Miss) DCS			38 Cruachan Street, Glasgow G46 8LY	0141-638 9035

61 Glasgow Castlemilk: East (H) (0141-634 2444)
John D. Miller BA BD   1971
Ann Lyall (Miss) DCS
15 Castlemilk Drive, Glasgow G45 9TL   0141-631 1244
117 Barlia Drive, Glasgow G45 0AY   0141-631 3643

62 Glasgow Castlemilk: West (H) (0141-634 1480)
Janet P.H. MacMahon (Mrs) MSc BD   1992
156 Old Castle Road, Glasgow G44 5TW   0141-637 5451

63 Glasgow: Cathcart Old
Neil W. Galbraith BD CertMin   1987
21 Courthill Avenue, Cathcart, Glasgow G44 5AA   0141-633 5248 (Tel/Fax)

64 Glasgow: Cathcart South (H) (0141-637 6658)
Vacant
82 Merrylee Road, Glasgow G43 2QZ   0141-633 3744

65 Glasgow: Cathedral (High or St Mungo's)
William Morris KCVO DD PhD LLD JP   1951
1 Whitehill Grove, Newton Mearns, Glasgow G77 5DH   0141-639 6327

66 Glasgow: Colston Milton (0141-772 1922)
Christopher D. Park BSc BD   1977
118 Birsay Road, Glasgow G22 7QP   0141-772 1958

67 Glasgow: Colston Wellpark (H)
Christine M. Goldie (Miss) LLB BD MTh   1984
16 Bishop's Gate Gardens, Colston, Glasgow G21 1XS   0141-589 8866

68 Glasgow: Cranhill (H) (0141-774 5593)
James A. Trevorrow LTh   1971
31 Lethamhill Crescent, Glasgow G33 2SH
[E-mail: jimtrevorrow@compuserve.com]   0141-770 6873

69 Glasgow: Croftfoot (H) (0141-637 3913)
John M. Lloyd BD CertMin   1984
20 Victoria Road, Burnside, Rutherglen, Glasgow G73 3QG
[E-mail: johnmlloyd@compuserve.com]   0141-647 5524

70 Glasgow: Dennistoun Blackfriars (H)
Vacant
41 Broompark Drive, Glasgow G31 2JB   0141-554 8667

71 Glasgow: Dennistoun Central (H) (0141-554 1350)
Adah Younger (Mrs) BD   1978   1996
45 Broompark Drive, Glasgow G31 2JB
[E-mail: adah@younger31.prestel.co.uk]   0141-550 4487

72 Glasgow: Drumchapel Drumry St Mary's (0141-944 1998)
Brian S. Sheret MA BD DPhil   1982   2002
8 Fruin Road, Glasgow G15 6SQ   0141-944 4493

73 Glasgow: Drumchapel St Andrew's (0141-944 3758)
John S. Purves LLB BD   1983   1984
6 Firdon Crescent, Glasgow G15 6QQ   0141-944 4566

74	**Glasgow: Drumchapel St Mark's** Alistair J. MacKichan MA BD	1984	2001	146 Garscadden Road, Glasgow G15 6PR	0141-944 5440
75	**Glasgow: Eastbank** See Carntyne Old				
76	**Glasgow: Easterhouse St George's and St Peter's (E) (0141-781 0800)** Malcolm Cuthbertson BA BD	1984		3 Barony Gardens, Baillieston, Glasgow G69 6TS [E-mail: malcuth@aol.com]	0141-573 8200 (Tel) 0141-773 4878 (Fax)
77	**Glasgow: Eastwood** Moyna McGlynn (Mrs) BD PhD	1999		54 Mansewood Road, Glasgow G43 1TL	0141-632 0724
78	**Glasgow: Gairbraid (H)** Ian C. MacKenzie MA BD	1970	1971	1515 Maryhill Road, Glasgow G20 9AB [E-mail: ian@revmac.freeserve.co.uk]	0141-946 1568
79	**Glasgow: Gardner Street (GE)** Roderick Morrison MA BD	1974	1994	148 Beechwood Drive, Glasgow G11 7DX	0141-563 2638
80	**Glasgow: Garthamlock and Craigend East (E)** Valerie J. Duff (Miss) DMin	1993	1996	175 Tillycairn Drive, Garthamlock, Glasgow G33 5HS	0141-774 6364
81	**Glasgow: Gorbals** Ian F. Galloway BA BD	1976	1996	44 Riverside Road, Glasgow G43 2EF	0141-649 5250
82	**Glasgow: Govan Old (Tel/Fax: 0141-440 2466)** Vacant Michael S. Edwards BD (Assoc)	1982	1996	4 Dalziel Quadrant, Pollokshields, Glasgow G41 4NR 108 Cleveden Road, Glasgow G12 0JT [E-mail: michaeledwards@net.ntl.com]	0141-427 0321 0141-579 7115
83	**Glasgow: Govanhill Trinity** Bernard P. Lodge BD	1967	2002	6 Darluith Park, Brookfield, Johnstone PA5 8DD	01505 320378
84	**Glasgow: High Carntyne (0141-778 4186)** Peter W. Nimmo BD ThM	1996	1998	165 Smithycroft Road, Glasgow G33 2RD [E-mail: peternimmo@minister.com]	0141-770 6464
85	**Glasgow: Hillington Park (H)** Ian Morrison BD	1991	1997	61 Ralston Avenue, Glasgow G52 3NB [E-mail: iain@mor77.freeserve.co.uk]	0141-882 7000

86	**Glasgow: Householdwood St Christopher's** May M. Allison (Mrs) BD	1988	2001	12 Leverndale Court, Crookston, Glasgow G53 7SJ	0141-810 5953
87	**Glasgow: Hyndland (H) (0141-339 1804)** John C. Christie BSc BD	1990		24 Hughenden Gardens, Glasgow G12 9YH	0141-334 1002
88	**Glasgow: Ibrox (H) (0141-427 0896)** C. Blair Gillon BD	1975	1980	3 Dargarvel Avenue, Glasgow G41 5LD [E-mail: cb@gillon3.freeserve.co.uk]	0141-427 1282 (Tel/Fax) 07786 326905 (Mbl)
89	**Glasgow John Ross Memorial Church for Deaf People** **(Voice Text: 0141-420 1759; Text Only: 0141-429 6682; Fax: 0141-429 6860; ISDN Video Phone: 0141-418 0579)** Richard C. Durno DSW CQSW 1989 1998 31 Springfield Road, Bishopbriggs, Glasgow G64 1PJ (Voice/Text) 0141-772 1052 [E-mail: richard@deafconnections.co.uk] [www.deafconnections.co.uk]				
90	**Glasgow: Jordanhill (Tel/Fax: 0141-959 2496)** Colin C. Renwick BMus BD	1989	1996	96 Southbrae Drive, Glasgow G13 1TZ [E-mail: jordchurch@aol.com]	0141-959 1310 (Tel) 0141-959 2496 (Fax)
91	**Glasgow: Kelvin Stevenson Memorial (0141-339 1750)** Vacant			94 Hyndland Road, Glasgow G12 9PZ	0141-334 5352
92	**Glasgow: Kelvinside Hillhead** Jennifer Macrae (Mrs) MA BD	1998	2000	39 Athole Gardens, Glasgow G12 9BQ [E-mail: jmacrae@supanet.com]	0141-339 2865
93	**Glasgow: Kenmuir Mount Vernon** See Carmyle				
94	**Glasgow: King's Park (H) (0141-632 1131)** G. Stewart Smith MA BD STM	1966	1979	1101 Aikenhead Road, Glasgow G44 5SL	0141-637 2803 (Tel/Fax)
95	**Glasgow: Kinning Park (0141-427 3063)** Margaret H. Johnston (Miss) BD	1988	2000	168 Arbroath Avenue, Cardonald, Glasgow G52 3HH	0141-810 3782
96	**Glasgow: Knightswood St Margaret's (H)** Vacant			26 Airthrey Avenue, Glasgow G14 9LJ	0141-959 1094
97	**Glasgow: Langside (0141-632 7520)** John Owain Jones MA BD FSAScot	1981	1998	36 Madison Avenue, Glasgow G44 5AQ	0141-637 0797
98	**Glasgow: Lansdowne** Roy J.M. Henderson MA BD DipMin	1987	1992	18 Woodlands Drive, Glasgow G4 9EH [E-mail: rhende1961@aol.com]	0141-339 2794
	Helen M. Hughes (Miss) DCS			Flat 2/2, 43 Burnbank Terrace, Glasgow G20 6UQ	0141-333 9459

99	**Glasgow: Linthouse St Kenneth's** David A. Keddie MA BD	1966	2001	21 Ilay Road, Bearsden, Glasgow G61 1QG	0141-577 1408
100	**Glasgow: Lochwood (H) (0141-771 2649)** Stuart M. Duff BA	1997		42 Rhindmuir Road, Swinton, Glasgow G69 6AZ [E-mail: stuart@duff58.freeserve.co.uk]	0141-773 2756
101	**Glasgow: Martyrs', The** Ewen MacLean BA BD	1995		30 Louden Hill Road, Robroyston, Glasgow G33 1GA [E-mail: ewenmaclean@beeb.net]	0141-558 7451
102	**Glasgow: Maryhill (H) (0141-946 3512)** Anthony J.D. Craig BD	1987		111 Maxwell Avenue, Glasgow G61 1HT [E-mail: craig.glasgow@ntlworld.com]	0141-570 0642
	James Hamilton DCS			6 Beckfield Gate, Robroyston, Glasgow G33 1SW	0141-558 3195
103	**Glasgow: Merrylea (0141-637 2009)** David P. Hood BD CertMin DipIOB(Scot)	1997		37 Burnhead Road, Newlands, Glasgow G43 2SU	0141-637 6700
104	**Glasgow: Mosspark (H) (0141-882 2240)** Alan H. MacKay BD	1974	2002	396 Kilmarnock Road, Glasgow G43 2DJ [E-mail: alanhmackay@aol.com]	0141-632 1247
105	**Glasgow: Mount Florida (H) (0141-561 0307)** Hugh M. Wallace MA BD	1981	1987	90 Mount Annan Drive, Glasgow G44 4RZ	0141-589 5381
106	**Glasgow: New Cathcart (H)** Vacant			'Kilrenny', 30 Elmore Avenue, Glasgow G44 5AD	0141-637 7373
107	**Glasgow: New Govan (H)** Robert G. McFarlane BD	2001		19 Dumbreck Road, Glasgow G41 5LJ	0141-427 3197
108	**Glasgow: Newlands South (H) (0141-632 3055)** John D. Whiteford MA BD	1989	1997	24 Monreith Road, Glasgow G43 2NY	0141-632 2588
109	**Glasgow: North Kelvinside** William G. Alston	1961	1971	41 Mitre Road, Glasgow G14 9LE	0141-954 8250
110	**Glasgow: Partick South** Alan L. Dunnett LLB BD	1994	1997	17 Munro Road, Glasgow G13 1SQ [E-mail: dustydunnett@prtck.freeserve.co.uk]	0141-959 3732

111 Glasgow: Partick Trinity (H)
Stuart J. Smith BEng BD — 1994 — 99 Balshagray Avenue, Glasgow G11 7EQ [E-mail: stuart@stuartandelspeth.freeserve.co.uk] — 0141-576 7149

112 Glasgow: Penilee St Andrew (H) (0141-882 2691)
Vacant — 80 Tweedsmuir Road, Glasgow G52 2RX — 0141-882 3432

113 Glasgow: Pollokshaws
Margaret Whyte (Mrs) BA BD — 1988 2000 — 33 Mannering Road, Glasgow G41 3SW — 0141-649 0458

114 Glasgow: Pollokshields (H)
David R. Black MA BD — 1986 1997 — 36 Glencairn Drive, Glasgow G41 4PW — 0141-423 4000

115 Glasgow: Possilpark
Vacant — 11E 231 Westercommon Road, Glasgow G22 5ND — 0141-336 3127

116 Glasgow: Priesthill and Nitshill
Douglas M. Nicol BD CA — 1987 1996 — 36 Springkell Drive, Glasgow G41 4EZ — 0141-427 7877
Thomas C. Houston BA (Assoc) — 1975 2000 — 1/1 31 Barrachnie Drive, Glasgow G69 6SH — 0141-588 2442

117 Glasgow: Queen's Park (0141-423 3654)
T. Malcolm F. Duff MA BD — 1985 2000 — 5 Alder Road, Glasgow G43 2UY [E-mail: malcolm@dufftmf.freeserve.co.uk] — 0141-637 5491

118 Glasgow: Renfield St Stephen's (0141-332 4293; Fax: 0141-332 8482)
Peter M. Gardner MA BD — 1988 2002 — 101 Hill Street, Glasgow G3 6TY — 0141-353 3395

119 Glasgow: Robroyston (New Charge Development)
Keith McKillop MB ChB BD — 1999 — 7 Beckfield Drive, Robroyston, Glasgow G33 1SR — 0141-558 1874

120 Glasgow: Ruchazie (0141-774 2759)
William F. Hunter MA BD — 1986 1999 — 18 Borthwick Street, Glasgow G33 3UU [E-mail: bhunter@fish.co.uk] — 0141-774 6860
Janet Anderson (Miss) DCS — 322 Gartcraig Road, Glasgow G33 2TB — 0141-774 5329

121 Glasgow: Ruchill (0141-946 0466)
John C. Matthews MA BD — 1992 — 9 Kirklee Road, Glasgow G12 0RQ [E-mail: jmatthews@kirklee9.fsnet.co.uk] — 0141-357 3249

122 Glasgow: St Andrew's East (0141-554 1485)
Janette G. Reid (Miss) BD — 1991 — 43 Broompark Drive, Glasgow G31 2JB — 0141-554 3620

123 Glasgow: St Columba (GE) (0141-221 3305)
Donald Michael MacInnes — 2002 — 1 Reelick Avenue, Peterson Park, Glasgow G13 4NF — 0141-952 0948

124 Glasgow: St David's Knightswood (0141-959 1024; E-mail: dringlis@stdavidschurch.freeserve.co.uk)
W. Graham M. Thain LLB BD   1988   1999   60 Southbrae Drive, Glasgow G13 1QD   0141-959 2904
[E-mail: thains@btclick.com]

125 Glasgow: St Enoch's Hogganfield (H) (0141-770 5694; Fax: 0870 284 0084; E-mail: church@st-enoch.org.uk; Website: www.st-enoch.org.uk)
Andrew J. Philip BSc BD   1996   43 Smithycroft Road, Glasgow G33 2RH   0141-770 7593
0870 284 0085 (Fax)
[E-mail: andrewphilip@minister.com]

126 Glasgow: St George's Tron (0141-221 2141)
Sinclair B. Ferguson MA BD PhD   1971   1998   12 Dargarvel Avenue, Glasgow G41 5LU   0141-427 1402
John Rushton BVMS BD (Assoc)   1983   2000   29 Brent Avenue, Thornliebank, Glasgow G46 8JU   0141-638 0837
[E-mail: johnsusanrushton@bigfoot.com]

127 Glasgow: St James' (Pollok) (0141-882 4984)
Helen Hamilton (Miss) BD   1991   30 Ralston Avenue, Glasgow G52 3NA   0141-883 7405
[E-mail: helend.hamilton@hotmail.com]
Ann Merrilees (Miss) DCS   0/1 15 Crookston Grove, Glasgow G52 3PN   0141-883 2488

128 Glasgow: St John's Renfield (0141-339 7021; Website: www.stjohns-renfield.org.uk)
Dugald J.R. Cameron BD DipMin MTh   1990   1999   26 Leicester Avenue, Glasgow G12 0LU   0141-339 4637
[E-mail: dugald@stjohns-renfield.org.uk]

129 Glasgow: St Luke's and St Andrew's
Ian C. Fraser BA BD   1983   1995   10 Chalmers Street, Glasgow G40 2HA   0141-556 3883
[E-mail: stluke@cqm.co.uk]

130 Glasgow: St Margaret's Tollcross Park
George M. Murray LTh   1995   31 Kenmuir Avenue, Sandyhills, Glasgow G32 9LE   0141-778 5060

131 Glasgow: St Nicholas' Cardonald
Roderick I.T. MacDonald BD   1992   104 Lamington Road, Glasgow G52 2SE   0141-882 2065

132 Glasgow: St Paul's (0141-770 8559)
R. Russell McLarty MA BD   1985   38 Lochview Drive, Glasgow G33 1QF   0141-770 9611

133 Glasgow: St Rollox
Vacant   42 Melville Gardens, Bishopbriggs, Glasgow G64 3DE   0141-772 2848

134 Glasgow: St Thomas' Gallowgate
Irene A. Bristow (Mrs) BD   1989   1997   8 Helenvale Court, Glasgow G31 4LH   0141-554 0997
Karen Hamilton (Mrs) DCS   6 Beckfield Gate, Robroyston, Glasgow G33 1SW   0141-558 3195

135 Glasgow: Sandyford Henderson Memorial (H)
C. Peter White BVMS BD MRCVS 1974 66 Woodend Drive, Glasgow G13 1TG 0141-954 9013
[E-mail: revcpw@aol.com]

136 Glasgow: Sandyhills
John P.F. Martindale 1994 60 Wester Road, Glasgow G32 9JJ 0141-778 2174
BD BSc MSc FRICS MBIM

137 Glasgow: Scotstoun (T)
Richard Cameron BD DipMin 2000 15 Northland Drive, Glasgow G14 9BE 0141-959 4637
[E-mail: rev.rickycam@virgin.net]

138 Glasgow: Shawlands (0141-649 2012)
Alastair D. McLay BSc BD 1989 2001 29 St Ronan's Drive, Glasgow G41 3SQ 0141-649 2034
[E-mail: alastair@mclay79.freeserve.co.uk]

139 Glasgow: Sherbrooke St Gilbert's (H) (0141-427 1968)
Vacant 9 Springkell Gate, Glasgow G41 4BY 0141-423 3912

140 Glasgow: Shettleston Old (T) (H) (0141-778 2484)
David K. Speed LTh 1969 1999 57 Mansionhouse Road, Mount Vernon, Glasgow G32 0RP 0141-778 8904

141 Glasgow: South Carntyne (H) (0141-778 1343)
Vacant 47 Broompark Drive, Glasgow G31 2JB 0141-554 5930

142 Glasgow: South Shawlands (T) (0141-649 4656)
Fiona Gardner (Mrs) BD MA MLitt 1997 391 Kilmarnock Road, Glasgow G43 2NU 0141-632 0013

143 Glasgow: Springburn (H) (0141-557 2345)
Alan A. Ford BD 1977 3 Tofthill Avenue, Bishopbriggs, Glasgow G64 3PA 0141-762 1844
[E-mail: alanford@springburnchurch.freeserve.co.uk] 0771 045 5737 (Mbl)

144 Glasgow: Temple Anniesland (0141-959 1814)
John Wilson BD 1985 76 Victoria Park Drive North, Glasgow G14 9PJ 0141-959 5835
[E-mail: jwilson@crowroad0.freeserve.co.uk]

145 Glasgow: Toryglen (H)
Vacant 28 Snuffmill Road, Cathcart, Glasgow G44 5TR 0141-569 6892

146 Glasgow: Trinity Possil and Henry Drummond
Richard G. Buckley BD MTh 1990 50 Highfield Drive, Glasgow G12 0HL 0141-339 2870

147 Glasgow: Tron St Mary's
William T.S. Wilson BSc BD 1999 3 Hurly Hawkin', Bishopbriggs, Glasgow G64 1YL 0141-772 8555
[E-mail: william.mairi@ntlworld.com]

148 Glasgow: Victoria Tollcross

Richard Coley LTh	1971	228 Hamilton Road, Glasgow G32 9QU	0141-778 2413

149 Glasgow: Wallacewell

John B. MacGregor BD	1999	54 Etive Crescent, Bishopbriggs, Glasgow G64 1ES	0141-772 1453
Joanna Love (Mrs) DCS		92 Everard Drive, Colston, Glasgow G21 1XQ	0141-563 5859

150 Glasgow: Wellington (H) (0141-339 0454)

M. Leith Fisher MA BD	1967 1990	27 Kingsborough Gardens, Glasgow G12 9NH [E-mail: leith@minister22.freeserve.co.uk]	0141-339 3627

151 Glasgow: Whiteinch (New Charge Development)

Alan McWilliam BD	1993 2000	65 Victoria Park Drive South, Glasgow G14 9NX [E-mail: alanmcwilliam@netscape.net]	0141-576 9020

152 Glasgow: Yoker (T)

Vacant		15 Coldingham Avenue, Glasgow G14 0PX	0141-952 3620
Kenneth MacDonald MA BA (Aux)	2001	5 Henderland Road, Bearsden, Glasgow G61 1AH	0141-943 1103

Name	Years	Charge	Address	Phone
Aitken, Andrew J. BD APhS MTh PhD	1951 1981	(Tollcross Central with Park)	18 Dorchester Avenue, Glasgow G12 0EE	0141-357 1617
Alexander, Eric J. MA BD	1958 1997	(St George's Tron)	PO Box 14725, St Andrews KY16 8WB	ex-directory
Allan, A.G.	1959 1989	(Candlish Polmadie)	30 Dalrymple Drive, East Mains, East Kilbride, Glasgow G74 4LF	01355 226190
Barr, Alexander C. MA BD	1950 1992	(St Nicholas' Cardonald)	25 Fisher Drive, Phoenix Park, Paisley PA1 2TP	0141-848 5941
Beattie, John A.	1951 1984	(Dalmuir Overtoun)	0/1, 15 Kelvindale Gardens, Kelvindale Road, Glasgow G20 8DW	0141-946 5978
Bell, John L. MA BD FRSCM DUniv	1978 1988	Iona Community	Flat 2/1, 31 Lansdowne Crescent, Glasgow G20 6NH	0141-334 0688
Brain, Ernest J.	1955 1985	(Liverpool St Andrew's)	14 Chesterfield Court, 1240 Great Western Road, Glasgow G12 0BJ	0141-357 2249
Brain, Isobel J. (Mrs) MA	1987 1997	(Ballantrae)	14 Chesterfield Court, 1240 Great Western Road, Glasgow G12 0BJ	0141-357 2249
Brice, Dennis G. BSc BD	1981	(Taiwan)	18 Hermitage Avenue, West Hadleigh, Essex	01702 555333
Bryden, William A. BD	1977 1984	(Yoker Old with St Matthew's)	145 Bearsden Road, Glasgow G13 1BS	0141-959 5213
Bull, Alister W. BD DipMin	1994 2001	Chaplain: Royal Hospital for Sick Children	Yorkhill NHS Trust, Yorkhill, Glasgow G3 8SJ	0141-201 0595
Campbell, A. Iain MA DipEd	1961 1997	(Busby)	430 Clarkston Road, Glasgow G44 3QF	0141-637 7460
Campbell, Colin MA BD	1940 1989	(Williamwood)	4 Golf Road, Clarkston, Glasgow G76 7LZ	0141-638 1215
Cartledge, G.R.G. MA BD STM	1977 1993	Religious Education	5 Briar Grove, Newlands, Glasgow G43 2TD	0141-637 3228
Chester, Stephen J. BA BD	1999	RE Teacher, International Christian College	42 Drumlochy Road, Ruchazie, Glasgow G33 3RE	0141-774 4666
Coleman, Sidney H. BA BD MTh	1961 2001	(Glasgow Merrylea)	'Blaven', 11 Clyde Place, Perth PH2 0EZ	01738 565072
Cullen, William T. BA LTh	1984 1996	(Kilmarnock: St John's Onthank)	71 Fenwick Road, Giffnock, Glasgow G46 6AX	0141-637 8244
Cunningham, Alexander MA BD	1961 2002	(Presbytery Clerk)	The Glen, 103 Glenmavis Road, Airdrie ML6 0PQ	01236 763012
Cunningham, James S.A. MA BD BLitt PhD	1992 2000	(Glasgow: Barlanark Greyfriars)	'Kirkland', 5 Inveresk Place, Coatbridge ML5 2DA	01236 421541
Currie, Robert MA	1955 1990	(Community Minister)	Flat 3/2, 13 Redlands Road, Glasgow G12 0SJ	0141-334 5111

Name	Appointment			Address	Telephone
Dunnett, Linda (Mrs) DCS	Frontier Youth Trust, West of Scotland Development Officer	1945	1985	759B Argyle Street, Glasgow G3 8DS	(Office) 0141-204 4800
Fairweather, Ian C.M. MA BD	(Jordanhill College of Education)	1940	1976	17 Munro Road, Glasgow G13 1SQ	0141-959 3732
Fenton, Robert J. MA	(St Kiaran's Dean Park)	1969	2000	86 Whittinghame Court, Glasgow G12 0BH	0141-334 7577
Finlay, William P. MA BD	(Glasgow: Townhead Blochairn)	1971	2000	Eastwoodhill, 238 Fenwick Road, Glasgow G46 6UU	0141-638 5127
Forbes, George A.R. BD	(Kirkintilloch: Hillhead)	1984	1987	High Corrie, Brodick, Isle of Arran KA27 8JB	01770 810689
Forrest, Gavin W. MA BD	(Whitburn South)	1948	1982	28 Murrayfield, Bishopbriggs, Glasgow G64 3DS	0141-762 0272
Galloway, Allan D. MA BD STM PhD FRSE	(University of Glasgow)			12 Vancouver Road, Glasgow G14 9HJ	0141-954 9110
Gibson, H. Marshall MA BD	(St Thomas' Gallowgate)	1957	1996	5 Straid Bheag, Barremman, Clynder, Helensburgh G84 0QX	01436 83432
Gibson, Michael BD STM	(Glasgow: Giffnock: The Park)	1974	2001	39 Burnbroom Drive, Glasgow G69 7XG	0141-771 0749
Goss, Alister BD	Industrial Mission Organiser	1975	1998	12 Mile End Park, Pocklington, York YO42 2TH	
Gregson, Elizabeth M. (Mrs) BD	(Drumchapel: St Andrew's)	1996	2001	79 Weymouth Crescent, Gourock PA19 1HR	01475 638944
Grimstone, A. Frank MA	(Calton Parkhead)	1949	1986	17 Westfields, Bishopbriggs, Glasgow G64 3PL	0141-563 1918
Haley, Derek BD DPS	(Chaplain: Gartnavel Royal)	1960	1999	144C Howth Drive, Parkview Estate, Anniesland, Glasgow G13 1RL	0141-954 1009
Harper, Anne J.M. (Miss) BD STM MTh CertSocPsych				9 Kinnaird Crescent, Bearsden, Glasgow G61 2BN	0141-942 9281
Haughton, Frank MA BD	Hospital Chaplain	1979	1990	122 Greenock Road, Bishopton PA7 5AS	01505 862466
Herron, Andrew DD LLD	(Kirkintilloch: St Mary's)	1942	2000	64 Regent Street, Kirkintilloch, Glasgow G66 1JF	0141-777 6802
Hope, Evelyn P. (Miss) BA BD	(Presbytery Clerk)	1934	1981	c/o Park, 3 Berryhill Drive, Giffnock, Glasgow G46 7AS	0141-638 3305
Hunter, Alastair G. MSc BD	(Wishaw: Thornlie)	1990	1998	Flat 0/1, 48 Moss-side Road, Glasgow G41 3UA	0141-649 1522
Hunter, George	University of Glasgow	1976	1980	487 Shields Road, Glasgow G41 2RG	0141-429 1687
Hutcheson, J. Murray MA	(Scotstoun West)	1950	1987	Flat 1C, 256 Great Western Road, Glasgow G4 9EJ	0141-332 7228
Hutchison, Henry MA BEd BD MLitt PhD LLCM	(Possilpark)	1943	1987	88 Ainslie Road, Kildrum, Cumbernauld, Glasgow G67 2ED	01236 631168
Irvine, Euphemia H.C. (Mrs) BD	(Carmunnock)	1948	1993	4A Briar Grove, Newlands, Glasgow G43 2TG	0141-637 2766
Johnston, Robert W.M. MA BD STM	(Milton of Campsie)	1972	1988	32 Baird Drive, Bargarran, Erskine PA8 6BB	0141-812 2777
Johnstone, H. Martin J. MA BD MTh	(Temple Anniesland)	1964	1999	13 Kilmardinny Crescent, Bearsden, Glasgow G61 3ND	0141-931 5862
Jolly, John BA	Urban Priority Areas Adviser	1989	2000	3 Herries Road, Glasgow G41 4DE	0141-423 3760
Jones, E. Gwynfai BA	(Old Partick)	1950	1990	10 Kensington Court, 20 Kensington Road, Glasgow G12 9NX	0141-339 9815
Langlands, Cameron H. BD MTh ThM	(Glasgow: St Rollox)	1964	2002	50 Melville Gardens, Bishopbriggs, Glasgow G64 3DD	0141-563 1770
Leask, Rebecca M. (Mrs)	Hospital Chaplain	1995	1999	Flat 3/2, 59 Nursery Street, Glasgow G41 2PL	0141-424 1530
Levison, C.L. MA BD	(Callander: St Bride's)	1977	1985	1 Woodrow Court, 17 Woodrow Road, Glasgow G41 5TN	0141-427 2260
Lewis, E.M.H. MA	Health Care Chaplaincy Training and Development Officer	1972	1998	5 Deaconsbank Avenue, Stewarton Road, Glasgow G46 7UN	0141-620 3492
Liddell, Matthew MA BD	(Drumchapel St Andrew's)	1962	1993	7 Cleveden Place, Glasgow G12 0HG	0141-334 5411
Lunan, David W. MA BD	(St Paul's (Outer High) and St David's (Ramshorn))	1943	1982	17 Traquair Drive, Glasgow G52 2TB	0141-810 3776
McAreavey, William BA	Presbytery Clerk	1970	2002	142 Hill Street, Glasgow G3 6UA	0141-353 3687
Macarthur, J.M.M.	(Kelvin Stevenson Memorial)	1950	2001	94 Hyndland Road, Glasgow G12 9PZ	0141-334 5352
Macaskill, Donald MA BD PhD	(St Columba)	1994	1994	5 Polquhap Gardens, Thorncroft Park, Crookston, Glasgow G53 7FW [E-mail: polquhap@quista.net]	0141-891 5385
Macaskill, Marjory (Mrs) LLB BD	Board of Parish Education / Chaplain: University of Strathclyde	1990	1998	44 Forfar Avenue, Cardonald, Glasgow G52 3JQ	0141-883 5956

Name			Charge / Appointment	Address	Tel.
MacBain, Iain W.	1971	1993	(Coatbridge: Coatdyke)	24 Thornyburn Drive, Baillieston, Glasgow G69 7ER	0141-771 7030
MacDonald, Anne (Miss) BA DCS			Hospital Chaplain	62 Berwick Drive, Glasgow G52 3JA	0141-883 5618
Macdonald, Murdo Ewen DD	1939	1984	(University of Glasgow)	Eastwoodhill, 238 Fenwick Road, Glasgow G46 6UU	0141-638 5127
McDonald, Ross J. BA BD ThM	1998		Director/Chaplain: Lodging House Mission	35 East Campbell Street, Glasgow G1 5DT	0141-552 0285
Macfadyen, Anne M. (Mrs) BSc BD	1995		Auxiliary Minister	295 Mearns Road, Glasgow G77 5LT	0141-639 3605
Macfarlane, Thomas G. BSc PhD BD	1956	1992	(South Shawlands)	Flat 0/2, 19 Corrour Road, Glasgow G43 2DY	0141-632 7966
McKenzie, Mary O. (Miss)	1976	1996	(Edinburgh Richmond Craigmillar)	4 Dunellan Avenue, Moodiesburn, Glasgow G69 0GB	01236 870180
McKeown, Paul	2000		Community Minister: Ruchill	G/R, 10 Jedburgh Gardens, Glasgow G20 6BP [E-mail: prmckeown@supanet.com]	0141-946 6409
McLaren D. Muir MA BD MTh PhD	1971	2001	(Mosspark)	112 Nether Auldhouse Road, Glasgow G43 2YT	0141-649 4268
McLean, John MA	1948	1977	(St Andrew's Plantation)	34 Rowan Court, Worcester Road, Droitwich Spa, Worcs WR9 8AH	
MacLeod, William J. DipTh	1963	1988	(Kirkintilloch St David's Memorial)	42 Hawthorn Drive, Banknock, Bonnybridge FK4 1LF	01324 840667
MacMahon, Janet P.H. (Mrs) MSc BD	1992	1992	Chaplain: Southern General Hospital	6 Jubilee Gardens, Bearsden, Glasgow G61 2RT	0141-942 3671
Macnaughton, J.A. MA BD	1949	1989	(Hyndland)	62 Lauderdale Gardens, Glasgow G12 9QW	0141-339 1294
MacPherson, James B. DCS			(Deacon)	13 Leslie Street, Glasgow G41 2LQ	0141-423 6868
MacQuarrie, Stuart BD BSc JP	1984	2001	Chaplain: Glasgow University	The Chaplaincy Centre, University of Glasgow, Glasgow G12 8QQ	0141-330 5419
Millar, David A.R. MA	1956	1989	(University of Glasgow)	310A Albert Drive, Glasgow G41 5RS	0141-429 2249
Millar, James	1949	1989	(Shawlands Old)	9 Glenbank Court, Glasgow G46 7EJ	0141-638 6250
Mitchell, David BD MSc DipPTheol	1988	1998	Chaplain: Marie Curie Hospice, Glasgow	48 Leglin Wood Drive, Wallacewell Park, Glasgow G21 3PL [E-mail: davidmitchell@chaplain48.freeserve.co.uk]	0141-558 4679
Morton, Thomas MA BD LGSM	1945	1986	(Rutherglen Stonelaw)	54 Greystone Avenue, Burnside, Rutherglen, Glasgow G73 3SW	0141-647 2682
Muir, Fred C. MA BD ThM ARCM	1961	1997	(Stepps)	20 Alexandra Avenue, Stepps, Glasgow G33 6BP	0141-779 2504
Myers, Frank BA	1952	1978	(Springburn)	18 Birmingham Close, Grantham NG31 8SD	01476 594430
Newlands, George M. MA BD PhD	1970	1986	University of Glasgow	2/19 Succoth Court, Edinburgh EH12 6BZ	0131-337 4941
Philip, Robert A. BA BD	1953	1996	(Sandyford Henderson Memorial)	44 Beech Avenue, Bearsden, Glasgow G61 3EX	0141-942 1327
Porter, Richard MA	1937	1981	(Stepps St Andrew's)	2 Hockley Court, Weston Park West, Bath BA1 4AR	01225 333041
Ramsay, W.G.	1953	1988	(Govanhill)	58 Hillend Road, Glasgow G76 7XT	0141-639 4169
Reid, Ian M.A. BD	1967	1999	(Springburn) / Hospital Chaplain	53 Kelvinvale, Kirkintilloch, Glasgow G66 1RD; Chaplains Office, Victoria Infirmary, Langside Road, Glasgow G42 9TT	0141-776 2915
Robertson, Archibald MA BD	1957	1999	(Eastwood)	19 Canberra Court, Braidpark Drive, Glasgow G46 6NS	0141-637 7572
Robertson, Blair MA BD ThM	1990	1998	Chaplain: Southern General Hospital	c/o Chaplain's Office, Southern General Hospital, 1345 Govan Road, Glasgow G51 4TF	
Ross, Donald M. MA	1953	1994	(Industrial Mission Organiser)	14 Cartsbridge Road, Busby, Glasgow G76 8DH	0141-201 2156
Ross, James MA BD	1968	1998	(Kilsyth: Anderson)	53 Turnberry Gardens, Westerwood, Cumbernauld, Glasgow G68 0AY	0141-644 2220
Saunders, Keith BD	1983	1999	Hospital Chaplain	Western Infirmary, Dumbarton Road, Glasgow G11 6NT	01236 730501
Scrimgeour, Alice M. (Miss) DCS	1960	1996	(Deaconess)	265 Golfhill Drive, Glasgow G31 2PB	0141-211 2000
Shackleton, William			(Greenock: Wellpark West)	3 Tynwald Avenue, Burnside, Glasgow G73 4RN	0141-564 9602
Shanks, Norman J. MA BD	1983	1988	Iona Community	1 Marchmont Terrace, Glasgow G12 9LT	0141-569 9407
Simpson, Neil A. BA BD PhD	1992	2001	(Glasgow: Yoker Old with Yoker St Matthew's)		0141-339 4421

Name	Designation			Address	Phone
Smillie, Andrew M. LTh	(Cathcart South)	1990	2001	14 Strathview Place, Comrie, Crieff PH6 2GH	01764 670625
Smith, A. McLaren	(Cumbrae)	1971	1997	27 Fenwick Road, Glasgow G46 6AU	
Smith, Hilda C. (Miss) MA BD	Hospital Chaplain	1992	2001	107 Athelstane Road, Glasgow G13 3QY	0141-954 6497
Smith, J. Rankine MA BD	(Barmulloch)	1945	1982	44 Middlemuir Road, Lenzie, Glasgow G66 4ND	0141-776 0870
Smith, James S.A.	(Drongan, The Schaw Kirk)	1956	1991	146 Aros Drive, Glasgow G52 1TJ	0141-883 9666
Spence, Elisabeth G.B. (Miss) BD DipEd	Industrial Missioner: Glasgow Area	1995	2000	45 Selvieland Road, Glasgow G52 4AS	0141-883 8973
Stewart, Norma D. (Miss) MA MEd BD	(Glasgow: Strathbungo Queens Park)	1977	2000	127 Nether Auldhouse Road, Glasgow G43 2YS	0141-637 6956
Sutherland, Denis I.	(Hutchesontown)	1963	1995	19 Boyd Orr Crescent, Kilmaurs, Kilmarnock KA3 2QB	01563 520641
Sutherland, Elizabeth W. (Miss) BD	(Balornock North with Barmulloch)	1972	1996	20 Kirkland Avenue, Blanefield, Glasgow G63 9BZ	01360 770154
Tait, Alexander	(St Enoch's Hogganfield)	1967	1995	8 Mossbank Drive, Hogganfield, Glasgow G33 1LS	0141-770 7850
Turner, Angus BD	(Industrial Chaplain)	1976	1998	46 Keir Street, Pollokshields, Glasgow G41 2LA	0141-424 0493
Tuton, Robert M. MA	(Shettleston: Old)	1957	1995	6 Holmwood Gardens, Uddingston, Glasgow G71 7BH	01698 321108
Walker, A.L.	(Trinity Possil and Henry Drummond)	1955	1988	11 Dundas Avenue, Torrance, Glasgow G64 4BD	01360 622281
Webster, John G. BSc	(St John's Renfield)	1964	1998	Plane Tree, King's Cross, Brodick, Isle of Arran KA27 8RG	01770 700747
White, Elizabeth (Miss) DCS	(Deaconess)			Woodside House, Rodger Avenue, Rutherglen, Glasgow G73 3QZ	

GLASGOW ADDRESSES

Banton	Kelvinhead Road, Banton
Bishopbriggs	
Kenmure	Viewfield Road, Bishopbriggs
Springfield	Springfield Road
Blairbeth Rodger Memorial	Kirkcriggs Gardens
Broom	Mearns Road, Newton Mearns
Burnside	Church Avenue, Burnside
Busby	Church Road, Busby
Cadder	Cadder Road, Glasgow
Cambuslang	
Flemington Hallside	265 Hamilton Road
Old	Cairns Road
St Andrew's	Main Street x Clydeford Road
Trinity St Paul's	Main Street
Campsie	Main Street, Lennoxtown
Chryston	Main Street, Chryston
Eaglesham	Montgomery Street, Eaglesham
Gartcosh	113 Lochend Road, Gartcosh
Giffnock	
Orchardhill	Church Road
South	Eastwood Toll
The Park	Ravenscliffe Drive
Glenboig	138 Main Street, Glenboig
Greenbank	Eaglesham Road, Clarkston
Kilsyth	
Anderson	Kingston Road
Burns and Old	Church Street
Kirkintilloch	
Hillhead	Newdyke Road
St Columba's	Waterside Road nr Old Aisle Road
St David's Mem Pk	Alexander Street
St Mary's	Cowgate
Lenzie Old	Kirkintilloch Road x Garngaber Avenue
Union	Moncrieff Ave x Kirkintilloch Road
Maxwell	Waterfoot Road
Mearns Castle	Mearns Road, Newton Mearns
Mearns	
Milton of Campsie	Antermony Road, Milton of Campsie
Netherlee	Ormonde Drive x Ormonde Avenue
Newton Mearns	Ayr Road, Newton Mearns
Rutherglen	
Old	Main Street at Queen Street
Stonelaw	Stonelaw Road x Dryburgh Avenue
Wardlawhill	Hamilton Road
West	Glasgow Road nr Main Street
Stamperland	Stamperland Gardens, Clarkston
Stepps	Whitehill Avenue
Thornliebank	61 Spiersbridge Road
Torrance	School Road, Torrance
Twechar	Main Street, Twechar
Williamwood	Vardar Avenue x Seres Ave, Clarkston

Glasgow

Church	Address
Anderston Kelvingrove	Argyle Street x Elderslie Street
Baillieston	
Mure Memorial	Beech Avenue, Garrowhill
St Andrew's	Church Street
Balshagray Victoria Pk	Broomhill Cross
Barlanark Greyfriars	Edinburgh Road x Hallhill Road
Battlefield East	1216 Cathcart Road
Blawarthill	Millbrix Avenue
Bridgeton St Francis in the East	26 Queen Mary Street
Broomhill	Randolph Rd x Marlborough Ave
Calton Parkhead	122 Helenvale Street
Cardonald	2155 Paisley Road West
Carmunnock	Kirk Road, Carmunnock
Carmyle	South Carmyle Avenue
Carntyne Old	862 Shettleston Road
Carnwadric	556 Boydstone Road, Thornliebank
Castlemilk	
East	Barlia Terrace
West	Carmunnock Road
Cathcart	
Old	119 Clarkston Road
South	92 Clarkston Road
Cathedral	Cathedral Square
Colston Milton	Egilsay Crescent
Colston Wellpark	1378 Springburn Road
Cranhill	Bellrock Crescent x Bellrock Street
Croftfoot	Croftpark Ave x Crofthill Road
Dennistoun	
Blackfriars	Whitehill Street
Central	Armadale Street
Drumchapel	
Drumry St Mary's	Drumry Road East
St Andrew's	Garscadden Road
St Mark's	Kinfauns Drive
Eastbank	679 Old Shettleston Road
Easterhouse St George's and St Peter's	Boyndie Street
Eastwood	Mansewood Road
Fernhill and Cathkin	Neilvaig Drive
Gairbraid	1517 Maryhill Road

Church	Address
Gardner Street	Gardner Street x Muirpark Street
Garthamlock and Craigend East	Porchester Street x Balveny Street
Gorbals	Eglinton Street x Cumberland Street
Govan Old	866 Govan Road
Govanhill Trinity	Daisy Street nr Allison Street
High Carntyne	358 Carntynehall Road
Hillington Park	24 Berryknowes Road
Househillwood St Christopher's	Meikle Road
Hyndland	Hyndland Road, opp Novar Drive
Ibrox	Carillon Road x Clifford Street
John Ross Memorial	100 Norfolk Street G5 9EJ
Jordanhill	Woodend Drive x Munro Road
Kelvin Stevenson Mem	Belmont Street at Belmont Bridge
Kelvinside Hillhead	Huntly Gardens
Kenmuir Mount Vernon	London Road, Mount Vernon
King's Park	242 Castlemilk Road
Kinning Park	Eaglesham Place
Knightswood St Margaret's	Knightswood Cross
Langside	Ledard Road x Lochleven Road
Lansdowne	Gt Western Road at Kelvin Bridge
Linthouse St Kenneth's	9 Skipness Drive
Lochwood	Lochend Road x Liff Place
Martyrs', The	
Maryhill	St Mungo Avenue
	1990 Maryhill Road
Merrylea	78 Merrylee Road
Mosspark	149 Ashkirk Drive
Mount Florida	1123 Cathcart Road
New Cathcart	Newlands Road nr Clarkston Road
New Govan	Govan Cross
Newlands South	Riverside Road x Langside Drive
North Kelvinside	153 Queen Margaret Drive
Partick South	Dumbarton Road
Trinity	20 Lawrence Street
Penilee St Andrew	Bowfield Cres x Bowfield Avenue
Pollokshaws	223 Shawbridge Street
Pollokshields	Albert Drive x Shields Road
Possilpark	124 Saracen Street
Priesthill and Nitshill	Freeland Drive x Muirshiel Cres

Church	Address
Queen's Park	170 Queen's Drive
Renfield St Stephen's	260 Bath Street
Robroyston	
Ruchazie	Elibank Street x Milncroft Road
Ruchill	Shakespeare Street nr Maryhill Rd
St Andrew's East	681 Alexandra Parade
St Columba	300 St Vincent Street
St David's Knightswood	Boreland Drive nr Lincoln Avenue
St Enoch's Hogganfield	860 Cumbernauld Road
St George's Tron	163 Buchanan Street
St James' (Pollok)	Lyoncross Road x Byrebush Road
St John's Renfield	22 Beaconsfield Road
St Luke's and St Andrew's	Well Street at Bain Square
St Margaret's Tollcross Pk	179 Braidfauld Street
St Nicholas' Cardonald	Hartlaw Crescent nr Gladsmuir Road
St Paul's Provanmill	Langdale Street x Greenrig Street
St Rollox	Fountainwell Road
St Thomas Gallowgate	Gallowgate opp Bluevale Street
Sandyford-Henderson Memorial	Kelvinhaugh Street at Argyle Street
Sandyhills	28 Baillieston Rd x Sandyhills Rd
Scotstoun	Earlbank Avenue x Ormiston Avenue
Shawlands	Shawlands Cross
Sherbrooke St Gilbert's	Nithsdale Rd x Sherbrooke Avenue
Shettleston Old	99–111 Killin Street
South Carntyne	538 Carntyne Road
South Shawlands	Regwood Street x Deanston Drive
Springburn	Springburn Road x Atlas Street
Temple Anniesland	869 Crow Road
Toryglen	Glenmore Ave nr Prospecthill Road
Trinity Possil and Henry Drummond	Crowhill Street x Broadholm Street
Tron St Mary's	128 Red Road
Victoria Tollcross	1134 Tollcross Road
Wallacewell	57 Northgate Road
	Ryehill Road x Quarrywood Road
Wellington	University Ave x Southpark Avenue
Whiteinch	Whiteinch Neighbourhood Centre, Dumbarton Road
Yoker	Dumbarton Road at Hawick Street

(17) HAMILTON

Meets at Motherwell: Dalziel St Andrew's Parish Church Halls, on the first Tuesday of February, March, May, September, October, November, December, and on the third Tuesday of June.

Presbytery Office:		18 Haddow Street, Hamilton ML3 7HX [E-mail: akph54@uk.uumail.com]	01698 286837 (Tel) 01698 457258 (Fax)
Clerk:	REV. JAMES H. WILSON LTH	21 Austine Drive, Hamilton ML3 7YE [E-mail: wilsonjh@blueyonder.co.uk]	01698 457042
Treasurer:	MR DAVID FORRESTER CA	Belmont, Lefroy Street, Coatbridge ML5 1PN	01236 421892

1 **Airdrie Broomknoll (H) (Tel: 01236 762101; E-mail: airdrie-broomknoll@presbyteryofhamilton.co.uk)**
linked with Calderbank (E-mail: calderbank@presbyteryofhamilton.co.uk)
Andrew Thomson BA   1976   2000   38 Commonhead Street, Airdrie ML6 6NS   01236 602538

2 **Airdrie Clarkston (E-mail: airdrie-clarkston@presbyteryofhamilton.co.uk)**
Thomas L. Pollock   1982   1992   Forrest Street, Airdrie ML6 7BE   01236 769676
JP BA BD MTh FSAScot   [E-mail: tom.pollock@totalise.co.uk]

3 **Airdrie: Flowerhill (H) (E-mail: airdrie-flowerhill@presbyteryofhamilton.co.uk)**
Andrew Gardner BSc BD PhD   1997   31 Victoria Place, Airdrie ML6 9BX   01236 763025
[E-mail: andrewgar@supanet.com]

4 **Airdrie: High (H) (E-mail: airdrie-high@presbyteryofhamilton.co.uk)**
W. Richard Houston BSc BD   1998   17 Etive Drive, Airdrie ML6 9QL   01236 762010
[E-mail: richard.houston@virgin.net]

5 **Airdrie: Jackson (Tel: 01236 733508; E-mail: airdrie-jackson@presbyteryofhamilton.co.uk)**
Sharon E.F. Colvin (Mrs)   1985   1998   48 Dunrobin Road, Airdrie ML6 8LR   01236 763154
BD LRAM LTCL

6 **Airdrie: New Monkland (H) (E-mail: airdrie-newmonkland@presbyteryofhamilton.co.uk)**
linked with Greengairs (E-mail: greengairs@presbyteryofhamilton.co.uk)
Randolph Scott MA BD   1991   2001   3 Dykehead Crescent, Airdrie ML6 6PU   01236 763554

7 **Airdrie: St Columba's (E-mail: airdrie-stcolumbas@presbyteryofhamilton.co.uk)**
Margaret F. Currie BEd BD   1980   1987   52 Kennedy Drive, Airdrie ML6 9AW   01236 763173
[E-mail: mfcstcol@surfaid.org]

8 Airdrie: The New Wellwynd (H) (E-mail: airdrie-newwellwynd@presbyteryofhamilton.co.uk)
Robert A. Hamilton BA BD   1995   2001   20 Arthur Avenue, Airdrie ML6 9EZ   01236 763022
[E-mail: robbie.hamilton13@btopenworld.com]

9 Bargeddie (H) (E-mail: bargeddie@presbyteryofhamilton.co.uk)
John Fairful BD   1994   2001   Bargeddie, Baillieston, Glasgow G69 6UB   0141-771 1322

10 Bellshill: Macdonald Memorial (E-mail: bellshill-macdonald@presbyteryofhamilton.co.uk) linked with Bellshill: Orbiston
Allan McKenzie BSc BD   1988   2001   32 Adamson Street, Bellshill ML4 1DT   01698 849114

11 Bellshill: Orbiston (E-mail: bellshill-orbiston@presbyteryofhamilton.co.uk) See Bellshill: Macdonald Memorial

12 Bellshill: West (H) (01698 747581) (E-mail: bellshill-west@presbyteryofhamilton.co.uk)
Agnes A. Moore (Miss) BD   1987   2001   16 Croftpark Street, Bellshill ML4 1EY   01698 842877

13 Blantyre: Livingstone Memorial (E-mail: blantyre-livingstone@presbyteryofhamilton.co.uk)
Vacant   286 Glasgow Road, Blantyre, Glasgow G72 9DB   01698 823794

14 Blantyre: Old (H) (E-mail: blantyre-old@presbyteryofhamilton.co.uk)
Rosemary A. Smith (Ms) BD   1997   The Manse, Craigmuir Road, High Blantyre, Glasgow G72 9UA   01698 823130

15 Blantyre: St Andrew's (E-mail: blantyre-standrews@presbyteryofhamilton.co.uk)
J. Peter N. Johnston BSc BD   2001   332 Glasgow Road, Blantyre, Glasgow G72 9LQ   01698 828633

16 Bothwell (H) (E-mail: bothwell@presbyteryofhamilton.co.uk)
James M. Gibson TD LTh LRAM   1978   1989   Manse Avenue, Bothwell, Glasgow G71 8PQ   01698 853189 (Tel)
[E-mail: jamesgibson@msn.com]   01698 853229 (Fax)

17 Calderbank See Airdrie Broomknoll

18 Caldercruix and Longriggend (H) (E-mail: caldercruix@presbyteryofhamilton.co.uk)
Ian M. Watson LLB DipLP BD   1998   Main Street, Caldercruix, Airdrie ML6 7RF   01236 842279

19 Carfin (E-mail: carfin@presbyteryofhamilton.co.uk) linked with Newarthill (E-mail: newarthill@presbyteryofhamilton.co.uk)
James Weir BD   1991   2002   Church Street, Newarthill, Motherwell ML1 5HS   01698 860316
[E-mail: jimweir@beeb.net]

20 Chapelhall (H) (E-mail: chapelhall@presbyteryofhamilton.co.uk)
James R. Nelson BD DipTheol   1986   Chapelhall, Airdrie ML6 8SG   01236 763439

21 Chapelton (E-mail: chapelton@presbyteryofhamilton.co.uk)
linked with Strathaven: Rankin (H) (E-mail: strathaven-rankin@presbyteryofhamilton.co.uk)
Shaw J. Paterson BSc BD   1991   15 Lethame Road, Strathaven ML10 6AD   01357 520019 (Tel)
[E-mail: shaw@patersonj.freeserve.co.uk]   01357 529316 (Fax)

22 Cleland (H) (E-mail: cleland@presbyteryofhamilton.co.uk)
John A. Jackson BD   1997   Bellside Road, Cleland, Motherwell ML1 5NP   01698 860260

23 Coatbridge: Blairhill Dundyvan (H) (E-mail: coatbridge-blairhill@presbyteryofhamilton.co.uk)
John M. Black MA BD   1963 1991   18 Blairhill Street, Coatbridge ML5 1PG   01236 432304

24 Coatbridge: Calder (H) (E-mail: coatbridge-calder@presbyteryofhamilton.co.uk)
Vacant   26 Bute Street, Coatbridge ML5 4HF   01236 421516
James Zambonini LIA Dip (Aux)   1997 2002   100 Old Manse Road, Wishaw ML2 0EP   01698 350889

25 Coatbridge: Clifton (H) (E-mail: coatbridge-clifton@presbyteryofhamilton.co.uk)
Vacant   132 Muiryhall Street, Coatbridge ML5 3NH   01236 421181

26 Coatbridge: Middle (E-mail: coatbridge-middle@presbyteryofhamilton.co.uk)
James Grier BD   1991 1996   47 Blair Road, Coatbridge ML5 1JQ   01236 432427

27 Coatbridge: Old Monkland (E-mail: coatbridge-oldmonkland@presbyteryofhamilton.co.uk)
Vacant   Old Monkland Manse, Coatbridge ML5 5QT   01236 423788

28 Coatbridge: St Andrew's (E-mail: coatbridge-standrews@presbyteryofhamilton.co.uk)
Ian G. Wotherspoon BA LTh   1967 1994   77 Eglinton Street, Coatbridge ML5 3JF   01236 437271
[E-mail: wotherspoonrig@aol.com]

29 Coatbridge: Townhead (H) (E-mail: coatbridge-townhead@presbyteryofhamilton.co.uk)
Vacant   Crinan Crescent, Coatbridge ML5 2LH   01236 423150

30 Dalserf (E-mail: dalserf@presbyteryofhamilton.co.uk)
D. Cameron McPherson BSc BD   1982   Manse Brae, Dalserf, Larkhall ML9 3BN   01698 882195

31 East Kilbride: Claremont (H) (Tel: 01355 238088; E-mail: ek-claremont@presbyteryofhamilton.co.uk)
John K. Collard MA BD   1986 1991   17 Deveron Road, East Kilbride, Glasgow G74 2HR   01355 248526
Paul Cathcart DCS   5A Atholl Gardens, Rutherglen, Glasgow G73 5HF   0141-569 6865

32 East Kilbride: Greenhills (E) (Tel: 01355 221746; E-mail: ek-greenhills@presbyteryofhamilton.co.uk)
John Brewster MA BD DipEd   1988   21 Turnberry Place, East Kilbride, Glasgow G75 8TB   01355 242564
[E-mail: johnbrewster1@activemail.co.uk]

33 East Kilbride: Moncreiff (H) (Tel: 01355 223328; E-mail: ek-moncreiff@presbyteryofhamilton.co.uk)
Alastair S. Lusk BD   1974 1983   16 Almond Drive, East Kilbride, Glasgow G74 2HX   01355 238639

34   **East Kilbride: Mossneuk (E) (Tel: 01355 260954; E-mail: ek-mossneuk@presbyteryofhamilton.co.uk)**
John L. McPake BA BD PhD   1986   2000   30 Eden Grove, Mossneuk, East Kilbride, Glasgow   G75 8XU   01355 234196

35   **East Kilbride: Old (H) (E-mail: ek-old@presbyteryofhamilton.co.uk)**
Anne S. Paton BA BD   2001   40 Maxwell Drive, East Kilbride, Glasgow   G74 4NG   01355 220732

36   **East Kilbride: South (H) (E-mail: ek-south@presbyteryofhamilton.co.uk)**
John C. Sharp BSc BD PhD   1980   7 Clamps Wood, East Kilbride, Glasgow   G74 2HB   01355 247993
    [E-mail: johncsharp@btinternet.com]

37   **East Kilbride: Stewartfield (New Charge Development)**
Douglas W. Wallace MA BD   1981   2001   8 Thistle Place, Stewartfield, East Kilbride, Glasgow   G74 4RH   01355 260879

38   **East Kilbride: West (H) (E-mail: ek-west@presbyteryofhamilton.co.uk)**
Kenneth Mayne   2001   1 Barr Terrace, East Kilbride, Glasgow   G74 1AP   01355 239891

39   **East Kilbride: Westwood (H) (Tel: 01355 245657; E-mail: ek-westwood@presbyteryofhamilton.co.uk)**
Kevin Mackenzie BD DPS   1989   1996   16 Inglewood Crescent, East Kilbride, Glasgow   G75 8QD   01355 223992
    [E-mail: kevin@westwood-church.org.uk]

40   **Glasford (E-mail: glassford@presbyteryofhamilton.co.uk) linked with Strathaven East (E-mail: strathaven-east@presbyteryofhamilton.co.uk)**
William T. Stewart BD   1980   68 Townhead Street, Strathaven   ML10 6BA   01357 521138

41   **Greengairs**   See Airdrie: New Monkland

42   **Hamilton: Burnbank (E-mail: hamilton-burnbank@presbyteryofhamilton.co.uk) linked with Hamilton North (H) (E-mail: hamilton-north@presbyteryofhamilton.co.uk)**
Raymond D. McKenzie BD   1978   1987   9 South Park Road, Hamilton   ML3 6PJ   01698 424609

43   **Hamilton: Cadzow (H) (Tel: 01698 428695; E-mail: hamilton-cadzow@presbyteryofhamilton.co.uk)**
Arthur P. Barrie LTh   1973   1979   3 Carlisle Road, Hamilton   ML3 7BZ   01698 421664 (Tel)
    01698 891126 (Fax)

44   **Hamilton: Gilmour and Whitehill (H) (E-mail: hamilton-gilmourwhitehill@presbyteryofhamilton.co.uk)**
Ronald J. Maxwell Stitt   1977   2000   86 Burnbank Centre, Burnbank, Hamilton   ML3 0NA   01698 284201
    LTh BA ThM BREd DMin FSAScot

45   **Hamilton: Hillhouse (E-mail: hamilton-hillhouse@presbyteryofhamilton.co.uk)**
David W.G. Burt BD DipMin   1989   1998   66 Wellhall Road, Hamilton   ML3 9BY   01698 422300
William Wishart DCS   17 Swift Bank, Earrock, Hamilton   ML3 8PX   01698 429371
    [E-mail: bill@hillhousechurch.co.uk]

46   **Hamilton: North**   See Hamilton: Burnbank

47 Hamilton: Old (H) (Tel: 01698 281905; E-mail: hamilton-old@presbyteryofhamilton.co.uk)
John M.A. Thomson TD JP BD ThM   1978   2001   1 Chateau Grove, Hamilton ML3 7DS   01698 422511
[E-mail: johnt@hopc.demon.co.uk]

48 Hamilton: St Andrew's (T) (E-mail: hamilton-standrews@presbyteryofhamilton.co.uk)
Norma Moore (Ms) MA BD   1995   15 Bent Road, Hamilton ML3 6QB   01698 891361
[E-mail: norma.moore@blueyonder.co.uk]

49 Hamilton: St John's (H) (Tel: 01698 283492; E-mail: hamilton-stjohns@presbyteryofhamilton.co.uk)
Robert M. Kent MA BD   1973   1981   12 Castlehill Crescent, Hamilton ML3 7DG   01698 425002
[E-mail: robert@bobkent.fsnet.co.uk]

50 Hamilton: South (H) (Tel: 01698 281014; E-mail: hamilton-south@presbyteryofhamilton.co.uk)
linked with Quarter (E-mail: quarter@presbyteryofhamilton.co.uk)
Fraser K. Turner LTh   1994   The Manse, Limekilnburn Road, Quarter, Hamilton ML3 7XA   01698 424511
[E-mail: fraseratq@yahoo.co.uk]

51 Hamilton: Trinity (Tel: 01698 284254; E-mail: hamilton-trinity@presbyteryofhamilton.co.uk)
Karen E. Harbison (Mrs) MA BD   1991   69 Buchan Street, Hamilton ML3 8JY   01698 425326

52 Hamilton: West (H) (Tel: 01698 284670; E-mail: hamilton-west@presbyteryofhamilton.co.uk)
William M. Murdoch BSc PhD BD STM   1980   2001   43 Bothwell Road, Hamilton ML3 0BB   01698 458770

53 Holytown (E-mail: holytown@presbyteryofhamilton.co.uk)
James S. Salmond BA BD MTh ThD   1979   Holytown, Motherwell ML1 5RU   01698 832622

54 Kirk o' Shotts (H) (E-mail: kirk-o-shotts@presbyteryofhamilton.co.uk)
Sheila M. Spence (Mrs) MA BD   1979   The Manse, Kirk o' Shotts, Salsburgh, Shotts ML7 4NS   01698 870208
[E-mail: sm-spence@hotmail.com]

55 Larkhall: Chalmers (H) (E-mail: larkhall-chalmers@presbyteryofhamilton.co.uk)
James S.G. Hastie CA BD   1990   Quarry Road, Larkhall ML9 1HH   01698 882238
[E-mail: jhastie@chalmers0.demon.co.uk]   0870 056 2133 (Fax)

56 Larkhall: St Machan's (H) (E-mail: larkhall-stmachans@presbyteryofhamilton.co.uk)
Vacant   2 Orchard Gate, Larkhall ML9 1HG   01698 882457

57 Larkhall: Trinity (E-mail: larkhall-trinity@presbyteryofhamilton.co.uk)
Lindsay Schluter (Miss) ThE CertMin   1995   13 Machan Avenue, Larkhall ML9 2HE   01698 881401

58 Motherwell: Crosshill (H) (E-mail: mwell-crosshill@presbyteryofhamilton.co.uk)
W. Stuart Dunn LTh   1970   1982   15 Orchard Street, Motherwell ML1 3JE   01698 263410

59 Motherwell: Dalziel St Andrew's (H) (Tel: 01698 264097; E-mail: mwell-dalzielstandrews@presbyteryofhamilton.co.uk)
Derek W. Hughes BSc BD DipEd   1990   1996   4 Pollock Street, Motherwell ML1 1LP   01698 263414
[E-mail: derek@hughes04.freeserve.co.uk]
Colin M. Brough BSc BD (Assoc)   1998   5 Bredin Way, Motherwell ML1 3PD   01698 252527
[E-mail: colin.brough@btinternet.com]

60 **Motherwell: Manse Road (E-mail: mwell-manseroad@presbyteryofhamilton.co.uk)**
Vacant   10 Hamilton Drive, Motherwell ML1 2QA   01698 267345

61 **Motherwell: North (E-mail: mwell-north@presbyteryofhamilton.co.uk)**
Derek H.N. Pope BD   1987 1995   Kirkland Street, Motherwell ML1 3JW   01698 266716

62 **Motherwell: St Margaret's (E-mail: mwell-stmargarets@presbyteryofhamilton.co.uk)**
Andrew M. Campbell BD   1984   70 Baron's Road, Motherwell ML1 2NB   01698 263803

63 **Motherwell: St Mary's (H) (E-mail: mwell-stmarys@presbyteryofhamilton.co.uk)**
David W. Doyle MA BD   1977 1987   19 Orchard Street, Motherwell ML1 3JE   01698 263472

64 **Motherwell: South Dalziel (H) (E-mail: mwell-southdalziel@presbyteryofhamilton.co.uk)**
Phyllis M. Wilson (Mrs) DipCom DipRE   1985 1994   62 Manse Road, Motherwell ML1 2PT   01698 263054
[E-mail: phylandtomwilson@ukonline.co.uk]

65 **Newarthill** See Carfin

66 **Newmains: Bonkle (H) (E-mail: bonkle@presbyteryofhamilton.co.uk)**
   linked with Newmains: Coltness Memorial (H) (E-mail: coltness@presbyteryofhamilton.co.uk)
Vacant   5 Kirkgate, Newmains, Wishaw ML2 9BT   01698 383858
John McAlpine BSc (Aux)   1998   201 Bonkle Road, Newmains, Wishaw ML2 9AA   01698 384610

67 **Newmains: Coltness Memorial** See Newmains: Bonkle

68 **New Stevenston: Wrangholm Kirk (E-mail: wrangholm@presbyteryofhamilton.co.uk)**
Vacant   222 Clydesdale Street, New Stevenston, Motherwell ML1 4JQ   01698 832533

69 **Overtown (E-mail: overtown@presbyteryofhamilton.co.uk)**
Nan Low (Mrs) BD   2002   The Manse, Main Street, Overtown, Wishaw ML2 0QP   01698 372330

70 **Quarter** See Hamilton: South

71 **Shotts: Calderhead Erskine (E-mail: calderhead-erskine@presbyteryofhamilton.co.uk)**
Ian G. Thom BSc PhD BD   1990 2000   The Manse, Kirk Road, Shotts ML7 5ET   01501 820042
[E-mail: the.thoms@btinternet.com]

72 **Stonehouse: St Ninian's (H) (E-mail: stonehouse@presbyteryofhamilton.co.uk)**
Vacant   4 Hamilton Way, Stonehouse ML9 3PU   01698 792364

73 **Strathaven: Avendale Old and Drumclog (H) (Tel: 01357 529748; E-mail: strathaven-avendaleold@presbyteryofhamilton.co.uk and**
   E-mail: drumclog@presbyteryofhamilton.co.uk)
Alan W. Gibson BA BD   2001   Kirk Street, Strathaven ML10 6BA   01357 520077
[E-mail: awgibson82@hotmail.com]

74 **Strathaven: East** See Glasford

75 Strathaven: Rankin See Chapelton

76 **Strathaven: West (E-mail: strathaven-west@presbyteryofhamilton.co.uk)**
Una B. Stewart (Ms) BD DipEd   1995   2002   6 Avenel Crescent, Strathaven ML10 6JF   01357 529086
[E-mail: rev.ubs@virgin.net]

77 **Uddingston: Burnhead (H) (E-mail: uddingston-burnhead@presbyteryofhamilton.co.uk)**
Sandi McGill (Ms) BD   2002   90 Laburnum Road, Uddingston, Glasgow G71 5DB   01698 813716
[E-mail: sandi.mcgill@btopenworld.com]
Raymond Deans DCS   22 Garrowhill Drive, Garrowhill, Glasgow G69 6HL   0141-771 6847

78 **Uddingston: Old (H) (Tel: 01698 8140015; E-mail: uddingston-old@presbyteryofhamilton.co.uk)**
Norman B. McKee BD   1987   1994   1 Belmont Avenue, Uddingston, Glasgow G71 7AX   01698 814757
[E-mail: normanb.mckee@belmont89.freeserve.co.uk]

79 **Uddingston: Park (T) (H) (E-mail: uddingston-park@presbyteryofhamilton.co.uk)**
W. Bruce McDowall BA BD   1989   1999   25 Douglas Gardens, Uddingston, Glasgow G71 7HB   01698 817256

80 **Uddingston: Viewpark (H) (E-mail: uddingston-viewpark@presbyteryofhamilton.co.uk)**
Michael G. Lyall BD   1993   2001   14 Holmbrae Road, Uddingston, Glasgow G71 6AP   01698 813113

81 **Wishaw: Cambusnethan North (H) (E-mail: wishaw-cambusnethannorth@presbyteryofhamilton.co.uk)**
Mhorag Macdonald (Ms) MA BD   1989   350 Kirk Road, Wishaw ML2 8LH   01698 381305
[E-mail: mhorag@mhorag.force9.co.uk]

82 **Wishaw: Cambusnethan Old (E-mail: wishaw-cambusnethanold@presbyteryofhamilton.co.uk)**
and Morningside (E-mail: wishaw-morningside@presbyteryofhamilton.co.uk)
Iain C. Murdoch MA LLB DipEd BD   1995   22 Coronation Street, Wishaw ML2 8LF   01698 384235
[E-mail: iaincmurdoch@btopenworld.com]

83 **Wishaw: Chalmers (H) (Tel: 01698 375306; E-mail: wishaw-chalmers@presbyteryofhamilton.co.uk)**
Ian O. Coltart CA BD   1988   161 Kirk Road, Wishaw ML2 7BZ   01698 372464

84 **Wishaw: Craigneuk and Belhaven (H) (E-mail: wishaw-craigneukbelhaven@presbyteryofhamilton.co.uk)**
Scott Raby LTh   1991   100 Glen Road, Wishaw ML2 7NP   01698 372495
[E-mail: revscott@rabyfamily28.freeserve.co.uk]

85 **Wishaw: Old (H) (Tel: 01698 376080; E-mail: wishaw-old@presbyteryofhamilton.co.uk)**
Vacant   130 Glen Road, Wishaw ML2 7NP   01698 375134

86 **Wishaw: St Mark's (E-mail: wishaw-stmarks@presbyteryofhamilton.co.uk)**
Henry J.W. Findlay MA BD   1965   1967   Coltness Road, Wishaw ML2 7EX   01698 384596 (Tel)
01698 386025 (Fax)

87 **Wishaw: Thornlie (H) (E-mail: wishaw-thornlie@presbyteryofhamilton.co.uk)**
Klaus O.F. Buwert LLB BD   1984   1999   West Thornlie Street, Wishaw ML2 7AR   01698 372356 (Tel)
[E-mail: revklausb@aol.com]   07801 533548 (Mbl)

Name			Charge	Address	Tel
Allan, James B. BA	1965	1993	(Motherwell: South Dalziel)	42 Catherine Street, Motherwell ML1 2RN	01698 264756
Anderson, Catherine B. (Mrs) DCS	1944	1984	(Deaconess)	13 Mosshill Road, Bellshill ML4 1NQ	01698 745907
Baird, George W. MA	1951	1986	(Crimond with St Fergus)	42 Neilsland Drive, Motherwell ML1 3EB	01698 262088
Beattie, William G. BD BSc	1974	2001	(Hamilton St Andrew's)	33 Dungavel Gardens, Hamilton ML3 7PE	01698 423804
Cook, J. Stanley BD Dip PSS			(Hamilton: West)	Mansend, 137A Old Manse Road, Netherton, Wishaw ML2 0EW	01698 299600

[E-mail: stancook@lineone.net]

Cowper, Macknight C. MA BD STM	1947	1983	(East Kilbride West)	17 Manor Place, Edinburgh EH3 7DH	0131-225 6214
Davidson, James BD DipAFH	1989	2002	(Wishaw Old)	13 Redburn Place, Irvine KA12 9BQ	01294 279835
Fraser, James P.	1951	1988	(Strathaven Avendale Old and Drumclog)	26 Hamilton Road, Strathaven ML10 6JA	01357 522758
Gilchrist, Kay (Miss) BD	1996	1999	(Chaplain: Rachel House)	45 Hawthorn Drive, Craigneuk, Airdrie ML6 8AP	01698 262733
Handley, John	1954	1993	(Motherwell: Clason Memorial)	12 Airbles Crescent, Motherwell ML1 3AR	01698 826177
Hunter, James E. LTh	1974	1997	(Blantyre: Livingstone Memorial)	57 Dalwhinnie Avenue, Blantyre. Glasgow G72 9NQ	01236 761753
King, Crawford S. MA	1958	1984	(Glenboig)	77 Faskine Avenue, Airdrie ML6 9EA	01236 763248
Learmonth, Adam J.	1966	1993	(Airdrie: Wellwynd)	3 Drumbathie Terrace, Airdrie ML6 7EU	

[E-mail: adamlearmonth@bosinternet.com]

McCabe, George	1963	1996	(Airdrie: High)	Flat 8, Park Court, 2 Craighouse Park, Edinburgh EH10 5LD	0131-447 9522
McDonald, John A. MA BD	1978	1997	(Cumbernauld: Condorrat)	17 Thomson Drive, Bellshill ML4 3ND	
Martin, James MA BD DD	1946	1987	(Glasgow: High Carntyne)	9 Magnolia Street, Wishaw ML2 7EQ	01698 385825
Melrose, J.H. Loudon MA BD MEd	1955	1996	(Gourock: Old Gourock & Ashton [Assoc])	24 Avonbridge Drive, Hamilton ML3 7EJ	01698 891033
Munton, James G. BA	1969	2002	(Coatbridge: Old Monkland)	2 Moorcroft Drive, Airdrie ML6 8ES	01236 754848

[E-mail: jacjim@supanet.com]

Niven, William LTCL	1955	1994	(Lesmahagow: Old)	92 Linden Lea, Hamilton ML3 9AG	01698 420653
Price, Peter O. CBE QHC BA FPhS	1960	1996	(Blantyre Old)	20A Old Bothwell Road, Bothwell, Glasgow G71 8AW	01698 854032

[E-mail: peteroprice@aol.com]

Rogerson, Stuart D. BSc BD	1980	2001	(Strathaven: West)	17 Westfield Park, Strathaven ML10 6XH	01357 523321

[E-mail: srogerson@cnetwork.co.uk]

Thorne, Leslie W. BA LTh	1987	2001	(Coatbridge: Clifton)	'Hatherleigh', 9 Chatton Walk, Coatbridge ML5 4FH	01236 432241
Wilson, James H. LTh	1970	1996	(Cleland)	21 Austine Drive, Hamilton ML3 7YE	01698 457042

[E-mail: wilsonjh@blueyonder.co.uk]

Wyllie, Hugh R. MA DD FCIBS	1962	2000	(Hamilton Old)	18 Chantinghall Road, Hamilton ML3 8NP	01698 420002

HAMILTON ADDRESSES

Airdrie
Broomknoll — Broomknoll Street
Clarkston — Forrest Street
Flowerhill — 89 Graham Street
High — North Bridge Street
Jackson — Glen Road
New Monkland — Glenmavis
St Columba's — Thrashbush Road
The New Wellwynd — Wellwynd

Coatbridge
Blairhill Dundyvan — Blairhill Street
Calder — Calder Street
Clifton — Muiryhall Street x Jackson Street
Middle — Bank Street
Old Monkland — Woodside Street
St Andrew's — Church Street
Townhead — Crinan Crescent

East Kilbride
Claremont — High Common Road, St Leonard's
Greenhills — Greenhills Centre
Moncreiff — Calderwood Road
Mossneuk — Eden Drive
Old — Montgomery Street
South — Baird Hill, Murray
West — Kittoch Street
Westwood — Belmont Drive, Westwood

Hamilton
Burnbank — High Blantyre Road
Cadzow — Woodside Walk
Gilmour and Whitehill — Glasgow Road, Burnbank
Hillhouse — Abbotsford Road, Whitehill
North — Clerkwell Road
Old — Windmill Road
St Andrew's — Leechlee Road
St John's — Avon Street
South — Duke Street
Trinity — Strathaven Square off North Road
West — Burnbank Road

Motherwell
Crosshill — Windmillhill Street x
Airbles Street
Dalziel St Andrew's — Merry Street and Muir Street
Manse Road — Gavin Street
North — Chesters Crescent
St Margaret's — Shields Road
St Mary's — Avon Street
South Dalziel — 504 Windmillhill Street

Uddingston
Burnhead — Kirk Road
Old — East Academy Street
Park — Craigneuk Street
Viewpark — Main Street
Wishaw
Cambusnethan — Coltness Road
North — West Thornlie Street

Old — Laburnum Road
Chalmers
Craigneuk and — Old Glasgow Road.
Belhaven — Main Street
Old — Old Edinburgh Road
St Mark's
Thornlie — Kirk Road

01360 550098 (Tel)
01360 551198 (Fax)
07710 866982 (Mbl)

(18) DUMBARTON

Meets at Dumbarton in Riverside Church Halls, on the first Tuesday of February, March, April, May, October, November, December, and on the second Tuesday of June and September (and April when the first Tuesday falls in Holy Week).

Clerk: REV. DAVID P. MUNRO MA BD STM   14 Birch Road, Killearn, Glasgow G63 9SQ   01360 550098 (Tel)
[E-mail: akph43@uk.uumail.com]
[E-mail: dmunro@uk.uumail.com]

Alexandria
Elizabeth W. Houston (Miss) MA BD DipEd   1985   1995   32 Ledrish Avenue, Balloch, Alexandria G83 8JB   01389 751933
Archibald M. Ferguson   1989   2001   The Whins, Barrowfield, Cardross, Dumbarton G82 5NL   01389 841517
MSc PhD CEng FRINA (Aux)

Arrochar linked with Luss
H. Dane Sherrard BD DMin   1971   1998   Luss, Alexandria G83 8NZ   01436 860240
[E-mail: dane@cadder.demon.co.uk]   07801 939138 (Mbl)

Baldernock (H)
Andrew P. Lees BD   1984   2002   The Manse, Bardowie, Milngavie, Glasgow G62 6ES   01360 620471

Bearsden: Killermont (H)
Vacant   8 Clathic Avenue, Bearsden, Glasgow G61 2HF   0141-942 0021

Bearsden: New Kilpatrick (H) (0141-942 8827)
David D. Scott BSc BD   1981   1999   51 Manse Road, Bearsden, Glasgow G61 3PN   0141-942 0035
[E-mail: nkb@btopenworld.com]

Bearsden: North (H) (0141-942 2818)
Keith T. Blackwood BD Dip Min   1997   5 Fintry Gardens, Bearsden, Glasgow G61 4RJ   0141-942 0366
[E-mail: kblackwood@totalise.co.uk]   07961 442972 (Mbl)

Bearsden: South (H)
John W.F. Harris MA — 1967 1987 — 61 Drymen Road, Bearsden, Glasgow G61 2SU [E-mail: jwfh@globalnet.co.uk] — 0141-942 0507 / 07711 573877 (Mbl)

Bearsden: Westerton Fairlie Memorial (H) (0141-942 6960)
Eric V. Hudson LTh — 1971 1990 — 3 Canniesburn Road, Bearsden, Glasgow G61 1PW [E-mail: evhudson@canniesburn.fsnet.co.uk] — 0141-942 2672

Alistair E. Ramage BA ADB CertEd (Aux) — 1996 — 16 Claremont Gardens, Milngavie, Glasgow G62 6PG [E-mail: a.ramage@gcal.ac.uk] — 0141-956 2897

Bonhill (H) (01389 756516)
Ian H. Miller BA BD — 1975 — 1 Glebe Gardens, Bonhill, Alexandria G83 9NZ — 01389 753039

Cardross (H) (01389 841322)
Andrew J. Scobie MA BD — 1963 1965 — Cardross, Dumbarton G82 5LB [E-mail: ascobie55@cardross.dunbartonshire.co.uk] — 01389 841289 / 07889 670252 (Mbl)

Clydebank: Abbotsford (E-mail: abbotsford@lineone.net; Website: http://www.abbotsford.org.uk)
Roderick G. Hamilton MA BD — 1992 1996 — 35 Montrose Street, Clydebank G81 2PA [E-mail: rghamilton@ntlworld.com] — 0141-952 5151

Clydebank: Faifley
Gregor McIntyre BSc BD — 1991 — Kirklea, Cochno Road, Hardgate, Clydebank G81 6PT [E-mail: mail@gregormcintyre.com] — 01389 876836

Agnes Tait (Mrs) DCS — 2 Lennox Drive, Faifley, Clydebank G81 5JU — 01389 873196

Clydebank: Kilbowie St Andrew's
Vacant — 5 Melfort Avenue, Clydebank G81 2HX — 0141-951 2455

Clydebank: Radnor Park
Margaret J.B.Yule (Mrs) BD — 1992 — Spencer Street, Clydebank G81 3AS [E-mail: mjbyule@tinyworld.co.uk] — 0141-951 1007

Clydebank: St Cuthbert's (T) linked with Duntocher (H)
David Donaldson MA BD — 1969 2002 — The Manse, Roman Road, Duntocher, Clydebank, Glasgow G81 6BT — 01389 878846

Craigrownie linked with Rosneath St Modan's (H)
Malcolm Wright LTh — 1970 1984 — Edenkiln, Argyll Road, Kilcreggan, Helensburgh G84 0JW [E-mail: malcolm_wright@compuserve.com] — 01436 842274

Dalmuir Barclay (0141-941 3988)
James F. Gatherer BD — 1984 — Parkhall Road, Dalmuir, Clydebank G81 3RJ — 0141-941 3317

Dumbarton: Riverside (H) (01389 742551)
Robert J. Watt BD — 1994 — 2002 — 5 Kirkton Road, Dumbarton G82 4AS
[E-mail: rjw@perth94.freeserve.co.uk]
01389 762512

Dumbarton: St Andrew's (H)
Leslie G. Donaghy — 1990 — 1998 — 17 Mansewood Drive, Dumbarton G82 3EU
BD DipMin PGCE FSAScot
[E-mail: info@bellsmyre.co.uk]
01389 604259
07654 553473 (Pager)

Dumbarton: West Kirk (H)
Christine Liddell (Miss) BD — 1999 — 3 Havoc Road, Dumbarton G82 4JW
[E-mail: thewestkirk@aol.com]
01389 604840

Duntocher (H)   See Clydebank: St Cuthbert's

Garelochhead (01436 810589)
Alastair S. Duncan MA BD — 1989 — Old School Road, Garelochhead, Helensburgh G84 0AT
[E-mail: gpc@churchuk.net]
01436 810022

Helensburgh: Park (H) (01436 671714)
James H. Brown BD — 1977 — 35 East Argyle Street, Helensburgh G84 7EL
[E-mail: jh@jhbrown.freeserve.co.uk]
01436 672209
07941 173299 (Mbl)

Helensburgh: St Columba (H)
Frederick M. Booth LTh — 1970 — 1982 — 46 Suffolk Street, Helensburgh G84 9QZ
01436 672054

Helensburgh: The West Kirk (H) (01436 676880)
David W. Clark MA BD — 1975 — 1986 — 37 Campbell Street, Helensburgh G84 9NH
[E-mail: clarkdw@lineone.net]
01436 674063

Jamestown (H)
Vacant — Appin House, Drymen Road, Balloch, Alexandria G83 8HT
01389 752734

Kilmaronock Gartocharn
Vacant — Kilmaronock Manse, Alexandria G83 8SB
01360 660295

Luss   See Arrochar

Milngavie: Cairns (H) (0141-956 4868)
Andrew Frater BA BD — 1987 — 1994 — 4 Cairns Drive, Milngavie, Glasgow G62 8AJ
[E-mail: clancarp@aol.com]
0141-956 1717

Milngavie: St Luke's (0141-956 4226)
Ramsay B. Shields BA BD — 1990 — 1997 — 70 Hunter Road, Milngavie, Glasgow G62 7BY
[E-mail: rbshields@ntlworld.com]
0141-577 9171 (Tel)
0141-577 9181 (Fax)

Milngavie: St Paul's (H) (0141-956 4405)
Fergus C. Buchanan MA BD | 1982 · 1988 | 8 Buchanan Street, Milngavie, Glasgow G62 8DD | 0141-956 1043
[E-mail: f.c.buchanan@btinternet.com]

Old Kilpatrick Bowling
Jeanette Whitecross (Mrs) BD | 2002 | Old Kilpatrick, Glasgow G60 5JQ | 01389 873130

Renton Trinity (H)
Ian Wilkie | 2001 | 38 Main Street, Renton, Dumbarton G82 4PU | 01389 752017 / 07751 155552 (Mbl)

Rhu and Shandon (H)
J. Colin Caskie BA BD | 1977 2002 | 11 Ardenconnel Way, Rhu, Helensburgh G84 8LX | 01436 820213

Rosneath St Modan's See Craigrownie

Name	Years	Charge / Appointment	Address	Tel
Crombie, W.M.D. MA BD	1947 1987	(Calton New with St Andrew's)	32 Westbourne Drive, Bearsden, Glasgow G61 4BH	0141-943 0235
Davidson, Professor Robert MA BD DD FRSE	1956 1991	(University of Glasgow)	30 Dungoyne Drive, Bearsden, Glasgow G61 3AP	0141-942 1810
Easton, I.A.G. MA FIPM	1945 1988	Lecturer	6 Edgehill Road, Bearsden, Glasgow G61 3AD	0141-942 4214
Hamilton, David S.M. MA BD STM	1958 1996	(University of Glasgow)	2 Roselea Drive, Milngavie, Glasgow G62 8HQ	0141-956 1839
Houston, Peter M. FPhS	1952 1997	(Renfrew Old)	25 Honeysuckle Lane, Jamestown, Alexandria G83 8PL	01389 721165 / 07770 390936 (Mbl)
Hunter, G. Lindsay BD PhD APhS	1949 1990	(Teacher: Religious Education)	16 Restway Wall, Chepstow, Gwent NP6 5EF	01291 629445
Jack, Robert MA BD	1950 1996	(Bearsden: Killermont)	142 Turnhill Drive, Erskine PA8 7AH	0141-812 8370
Lawson, Alexander H. ThM ThD FPhS	1950 1988	(Clydebank: Kilbowie)	1 Glebe Park, Mansewood, Dumbarton G82 3HE	01389 742030
McFadzean, Iain MA BD	1989 1999	Chaplain: Royal Navy	Lochhaven, Portincaple, Garelochhead, Helensburgh G84 0EU	01436 810811
Macfarlane, William J.E. MA BD	1953 1987	(Alexandria St Andrew's)	3 Inchfad Road, Balloch, Alexandria G83 8SY	01389 758185
McIntyre, J. Ainslie MA BD	1963 1984	(University of Glasgow)	60 Bonnaughton Road, Bearsden, Glasgow G61 4DB [E-mail: jamcintyre@hotmail.com]	0141-942 5143 / 07050 295103 (Mbl)
Mackenzie, Ian M. MA	1967 1989	(BBC)	1 Glennan Gardens, Helensburgh G84 8XT	01436 673429
Morton, Andrew Q. MA BSc BD FRSE	1949 1987	(Culross and Torryburn)	4 Upper Adelaide Street, Helensburgh G84 7HT	01436 675152
Munro, David P. MA BD STM	1953 1996	(Bearsden: North)	14 Birch Road, Killearn, Glasgow G63 9SQ	01360 550098
Paul, Alison (Miss) MA BD Dip Theol	1986 2001	(Rhu and Shandon)	30 Perrays Drive, Lennox Gardens, Dumbarton G82 5HT	01389 733698
Rae, Scott M. MBE BD CPS	1976 2002	Chaplain: Royal Navy	HMS Neptune, Faslane, Helensburgh G84 8HL	
Spence, C.K.O. MC TD MA BD	1949 1983	(Craigrownie)	8B Cairndhu Gardens, Helensburgh G84 8PG	
Steven, Harold A.M. LTh FSA Scot	1970 2001	(Baldernock)	9 Cairnhill Road, Bearsden, Glasgow G61 1AT	01436 678838
Wilson, Roy DA ARIBA ARIAS	1986 2002	Auxiliary Minister with Presbytery Clerk	20 William Ure Place, Bishopbriggs, Glasgow G64 3BH	0141-942 1598 / 0141-563 1829

DUMBARTON ADDRESSES

Clydebank
Abbotsford — Town Centre
Faifley — Faifley Road
Kilbowie St Andrew's — Kilbowie Road
Radnor Park — Radnor Street
St Cuthbert's — Linnvale

Dumbarton
Riverside
St Andrew's
West Kirk

High Street
Off Bonhill Road
West Bridgend

Helensburgh
Park
St Columba
The West Kirk

Charlotte Street
Sinclair Street
Colquhoun Square

(19) SOUTH ARGYLL

Meets on first Wednesday of February (at Clachan), March (at Ardrishaig), June (island), November (at Clachan) and December (at Tarbert) and first Tuesday of May and September (at Tarbert).

Clerk: MR HUGH PATERSON   South Lodge, Whitehouse, Tarbert, Argyll PA29 6XR   **01880 730221**
[E-mail: akph73@uk.uumail.com]
[E-mail: patersonhw@hotmail.com]

Ardrishaig (H) linked with South Knapdale
David Carruthers BD   1998   Ardrishaig, Argyll PA30 8HD   01546 603269

Campbeltown: Highland (H)
Michael J. Lind LLB BD   1984   1997   Kirk Street, Campbeltown, Argyll PA28 6BN   01586 551146

Campbeltown: Lorne and Lowland (H)
Vacant   Castlehill, Campbeltown, Argyll PA28 6AN   01586 552468

Craignish linked with Kilninver and Kilmelford
Michael J. Erskine MA BD   1985   1992   Kilmelford, by Oban, Argyll PA34 4XA   01852 200373

Cumlodden, Lochfyneside and Lochgair
Roderick MacLeod
MA BD PhD(Edin) PhD(Open)   1966   1985   Furnace, Inveraray, Argyll PA32 8XU   01499 500288

Gigha and Cara (H) (GD)
Rosemary Legge (Mrs) BSc BD MTh   1992   2002   Gigha, Argyll PA41 7AA   01583 505245

Glassary and Kilmartin and Ford
Vacant   Kilmichael Glassary, Lochgilphead, Argyll PA31 8QA   01546 606926

Charge / Minister			Address	Tel
Glenaray and Inveraray W. Brian Wilkinson MA BD	1968	1993	Inveraray, Argyll PA32 8XT [E-mail: brianwilkinson@freeuk.com]	01499 302060
Jura (GD) [Dwin Capstick]		1999	Craighouse, Isle of Jura PA60 7XG	01496 820384
Kilarrow (H) linked with Kilmeny Anne McIvor (Miss) SRD BD	1996		Bowmore, Isle of Islay PA43 7LH	01496 810271
Kilberry linked with Tarbert (H) Vacant			Tarbert, Argyll PA29 6TY	01880 820288
Kilcalmonell linked with Skipness Charles R. Wood LTh DipYL FRGS	1993		Whitehouse, Tarbert, Argyll PA29 6XS	01880 730224
Kilchoman (GD) linked with Portnahaven (GD) Vacant			Port Charlotte, Isle of Islay PA48 7TX	01496 850241
Kildalton and Oa (GD) (H) Norman MacLeod BTh	1999		Port Ellen, Isle of Islay PA42 7DB	01496 302447
Killean and Kilchenzie (H) John H. Paton JP BSc BD	1983	1984	Muasdale, by Tarbert, Argyll PA29 6XD [E-mail: jonymar@globalnet.co.uk]	01583 421249
Kilmeny See Kilarrow				
Kilninver and Kilmelford See Craignish				
Lochgilphead Alastair H. Gray MA BD	1978	1996	Manse Brae, Lochgilphead, Argyll PA31 8QZ [E-mail: a.gray1@tinyworld.co.uk]	01546 602238
North Knapdale Vacant			Tayvallich, by Lochgilphead, Argyll PA31 8PG	01546 870611
Portnahaven See Kilchoman				
Saddell and Carradale (H) Alistair J. Dunlop MA FSAScot	1965	1979	Carradale, by Campbeltown, Argyll PA28 6QG	01583 431253
Skipness See Kilcalmonell				

Southend (H)
Martin R. Forrest BA MA BD   1988   2001   Southend, Campbeltown, Argyll PA28 6RQ   01586 830274

South Knapdale See Ardrishaig
Tarbert See Kilberry

Bristow W.H.G. BEd HDipRE DipSpecEd	1951 2002	(Part-time Hospital Chaplain: Campbeltown)	Laith Cottage, Southend, Campbeltown, Argyll PA28 6RU	01586 830667
Campbell, Margaret M. (Miss) DCS		(Deaconess)	Tigh-an-Rudha, Pier Road, Port Ellen, Isle of Islay PA42 7DJ	01496 302006
Carmichael, Robert C.M. MA	1948 1991	(Craignish with Kilninver and Kilmelford)	13 The Glebe, Kilmelford, Argyll PA34 4AF	01852 200346
Davidson David W. (Aux)	1987 1998	Moderator's Chaplain	Grainail, Glenegedale, Port Ellen, Isle of Islay PA42 7AS	01496 302194
Forrest, Janice (Mrs) DCS		Part-time Hospital Chaplain: Campbeltown	The Manse, Southend, Campbeltown, Argyll PA28 6RQ	01586 830274
Gibson, Frank S. BL BD STM DSWA DD	1963 1995	(Kilarrow with Kilmeny)	163 Gilbertstoun, Edinburgh EH15 2RG	0131-657 5208
Henderson, Charles M.	1952 1989	(Campbeltown Highland)	Springbank House, Askomill Walk, Campbeltown PA28 6EP	01586 552759
Hood, H. Stanley C. MA BD	1966 2000	(London: Crown Court)	10 Dalriada Place, Kilmichael, Glassary, Lochgilphead PA31 8QA	01546 606168
Montgomery, David	1961 1996	(North Knapdale)	Flat 1, 99 Quarry Street, Hamilton ML3 7AG	01698 200029
Morrison, Angus W. MA BD	1959 1999	(Kildalton and Oa)	1 Livingstone Way, Port Ellen, Isle of Islay PA42 7EP	01496 300043
Ritchie, Malcolm A.	1955 1990	(Kilbrandon and Kilchattan)	Roadside Cottage, Tayvallich, Argyll PA31 8PN	01546 870616
Stewart, Jean E. (Mrs)	1983 1989	(Kildalton and Oa)	Tigh-na-Truain, Port Ellen, Isle of Islay PA42 7AH	01496 302068

SOUTH ARGYLL Communion Sundays

Parish	Sundays
Ardrishaig	4th Apr, 1st Nov
Campbeltown	
Highland	1st May, Nov
Lorne and Lowland	1st May, Nov
Craignish	1st Jun, Nov
Cumlodden, Lochfyneside and Lochgair	1st May, 3rd Nov
Gigha and Cara	1st May, Nov
Glassary, Kilmartin and Ford	1st Apr, Sep
Glenaray and Inveraray	1st Apr, Jul, Oct, Dec
Inverlussa and Bellanoch	2nd May, Nov
Jura	Passion Sun., 2nd Jul, 3rd Nov
Kilarrow	1st Mar, Jun, Sep, Dec
Kilberry with Tarbert	1st May, Oct
Kilcalmonell	1st Jul, 3rd Nov
Kilchoman	1st Jul, 2nd Dec, Easter
Kildalton	Last Jan, Jun, Oct, Easter
Killean and Kilchenzie	1st Mar, Jul, Oct
Kilmeny	2nd May, 3rd Nov
Kilninver and Kilmelford	2nd Jun, Oct
Lochgair	2nd Oct (Gaelic)
Lochgilphead	1st Apr, Nov
North Knapdale	3rd Oct, 2nd May
Portnahaven	3rd Jul
Saddell and Carradale	2nd May, 1st Nov
Skipness	2nd May, Nov
Southend	1st Jun, Dec
South Knapdale	4th Apr, 1st Nov
Tayvallich	2nd May, Nov

(20) DUNOON

Meets at Dunoon St John's, on the first Tuesday of February, April, June and November; at Rothesay Trinity on the first Tuesday of March, October and December; and at the Moderator's Church on the first Tuesday of September.

Clerk: REV. RONALD SAMUEL TD BSc BD STM   9 Bishop Terrace, Rothesay, Isle of Bute PA20 9HF   01700 504378 (Tel/Fax)
[E-mail: akph48@uk.uumail.com]

Bute United
John Murning BD   1988   2000   10 Bishop Terrace, Rothesay, Isle of Bute PA20 9HF   01700 502407
[E-mail: bridgebuilder@supanet.com]

Dunoon: St John's linked with Sandbank (H)
Joseph Stewart LTh   1979   1989   23 Bullwood Road, Dunoon, Argyll PA23 7QJ   01369 702128

Dunoon: The High Kirk (H)
I. Pat Lang (Miss) BSc   1996   1 Royal Crescent, Dunoon, Argyll PA23 7AH   01369 701291
[E-mail: patlang@tinyworld.co.uk]

Innellan (H) linked with Toward (H)
Vacant   7A Matheson Lane, Innellan, Argyll PA23 7SH   01369 830276

Kilfinan linked with Kyles (H)
David J. Kellas MA BD   1966   1998   Tighnabruaich, Argyll PA21 2DX   01700 811887 (Tel/Fax)
[E-mail: davidkellas@britishlibrary.net]

Kilmodan and Colintraive
Robert M. Donald BA   1969   1998   Glendaruel, Colintraive, Argyll PA22 3AA   01369 820232 (Tel/Fax)
[E-mail: robdon@colglen.freeserve.co.uk]

Kilmun (St Munn's) (H) linked with Strone (H) and Ardentinny
Evelyn M. Young (Mrs) BSc BD   1984   1997   Blairmore, Dunoon, Argyll PA23 8TE   01369 840313

Kirn (H)
Vacant   Stewart Street, Kirn, Dunoon, Argyll PA23 8DS   01369 702220

Kyles See Kilfinan

Lochgoilhead (H) and Kilmorich
James Macfarlane PhD   1991   2000   Lochgoilhead, Argyll PA24 8AA   01301 703059
[E-mail: macfarlane-cofs@beeb.net]

Rothesay: Trinity (H)
Vacant
12 Crichton Road, Rothesay, Isle of Bute PA20 9JR   01700 502797

Sandbank See Dunoon: St John's

Strachur and Strathlachlan
Robert K. Mackenzie MA BD PhD   1976 1998   Strachur, Argyll PA27 8DG   01369 860246
[E-mail: rkmackenzie@strachurmanse.fsnet.co.uk]

Strone and Ardentinny See Kilmun
Toward (H) See Innellan

Name			Charge	Address		Tel
Cumming, David P.L. MA	1957	1997	(Kilmodan and Colintraive)	Shillong, Tarbat Ness Road, Portmahomack, Ross-shire	IV20 1YA	01862 871794
Erskine, Austin U.	1986	2001	(Anwoth and Girthon with Borgue)	99 Sandhaven, Sandbank, Dunoon, Argyll PA23 8QW		01369 701295

[E-mail: austin@erskine81.freeserve.co.uk]

Name			Charge	Address		Tel
Fenemore, John H.C.	1980	1993	(Edinburgh Colinton Mains)	Seaford Cottage, 74E Shore Rd, Innellan PA23 7TR		01369 830678
Forrest, Alan B. MA	1956	1993	(Uphall: South)	126 Shore Road, Innellan, Dunoon PA23 7SX		01369 830424
Gisbey, John E. MA BD MSc	1964	2002	(Thornhill)	Kames Haven, Chapel Lane, Isle of Bute PA20 0LQ		01700 503346
Hamilton, Patrick J.R. MA	1948	1979	(East Kilbride South)	La Madrugada, Tighnabruaich PA21 2BE		01700 811586
Inglis, Donald B.C. MA MEd BD	1975	2000	(Turriff St Andrew's)	'Lindores', 11 Bullwood Road, Dunoon PA23 7QJ		01369 701334

[E-mail: dbcinglis@aol.com]

Name			Charge	Address		Tel
Mackenzie, Iain MA BD	1967	2000	(Tarbat)	3 Southern Beeches, Sandbank, Dunoon PA23 8PD		01369 703507

[E-mail: iandg@imackenzie.fsnet.co.uk]

Name			Charge	Address		Tel
Marshall, James S. BA BD FFA MDiv	1986	1989	(Lochgoilhead and Kilmorich)	12 Manse Gardens, Strachur, Cairndow PA27 8DS		01369 860544
Miller, Harry Galbraith MA BD	1941	1985	(Iona and Ross of Mull)	16 Lobnitz Avenue, Renfrew PA4 0TG		0141-886 2147
Samuel, Ronald TD BSc BD STM	1960	2000	(Rothesay Trinity)	9 Bishop Terrace, Rothesay PA20 9HF		(Tel/Fax) 01700 504378

[E-mail: ronald.samuel@ukgateway.net]

Name			Charge	Address		Tel
Stewart, Donald MA	1944	1984	(Fenwick)	Seafield, Toward, Dunoon PA23 7UG		01369 870206
Watson, James LTh	1968	1994	(Bowden with Lilliesleaf)	7 Lochan Avenue, Kirn, Dunoon PA23 8HT		01369 702851

DUNOON Communion Sundays

Bute United	1st Feb, May, Nov	Kilmun	1st Mar, Jun, Oct
Dunoon		Kirn	1st May, Nov
St John's	1st Mar, Jun, Nov	Kyles	Last Apr, Oct
The High Kirk	1st Feb, Jun, Oct	Lochgoilhead and	
Innellan	1st Mar, Jun, Sep, Dec	Kilmorich	2nd Mar, Jun, Sep, Nov
Kilfinan	Last Apr, Oct	Rothesay Trinity	1st Aug, Easter
Kilmodan and	1st Apr, Sep	Sandbank	1st Feb, May, Nov
Colintraive	Last Jun, Nov		1st Jan, May, Nov

Strachur and Strathlachlan	1st Mar, Jun, Nov
Strone and Ardentinny	Last Feb, Jun, Oct
Toward	Last Feb, May, Aug, Nov

(21) LORN AND MULL

Meets at Oban, in the Church of Scotland Centre, Glencruitten Road, on the first Wednesday of February and December, and on the first Tuesday of June and October.

| Clerk: | REV. JEFFREY A. McCORMICK BD | The Manse, Ardchattan, Connel, Argyll PA37 1QZ
[E-mail: akph64@uk.uumail.com] | **01631 710364** |

Appin linked with Lismore

John A.H. Murdoch BA BD DPSS	1979	2001	Appin, Argyll PA38 4DD	01631 730206

Ardchattan (H)

| Jeffrey A. McCormick BD | 1984 | Ardchattan, Connel, Argyll PA37 1QZ | 01631 710364 |

Coll

| Continuing Vacancy | Arinagour, Isle of Coll PA78 6SY | 01879 230366 |

Colonsay and Oronsay linked with Kilbrandon and Kilchattan

| Freda Marshall (Mrs) BD FCII | 1993 | 1997 | The Manse, Winterton Road, Balvicar, Argyll PA34 4TF
[E-mail: f.marshall@ukonline.co.uk] | 01852 300240 |

Connel

| Vacant | St Oran's Manse, Connel, Argyll PA37 1PJ
[E-mail: ronniegall@aol.com] | 01631 710242 |

Glenorchy and Innishael linked with Strathfillan

| John Shedden BD | 1971 | 2001 | The Manse, Dalmally, Argyll PA33 1AS | 01838 200386 |

Iona linked with Kilfinichen and Kilvickeon and the Ross of Mull

| Robert C. Nelson BA BD (Locum Associate) | 1980 | 2002 | Bunessan, Isle of Mull PA67 6DW | 01681 700227 |

Kilbrandon and Kilchattan See Colonsay and Oronsay

Kilchrenan and Dalavich linked with Muckairn

| Margaret R.M. Millar (Miss) BTh | 1977 | 1996 | Taynuilt, Argyll PA35 1HW
[E-mail: macoje@aol.com] | 01866 822204 |

Kilfinichen and Kilvickeon and the Ross of Mull See Iona

Kilmore (GD) and Oban
Andrew B. Campbell BD DPS MTh   1979   Kilmore and Oban Manse, Ganavan, Oban, Argyll PA34 5TU   01631 562322
[E-mail: revabc@obancofs.freeserve.co.uk]
William Gray LTh (Assist)   1971   2000   Lochnagar, Longsdale Road, Oban PA34 5DZ   01631 567471

Lismore See Appin
Muckairn See Kilchrenan

Mull, Isle of, Kilninian and Kilmore linked with Salen (H) and Ulva
linked with Tobermory (GD) (H) linked with Torosay (H) and Kinlochspelvie
Alan T. Taylor BD   1980   Tobermory, Isle of Mull PA75 6PS   01688 302226
01688 302037 (Fax)

Salen and Ulva See Mull
Strathfillan See Glenorchy

Tiree (GD)
Vacant   Isle of Tiree PA77 6TN   01879 220377

Tobermory See Mull
Torosay and Kinlochspelvie See Mull

Grainger, Ian G.   1985 1991   (Maxton with Newtown)   Seaview, Ardtun, Bunessan, Isle of Mull PA67 6DH   01681 700457
Lamont, Archibald   1952 1994   (Kilcalmonell with Skipness)   8 Achlonan, Taynuilt, Argyll PA35 1JJ   01866 822385
MacKechnie, J.M. MBE MA   1938 1978   (Kilchrenan and Dalavich)   Eastwing, Manton Grounds, Windermere, Cumbria   01680 300507
Pollock, William MA BD PhD   1987 2002   (Isle of Mull Parishes)   Correay, Salen, Aros, Isle of Mull PA72 6JF
[E-mail: wpollock@salen.freeserve.co.uk]
Spencer, John MA BD   1962 2001   (Dumfries: Lincluden with Holywood)   Rhugarbh Cottage, North Shian, Appin, Argyll PA38 4BA   01631 730416
Troup, Harold J.G. MA   1951 1980   (Garelochhead)   Tighshee, Isle of Iona PA76 6SP   01681 700309

(22) FALKIRK

Meets at St Andrew's West, Falkirk, on the first Tuesday of September, October, November, December and March, and on the fourth Tuesday of January and June; and in Kildrum Church, Cumbernauld on the first Tuesday in May.

Clerk: REV. IAN W. BLACK MA BD   Zetland Manse, Ronaldshay Crescent, Grangemouth FK3 9JH   01324 472868
[E-mail: akph51@uk.uumail.com]   01324 471656 (Presby)
Treasurer: MR. I. MACDONALD   1 Jones Avenue, Larbert FK5 3ER   01324 553603

Airth (H)
Richard J. Hammond BA BD — 1993 — Airth, Falkirk FK2 8JQ — 01324 831474

Blackbraes and Shieldhill
James H.D.C. Drysdale LTh — 2002 — 1997 — Shieldhill, Falkirk FK1 2EG
[E-mail: jmdrysdl1@aol.com] — 01324 621938

Bo'ness: Old (H)
William McPherson BD DipEd — 1994 — 10 Dundas Street, Bo'ness EH51 0DG
[E-mail: willie.mcpherson@care4free.net] — 01506 822206

Bo'ness: St Andrew's
Albert O. Bogle BD MTh — 1981 — St Andrew's Manse, 11 Erngath Road, Bo'ness EH51 9DP
[E-mail: a.bogle@blueyonder.co.uk]
[Website: http://www.standonline.org.uk] — 01506 822195

Bonnybridge: St Helen's (H) (01324 815756)
Alisdair T. MacLeod-Mair MEd DipTheol — 2002 — 133 Falkirk Road, Bonnybridge FK4 1BA — 01324 812621 (Tel/Fax)

Bothkennar and Carronshore
Patricia A. Carruth (Mrs) BD — 1998 — 11 Hunter Place, Greenmount Park, Carronshore, Falkirk FK2 8QS — 01324 570525

Brightons (H)
Scott R.McL. Kirkland BD MAR — 1996 — The Manse, Maddiston Road, Brightons, Falkirk FK2 0JP
[E-mail: scott@kirklands.net] — 01324 712062 / 01324 713855 (2nd num)

Carriden (H)
R. Gordon Reid BSc BD AMIEE — 1993 — The Spires, Foredale Terrace, Carriden, Bo'ness EH51 9LW — 01506 822141

Cumbernauld: Abronhill (H)
Vacant
Marilyn Douglas (Miss) DCS — 26 Ash Road, Cumbernauld, Glasgow G67 3ED — 01236 723833
201 Almond Road, Cumbernauld, Glasgow G67 3LS — 01236 732136

Cumbernauld: Condorrat (H)
H. Taylor Brown BD CertMin — 1997 — 11 Rosehill Drive, Cumbernauld, Glasgow G67 4FD — 01236 721464
Janette McNaughton (Miss) DCS — 4 Dunellan Avenue, Moodiesburn, Glasgow G69 0GB — 01236 870180

Cumbernauld: Kildrum (H)
Vacant — Clouden Road, Cumbernauld, Glasgow G67 2JQ — 01236 723204
David Nicholson DCS — 2D Doon Side, Kildrum, Cumbernauld, Glasgow G67 2HX — 01236 732260

Cumbernauld: Old (H)
Catriona Ogilvie (Mrs) MA BD
Colin Ogilvie DCS
1999
Baronhill, Cumbernauld, Glasgow G67 2SD
6 Ranfurly Drive, Carrickstone, Cumbernauld, Glasgow G68 0DS
[E-mail: colinogilvie@lineone.net]
01236 721912
01236 728301

Cumbernauld: St Mungo's
Neil MacKinnon BD
1990 1999
The Manse, Fergusson Road, Cumbernauld, Glasgow G67 1LS
[E-mail: neil@box200.fsnet.co.uk]
01236 721513

Denny: Dunipace (H)
Jean W. Gallacher (Miss) BD
1989
Dunipace Manse, Denny FK6 6QJ
01324 824540

Denny: Old
Vacant
31 Duke Street, Denny FK6 6NR
01324 824508

Denny: Westpark (H)
Andrew Barrie BSc BD
1984 2000
13 Baxter Crescent, Denny FK6 5EZ
[E-mail: andrew.barrie@blueyonder.co.uk]
[Website: http://www.westparkchurch.org.uk]
01324 876224

Falkirk: Bainsford
Michael R. Philip BD
1978 2001
1 Valleyview Place, Newcarron Village, Falkirk FK2 7JB
[E-mail: mrphilip@btinternet.com]
01324 621087

Falkirk: Camelon Irving (H)
Sally Foster Fulton (Mrs) BA BD
1999
8 Macintosh Place, Falkirk FK1 5UL
01324 623035

Falkirk: Camelon St John's
Stuart Sharp MTheol DipPA
Margaret Corrie (Miss) DCS
2001
24 Rennie Street, Falkirk FK1 5QW
44 Sunnyside Street, Falkirk FK1 4BH
01324 623631
01324 670656

Falkirk: Erskine (H)
Glen D. Macaulay BD
1999
Burnbrae Road, Falkirk FK1 5SD
01324 623701

Falkirk: Grahamston United (H)
Neil W. Barclay BSc BEd BD
1986 2002
30 Russel Street, Falkirk FK2 7HS
01324 624461

Falkirk: Laurieston linked with Redding and Westquarter
Geoffrey H. Smart LTh
1994 2002
11 Polmont Road, Laurieston, Falkirk FK2 9QQ
01324 621196

Falkirk: Old and St Modan's (H)
A. Sheila Blount (Mrs) BD BA
1978 1998
9 Major's Loan, Falkirk FK1 5QF
[E-mail: asblount@fish.co.uk]
01324 623063

Ronald W. Smith BA BEd BD (Assoc)
1979
19 Neilson Street, Falkirk FK1 5AQ
01324 621058

Falkirk: St Andrew's West (H)
Alastair M. Horne BSc BD
1989 1997
1 Maggiewood's Loan, Falkirk FK1 5SJ
01324 623308

Charge / Minister		Address	Tel
Falkirk: St James'			
Eric G. McKimmon BA BD MTh	1983 1992	13 Wallace Place, Falkirk FK2 7EN	01324 622757
Grangemouth: Dundas			
Douglas B. Blair LTh	1969	5 Abbotsgrange Road, Grangemouth FK3 9JD	01324 482467
Grangemouth: Kerse (H) (01324 482487)			
Andrew C. Donald BD DPS	1992	8 Naismith Court, Grangemouth FK3 9BQ	01324 482109
Grangemouth: Kirk of the Holy Rood			
Vacant		Bowhouse Road, Grangemouth FK3 0EX	01324 471595
Grangemouth: Zetland (H)			
Ian W. Black MA BD	1976 1991	Ronaldshay Crescent, Grangemouth FK3 9JH	01324 472868
Colin Mailer (Aux)	1996 1999	Innis Chonain, Back Row, Polmont, Falkirk FK2 0RD	01324 712401
Haggs (H)			
Helen F. Christie (Mrs) BD	1998	5 Watson Place, Dennyloanhead, Bonnybridge FK4 2BG	01324 813786
David Wandrum (Aux)	1993 2001	5 Cawder View, Carrickstone Meadows, Cumbernauld, Glasgow G68 0BN	01236 723288
Larbert: East			
Melville D. Crosthwaite BD DipEd DipMin	1984 1995	1 Cortachy Avenue, Carron, Falkirk FK2 8DH	01324 562402
Larbert: Old (H)			
Clifford A.J. Rennie MA BD	1973 1985	38 South Broomage Avenue, Larbert FK2 3ED	01324 562868
Larbert: West (H)			
Gavin Boswell BTheol	1993 1999	11 Carronvale Road, Larbert FK5 3LZ	01324 562878
Muiravonside			
Joan Ross (Miss) BSc BD PhD	1999	Maddiston, Falkirk FK2 0LX	01324 712876
Polmont: Old			
William G. McKaig BD	1978 2000	Polmont, Falkirk FK2 0QY	01324 713081
Redding and Westquarter See Falkirk: Laurieston			
Slamannan			
Raymond Thomson BD DipMin	1992	Slamannan, Falkirk FK1 3EN	01324 851307
Stenhouse and Carron (H)			
Robert K. Hardie MA BD	1968 1969	Stenhousemuir, Larbert FK5 4BU	01324 562393

Name	Years	Charge / Position	Address	Telephone
Allan, Robert S.T. LLB DipLP BD	1991 1999	Education and Development Officer, Department of Ministry	1 Lime Grove, Larbert FK5 3LY	01324 562500
Blount, Graham K. LLB BD PhD	1976 1998	Parliamentary Officer	(Office) 14 Johnston Terrace, Edinburgh EH1 2PW [E-mail: gkblount@dial.pipex.com] (Home) 9 Majors Loan, Falkirk FK1 5QF	(Tel) 0131-622 2278 (Fax) 0131-622 7226 01324 623063
Brown, James BA BD DipHSW DipPsychol	1973 2001	(Abercorn with Dalmeny)	Fern Cottage, 3 Philipstone Lane, Bo'ness EH51 9JP	01506 822454
Chalmers, George A. MA BD MLitt	1962 2002	(Catrine with Sorn)	3 Cricket Place, Brightons, Falkirk FK2 0HZ	01324 712030
Fulton, R. Stuart M. BA BD	1991 1998	Specialist Adviser in Chaplaincy to HM Prison Services	(Office) c/o Scottish Prison Service HQ, Calton House, 5 Redheugh Rig, Edinburgh EH12 9DQ (Home) 8 Macintosh Place, Falkirk FK1 5UL	0131-244 8459
Goodman, Richard A.	1976 1986	(Isle of Mull Associate)	13/2 Glenbrae Court, Falkirk FK1 1YT	01324 683035
Heriot, Charles R. JP BA	1962 1996	(Brightons)	20 Eastcroft Drive, Polmont, Falkirk FK2 0SU	01324 621315
Hill, Stanley LTh	1967 1998	(Muiravonside)	28 Creteil Court, Falkirk FK1 1UL	01324 711352
Holland, John C.	1976 1985	(Strone and Ardentinny)	7 Polmont Park, Polmont, Falkirk FK2 0XT	01324 634483
Kellock, Chris N. MA BD	1998	Chaplain: RAF	Chaplaincy Services, HQPTC, RAF Innsworth, Gloucester GL3 1EZ	01324 712716
McCallum, John	1962 1998	(Falkirk: Irving Camelon)	11 Burnbrae Gardens, Falkirk FK1 5SB	01324 619766
McDonald, William G. MA BD	1959 1975	(Falkirk: Grahamston United)	38 St Mary Street, St Andrews KY16 8AZ	
McDowall, Ronald J. BD	1980 2001	(Falkirk: Laurieston with Redding and Westquarter)	'Kailas', Windsor Road, Falkirk FK1 5EJ	01324 871947
Maclaren, William B. MA JP	1944 1983	(Bothkennar and Carronshore)	7 Malcolm Drive, Stenhousemuir, Larbert FK5 4JP	01324 551274
McMullin, Andrew MA	1960 1996	(Blackbraes and Shieldhill)	33 Eastcroft Drive, Polmont, Falkirk FK2 0SU	01324 624938
Martin, Neil DCS		(Deacon)	3 Strathmiglo Place, Stenhousemuir, Larbert FK5 4UQ	01324 551362
Mathers, Daniel L. BD	1982 2001	(Grangemouth: Charing Cross and West)	10 Eccall Road, Brightons, Falkirk FK2 0RS	01324 872253
Maxton, Ronald M. MA	1955 1995	(Dollar: Associate)	5 Rulley View, Denny FK6 6QQ	01324 825441
Miller, Elsie M. (Miss) DCS		(Deacon)	30 Swinton Avenue, Rowansbank, Baillieston, Glasgow G69 6JR	0141-771 0857
Munroe, Henry BA LTh LTl	1971 1988	(Denny Dunipace North with Old)	Viewforth, High Road, Maddiston, Falkirk FK2 0BL	01324 712446
Murray, Eric J.	1958 1995	(Larbert: East)	21 Redpath Drive, Greenmount Park, Carron, Falkirk FK5 8QL	01324 563764
Paul, Iain BSc PhD BD PhD	1976 1991	(Wishaw Craigneuk and Belhaven)	116 Tryst Road, Larbert FK5 4QJ	01324 562641
Scott, Donald H. BA BD	1987 2002	Prison Chaplain	Polmont Young Offenders' Institution, Newlands Road, Brightons, Falkirk FK2 0DE	01324 711558
Smith, Richard BD	1976 2002	(Denny Old)	Easter Wayside, 46 Kennedy Way, Airth, Falkirk FK2 8GB	
Talman, Hugh MA	1943 1987	(Polmont Old)	Niagara, 70 Lawers Crescent, Polmont, Falkirk FK2 0RQ	01324 711240
Whiteford, Robert S. MA	1945 1986	(Shapinsay)	3 Wellside Court, Wellside Place, Falkirk FK1 5RG	01324 610562

FALKIRK ADDRESSES

Falkirk
Bainsford — Hendry Street, Bainsford
Camelon — Dorrator Road, Camelon
Irving — Glasgow Road x Stirling Road
St John's — Cockburn Street x Hodge Street
Erskine

Grahamston — Bute Street
Laurieston — Main Falkirk Road
Old and St Modan's — Kirk Wynd
St Andrew's West — Newmarket Street
St James' — Thornhill Road x Firs Street

Grangemouth
Charing Cross and West — Charing Cross
Dundas — Bo'ness Road
Kerse — Abbot's Road
Kirk of the Holy Rood — Bowhouse Road
Zetland — Ronaldshay Crescent

(23) STIRLING

Meets at the Moderator's Church on the second Thursday of September, and at Stirling Management Centre, Stirling University on the second Thursday of every other month except January, July and August when there is no meeting.

Presbytery Office:		St Columba's Church, Park Terrace, Stirling FK8 2NA	01786 449522 (Tel)
		[E-mail: akph75@uk.uumail.com]	01786 473930 (Fax)
		[E-mail: stirling-presbytery@uk.uumail.com]	(Mon–Fri: 9:30am–12 noon)
Clerk:	REV. GEORGE G. CRINGLES BD	St Blane's Manse, 49 Roman Way, Dunblane FK15 9DJ	01786 822268
Depute Clerk:	MR ALASTAIR ROSS	18 Fir Road, Doune FK16 6HU	01786 841648
Treasurer:	MR DONALD INGLIS	34 Buchanan Drive, Stirling FK9 5HE	01786 461013

Aberfoyle (H) linked with Port of Menteith (H)

James Daniel Gibb BA LTh	1994	2000	The Manse, Loch Ard Road, Aberfoyle, Stirling FK8 3SZ	01877 382391
			[E-mail: rev.danny@gibb.fsworld.co.uk]

Alloa: North (H)

Elizabeth Clelland (Mrs) BD	2002	30 Claremont, Alloa FK10 2DF	01259 210403

Alloa: St Mungo's (H)

Alan F.M. Downie MA BD	1977	1996	37a Claremont, Alloa FK10 2DG	01259 213872
			[E-mail: alan@stmungos.freeserve.co.uk]

Alloa: West

Irene C. Gillespie (Mrs) BD	1991	2001	29 Claremont, Alloa FK10 2DF	01259 214204

Alva

James N.R. McNeil BSc BD	1990	1997	The Manse, 34 Ochil Road, Alva FK12 5JT	01259 760262

Balfron linked with Fintry (H)

John Turnbull LTh	1994	Balfron, Glasgow G63 0SX	01360 440285

Balquhidder linked with Killin and Ardeonaig (H)

John Lincoln MPhil BD	1986	1997	The Manse, Killin FK21 8TN	01567 820247
			[E-mail: gm0jol@zetnet.co.uk]

Bannockburn: Allan (H)

Jim Landels BD CertMin	1990	Bogend Road, Bannockburn, Stirling FK7 8NP	01786 814692
		[E-mail: revjimlandels@btinternet.com]
Marina Brown (Mrs) MA (Aux)	2000	3 Lover's Loan, Dollar FK14 7AB	01259 743870

Bannockburn: Ladywell (H)

Elizabeth M.D. Robertson (Miss) BD CertMin	1997		57 The Firs, Bannockburn FK7 0EG [E-mail: lizr@tinyonline.uk]	01786 812467

Bridge of Allan: Chalmers (H)

Vacant			34 Kenilworth Road, Bridge of Allan, Stirling FK9 4EH	01786 832118

Bridge of Allan: Holy Trinity (H) (01786 834155)

John C. Nicol MA BD	1965		29 Keir Street, Bridge of Allan, Stirling FK9 4QJ [E-mail: johncnicol@aol.com]	01786 832093

Buchanan linked with Drymen

Alexander J. MacPherson BD	1986	1997	Buchanan Manse, Drymen, Glasgow G63 0AQ	01360 870212

Buchlyvie (H) linked with Gartmore (H)

Moira G. MacCormick BA LTh	1986		8 Culbowie Crescent, Buchlyvie, Stirling FK8 3NH [E-mail: MoiraMacCormick@compuserve.com]	01360 850249

Callander (H) (Tel/Fax: 01877 331409)

Iain M. Goring BSc BD	1976	1985	3 Aveland Park Road, Callander FK17 8FD [E-mail: gorings@gfki7.freeserve.co.uk]	01877 330097
June Cloggie (Mrs) (Aux)	1997	1998	8 Trossachs Road, Aberfoyle FK8 3SW	01877 382382

Cambusbarron: The Bruce Memorial (H)

Brian G. Webster BSc BD	1998		14 Woodside Court, Cambusbarron, Stirling FK7 9PH [E-mail: revwebby@aol.com]	01786 450579

Clackmannan (H)

J. Gordon Mathew MA BD	1973	1999	The Manse, Port Street, Clackmannan FK10 4JH [E-mail: jgmatthew@lineone.net]	01259 211255

Cowie (H) linked with Plean

Vacant			The Manse, Plean, Stirling FK7 8BX	01786 813287

Dollar (H) linked with Glendevon linked with Muckhart

John P.S. Purves BSc BD	1978	1990	2 Manse Road, Dollar FK14 7AJ [E-mail: dollar.parish@btinternet.com]	01259 743432
Margaret McArthur BD DipMin (Assoc)	1995		The Manse, Muckhart, Dollar FK14 7JN	01259 781464
Jean S. Watson (Miss) MA (Aux)	1993	1998	29 Strachan Crescent, Dollar FK14 7HL	01259 742872

Drymen See Buchanan

Dunblane: Cathedral (H)

Colin G. McIntosh BSc BD	1976	1988	Cathedral Manse, Dunblane FK15 0AQ	01786 822205

Dunblane: St Blane's (H)
George G. Cringles BD   1981   1988   49 Roman Way, Dunblane FK15 9DJ   01786 822268
Alistair A.B. Cruickshank MA (Aux)   1991   2000   2A Chapel Place, Dollar FK14 7DW   01259 742549

Fallin
Eleanor D. Muir (Miss) MTheol DipPTheol   1986   4 King Street, Fallin, Stirling FK7 7JY   01786 812243

Fintry See Balfron

Gargunnock linked with Kilmadock linked with Kincardine in Menteith
Richard S. Campbell LTh   1993   2001   The Manse, Gargunnock, Stirling FK8 3BQ   01786 860678

Gartmore See Buchlyvie
Glendevon See Dollar

Killearn (H)
Philip R.M. Malloch LLB BD   1970   1993   2 The Oaks, Killearn, Glasgow G63 9SF   01360 550045
                                                                        [E-mail: pmalloch@killearnkirk.freeserve.co.uk]

Killin and Ardeonaig (H) See Balquhidder
Kilmadock See Gargunnock
Kincardine in Menteith See Gargunnock

Kippen (H) linked with Norrieston
Gordon MacRae BA BD   1985   1998   The Manse, Kippen, Stirling FK8 3DN   01786 870229

Lecropt (H)
William M. Gilmour MA BD   1969   1983   5 Henderson Street, Bridge of Allan, Stirling FK9 4NA 01786 832382

Logie (H)
Regine U. Cheyne (Mrs) MA BSc BD   1988   2000   128 Causewayhead Road, Stirling FK9 5HJ   01786 463060

Menstrie (H)
George T. Sherry LTh   1977   The Manse, Menstrie FK11 7EA   01259 761461

Muckhart See Dollar
Norrieston See Kippen
Plean See Cowie
Port of Menteith See Aberfoyle

Sauchie and Coalsnaughton
Vacant   Parish Church Manse, Main Street, Sauchie, Alloa FK10 3JX 01259 212037

Stirling: Allan Park South (H) linked with Church of the Holy Rude (H)
Morris C. Coull BD — 1974 1996 — 22 Laurelhill Place, Stirling FK8 2JH — 01786 473999

Stirling: Church of the Holy Rude (H) See Allan Park South (H)

Stirling: North (H)
Paul M.N. Sewell MA BD — 1970 1978 — 18 Shirra's Brae Road, Stirling FK7 0BA — 01786 475378

Stirling: St Columba's (H) (01786 449516)
Kenneth G. Russell BD CCE — 1986 2001 — 5 Clifford Road, Stirling FK8 2AQ [E-mail: kenrussell1000@hotmail.com] — 01786 475802

Stirling: St Mark's
Rodney P.T. Robb — 1995 — 176 Drip Road, Stirling FK8 1RR — 01786 473716

Stirling: St Ninian's Old (H)
Gary J. McIntyre BD DipMin — 1993 1998 — 7 Randolph Road, Stirling FK8 2AJ — 01786 474421

Stirling: Viewfield (T)(H)
Ian Taylor BD ThM — 1995 — 7 Windsor Place, Stirling FK8 2HY [E-mail: taylorian@btinternet.com] — 01786 474534

Strathblane (H)
Alex H. Green MA BD — 1986 1995 — Strathblane, Glasgow G63 9AQ — 01360 770226

Tillicoultry (H)
James Cochrane LTh — 1994 2000 — The Manse, Dollar Road, Tillicoultry FK13 6PD [E-mail: jc@cochranemail.co.uk] — 01259 750340 / 01259 752951 (Fax)

Tullibody St Serf's (H)
John Brown MA BD — 1995 2000 — 16 Menstrie Road, Tullibody, Alloa FK10 2RG [E-mail: john@browntj.fsnet.co.uk] — 01259 213236

Name				Address	Telephone
Aiken, E. Douglas MA	1961	1998	(Clackmannan)	1 Dolan Grove, Saline, Dunfermline KY12 9UP	01383 852730
Benson, James W. BA BD DipEd	1975	1996	(Balquhidder)	1 Sunnyside, Dunblane FK15 9HA	01786 822624
Blackley, Jean R.M. (Mrs) BD	1989	2001	(Banton with Twechar)	8 Rodders Grove, Alva, Clackmannan FK12 5RR	01259 760198
Burnett, John B.	1964	1985	(Dollar: Associate)	30 Manor House Road, Dollar FK14 7HB	01259 742892
Campbell, Patrick D.G. MA	1949	1984	(Geneva)	30 Harviestoun Road, Dollar FK14 7HG	01259 742172
Cheyne, Magnus	1963	1996	(Community Minister: Shetland)	128 Causewayhead Road, Stirling FK9 5HJ	01786 463060
Craig, Maxwell D. BD ThM	1966	2000	(Jerusalem: St Andrew's: Locum)	9 Kilbryde Crescent, Dunblane FK15 9BA	01786 823147
Doherty, Arthur James DipTh	1957	1993	(Strathblane)	1 Murdiston Avenue, Callander FK17 8AY	
Fleming, Alexander F. MA BD	1966	1995	(Fintry)	4 Horsburgh Avenue, Kilsyth, Glasgow G65 9BZ	01236 821461
Gallan, Alex MA	1955	1989	(Wishaw Cambusnethan North)	16 Dundas Road, Stirling FK9 5QQ	01786 470796
Gaston, A. Ray C. MA BD	1969	2002	(Leuchars: St Athernase)	13 Manse Road, Dollar FK14 7AL	01259 743202

Name				Address	Tel.
Izett, William A.F.	1968	2000	(Law)	1 Duke Street, Clackmannan FK10 4EF	01259 724 203
Jamieson, G.T. BA	1936	1969	(Stirling: Viewfield)	10 Grendon Court, Snowdon Place, Stirling FK8 2JX	01786 461646
Jamieson, John LTh	1967	1993	(Balfron)	Ardnablane, Dunblane FK15 0QR	01786 823610
McIntosh, Hamish N.M. MA	1949	1987	(Fintry)	1 Forth Crescent, Stirling FK8 1LE	01786 470453
MacRae, Elaine H. (Mrs) BD	1985	1998	Prison Chaplain	The Manse, Kippen, Stirling FK8 3DN	01786 870229
McRae, Malcolm H. MA PhD	1986	1994	(Coalsnaughton)	10B Victoria Place, Stirling FK8 2QU	
Orrock, Archibald A. MA BD	1938	1982	(Teacher: Religious Instruction)	3 Kilbryde Court, Dunblane FK15 9AX	01786 822821
Ovens, Samuel B. BD	1982	1993	(Slamannan)	17 Swinburne Drive, Sauchie, Alloa FK10 3EQ	01259 222723
Pryce, Stuart F.A.	1963	1997	(Dumfries: St George's)	36 Forth Park, Bridge of Allan, Stirling FK9 5NT	01786 831026
Reid, Alan A.S. MA BD STM	1962	1995	(Bridge of Allan: Chalmers)	Wayside Cottage, Bridgend, Ceres, Cupar KY15 5LS	01334 828509
Reid, David T. BA BD	1954	1993	(Cleish linked with Fossoway St Serf's and Devonside)		
Rennie, James B. MA	1959	1992	(Leochel Cushnie and Lynturk with Tough)	14 Argyle Park, Dunblane FK15 9DZ	01786 824863
Robertson, Alex	1974	1993	(Baldernock)	17 Oliphant Court, Riverside, Stirling FK8 1US	01786 841894
Sangster, Ernest G. BD ThM	1958	1997	(Alva)	4 Moray Park, Moray Street, Doune FK16 6DJ	
Scott, James F.	1957	1997	(Dyce)	6 Law Hill Road, Dollar FK14 7BG	
Scoular, J. Marshall	1954	1996	(Kippen)	5 Gullipen View, Callander FK17	01786 825976
Silcox, John R. BD	1976	1984	School Chaplain	2H Buccleuch Court, Dunblane FK15 0AH	01786 824944
Stewart, Angus T. MA BD PhD	1962	1999	(Glasgow: Greenbank)	Queen Victoria School, Dunblane FK15 0JA	01360 850117
Stirling, J. BSc BD	1962	1998	(Stirling: St Ninian's Old)	Mansefield, Station Road, Buchlyvie, Stirling FK8 3NE	01738 442953
Symington, Robert C. BA	1954	1997	(Community Minister: Lorn and Mull)	42 Fairies Road, Perth PH1 1LZ	01786 823902
Todd, A. Stewart MA BD DD	1952	1993	(Aberdeen: St Machar's Cathedral)	3 Belmont, The Crescent, Dunblane FK15 0DW	01877 384662
Watt, Robert MA BD	1943	1982	(Aberdeen: Woodside South)	Culearn, Balquhidder, Lochearnhead FK19 8PB	01786 823632
Wright, John P. BD	1977	2000	(Glasgow: New Govan)	1 Coldstream Avenue, Dunblane FK15 9JN	01786 480840
				Plane Castle, Airth, Falkirk FK2 8SF	

STIRLING ADDRESSES

Allan Park South	Dumbarton Road	St Ninians Old	Kirk Wynd
Holy Rude	St John Street	St Ninians Viewfield	Barnton Street
North	Springfield Road	St Columba's	Park Terrace
St Mark's	Drip Road		

(24) DUNFERMLINE

Meets at Dunfermline, in the Abbey Church Hall, Abbey Park Place on the first Thursday of each month, except January, July and August when there is no meeting, and June when it meets on the last Thursday.

Clerk: REV. WILLIAM E. FARQUHAR BA BD — Townhill Manse, Dunfermline KY12 0EZ [E-mail: akph46@uk.uumail.com] — 01383 723835 (Tel/Fax)

Charge / Minister	Year(s)	Address	Telephone
Aberdour St Fillan's (H) Peter B. Park BD MCIBS	1997	36 Bellhouse Road, Aberdour, Fife KY3 0TL	01383 860349
Ballingry and Lochcraig Vacant		122 Mid Street, Kirkcaldy KY1 2PN	01592 205139
Beath and Cowdenbeath North (H) David W. Redmayne BSc BD	2001	10 Stuart Place, Cowdenbeath KY4 9BN	01383 511033
Cairneyhill (H) (01383 882352) linked with Limekilns (H) (01383 873337) Norman M. Grant BD	1990	Limekilns, Dunfermline KY11 3HT	01383 872341
Carnock and Oakley (H) Elizabeth S.S. Kenny (Miss) BD RGN SCM	1989	Carnock, Dunfermline KY12 9JG	01383 850327
Cowdenbeath: Trinity (H) David G. Adams BD	1991 1999	66 Barclay Street, Cowdenbeath KY4 9LD	01383 515089
Culross and Torryburn (H) Thomas Moffat BSc BD	1976 2000	Culross, Dunfermline KY12 8JD	01383 880231
Dalgety (H) Donald G.B. McCorkindale BD DipMin	1992 2000	9 St Colme Drive, Dalgety Bay, Dunfermline KY11 9LQ [E-mail: donald@dalgety-church.co.uk] [Website: http://www.dalgety-church.co.uk]	01383 822316 (Tel/Fax)
Ian Cunningham DCS		5 Forth Court, Dalgety Bay, Dunfermline KY11 5SF [E-mail: ian@dalgety-church.co.uk]	
Dunfermline: Abbey (H) Alistair L. Jessamine MA BD	1979 1991	12 Garvock Hill, Dunfermline KY12 7UU	01383 721022
Dunfermline: Gillespie Memorial (H) (01383 621253) A. Gordon Reid BSc BD	1982 1988	4 Killin Court, Dunfermline KY12 7XF	01383 723329

Dunfermline: North
Gordon F.C. Jenkins MA BD PhD — 1968   1998 — 13 Barbour Grove, Dunfermline KY12 9YB — 01383 721061

Dunfermline: St Andrew's Erskine
Anne Allison (Mrs) BSc PhD BD — 2000 — 71A Townhill Road, Dunfermline KY12 0BN — 01383 734657

Dunfermline: St Leonard's (01383 620106)
Alexander B. Mitchell BD — 1981 — 12 Torvean Place, Dunfermline KY11 4YY — 01383 721054
Andrew E. Paterson (Aux) — 1994 — 61 Elmwood Terrace, Kelty KY4 0LL — 01383 830998

Dunfermline: St Margaret's
Fiona Richard (Mrs) BA BD — 1996 — 38 Garvock Hill, Dunfermline KY12 7UU — 01383 723955

Dunfermline: St Ninian's
Elizabeth A. Fisk (Mrs) BD — 1996 — 51 St John's Drive, Dunfermline KY12 7TL — 01383 722256

Dunfermline: Townhill and Kingseat (H)
William E. Farquhar BA BD — 1987 — 161 Main Street, Townhill, Dunfermline KY12 0EZ — 01383 723835

Inverkeithing: St John's linked with North Queensferry (T)
Sheila Munro (Ms) BD — 1995 — 34 Hill Street, Inverkeithing KY11 1AB — 01383 412422

Inverkeithing: St Peter's (01383 412626)
George G. Nicol BD DPhil — 1982   1988 — 20 Struan Drive, Inverkeithing KY11 1AR — 01383 410032

Kelty
Scott Burton BD DipMin — 1999 — 15 Arlick Road, Kelty KY4 0BH — 01383 830291

Limekilns See Cairneyhill

Lochgelly: Macainsh
Vacant — 82 Main Street, Lochgelly KY5 9AA — 01592 780435

Lochgelly: St Andrew's (T) (H)
Vacant — Station Road, Lochgelly KY5 9QX — 01592 780319

North Queensferry See Inverkeithing: St John's

Rosyth
Violet C.C. McKay (Mrs) BD — 1988   2002 — 42 Woodside Avenue, Rosyth KY11 2LA — 01383 412776
Morag Crawford (Miss) DCS — 118 Wester Drylaw Place, Edinburgh EH4 2TG — 0131-332 2253

Saline and Blairingone
Vacant

Main Street, Saline, Dunfermline KY12 9PL   01383 852240

Tulliallan and Kincardine

Jock Stein MA BD	1973	2002	62 Toll Road, Kincardine, Alloa FK10 4QZ	01259 730538
Margaret E. Stein (Mrs) DA BD DipRE	1984	2002	62 Toll Road, Kincardine, Alloa FK10 4QZ	01259 730538

Archibald, D.Y. BA BD MPhil	1949	1983	(Cairneyhill with Torryburn and Newmills)	Flat 31, Runnymeade Court, Park Hill Rise, Croydon CR0 5JF	020 8681 8398
Britchfield, Alison E.P. (Mrs) MA BD	1986	1992	Chaplain RN	13 Tregoning Road, Torpoint, Cornwall PL11 2LX	01752 818430
Brown, Peter MA BD FRAScot	1953	1987	(Holm)	24 Inchmickery Avenue, Dalgety Bay, Dunfermline KY11 5NF	01383 822456
Campbell, John MA	1943	1978	(Urquhart)	15 Foulden Place, Dunfermline KY12 7TQ	01383 738055
Mackenzie, R.P. MA BD	1936	1980	(Dunfermline: St Leonard's)	23 Foulis Crescent, Juniper Green, Edinburgh EH14 5BN	0131-453 3599
Macpherson, Stewart M. MA	1953	1990	(Dunfermline: Abbey)	176 Halbeath Road, Dunfermline KY11 4LB	01383 722851
Orr, J. McMichael MA BD PhD	1949	1986	(Aberfoyle with Port of Menteith)	9 Overhaven, Limekilns, Dunfermline KY11 3JH	01383 872245
Pogue, Victor C. BA BD	1945	1980	(Baird Research Fellow)	5/2 Plewlands Court, Edinburgh EH10 5JY	0131-445 1628
Reid, David MSc LTh FSAScot	1961	1992	(St Monans with Largoward)	North Lethans, Saline, Dunfermline KY12 9TE	01383 733144
Ross, Evan J. LTh	1986	1998	(Cowdenbeath: West with Mossgreen and Crossgates)	43 Auld Mart Road, Milnathort, Kinross KY13 7FR	01577 861484
Scott, John LTh	1969	1996	(Aberdour St Fillan's)	32 White's Quay, St David's Harbour, Dalgety Bay, Dunfermline KY11 5HT	01383 820896
Smith, T. Forrest	1959	1986	(Arbuthnott with Kinneff)	71 Whitehills Gardens, Musselburgh EH21 6PH	
Stuart, Anne (Miss) DCS			(Deaconess)	19 St Colme Crescent, Aberdour, Burntisland KY3 0ST	01383 860049
Whyte, Isabel H. (Mrs) BD		1993	Chaplain: Queen Margaret Hospital, Dunfermline	14 Carlingnose Point, North Queensferry, Inverkeithing KY11 1ER	01383 410732

(25) KIRKCALDY

Meets at Kirkcaldy, in St Brycedale Hall, on the first Tuesday of February, March, April, May, November and December, on the second Tuesday of September, and on the fourth Tuesday of June.

Clerk:	MR ANDREW MOORE	Annandale, Linksfield Street, Leven KY8 4HX [E-mail: akph59@uk.uumail.com]	01333 426984
Depute Clerk:	MR IAN WALKER	62 Centenary Court, Leven KY8 4AL [E-mail: walkerleven@aol.com]	01333 301332

Auchterderran St Fothad's linked with Kinglassie

J. Ewen R. Campbell MA BD	1967	1977	7 Woodend Road, Cardenden, Lochgelly KY5 0NE	01592 720213

Auchtertool linked with Kirkcaldy Linktown (H) (01592 641080)
Catriona M. Morrison (Mrs) MA BD   1995   2000   16 Raith Crescent, Kirkcaldy KY2 5NN   01592 265536

Buckhaven (01592 715577)
Vacant   181 Wellesley Road, Buckhaven, Leven KY8 1JA   01592 712870

Burntisland (H)
Alan Sharp BSc BD   1980   2001   21 Ramsay Crescent, Burntisland KY3 9JL   01592 874303
[E-mail: alansharp@compuserve.com]

Denbeath linked with Methilhill
Elizabeth F. Cranfield (Miss) MA BD   1988   9 Chemiss Road, Methilhill, Leven KY8 2BS   01592 713142

Dysart (H)
Tilly Wilson (Miss) MTh   1990   1998   1 School Brae, Dysart, Kirkcaldy KY1 2XB   01592 655887

Glenrothes: Christ's Kirk (H)
James MacMillan BD   1997   12 The Limekilns, Glenrothes KY6 3QJ   01592 620536

Glenrothes: St Columba's (01592 752539)
Alistair G. McLeod   1988   40 Liberton Drive, Glenrothes KY6 3PB   01592 744558

Glenrothes: St Margaret's (H) (01592 610310)
John P. McLean BSc BPhil BD   1994   8 Alburne Park, Glenrothes KY7 5RB   01592 752241
[E-mail: john@stmargaretschurch.org.uk]

Glenrothes: St Ninian's (H) (01592 610560)
Linda J. Dunbar (Ms) BSc BA BD PhD   2000   1 Cawdor Drive, Glenrothes KY6 2HN   01592 611963 (Tel/Fax)
[E-mail: linda.dunbar0@ouvip.com]
Linda Black (Miss) BSc DCS   378 Alwyn Green, Glenrothes KY7 6TS

Innerleven East (H)
James L. Templeton BSc BD   1975   77 McDonald Street, Methil, Leven KY8 3AJ   01333 426310

Kennoway, Windygates and Balgonie: St Kenneth's (Tel: 01333 351372; E-mail: administration@st-kenneths.freeserve.co.uk)
Richard Baxter MA BD   1997   2 Fernhill Gardens, Windygates, Leven KY8 5DZ   01333 352329
[E-mail: richard-baxter@msn.com]

Kinghorn
James Reid BD   1985   1997   17 Myre Crescent, Kinghorn, Burntisland KY3 9UB   01592 890269
[E-mail: jim17reid@aol.com]

Kinglassie See Auchterderran St Fothad's

Kirkcaldy: Abbotshall (H)
Bryan L. Tomlinson TD   1969   1980   83 Milton Road, Kirkcaldy KY1 1TP   01592 260315
[E-mail: abbkirk@blueyonder.co.uk]

Kirkcaldy: Linktown (01592 641080) See Auchtertool

Kirkcaldy: Pathhead (H) (Tel/Fax: 01592 204635; E-mail: pathhead@btinternet.com)
John D. Thomson BD   1985   1993   73 Loughborough Road, Kirkcaldy KY1 3DD   01592 652215
[Website: www.pathheadparishchurch.co.uk]
[E-mail: john.d.thomson@blueyonder.co.uk]
Maureen Paterson (Mrs) BSc (Aux)   1992   1994   91 Dalmahoy Crescent, Kirkcaldy KY2 6TA   01592 262300
[E-mail: m.e.paterson@btinternet.com]

Kirkcaldy: St Andrew's (H)
Donald M. Thomson BD   1975   2000   15 Harcourt Road, Kirkcaldy KY2 5HQ   01592 260816
[E-mail: dmaclthomson@aol.com]

Kirkcaldy: St Bryce Kirk (H) (Tel: 01592 640016; E-mail: office@stbee.freeserve.co.uk)
Ken Froude MA BD   1979   6 East Fergus Place, Kirkcaldy KY1 1XT   01592 264480
[E-mail: jkfroude@kfroude.freeserve.co.uk]

Kirkcaldy: St John's
Samuel M. McNaught MA BD MTh   1968   1975   25 Bennochy Avenue, Kirkcaldy KY2 5QE   01592 263821

Kirkcaldy: Templehall (H)
Vacant   Appin Crescent, Kirkcaldy KY2 6EJ   01592 260156

Kirkcaldy: Torbain
Ian Elston BD MTh   1999   91 Sauchenbush Road, Kirkcaldy KY2 5RN   01592 263015

Kirkcaldy: Viewforth (H) linked with Thornton
Anne J. Job   2000   66 Viewforth Street, Kirkcaldy KY1 3DJ   01592 652502

Leslie Trinity
David J. Smith BD DipMin   1992   1997   4 Valley Drive, Leslie, Glenrothes KY6 3BQ   01592 741008

Leven
Alan Miller BA MA BD   2000   2001   5 Forman Road, Leven KY8 4HH   01333 303339
[E-mail: alan.miller@ukgateway.net]

Markinch
Alexander R. Forsyth TD BA MTh   1973   2002   7 Guthrie Crescent, Markinch, Glenrothes KY7 6AY   01592 758264

Methil (H)
Allan B. Brown BD MTh   1995   2000   Alma House, 2 School Brae, Methilhill, Leven KY8 2BT   01592 713708
[E-mail: abbrown59@aol.com]

Methilhill See Denbeath
Thornton See Kirkcaldy: Viewforth

Wemyss
Kenneth W. Donald BA BD   1982   1999   33 Main Road, East Wemyss, Kirkcaldy KY1 4RE   01592 713260
[E-mail: kwdonald@4unet.co.uk]

Connolly, Daniel BD DipTheol DipMin	1983		Army Chaplain	2 CS Reg, RLC, BFPO 47
Cooper, M.W. MA	1944	1979	(Kirkcaldy Abbotshall)	Applegarth, Sunny Park, Kinross KY13 7BX — 01577 263204
Crawford, S.G. Victor	1980	1991	(Glasgow: Calton Parkhead)	Crofton, 65 Main Road, East Wemyss, Kirkcaldy KY1 4RL — 01592 712325
Dick, James S. MA BTh	1988	1997	(Glasgow: Ruchazie)	1 Hawkmuir, Kirkcaldy KY1 2AN — 01592 260289
Duncan, John C. BD MPhil	1987	2001	Army Chaplain	35 Engr Regt, Barker Barracks, Paderborn, BFPO 22
Elston, Peter K.	1963	2000	(Dalgety)	6 Cairngorm Crescent, Kirkcaldy KY2 5RF — 01592 205622
Forrester, Ian L. MA	1964	1996	(Friockheim, Kinnell with Inverkeilor and Lunan)	
Gatt, David W.	1981	1995	(Thornton)	8 Bennochy Avenue, Kirkcaldy KY2 5QE — 01592 260251
Gibson, Ivor MA	1957	1993	(Abercorn with Dalmeny)	15 Beech Avenue, Thornton, Kirkcaldy KY1 4AT — 01592 774328
Gordon, Ian D. LTh	1972	2001	(Markinch)	15 McInnes Road, Glenrothes KY7 6BA — 01592 759982
Howden, Margaret (Miss) DCS			(Deaconess)	2 Somerville Way, Glenrothes KY7 5GE — 01592 742487
McAlpine, Robin J. BDS BD	1988	1997	Adviser in Mission and Evangelism	38 Munro Street, Kirkcaldy KY1 1PY — 01592 205913
				10 Seton Place, Kirkcaldy KY2 6UX — 01592 643518
				[E-mail: robin.mcalpine@virgin.net]
McDonald, Iain J.M. MA BD	1984	1996	Chaplain, Kirkcaldy Acute Hospitals	26 Cairngorm Crescent, Kirkcaldy KY2 5RG — 01592 263012
McKenzie, Donald M. TD MA	1947	1986	(Auchtertool with Burntisland)	76 Forth Park Gardens, Kirkcaldy KY2 5TD — 01592 610281
MacLeod, Norman	1960	1988	(Orwell with Portmoak)	324 Muirfield Drive, Glenrothes KY6 2PZ — 01592 566129
Munro, Andrew MA BD PhD	1972	2000	(Glencaple with Lowther)	7 Dunvegan Avenue, Kirkcaldy KY2 5SG — 01592 620053
Reid, Martin R.B.C. BD	1960	1990	(Falkirk West)	13 Rothes Park, Leslie, Glenrothes KY6 3LL — 01334 473406
Simpson, Gordon M. MA BD	1959	1996	(Leslie Trinity)	37 Spottiswoode Gardens, St Andrews KY16 8SA — 01592 205510
Sutherland, William	1964	1993	(Bo'ness Old)	88 Dunrobin Road, Kirkcaldy KY2 5YT — 01592 741009
Taylor, John T.H.	1947	1983	(Glenrothes Christ's Kirk on the Green)	9 Douglas Road, Leslie, Glenrothes KY6 3JZ — 01337 857431
Thomson, Gilbert L. BA	1965	1996	(Glenrothes Christ's Kirk)	3 Fortharfield, Freuchie, Cupar KY15 7JJ — 01592 873616
Webster, Elspeth H. (Miss) DCS			(Deaconess)	82 Broomhill Avenue, Burntisland KY3 0BP — 01337 840646
Young, W. Finlayson MA	1943	1979	(Kinglassie)	17 Whitecraig Road, Newburgh, Cupar KY14 6BP

KIRKCALDY ADDRESSES

Abbotshall	Abbotshall Road	St Andrew's	Victoria Road x Victoria Gdns	Templehall	Beauly Place
Linktown	Nicol Street x High Street	St Bryce Kirk	St Brycedale Avenue x Kirk Wynd	Torbain	Lindores Drive
Old	Kirk Wynd	St John's	Elgin Street	Viewforth	Viewforth Street x Viewforth
Pathhead	Harriet Street x Church Street			Terrace	

(26) ST ANDREWS

Meets alternately at Cupar, in St John's Church Hall, and at St Andrews, in Martyrs Church Hall, on the second Wednesday of February, March, April, May, September, October, November and December, and on the last Wednesday of June.

| Clerk: | REV. PETER MEAGER MA BD CertMgmt | | 7 Lorraine Drive, Cupar KY15 5DY | 01334 656991 |
| | | | [E-mail: akph74@uk.uumail.com] | |

Abdie and Dunbog (H) linked with Newburgh (H)

| Lynn Brady (Miss) BD DipMin | 1996 | 2002 | 2 Guthrie Court, Cupar Road, Newburgh, Cupar KY14 6HA | 01337 842228 |
| | | | [E-mail: lynn@revbrady.freeserve.co.uk] | |

Anstruther

| Ian A. Cathcart BSc BD | 1994 | | The James Melville Manse, Anstruther KY10 3EX | 01333 311808 |

Auchtermuchty (H)

| Ann G. Fraser (Mrs) BD CertMin | 1990 | | 2 Burnside, Auchtermuchty, Cupar KY14 7AJ | 01337 828519 |
| | | | [E-mail: anngilfraser@bushinternet.com] | |

Balmerino (H) linked with Wormit (H)

| Graeme W. Beebee BD | 1993 | | 5 Westwater Place, Newport-on-Tay DD6 8NS | 01382 542626 |
| | | | [E-mail: beebees@btinternet.com] | |

Boarhills and Dunino linked with St Andrews Martyrs'

| J. Mary Henderson (Miss) MA BD DipEd PhD | 1990 | 2000 | 49 Irvine Crescent, St Andrews KY16 8LG | 01334 472948 |
| | | | [E-mail: jmh@smokeypuss.freeserve.co.uk] | |

Cameron linked with St Andrews: St Leonard's

| Alan D. McDonald LLB BD MTh | 1979 | 1998 | 1 Cairnhill Gardens, St Andrews KY16 8UR | 01334 472793 |
| | | | [E-mail: alan.d.mcdonald@talk21.com] | |

Carnbee linked with Pittenweem

| Charles G. Thrower BSc | 1965 | 1970 | The Manse, 2 Milton Place, Pittenweem, Anstruther KY10 2LR | 01333 311255 |
| | | | [E-mail: c-thrower@pittenweem2.freeserve.co.uk] | |

Cellardyke (H) linked with Kilrenny
David J.H. Laing BD DPS — 1976 — 1999
Toll Road, Cellardyke, Anstruther KY10 3BH
[E-mail: davith@v21mail.co.uk]
01333 310810

Ceres and Springfield
Matthew Z. Ross LLB BD FSAScot — 1998
The Manse, St Andrews Road, Ceres, Cupar KY15 5NQ
[E-mail: matthewross@beeb.net]
01334 828233 (Tel/Fax)
07050 191367 (Mbl)

Crail linked with Kingsbarns (H)
Vacant
Church Manse, St Andrews Road, Crail, Anstruther KY10 3UH
01333 450358

Creich, Flisk and Kilmany linked with Monimail
Mitchell Collins BD CPS — 1996
Creich Manse, Brunton, Cupar KY15 4PA
[E-mail: chellc@care4free.net]
01337 870332

Cupar: Old (H) and St Michael of Tarvit
Kenneth S. Jeffrey BA BD PhD — 2002
76 Hogarth Drive, Cupar KY15 5YH
[E-mail: ksjeffrey@btopenworld.com]
01334 653196

Cupar: St John's
Vacant
23 Hogarth Drive, Cupar KY15 5YH
01334 655851

Dairsie linked with Kemback linked with Strathkinness (H)
Alexander Strickland JP LTh — 1971 — 1981
Dairsie Manse, Dairsie, Cupar KY15 4RS
01334 653283

Edenshead and Strathmiglo
Thomas G.M. Robertson LTh — 1971 — 1984
The Manse, Strathmiglo, Cupar KY14 7QD
01337 860256

Elie (H) linked with Kilconquhar and Colinsburgh (H)
Iain F. Paton BD FCIS — 1980 — 1998
30 Bank Street, Elie, Leven KY9 1BW
[E-mail: iain-paton@tesco.net]
01333 330685

Falkland (01337 858442) linked with Freuchie (H)
John W. Jarvie BD CertMin MTh — 1990
1 Newton Road, Falkland, Cupar KY15 7AQ
[E-mail: jarvie@cwcom.net]
01337 857696

Freuchie (H) See Falkland

Howe of Fife
Marion J. Paton (Miss) BMus BD — 1991 — 1994
83 Church Street, Ladybank, Cupar KY15 7ND
[E-mail: marion@marionpaton.f9.co.uk]
01337 830513

Kemback See Dairsie
Kilconquhar and Colinsburgh See Elie

Kilrenny See Cellardyke
Kingsbarns See Crail

Largo and Newburn (H) linked with Largo St David's   1988
Rosemary Frew (Mrs) MA BD   The Manse, Church Place, Upper Largo, Leven KY8 6EH   01333 360286
[E-mail: rosemaryfrew@breathemail.net]

Largo St David's See Largo and Newburn

Largoward linked with St Monans (H)   2001
Donald G. MacEwan MA BD PhD   The Manse, St Monans, Anstruther KY10 2DD   01333 730258
[E-mail: maiadona@fish.co.uk]

Leuchars: St Athernase
Vacant   7 David Wilson Park, Balmullo, St Andrews KY16 0NP   01334 870038

Monimail See Creich, Flisk and Kilmany
Newburgh See Abdie and Dunbog

Newport-on-Tay (H)   1994
W. Kenneth Pryde DA BD   57 Cupar Road, Newport-on-Tay DD6 8DF   01382 543165 (Tel/Fax)
[E-mail: wkpryde@aol.com]

Pittenweem See Carnbee

St Andrews: Holy Trinity   1939 1949
Charles Armour MA   17 Queen's Gardens, St Andrews KY16 9TA   01334 474494

St Andrews: Hope Park (H)   1971 1996
A. David K. Arnott MA BD   20 Priory Gardens, St Andrews KY16 8XX   01334 472912 (Tel/Fax)
[E-mail: adka@st-andrews.ac.uk]

St Andrews: Martyrs' (H) See Boarhills and Dunino
St Andrews: St Leonard's (H) See Cameron
St Monans See Largoward
Strathkinness See Dairsie

Tayport   1990
Colin J. Dempster BD   27 Bell Street, Tayport DD6 9AP   01382 552861
[E-mail: demps@tayportc.fsnet.co.uk]

Wormit See Balmerino

Name		Ord	Ind	Address	Tel
Alexander, James S. MA BD BA PhD	University of St Andrews	1966	1973	5 Strathkinness High Road, St Andrews KY16 9RP	01334 472680
Bennett, Alestair TD MA	(Strathkinness)	1938	1976	7 Bonfield Park, Strathkinness, St Andrews KY16 9SY	01334 850249
Best, Ernest MA BD PhD DD	(University of Glasgow)	1949	1982	13 Newmill Gardens, St Andrews KY16 8RY	01334 473315
Bews, James MA	(Dundee Craigiebank)	1942	1981	21 Balrymonth Court, St Andrews KY16 8XT	01334 476087
Bogie, A.P. MA FSAScot	(Forgan)	1944	1979	7 Gourlay Wynd, St Andrews KY16 8HP	
Bradley, Ian MA BD DPhil	Lecturer: University of Aberdeen	1990	1990	4 Donaldson Gardens, St Andrews KY16 9DN	01334 475389
Brown, Lawson R. MA	(Cameron with St Andrew's St Leonard's)	1960	1997	10 Park Street, St Andrews KY16 8AQ	01334 473413
Buchan, Alexander MA BD	(North Ronaldsay with Sanday)	1975	1992	26 Allan Robertson Drive, St Andrews KY16 8EY	01334 473875
Buchan, Isabel C. (Mrs) BSc BD		1975		26 Allan Robertson Drive, St Andrews KY16 8EY	01334 473875
Cameron, James K. MA BD PhD FRHistS	(University of St Andrews)	1953	1989	Priorscroft, 71 Hepburn Gardens, St Andrews KY16 9LS	01334 473996
Casebow, Brian C. MA BD	(Edinburgh: Salisbury)	1959	1993	'The Rowans', 67 St Michael's Drive, Cupar KY15 5BP	01334 656385
Douglas, J.D. MA BD PhD		1957		2 Doocot Road, St Andrews KY16 8QP	01334 474876
Douglas, Peter C. JP	(Boarhills linked with Dunino)	1966	1993	The Old Schoolhouse, Flisk, Newburgh, Cupar KY14 6HN	01337 870218
Earnshaw, Philip BA BSc BD	(Glasgow: Pollokshields)	1986	1996	22 Castle Street, St Monans, Anstruther KY10 2AP	01333 730640
Edington, George L.	(Tayport)	1952	1989	64B Burghmuir Road, Perth PH1 1LH	
Fairlie, George BD BVMS MRCVS	(Crail with Kingsbarns)	1971	2002	41 Warrack Street, St Andrews KY18 8DR	01334 475868
Galloway, Robert W.C. LTh	(Cromarty)	1970	1998	22 Haughgate, Leven KY8 4SG	
Gibson, Henry M. MA BD PhD	(Dundee: The High Kirk)	1960	1999	4 Comerton Place, Drumoig, Leuchars, St Andrews KY16 0NQ	01382 542199
Gordon, Fiona S. (Mrs) DCS	(Deacon)			3 Cupar Road, Cupamuir, Cupar KY15 5RH	01334 652341
Gordon, Peter M. MA BD	(Airdrie West)	1958	1995	3 Cupar Road, Cupamuir, Cupar KY15 5RH [E-mail: machrie@madasafish.com]	01334 652341
Henney, William MA DD	(St Andrews Hope Park)	1957	1996	46 Hepburn Gardens, St Andrews KY16 9DF	01334 472560
Hill, Roy MA	(Lisbon)	1962	1997	Forgan Cottage, Kinnessburn Road, St Andrews KY16 8AO	01334 472121
Howieson, R.A. JP MA	(Newport-on-Tay St Thomas's)	1937	1977	3 Baker Lane, St Andrews KY16 9PJ	01334 473711
Kinnis, Robert L. MA BD	(Baillieston Mure Memorial)	1931	1972	Gibson House, St Andrews KY16 9JE	
Law, Arthur ACIB	(Kincardine in Menteith with Norrieston)	1968	1988	13 South Road, Cupar KY15 5JF	
Learmonth, Walter LTh	(Ceres with Springfield)	1968	1997	14 Marionfield Place, Cupar KY15 5JN	01334 654213
Lithgow, Thomas MA	(Banchory Devenick with Maryculter)	1945	1982	124 Balgarvie Crescent, Cupar KY15 4EG	01334 656290
McCartney, Alexander C. BTh	(Caputh and Clunie with Kinclaven)	1973	1995	10 The Glebe, Crail, Anstruther KY10 3UT	01334 655537
McFadyen, Gavin J.	(Whiteinch)	1963	1992	62 Toll Court, Lundin Links, Leven KY8 6HH	01333 451194
McGregor, Duncan J. FIMA	(Channelkirk with Lauder Old)	1982	1996	14 Mount Melville, St Andrews KY16 8NG	01333 320434
Macintyre, William J. MA BD DD	(Crail with Kingsbarns)	1951	1989	Tigh a' Ghobhainn, Lochton, Crail, Anstruther KY10 3XE	01334 478314 / 01333 450327
McKane, William MA PhD DLitt DD FBA	(University of St Andrews)	1949	1990	51 Irvine Crescent, St Andrews KY16 8LG	01334 473797
Mackenzie, A. Cameron MA	(Biggar)	1955	1995	Hedgerow, 5 Shiels Avenue, Freuchie, Cupar KY15 7JD	01337 857763
Mackenzie, J.A.R. MA	(Largo St David's)	1947	1987	8 Albert Street, Nairn IV12 4HP	01667 452827
MacNab, Hamish S.D. MA	(Kilrenny)	1948	1987	Fairhill, Northmuir, Kirriemuir DD8 4PF	01575 72564
McPhail, Peter MA BD	(Creich, Flisk and Kilmany)	1940	1982	44 Doocot Road, St Andrews KY16 8QP	01334 473093
Meager, Peter MA BD CertMgmt(Open)	(Elie with Kilconquhar and Colinsburgh)	1971	1998	7 Lorraine Drive, Cupar KY15 5DY [E-mail: akph74@uk.uumail.com]	01334 656991
Nicol, Robert M.	(Jersey: St Columba's)	1984	1996	35 Upper Greens, Auchtermuchty, Cupar KY14 7BX	01337 828327
Ord, J.K.	(Falkirk Condorrat)	1963		24 Forth Street, St Monance, Anstruther KY10 2AX	01333 730461

Name			Charge / Note	Address	Tel
Patterson, John W. BA BD	1948	1989	(St Andrews Martyrs)	34 Claybraes, St Andrews KY16 8RS	01334 473606
Portcmouth, Roland John NDD ATD	1980	1989	(Bendochy)	1 West Braes, Pittenweem, Anstruther KY10 2PS	01333 311448
Porteous, James K. DD	1944	1997	(Cupar St John's)	16 Market Street, St Andrews KY16 9NS	
Robb, Nigel J. FCP MA BD ThM MTh	1981	1998	Director of Educational Services, Board of Ministry	c/o 121 George Street, Edinburgh EH2 4YN [E-mail: nrobb@cofscotland.org.uk]	0131-225 5722
Robertson, Norma P. (Miss) BD	1993	2002	(Kincardine O'Neil with Lumphanan)	82 Hogarth Drive, Cupar KY15 5YU [E-mail: normapr@fish.co.uk]	01334 650595
Roy, Alan J. BSc BD	1960	1999	(Aberuthven with Dunning)	14 Comerton Place, Drumoig, Leuchars, St Andrews KY16 0NQ [E-mail: a.r.roy@ondigital.com]	01382 542225
Salters, Robert B. MA BD PhD	1966	1971	(University of St Andrews)	Vine Cottage, 119 South Street, St Andrews KY16 9UH	01334 473198
Scott, J. Miller MA BD FSAScot DD	1949	1988	(Jerusalem)	St Martins, 6 Trinity Place, St Andrews KY16 8SG	01334 479518
Shaw, Duncan LTh CPS	1984		Chaplain: RAF	Chaplain's Office, RAF Leuchars, St Andrews KY16 0JX	
Shaw, D.W.D. BA BD LLB WS DD	1960	1990	(University of St Andrews)	4/13 Succoth Court, Edinburgh EH12 6BZ	0131-337 2130
Sinclair, David I. BSc BD PhD DipSW	1990	1998	Secretary: Church and Nation Committee	42 South Road, Cupar KY15 5JF	01334 656957
Spowart, Mary G. (Mrs)	1978	1991	(Papa Westray with Westray)	Aldersyde, St Abbs Road, Coldingham, Eyemouth TD14 5NR	01890 771697
Stevenson A.L. LLB MLitt DPA FPEA	1984	1993	(Balmerino linked with Wormit)	41 Main Street, Dairsie, Cupar KY15 4SR	01334 870582
Stoddart, David L.	1961	1987	(Laggan with Newtonmore)	3 Castle Street, Anstruther KY10 3DD	01333 310668
Strong, Clifford LTh	1983	1995	(Creich, Flisk and Kilmany with Monimail)		
Taylor, Ian BSc MA LTh DipEd	1983	1997	(Abdie and Dunbog with Newburgh)	60 Maryknowe, Gauldry, Newport-on-Tay DD6 8SL	01382 330445
Thomson, P.G. MA BD MTh ThD	1947	1989	(Irvine Fullarton)	Lundie Cottage, Arncroach, Anstruther KY10 2RN	01333 720222
Torrance, Alan J. MA BD DrTheol	1984	1999	University of St Andrews	Fullarton, 2 Beech Walk, Crail, Anstruther KY10 3UN	01333 450423
				Kincaple House, Kincaple, St Andrews KY16 9SH	(Home) 01334 850755 (Office) 01334 462843
Turnbull, James J. MA	1940	1981	(Arbirlot with Colliston)	Woodlands, Beech Avenue, Ladybank, Cupar KY15 7NG	01337 830279
Walker, James B. MA BD DPhil	1975	1993	Chaplain: University of St Andrews	1 Gillespie Terrace, The Scores, St Andrews KY16 9AT [E-mail: jbw1@st-andrews.ac.uk]	(Tel) 01334 477471 (Fax) 01334 462697
Whyte, James A. MA LLD DD DUniv	1945	1987	(University of St Andrews)	13 Hope Street, St Andrews KY16 9HJ	01334 472323
Wilson, Robert McL. MA BD PhD DD FBA	1946	1983	(University of St Andrews)	10 Murrayfield Road, St Andrews KY16 9NB	01334 474331
Wright, Lynda (Miss) BEd DCS			Deacon: Retreat Leader, Key House	6 Key Cottage, High Street, Falkland, Cupar KY15 7BD	01337 857705

(27) DUNKELD AND MEIGLE

Meets at Pitlochry on the first Tuesday of September and December, on the third Tuesday of February, April and October, and at the Moderator's Church on the third Tuesday of June.

Clerk:	**REV. JOHN RUSSELL MA**	**Kilblaan, Gladstone Terrace, Birnam, Dunkeld PH8 0DP** **01350 728896**
		[E-mail: akph47@uk.uumail.com]

Aberfeldy (H) linked with Amulree and Strathbraan linked with Dull and Weem

Alexander M. Gunn MA BD	1967	1986	Taybridge Terrace, Aberfeldy PH15 2BS	01887 820656 (Tel/Fax)
			[E-mail: sandy@aberfeldypc.co.uk]	

Alyth (H)
Neil N. Gardner MA BD 1991 1998 Cambridge Street, Alyth, Blairgowrie PH11 8AW 01828 632104
[E-mail: nng@surfaid.org]

Amulree and Strathbraan See Aberfeldy

Ardler, Kettins and Meigle
Linda Stewart BD 2001 The Manse, Dundee Road, Meigle, Blairgowrie PH12 8SB 01828 640278

Bendochy linked with Coupar Angus Abbey
Bruce Dempsey BD 1997 Caddam Road, Coupar Angus, Blairgowrie PH13 9EF 01828 627331

Blair Atholl and Struan linked with Tenandry
Brian Ian Murray BD 2002 Blair Atholl, Pitlochry PH18 5SX 01796 481213
[E-mail: ian.murray@pgen.net]

Blairgowrie
Donald Macleod BD LRAM DRSAM 1987 2002 The Manse, Upper David Street, Blairgowrie PH10 6HB 01250 872146

Braes of Rannoch linked with Foss and Rannoch (H)
David G. Hamilton MA BD 1971 1998 Kinloch Rannoch, Pitlochry PH16 5QA 01882 632381
[E-mail: davidhamilton@onetel.net.uk]

Caputh and Clunie (H) linked with Kinclaven (H) (T)
Linda J. Broadley (Mrs) LTh DipEd 1996 Caputh Manse, Caputh, Perth PH1 4JH 01738 710520

Coupar Angus Abbey See Bendochy
Dull and Weem See Aberfeldy

Dunkeld (H)
R. Fraser Penny BA BD 1984 2001 Cathedral Manse, Dunkeld PH8 0AW 01350 727249
[E-mail: fraserpenn@aol.com]

Fortingall and Glenlyon linked with Kenmore and Lawers
Anne J. Brennan BSc BD MTh 1999 The Manse, Balnaskeag, Kenmore, Aberfeldy PH15 2HB 01887 830218
[E-mail: annebrennan@yahoo.co.uk]

Foss and Rannoch See Braes of Rannoch

Grantully, Logierait and Strathtay
Christine M. Creegan (Mrs) MTh 1993 2000 The Manse, Strathtay, Pitlochry PH9 0PG 01887 840251
[E-mail: christine@creegans.co.uk]

Kenmore and Lawers (H) See Fortingall and Glenlyon
Kinclaven See Caputh and Clunie

Kirkmichael, Straloch and Glenshee linked with Rattray (H) 1969 1998
Hugh C. Ormiston BSc BD MPhil PhD   The Manse, Alyth Road, Rattray, Blairgowrie PH10 7HF   01250 872462
[E-mail: hugh@ormistonh.fsnet.co.uk]

Pitlochry (H) (01796 472160)
Malcolm Ramsay BA LLB DipMin   1986 1998   Manse Road, Moulin, Pitlochry PH16 5EP   01796 472774
[E-mail: amramsay@aol.com]

Rattray See Kirkmichael Straloch and Glenshee

Tenandry See Blair Atholl and Struan

Name			(Charge)	Address	Phone
Barbour, Robin A.S. KCVO MC BD STM DD	1954	1982	(University of Aberdeen)	Fincastle, Pitlochry PH16 5RJ	01796 473209
Cassells, Alexander K. MA BD	1961	1997	(Leuchars St Athernase and Guardbridge)	Tighaness, Keltney Burn, Aberfeldy PH15 2LS	01887 830758
Dick, Tom MA	1951	1990	(Dunkeld)	Mo Dhachaidh, Callybrae, Dunkeld PH8 0EP	01350 727338
Duncan, James BTh FSAScot	1980	1995	(Blair Atholl and Struan)	25 Knockard Avenue, Pitlochry PH16 5JE	01796 474096
Forsyth, David Stuart MA	1948	1992	(Belhelvie)	Birchlea, 38 Fonab Crescent, Pitlochry PH16 5SR	01796 473708
Fulton, Frederick H. MA	1942	1983	(Clunie, Lethendy and Kinloch)	Grampian Cottage, Chapel Brae, Braemar, Ballater AB35 5YT	01339 741277
Grieve, David S.A. MA BD	1954	1991	(Arbirlot with Carmyllie with Colliston)	Dundarroch, Meigle Road, Alyth, Blairgowrie PH11 8EU	01828 632318
Henderson, John D. MA BD	1953	1992	(Cluny with Monymusk)	Aldersyde, George Street, Blairgowrie PH10 6HP	01250 875181
Knox, John W. MTheol	1992	1997	(Lochgelly: Macainsh)	Heatherlea, Main Street, Ardler, Blairgowrie PH12 8SR	01828 640731
Low, J.E. Stewart MA	1957	1997	(Tarbat)	47 Tay Avenue, Comrie, Crieff PH6 2PF	01764 679182
McAlister, D.J.B. MA BD PhD	1951	1989	(North Berwick Blackadder)	2 Duff Avenue, Moulin, Pitlochry PH16 5EN	01796 473591
Macdonald, James F. TD	1930	1984	(Bendochy with Kinclaven)	6 Cluny Court, Grant Road, Blairgowrie PH10 6PU	01250 875737
Macpherson, Norman J. TD	1954	1980	(Blairgowrie St Mary's South)	31 Glenburn Drive, Inverness IV2 4NE	01463 230536
MacVicar, Kenneth MBE DFC TD MA	1950	1990	(Kenmore with Lawers with Fortingall & Glenlyon)	Illeray, Kenmore, Aberfeldy PH15 2HE	01887 830514
Martin, Francis BL	1956	1991	(Pitlochry East)	58 West Moulin Road, Pitlochry PH16 5EQ	01796 472619
Robertson, Iain M. MA	1967	1992	(Carriden)	St Colme's, Perth Road, Birnam, Dunkeld PH8 0BH	01350 727455
Robertson, Matthew LTh	1968	2002	(Cawdor with Croy and Dalcross)	Inver, Strathtay, Pitlochry PH9 0PG	01887 840780
Russell, John MA	1959	2000	(Tillicoultry)	Kilblaan, Gladstone Terrace, Birnam, Dunkeld PH8 0DP	01350 728896
Shannon, W.G.H. MA BD	1955	1998	(Pitlochry)	19 Knockard Road, Pitlochry PH16 5HJ	01796 473533
Stewart, Walter T.A.	1964	1999	(Barry)	7A Tummel Crescent, Pitlochry PH16 5DF	01796 473422
Tait, Thomas W. BD	1972	1997	(Rattray)	20 Cedar Avenue, Blairgowrie PH10 6TT	01250 874833
White, Brock A. LTh	1971	2001	(Kirkcaldy: Templehall)	1 Littlewood Gardens, Blairgowrie PH10 6XZ	01250 870399
Young, G. Stuart	1961	1996	(Blairgowrie: St Andrew's)	7 James Place, Stanley, Perth PH1 4PD	01738 828473

(28) PERTH

Meets at Scone: Old, at 7:00pm, in the Elizabeth Ashton Hall, on the second Tuesday of every month except January, July and August, when there is no meeting, and on the last Tuesday of June, when it meets in the church of the incoming Moderator.

Clerk:	Rev. DEREK G. LAWSON LLB BD		
Presbytery Office:		209 High St, Perth PH1 5PB	01738 **451177** (Tel)
		[E-mail: akph70@uk.uumail.com]	01738 **638226** (Fax)

Abernethy and Dron linked with Arngask
Kenneth G. Anderson MA BD   1967   1988   Abernethy, Perth PH2 9JP   01738 850607

Almondbank Tibbermore
Donald Campbell BD   1998   Pitcairngreen, Perth PH1 3LT   01738 583217
[E-mail: revdonaldcampbell@btinternet.com]

Ardoch (H) linked with Blackford (H)
Hazel Wilson (Ms) MA BD DipEd DMS   1991   Braco, Dunblane FK15 9RE   01786 880217
[E-mail: hazel@feddal.freeserve.co.uk]

Arngask See Abernethy and Dron

Auchterarder (H)
Michael R.R. Shewan MA BD CPS   1985   1998   24 High Street, Auchterarder, Perth PH3 1DF   01764 662210

Auchtergaven and Moneydie
William McGregor LTh   1987   Bankfoot, Perth PH1 4BS   01738 787235
[E-mail: bill.mcgregor@ukonline.co.uk]

Blackford See Ardoch

Cargill Burrelton linked with Collace
Vacant   Woodside, Blairgowrie PH13 9NQ   01828 670352

Cleish (H) linked with Fossoway St Serf's and Devonside
A. David Macleod MA BD   1993   1994   Cleish, Kinross KY13 7LR   01577 850231 (Tel/Fax)
[E-mail: cleishrev@hotmail.com]

Collace See Cargill and Burrelton

Comrie (H) linked with Dundurn (H)
P.D. Thomson MA BD — 1968 1978 — Comrie, Crieff PH6 2HE
[E-mail: revpdt@the-manse.freeserve.co.uk] — 01764 670269

Crieff (H)
James W. MacDonald BD — 1976 2002 — 8 Strathearn Terrace, Crieff PH7 3AQ — 01764 653907

Dunbarney (H) linked with Forgandenny
W. Duncan Stenhouse MA BD — 1989 — Dunbarney Manse, Bridge of Earn, Perth PH2 9DY
[E-mail: duncan@stenhouse58.freeserve.co.uk] — 01738 812463

Dundurn See Comrie

Errol (H) linked with Kilspindie and Rait
John M. Pickering BSc BD DipEd — 1997 — Errol, Perth PH2 7PZ
[E-mail: john.m.pickering@talk21.com] — 01821 642279

Forgandenny See Dunbarney
Fossoway St Serf's and Devonside See Cleish

Fowlis Wester linked with Madderty linked with Monzie
Alexander F. Bonar LTh LRIC — 1988 1996 — Beechview, Abercairney, Crieff PH7 3NF
[E-mail: sandy.bonar@btinternet.com] — 01764 652116

Gask (H) linked with Methven and Logiealmond (H)
Brian Bain LTh — 1980 1986 — Methven, Perth PH1 3QD
[E-mail: brian@methvenmanse.freeserve.co.uk] — 01738 840274 (Tel/Fax)

Kilspindie and Rait See Errol

Kinross (H)
John P.L. Munro MA BD PhD — 1977 1998 — 15 Station Road, Kinross KY13 8TG
[E-mail: john@lochleven.freeserve.co.uk] — 01577 862952

Madderty See Fowlis Wester
Methven and Logiealmond See Gask
Monzie See Fowlis Wester

Muthill (H) linked with Trinity Gask and Kinkell
John Oswald BSc PhD BD — 1997 2002 — Muthill, Crieff PH5 2AR
[E-mail: revdocoz@bigfoot.com] — 01764 681205

Orwell (H) linked with Portmoak (H)
Vacant — 3 Perth Road, Milnathort, Kinross KY13 9XU — 01577 863461

Perth: Craigie (H)
William Thomson — 2001 — 46 Abbot Street, Perth PH2 0EE — 01738 623748

Perth: Kinnoull (H)
David I. Souter BD — 1996 — 2001 — 1 Mount Tabor Avenue, Perth PH2 7BT [E-mail: d.souter@virgin.net] — 01738 626046

Perth: Letham St Mark's (H)
James C. Stewart BD DipMin — 1997 — 35 Rose Crescent, Perth PH1 1NT [E-mail: jimstewartrev@lineone.net] — 01738 624167
Kenneth McKay DCS — 11F Balgowan Road, Perth PH1 2JG — 01738 621169

Perth: Moncreiffe (T)
Isobel Birrell (Mrs) BD — 1994 — 1999 — Rhynd Road, Perth PH2 8PT [E-mail: isobel.birrell3@ntlworld.com] — 01738 625694

Perth: North (01738 622298)
David W. Denniston BD DipMin — 1981 — 1996 — 127 Glasgow Road, Perth PH2 0LU [E-mail: david.denniston@virgin.net] — 01738 625728
Brian R. Hendrie BD (Assoc) — 1992 — 2000 — 98 Duncansby Way, Perth PH1 5XF [E-mail: brianandyvonne@98duncansby.freeserve.uk] — 01738 441029

Perth: Riverside (New Charge Development)
Alfred G. Drummond BD — 1991 — 2000 — 44 Hay Street, Perth PH1 5HS [E-mail: ncdriverside@uk.uumail.com] — 01738 621305
John Buchanan DCS — 22 Brora Court, North Muirton, Perth PH1 3DQ — 01738 631697

Perth: St John the Baptist's (H) (01738 626159)
David D. Ogston MA BD — 1970 — 1980 — 15 Comely Bank, Perth PH2 7HU [E-mail ogston@cwcom.net] — 01738 621755
Elizabeth Brown (Mrs) SRN (Aux) — 1996 — 25 Highfield Road, Scone, Perth PH2 6RN — 01738 552391 (Tel/Fax)

Perth: St Leonard's-in-the-Fields and Trinity (H) (01738 632238)
Gilbert C. Nisbet CA BD — 1993 — 2000 — 5 Strathearn Terrace, Perth PH2 0LS [E-mail: gcnisbet@stleonardsmanse.fsnet.co.uk] — 01738 621709

Perth: St Matthew's (Office: 01738 636757; Vestry: 01738 630725)
Ewen J. Gilchrist BD DipMin DipComm — 1982 — 1988 — 23 Kincarrathie Crescent, Perth PH2 7HH [E-mail: ewen.gilchrist@st-matthews.org.uk] — 01738 626828

Portmoak See Orwell

Redgorton linked with Stanley
Derek G. Lawson LLB BD   1998   22 King Street, Stanley, Perth PH1 4ND   01738 828247
[E-mail: lawson@stanley9835.freeserve.co.uk]

St Madoes and Kinfauns
Marc F. Bircham BD MTh   2000   Glencarse, Perth PH2 7NF   01738 860837
[E-mail: mf.bircham@virgin.net]

St Martin's linked with Scone New (H) (01738 553900)
Robert Sloan BD   1997   2001   24 Victoria Road, Scone, Perth PH2 6JW   01738 551467
[E-mail: robertsloan@lineone.net]

Scone: New See St Martin's

Scone: Old (H)
J. Bruce Thomson JP MA BD   1972   1983   Burnside, Scone, Perth PH2 6LP   01738 552030
[E-mail: jock.tamson@talk21.com]

Stanley See Redgorton

The Stewartry of Strathearn (H) (Tel: 01738 621674; Fax: 01738 643321; E-mail: stewartry@beeb.net)
Colin R. Williamson LLB BD   1972   2000   Aberdalgie, Perth PH2 0QD   01738 625854
[E-mail: stewartry@beeb.net]

Trinity Gask and Kinkell See Muthill

Alexander, William M. BD	1971	1998	(Berriedale and Dunbeath with Latheron)	23 Muirend Avenue, Perth PH1 1JL	01738 451190
Barr, George K. ARIBA BD PhD	1967	1993	(Uddingston: Viewpark)	7 Tay Avenue, Comrie, Crieff PH6 2PE	01764 670454
				[E-mail: gbarr2@compuserve.com]	
Barr, T. Leslie LTh	1969	1997	(Kinross)	8 Fairfield Road, Kelty KY4 0BY	01383 839330
Bartholomew, Julia (Mrs) BSc BD	2002		Auchterarder: Associate	Kippenhill, Dunning, Perth PH2 0RA	01764 684929
Bertram, Thomas A.	1972	1995	(Patna Waterside)	3 Scrimgeours Corner, 29 West High Street, Crieff PH7 4AP	01764 652066
Birrell, John M. MA LLB BD	1974	1996	Hospital Chaplain: Perth Royal Infirmary	Rhynd Road, Perth PH2 8QL	01738 625694
				[E-mail: john.birrell@tuht.scot.nhs.uk]	
Bonomy, William MA BD	1946	1987	(Inverkip)	Viewlands House, Viewlands Road, Perth PH1 1BL	
Brown, R. Russell MA	1940	1986	(Perth Kinnoull)	Viewlands House, Viewlands Road, Perth PH1 1BL	01738 632469
Buchan, William DipTheol BD	1987	2001	(Kilwinning Abbey)	34 Bridgewater Avenue, Auchterarder PH3 1DQ	01764 660306
Carr, W. Stanley MA	1951	1991	(Largs: St Columba's)	16 Gannochy Walk, Perth PH2 7LW	01738 627422
Cowie, J.L. MA	1950	1977	(Edinburgh: Richmond Craigmillar)	16 Curate Wynd, Kinross KY13 7DX	01577 864762
Denniston, Jane	2002		Board of Parish Education	127 Glasgow Road, Perth PH2 0LU	01738 565379
Donaldson, Robert B. BSocSc	1953	1997	(Kilchoman with Portnahaven)	11 Strathearn Court, Crieff PH7 3DS	01764 654976
Ferguson, John F. MA BD	1987	2001	(Perth: Kinnoull)	71 Burghmuir Road, Perth PH1 1LH	01738 561945
Fleming, Hamish K. MA	1966	2001	(Banchory Ternan East)	36 Earnmuir Road, Comrie, Crieff PH6 2EY	01764 679178
Galbraith, W. James L. BSc BD MICE	1973	1996	(Kilchrenan and Dalavich with Muckairn)	19 Mayfield Gardens, Kinross KY13 7GD	01577 863887

Name			Description	Address	Phone
Gordon, Elinor J. (Miss) BD	1988	2001	Board of World Mission	McPhail Flat, 14 Thirlestane Road, Edinburgh EH9 1AN	0131-447 5060
Gregory, J.C. LTh	1968	1992	(Blantyre St Andrew's)	2 Southlands Road, Auchterarder PH3 1BA	01764 664594
Grimson, John A. MA	1950	1986	(Glasgow Wellington: Associate)	29 Highland Road, Turret Park, Crieff PH7 4LE	01764 653063
Halliday, Archibald R. BD	1964	1999	(Duffus with Forres: St Leonard's with Rafford)	2 Pittenzie Place, Crieff PH7 3JL	01764 681275
Henry, Malcolm N. MA BD	1951	1987	(Perth Craigie)	Kelton, Castle Douglas DG7 1RU	01556 504144
Houston, Alexander M.	1939	1977	(Tibbermore)	120 Glasgow Road, Perth PH2 0LU	01738 628056
Hughes, Clifford E. MA BD	1993	2001	(Haddington: St Mary's)	Pavilion Cottage, Briglands, Rumbling Bridge, Kinross KY13 0PS	01577 840506
Kelly, T. Clifford	1973	1995	(Ferintosh)	7 Bankfoot Park, Scotlandwell, Kinross KY13 7JP	01592 840387
Lawson, James B. MA BD	1961	2002	(South Uist)	4 Cowden Way, Comrie, Crieff PH6 2NW	01764 679180
Lawson, Ronald G. MA BD	1964	1999	(Greenock: Wellpark Mid Kirk)	6 East Brougham Street, Stanley, Perth PH1 4NJ	01738 828871
McCormick, Alastair F.	1962	1998	(Creich with Rosehall)	14 Balmanno Park, Bridge of Earn, Perth PH2 9RJ	01738 813588
Macdonald, W.U. JP MA	1939	1984	(Aberdalgie and Dupplin with Forteviot)	30 Muircroft Terrace West, Perth PH1 1DY	01738 627948
MacKenzie, Donald W. MA	1941	1983	(Auchterarder The Barony)	81 Kingswell Terrace, Perth PH1 2DA	01738 633716
MacLean, Nigel R. MA BD	1940	1986	(Perth St Paul's)	9 Hay Street, Perth PH1 5HS	01738 626728
McLeish, D. Nairn MA	1938	1977	(Fisherton)	Wardside House, Muthill, Crieff PH5 2AS	01764 681275
MacMillan, Riada M. (Mrs) BD	1991	1998	(Perth: Craigend Moncreiffe with Rhynd)	73 Muirend Gardens, Perth PH1 1JR	01738 628867
McNaughton, David J.H. BA CA	1976	1995	(Killin and Ardeonaig)	30 Hollybush Road, Crieff PH7 3HB	01764 653028
McPhee, Duncan P.	1951	1980	(Braemar with Crathie: Associate)	Braemar Cottage, Ben Alder Place, Kirkcaldy KY2 5RH	01592 201984
McQuilken, John E. MA BD	1969	1992	(Glenaray and Inveraray)	18 Clark Terrace, Crieff PH7 3QE	01764 655764
Millar, Alexander M. MA BD MBA	1980	2001	Secretary Depute: National Mission	17 Mapledene Road, Scone, Perth PH2 6NX [E-mail: millar@millar62.freeserve.co.uk]	01738 550270
Millar, Archibald E. DipTh	1965	1991	(Perth St Stephen's)	7 Maple Place, Perth PH1 1RT	01738 621813
Ritchie, Bruce BSc BD	1977	2001	Board of World Mission	2 Laurel Avenue, Crieff PH7 3EN [E-mail: brucecrieff@compuserve.com]	01764 652531
Shirra, James MA	1945	1987	(St Martin's with Scone New)	17 Dunbarney Avenue, Bridge of Earn, Perth PH2 9BP	01738 812610
Simpson, James A. BSc BD STM DD	1960	2000	(Dornoch Cathedral)	'Dornoch', Perth Road, Bankfoot, Perth PH1 4ED	01738 787710
Stewart, Anne (Mrs) BD CertMin	1998		Hospital Chaplain	35 Rose Crescent, Perth PH1 1NT	01738 624167
Stewart, Gordon G. MA	1961	2000	(Perth: St Leonard's-in-the-Fields and Trinity)	'Balnoe', South Street, Rattray, Blairgowrie PH10 7BZ	01250 870626
Stewart, Robin J. MA BD STM	1959	1995	(Orwell with Portmoak)	Oakbrae, Perth Road, Murthly, Perth PH1 4HF	01738 710220
Tait, Henry A.G. MA BD	1966	1997	(Crieff: South and Monzievaird)	14 Shieling Hill Place, Crieff PH7 4ER	01764 652325
Taylor, A.H.S. MA BA BD	1957	1992	(Brydekirk with Hoddam)	41 Anderson Drive, Perth PH1 1LF	01738 626579
Whitson, William S. MA	1959	1999	(Cumbernauld: St Mungo's)	2 Chapman's Brae, Bathgate EH48 4LH	

PERTH ADDRESSES

Craigend Moncreiffe	Glenbruar Crescent	North	Mill Street near Kinnoull Street	St Leonard's-in-the-Fields and Trinity	Marshall Place
Craigie	Abbot Street	Riverside	At North Muirton Primary School, Uist Place	St Matthew's	Tay Street
Kinnoull	Dundee Rd near Queen's Bridge	St John's	St John's Street		
Letham St Mark's	Rannoch Road				

(29) DUNDEE

Meets at Dundee, Meadowside St Paul's Church Halls, Nethergate, on the second Wednesday of February, March, May, September, October, November and December, and on the fourth Wednesday of June.

Clerk:	REV. JAMES A. ROY MA BD	[E-mail: akph45@uk.uumail.com]
Presbytery Office:		Nicoll's Lane, Dundee DD2 3HG **01382 611415**

Abernyte linked with Inchture and Kinnaird linked with Longforgan (H)

Diana Hobson (Mrs) BA BD	2002	The Manse, Longforgan, Dundee DD2 5EU	01382 360238
Elizabeth Kay (Miss) DipYCS (Aux)	1993 1999	1 Kintail Walk, Inchture, Perth PH14 9RY	01828 686029
		[E-mail: lizkay@clara.co.uk]	

Auchterhouse (H) linked with Murroes and Tealing (T)

Sydney S. Graham BD DipYL MPhil	1987 1995	The Manse, Balgray, Tealing, Dundee DD4 0QZ	01382 380224
		[E-mail: graythom@sol.co.uk]	
Gordon Campbell MA CDipAF DipHSM (Aux)		2 Falkland Place, Kingoodie, Invergowrie, Dundee DD2 5DY	01382 561383

Dundee: Albany-Butterburn linked with St David's North

Gideon G. Scott MA BD ThM	1963 1973	2 Anstruther Road, Dundee DD4 7EA	01382 456579

Dundee: Balgay (H)

George K. Robson LTh DPS BA	1983 1987	150 City Road, Dundee DD2 2PW	01382 668806
		[E-mail: gkrobson@rev-balgay.freeserve]	

Dundee: Barnhill St Margaret's (H)

Fraser M.C. Stewart BSc BD	1980 2000	The Manse, Invermark Terrace, Broughty Ferry, Dundee DD5 2QU	01382 779278

Dundee: Broughty Ferry East (H) (01382 738264)

Vacant		8 West Queen Street, Broughty Ferry, Dundee DD5 1AR	01382 778972

Dundee: Broughty Ferry St Aidan's (T) (H)

Caroline Jackson (Mrs) MA BD	1995	63 Collingwood Street, Barnhill, Dundee DD5 2UF	01382 736828
		[E-mail: cjackson.aidan@virgin.net]	

Dundee: Broughty Ferry St James' (H)
Vacant
95 Seafield Road, Broughty Ferry, Dundee DD5 3AP   01382 779803

Dundee: Broughty Ferry St Luke's and Queen Street
C. Graham Taylor BSc BD FIAB   2001
22 Albert Road, Broughty Ferry, Dundee DD5 1AZ   01382 779212

Dundee: Broughty Ferry St Stephen's and West (H)
John U. Cameron BA BSc PhD BD ThD   1974
33 Camperdown Street, Broughty Ferry, Dundee DD5 3AA   01382 477403

Dundee: Camperdown (H) (01382 623958)
Vacant
James H. Simpson BSc (Aux)   1996   1999
Camperdown Manse, Myrekirk Road, Dundee DD2 4SF   01382 621383
11 Claypotts Place, Broughty Ferry, Dundee DD5 1LG   01382 776520

Dundee: Chalmers Ardler (H)
Kenneth D. Stott MA BD   1989   1997
The Manse, Turnberry Avenue, Dundee DD2 3TP   01382 827439
[E-mail: arkstott@aol.com]
Jane Martin (Miss) DCS
12A Carnoustie Court, Ardler, Dundee DD2 3RB   01382 813786

Dundee: Clepington linked with Dundee: Fairmuir
Stephen A. Blakey BSc BD   1977   2001
17A Claypotts Road, Broughty Ferry, Dundee DD5 1BS   01382 732221

Dundee: Craigiebank (H) (01382 457951) linked with Douglas and Angus (01382 739884)
Michael V.A. Mair MA BD   1967   1998
244 Arbroath Road, Dundee DD4 7SB   01382 452337
Edith F. McMillan (Mrs) MA BD (Assoc)   1981   1999
19 Americanmuir Road, Dundee DD3 9AA   01382 812423

Dundee: Douglas and Angus (01382 739884) See Dundee: Craigiebank

Dundee: Downfield South (H) (01382 810624)
Lezley J. Kennedy (Mrs) BD ThM MTh   2000
15 Elgin Street, Dundee DD3 8NL   01382 889498

Dundee: Dundee (St Mary's) (H) (01382 226271)
Keith F. Hall MA BD   1980   1994
33 Strathern Road, West Ferry, Dundee DD5 1PP   01382 778808

Dundee: Fairmuir (H) See Dundee: Clepington

Dundee: Lochee Old and St Luke's (T)
Vacant

Dundee: Lochee West
James A. Roy MA BD   1965   1973
Beechwood, 7 Northwood Terrace, Wormit, Newport-on-Tay
DD6 8PP   01382 543578
[E-mail: j.roy@btinternet.com]

Dundee: Logie and St John's Cross (H)
David S. Scott MA BD — 1987 1999 — 7 Hyndford Street, Dundee DD2 1HQ — 01382 641572

Dundee: Mains (H) (01382 812166)
Michael S. Goss BD DPS — 1991 — 9 Elgin Street, Dundee DD3 8NL [E-mail: gossdundee@aol.com] — 01382 825562

Jean Allan (Mrs) DCS — 12C Hindmarsh Avenue, Dundee DD3 7LW — 01382 827299

Dundee: Mains of Fintry (01382 508191)
Vacant — 4 Clive Street, Dundee DD4 7AW — 01382 458629

Dundee: Meadowside St Paul's (H) (01382 225420)
Maudeen I. MacDougall (Miss) BA BD — 1978 — 36 Blackness Avenue, Dundee DD2 1HH — 01382 668828

Dundee: Menzieshill
Harry J. Brown LTh — 1991 1996 — The Manse, Charleston Drive, Dundee DD2 4ED [E-mail: harrybrown@aol.com] — 01382 667446

David Sutherland (Aux) — 6 Cromarty Drive, Dundee DD2 2UQ — 01382 621473
Sarah Hankey (Miss) DCS — 9 Earn Crescent, Dundee DD2 4BS — 01382 641549

Dundee: Mid Craigie (T) (01382 506147)
Vacant — 96 Forfar Road, Dundee DD4 7BG — 01382 453926

Dundee: St Andrew's (H) (01382 224860)
Ian D. Petrie MA BD — 1970 1986 — 77 Blackness Avenue, Dundee DD2 1JN — 01382 641695

Dundee: St David's North See Dundee: Albany Butterburn

Dundee: Steeple (H) (01382 223880)
David M. Clark MA BD — 1989 2000 — 128 Arbroath Road, Dundee DD4 7HR — 01382 455411

Dundee: Stobswell (H)
Jane L. Barron (Mrs) BA DipEd BD MTh — 1999 — 23 Shamrock Street, Dundee DD4 7AH [E-mail: jane.ian@virgin.net] — 01382 459119

Dundee: Strathmartine (H) (01382 825817)
Stewart McMillan BD — 1983 1990 — 19 Americanmuir Road, Dundee DD3 9AA — 01382 812423

Dundee: The High Kirk (H) (01382 224433)
William B. Ross LTh CPS — 1988 2000 — 6 Adelaide Place, Dundee DD3 6LF — 01382 322955

Dundee: Trinity (H) (01382 459997)
Vacant

Dundee: West
Andrew T. Greaves BD   1985   2000   22 Hyndford Street, Dundee DD2 1HX   01382 646586

Dundee: Whitfield (E) (H) (01382 503012) (New Charge Development)
James L. Wilson BD CPS   1986   2001   75 Clepington Road, Dundee DD4 7BJ   01382 457430

Fowlis and Liff linked with Lundie and Muirhead of Liff (H) (01382 580550)
Vacant   149 Coupar Angus Road, Muirhead of Liff, Dundee DD2 5QN   01382 580210

Inchture and Kinnaird See Abernyte

Invergowrie (H)
Robert J. Ramsay LLB NP BD   1986   1997   2 Boniface Place, Invergowrie, Dundee DD2 5DW   01382 561118

Longforgan See Abernyte
Lundie and Muirhead of Liff See Fowlis and Liff

Monifieth: Panmure (H)
David B. Jamieson MA BD STM   1974   8A Albert Street, Monifieth, Dundee DD5 4JS   01382 532772

Monifieth: St Rule's (H)
Robert W. Massie LTh   1989   1999   Church Street, Monifieth, Dundee DD5 4JP   01382 532607
[E-mail: revrwm@lineone.net]

Monifieth: South
Donald W. Fraser MA   1958   1959   Queen Street, Monifieth, Dundee DD5 4HG   01382 532646

Monikie and Newbigging
Gordon R. Mackenzie BScAgr BD   1977   1985   59B Broomwell Gardens, Monikie, Dundee DD5 3QP   01382 370200
[E-mail: grmackenzie@talk21.com]

Murroes and Tealing See Auchterhouse

Barrett, Leslie M. BD FRICS   1991   2001   Chaplain: University of Abertay, Dundee   26 Shoregate, Crail, Anstruther KY10 3SU   01333 451599
[E-mail: leslie@abertay.ac.uk]

Chisholm, W. Douglas MA   1943   1983   (Monifieth North and Newbigging with Monikie)

Clarkson, Robert G.   1950   1989   (Dundee: Strathmartine)   8 Musgrave Road, Chinnor, Oxon OX9 4TF   01844 352029
Craig, Iain R. MA   1948   1988   (Invergowrie)   320 Strathmartine Road, Dundee DD3 8QG   01382 825380
Hope View, Burton Row, Brent Knoll, Highbridge, Somerset TA9 4BX   01278 760719

Craik, Sheila (Mrs) BD   1989   2001   (Dundee: Camperdown)   35 Haldane Terrace, Dundee DD3 0HT

Cramb, Erik M. LTh	1973 1989	Industrial Mission Organiser	65 Clepington Road, Dundee DD4 7BQ [E-mail: erikcramb@aol.com]	01382 458764
Douglas, Fiona C. (Miss) MA BD PhD	1989 1997	Chaplain: University of Dundee	10 Springfield, Dundee DD1 4JE	01382 344157
Gammack, George BD	1985 1999	(Dundee: Whitfield)	13A Hill Street, Broughty Ferry, Dundee DD5 2JP	01382 778636
Hamilton, James BA BD	1939 1982	(Auchterhouse)	Telford House, Blairlogie, Stirling FK9 5PX	01259 761721
Hawdon, John E. BA MTh AICS	1961 1995	(Dundee: Clepington)	22 Rosewood Terrace, Dundee DD2 1NS	01382 646212
Hudson, J. Harrison DipTh MA BD	1961 1999	(Dundee: St Peter's McCheyne)	22 Hamilton Avenue, Tayport DD6 9BW	01382 552052
Ingram, J.R.	1954 1978	(Chaplain: RAF)	48 Marlee Road, Broughty Ferry, Dundee DD5 3EX	01382 736400
Laidlaw, John J. MA	1964 1973	(Adviser in Religious Education)	14 Dalhousie Road, Barnhill, Dundee DD5 2SQ	01382 477458
Mackenzie, George R.R. MA BD	1942 1987	(Dundee: Logie and St John's Cross)	39 Middlebank Crescent, Dundee DD2 1HZ	01382 668491
McLeod, David C. BSc MEng BD	1969 2001	(Dundee: Fairmuir)	6 Carseview Gardens, Dundee DD2 1NE [E-mail: david.mcleod1@tesco.net]	01382 641371
McMillan, Hector G.	1964	(Hamilton North)	6 Kinghorne Terrace, Dundee DD3 6HX	01382 224803
Malvenan, Dorothy DCS	1964 1990	The Deaf Association, Dundee	Flat 19, 6 Craigie Street, Dundee DD4 6PF	01382 462495
Miller, Charles W. MA	1953 1994	(Fowlis and Liff)	'Palm Springs', Parkside, Auchterhouse, Dundee DD3 0RS	01241 856654
Milroy, Tom	1960 1992	(Monifieth: St Rule's)	9 Long Row, Westhaven, Carnoustie DD7 6BE	01382 320407
Mitchell, Jack MA BD CTh	1987 1996	(Dundee: Menzieshill)	10 Invergowrie Drive, Dundee DD2 1RF	01382 642301
Mowat, Gilbert M. MA	1948 1986	(Dundee: Albany-Butterburn)	7 Dunmore Gardens, Dundee DD2 1PP	01382 566013
Powrie, James E. LTh	1969 1995	(Dundee: Chalmers Ardler)	3 Kirktonhill Road, Kirriemuir DD8 4HU	01575 572503
Rae, Robert LTh	1968 1983	Chaplain: Dundee Acute Hospitals	14 Neddertown View, Liff, Dundee DD3 5RU	01382 581790
Robertson, Thomas P.	1963 2001	(Dundee: Broughty Ferry St James')	20 Kilnburn, Newport-on-Tay DD6 8DE	01382 542422
Rogers, James M. BA DB DCult	1955 1996	(Gibraltar)	24 Mansion Drive, Dunclaverhouse, Dundee DD4 9DD	01382 506162
Scroggie, John C.	1951 1985	(Mains)	4 Bell Tree Gardens, Balmossie, Dundee DD5 2LJ	01382 739354
Scoular, Stanley	1963 2000	(Rosyth)	31 Duns Crescent, Dundee DD4 0RY	01382 501653
Smith, Lilian MA DCS		(Deaconess)	6 Fintry Mains, Dundee DD4 9HF	01382 500052

DUNDEE ADDRESSES

Albany Butterburn	2 Hill Street
Balgay	200 Lochee Road
Barnhill St Margaret's	10 Invermark Terrace
Broughty Ferry	
East	370 Queen Street
St Aidan's	408 Brook Street
St James'	5 Fort Street
St Luke's and Queen Street	5 West Queen Street
St Stephen's and West	96 Dundee Road
Camperdown	22 Brownhill Road
Chalmers Ardler	Turnberry Avenue
Clepington	Isla Street x Main Street
Craigiebank	Craigie Avenue at Greendyke Road
Douglas and Angus	Balbeggie Place
Downfield South	Haldane Street off Strathmartine Road
Dundee (St Mary's)	Nethergate
Fairmuir	329 Clepington Road
High Kirk	119A Kinghorne Road
Lochee	
Old and St Luke's	Bright Street, Lochee
West	191 High Street, Lochee
Logie and	
St John's (Cross)	Shaftsbury Rd x Blackness Ave
Mains	Foot of Old Glamis Road
Mains of Fintry	Fintry Road x Fintry Drive
Meadowside St Paul's	114 Nethergate
Menzieshill	Charleston Drive, Lochee
Mid Craigie	Longtown Terrace
St Andrew's	2 King Street
St David's North	273 Strathmore Avenue
Steeple	Nethergate

Stobswell	Top of Albert Street
Strathmartine	513 Strathmartine Road
Trinity	73 Crescent Street
West	130 Perth Road
Whitfield	Haddington Crescent

(30) ANGUS

Meets at Forfar in St Margaret's Church Hall, on the first Tuesday of each month, except June when it meets on the last Tuesday, and January, July and August when there is no meeting.

Clerk: REV. MALCOLM I.G. ROONEY DPE BEd BD
Depute Clerk: MRS HELEN McLEOD MA
Presbytery Office: St Margaret's Church, West High Street, Forfar DD8 1BJ   01307 464224 (Tel)
[E-mail: akph36@uk.uumail.com]   01307 465589 (Fax)

Aberlemno linked with Guthrie and Rescobie
Brian Ramsay BD DPS   1980   1984   The Manse, Guthrie, Forfar DD8 2TP   01241 828243

Airlie Ruthven Kingoldrum linked with Glenisla (H) Kilry Lintrathen
Ben Pieterse BA BTh LTh   2001   Balduff House, Kilry, Blairgowrie PH11 8HS   01575 560260

Arbirlot linked with Carmyllie linked with Colliston
Vacant   The Manse, Arbirlot, Arbroath DD11 2NX   01241 875118

Arbroath: Knox's (H) linked with Arbroath: St Vigeans (H)
Ian G. Gough MA BD MTh   1974   1990   The Manse, St Vigeans, Arbroath DD11 4RD   01241 873206

Arbroath: Old and Abbey (H)
Valerie L. Allen (Miss) BMus MDiv   1990   1996   51 Cliffburn Road, Arbroath DD11 5BA   01241 872196 (Tel/Fax)
[E-mail: vl2allen@aol.com]

Arbroath: St Andrew's (H)
W. Martin Fair BA BD   1992   Albert Street, Arbroath DD11 1RA   01241 873238 (Tel/Fax)
[E-mail: martinfair@aol.com]

Arbroath: St Vigeans See Arbroath: Knox's

Arbroath: West Kirk (H)
Alasdair G. Graham BD DipMin   1981   1986   1 Charles Avenue, Arbroath DD11 2EY   01241 872244
[E-mail: alasdair.graham@lineone.net]

Barry
Wilma Cairns (Miss) BD — 1999 — 41 Corbie Drive, Carnoustie DD7 7NT — 01241 858701

Brechin: Cathedral (H)
Scott Rennie MA BD STM — 1999 — Chanonry Wynd, Brechin DD9 6JS — 01356 622783

Brechin: Gardner Memorial (H)
Moira Herkes (Mrs) BD — 1985 1999 — 36 Park Road, Brechin DD9 7AP — 01356 622789

Carmyllie See Arbirlot

Carnoustie
Vacant — 44 Terrace Road, Carnoustie DD7 7AR — 01241 852289

Carnoustie Panbride
Matthew S. Bicket BD — 1989 — 8 Arbroath Road, Carnoustie DD7 6BL
[E-mail: matthew@bicket.freeserve.co.uk] — 01241 854478 (Tel)
01241 855088 (Fax)

Colliston See Arbirlot

Dun linked with Hillside
Christine Houghton (Mrs) BD — 1997 — 4 Manse Road, Hillside, Montrose DD10 9FB
[E-mail: christinehoughton@hillsidemanse.freeserve.co.uk] — 01674 830288

Dunnichen, Letham and Kirkden
Allan F. Webster MA BD — 1978 1990 — 7 Braehead Road, Letham, Forfar DD8 2PG — 01307 818916

Eassie and Nevay linked with Newtyle
Carleen Robertson (Miss) BD — 1992 — 2 Kirkton Road, Newtyle, Blairgowrie PH12 8TS — 01828 650461

Edzell Lethnot (H) linked with Fern, Careston and Menmuir linked with Glenesk
Vacant — Glenesk Cottage, Dunlappie Road, Edzell, Brechin DD9 7UB — 01356 648455

Farnell linked with Montrose St Andrew's
Iain M. Douglas MA BD MPhil DipEd — 1960 1980 — 49 Northesk Road, Montrose DD10 8TQ — 01674 672060

Fern, Careston and Menmuir See Edzell Lethnot

Forfar: East and Old (H)
Graham Norrie MA BD — 1967 1978 — East Manse, Lour Road, Forfar DD8 2BB — 01307 464303

Forfar: Lowson Memorial (H)
Robert McCrum BD — 1982 1992 — 1 Jamieson Street, Forfar DD8 2HY
[E-mail: robert.mccrum@virgin.net] — 01307 462248

Forfar: St Margaret's (T) (H)

Jean B. Montgomerie (Miss) MA BD	1973 1998	15 Potters Park Crescent, Forfar DD8 1HH [E-mail: revjeanb@dial.pipex.com]	01307 466390 (Tel/Fax)

Friockheim Kinnell linked with Inverkeilor and Lunan

Vacant		18 Middlegate, Friockheim, Arbroath DD11 4TS	01241 828781

Glamis, Inverarity and Kinnettles (T)

John V. Gardner	1997 2000	10 Kirk Wynd, Glamis, Forfar DD8 1RT [E-mail: jvg66@hotmail.com]	01307 840206 (Tel) 01307 840724 (Fax)

Glenesk See Edzell Lethnot
Glenisla Kilry Lintrathen See Airlie Ruthven Kingoldrum

Glens, The and Kirriemuir Old

Malcolm I.G. Rooney DPE BEd BD	1993 1999	20 Strathmore Avenue, Kirriemuir DD8 4DJ [E-mail: malcolmrooney@gkopc.freeserve.co.uk]	01575 573724 07703 196091 (Mbl)

Guthrie and Rescobie See Aberlemno
Hillside See Dun

Inchbrayock linked with Montrose Melville South

David S. Dixon MA BD	1976 1994	The Manse, Ferryden, Montrose DD10 9SD	01674 672108

Inverkeilor and Lunan See Friockheim Kinnell

Kirriemuir: St Andrew's linked with Oathlaw Tannadice

David J. Taverner MCIBS ACIS BD	1996 2002	26 Quarry Park, Kirriemuir DD8 4DR [E-mail: rahereuk@hotmail.com]	01575 575561

Montrose: Melville South See Inchbrayock

Montrose: Old

Laurence A.B. Whitley MA BD PhD	1975 1985	2 Rosehill Road, Montrose DD10 8ST	01674 672447

Montrose: St Andrew's See Farnell
Newtyle See Eassie and Nevay
Oathlaw Tannadice See Kirriemuir: St Andrew's

Anderson, James W. BSc MTh	1986 1997	(Kincardine O'Neil with Lumphanan)	47 Glebe Road, Arbroath DD11 4HJ	
Brodie, James BEM MA BD STM	1955 1974	(Hurlford)	25A Keptie Road, Arbroath DD11 3ED	01241 873298
Brownlie, Gavin D. MA	1955 1990	(Arbroath: Ladyloan St Columba's)	12 Cliffburn Road, Arbroath DD11 5BB	01241 873062
Bruce, William C. MA BD	1961 1995	(Motherwell: Dalziel)	31 Kirkton Terrace, Carnoustie DD7 7BZ	01241 411078

		Name		Address	Tel
1964	1998	Butters, David	(Turriff: St Ninian's and Forglen)	68A Millgate, Friockheim, Arbroath DD11 4TN	01241 828030
1967	1999	Drysdale James P.R.	(Brechin: Gardner Memorial)	51 Airlie Street, Brechin DD9 6JX	01356 625201
1986	2001	Duncan, Robert F. MTheol	(Lochgelly: St Andrew's)	25 Rowan Avenue, Kirriemuir DD8 4TB	01575 573973
1975	1996	Finlay, Quintin BA BD	(North Bute)	1 Brougham Square, Northesk Road, Montrose DD10 8TD	01674 675522
1938	1981	Henderson, David C. CBE DD	(Glamis)	Isla View, Glenisla, Alyth, Blairgowrie PH11 8PH	01575 582256
1966	1995	Hodge, William N.T.	(Longside)	'Tullochgorum', 61 South Street, Forfar DD8 2BS	01307 461944
1952	1987	Jones, William	(Kirriemuir: St Andrew's)	14 Muir Street, Forfar DD8 3JY	01307 463193
1971	1984	Keith, Donald MA BD	(Chaplain RN)	82 Bo'ness Road, Grangemouth FK3 9DL	01324 484061
1978	1993	McKenzie, M.G. BA LLB	(South Ronaldsay and Burray)	18 Pearse Street, Brechin DD9 6JR	
1951	1986	MacKinnon, A.W.	(Fern, Careston and Menmuir with Oathlaw Tannadice)	19 Gallowhill, Brechin DD9 6BL	01356 623812
1954	1991	MacLeod, Ian I.S. MA BD	(Arbroath: St Andrew's)	13 Trinity Fields Crescent, Brechin DD9 6YF	01356 625599
1963	1994	Milton, Eric G.	(Blairdaff)	16 Bruce Court, Links Parade, Carnoustie DD7 7JE	01241 854928
1955	1989	Perry, Joseph B.	(Farnell)	19 Guthrie Street, Letham, Forfar DD8 2PS	01307 818741
1996	2001	Reid, Albert B. BD BSc	(Ardler, Kettins and Meigle)	1 Dundee Street, Letham, Forfar DD8 2PQ	01307 818416
1959	1976	Russell, A.C. CMG ED MA	(Aberlemno)	Balgavies Lodge, Forfar DD8 2TH	01307 818571
1965	1993	Smith, Hamish G.	(Auchterless with Rothienorman)	11A Guthrie Street, Letham, Forfar DD8 2PS	01307 818973
1935	1972	Stevens, David MA	(Glenesk)	Easter East Coates Cottage, Newburn, Upper Largo, Leven KY8 6JG	
1987	2002	Thomas, Martyn R.H. CEng MIStructE	(Fowlis and Liff with Lundie and Muirhead of Liff)	14 Kirkgait, Letham, Forfar DD8 2XQ	01307 818084
	2000	Thomas, Shirley (Mrs)	Auxiliary Minister	14 Kirkgait, Letham, Forfar DD8 2XQ	01307 818084
1960	1998	Tyre, Robert	(Aberdeen: St Ninian's with Stockethill)	8 Borrowfield Crescent, Montrose DD10 9BR	01674 676961
1952	1990	Warnock, Denis MA	(Kirkcaldy: Torbain)	19 Keptie Road, Arbroath DD11 3ED	01241 872740
1960	1996	Weatherhead, James L. CBE MA LLB DD	(Principal Clerk)	59 Brechin Road, Kirriemuir DD8 4DE	01575 572237
1961	1996	Youngson, Peter	(Kirriemuir: St Andrew's)	Coreen, Woodside, Northmuir, Kirriemuir DD8 4PG	01575 572832

ANGUS ADDRESSES

Arbroath
Old and Abbey	West Abbey Street
Knox's	Howard Street
St Andrew's	Hamilton Green
West Kirk	Keptie Street

Brechin
Cathedral	Bishops Close
Gardner Memorial	South Esk Street

Carnoustie
Carnoustie	Dundee Street
Panbride	Arbroath Road

Forfar
East: Old	East High Street
Lowson Memorial	Jamieson Street
St Margaret's	West High Street

Kirriemuir
Old	High Street
St Andrew's	Glamis Road

Montrose
Melville South	Castle Street
Old	High Street
St Andrew's	George Street

(31) ABERDEEN

Meets at St Mark's Church, Rosemount Viaduct, Aberdeen, on the first Tuesday of February, March April, May, September, October, November and December, and on the fourth Tuesday of June.

Clerk:	REV. IAN A. McLEAN BSc BD	
Presbytery Office:	Mastrick Church, Greenfern Road, Aberdeen AB16 6TR [E-mail: akph34@uk.uumail.com]	01224 690494 (Tel/Fax)
Hon. Treasurer:	MR A. SHARP	27 Hutchison Terrace, Aberdeen AB10 7NN	01224 315702

Aberdeen: Beechgrove (H) (01224 632102)
Iain M. Forbes BSc BD   1964   2000   156 Hamilton Place, Aberdeen AB15 5BB   01224 642615
[E-mail: church@beechgrove23.freeserve.co.uk]

Aberdeen: Bridge of Don Oldmachar (E) (01224 709299)
Jim Ritchie BD MTh DipTh   2000   60 Newburgh Circle, Aberdeen AB22 8QZ   01224 708137
[E-mail: revjim@tinyworld.co.uk]

Aberdeen: Cove (E)
Fyfe Blair BA BD   1989   1998   4 Charleston Way, Cove, Aberdeen AB12 3FA   01224 898030
[E-mail: ncdcove@uk.uumail.com]

Aberdeen: Craigiebuckler (H) (01224 315649)
Kenneth L. Petrie MA BD   1984   1999   185 Springfield Road, Aberdeen AB15 8AA   01224 315125
[E-mail: patandkenneth@aol.com]

Aberdeen: Denburn (H)
Vacant   122 Deswood Place, Aberdeen AB15 4DQ   01224 642845

Aberdeen: Ferryhill (H) (01224 213093)
John H.A. Dick MA MSc BD   1982   54 Polmuir Road, Aberdeen AB11 7RT   01224 586933
[E-mail: jhadick@fish.co.uk]

Aberdeen: Garthdee (H)
Vacant   27 Ramsay Gardens, Aberdeen AB10 7AE   01224 317452

Aberdeen: Gilcomston South (H) (01224 647144)
D. Dominic Smart BSc BD MTh   1988   1998   37 Richmondhill Road, Aberdeen AB15 5EQ   01224 314326
[E-mail: smartdd@lineone.net]

Aberdeen: Greyfriars John Knox (T) (01224 644719)
S. Ian Dennis BD | 1992 1997 | 41 Gray Street, Aberdeen AB10 6JD [E-mail: sid.dennis@virgin.net] | 01224 584594

Aberdeen: High Hilton (H) (01224 494717)
A. Peter Dickson BSc BD | 1996 | 24 Rosehill Drive, Aberdeen AB24 4JJ [E-mail: peter@highhilton.com] | 01224 484155

Aberdeen: Holburn Central (H) (01224 580967)
George S. Cowie BSc BD | 1991 1999 | 6 St Swithin Street, Aberdeen AB10 6XE [E-mail: gscowie@aol.com] | 01224 593302

Aberdeen: Holburn West (H) (01224 571120)
Duncan C. Eddie MA BD | 1992 1999 | 31 Cranford Road, Aberdeen AB10 7NJ [E-mail: nacnud@ceddie.freeserve.co.uk] | 01224 325873

Aberdeen: Mannofield (H) (01224 310087)
John F. Anderson MA BD FSAScot | 1966 1975 | 21 Forest Avenue, Aberdeen AB15 4TU [E-mail: mannofieldchurch@lineone.net] | 01224 315748

Aberdeen: Mastrick (H) (01224 694121)
Brian C. Rutherford BSc BD | 1977 1990 | 13 Beechgrove Avenue, Aberdeen AB15 5EZ | 01224 638011

Aberdeen: Middlefield (H)
Ernest Chapman | 1977 2000 | 73 Manor Avenue, Aberdeen AB16 7UT [E-mail: ernestochapman@aol.com] | 01224 685214

Aberdeen: New Stockethill (New Charge Development)
Ian M. Aitken | 1999 | 52 Ashgrove Road West, Aberdeen AB16 5EE [E-mail: ncdstockethill@dial.pipex.com] | 01224 686929

Aberdeen: North of St Andrew (T) (01224 643567)
Graeme W.M. Muckart MTh MSc FSAScot | 1983 1997 | 51 Osborne Place, Aberdeen AB25 2BX [E-mail: gw2m@clara.net] | 01224 646429

Aberdeen: Northfield
Scott C. Guy BD | 1989 1999 | 28 Byron Crescent, Aberdeen AB16 7EX [E-mail: scguy@xalt.co.uk] | 01224 692332
Duncan Ross DCS | | 64 Stewart Crescent, Aberdeen AB16 5SR [E-mail: duncan.ross@btinternet.com] | 01224 692519

Aberdeen: Queen's Cross (H) (01224 644742)
Robert F. Brown MA BD ThM | 1971 1984 | 1 St Swithin Street, Aberdeen AB10 6XH [E-mail: qxc@globalnet.co.uk] | 01224 322549

Aberdeen: Rosemount (H) (01224 620111)
A. David M. Graham BA BD | 1971 1983 | 22 Osborne Place, Aberdeen AB25 2DA | 01224 648041

Charge	Minister			Address	Tel
Aberdeen: Rubislaw (H) (01224 645477)	Andrew G.N. Wilson MA BD	1977	1987	45 Rubislaw Den South, Aberdeen AB15 4BD [E-mail: andrewg.wilson@virgin.net]	01224 314878
Aberdeen: Ruthrieston South (H) (01224 211730)	Hugh F. Kerr MA BD	1968	1985	39 Gray Street, Aberdeen AB10 6JD	01224 586762
Aberdeen: Ruthrieston West (H)	Sean Swindells BD DipMin	1996		451 Great Western Road, Aberdeen AB10 6NL [E-mail: seanswinl@aol.com]	01224 313075
Aberdeen: St Columba's Bridge of Don (H) (01224 825653)	Louis Kinsey BD DipMin	1991		151 Jesmond Avenue, Aberdeen AB22 8UG [E-mail: louis.kinsey@tinyworld.co.uk]	01224 705337
Aberdeen: St George's Tillydrone (H) (01224 482204)	Vacant			127 Clifton Road, Aberdeen AB24 3RH	01224 483976
	Ann V. Lundie (Miss) DCS			20 Langdykes Drive, Cove, Aberdeen AB12 3HW	01224 898416
Aberdeen: St John's Church for Deaf People (H) (01224 494566)	John R. Osbeck BD	1979	1991	15 Deeside Crescent, Aberdeen AB15 7PT [E-mail: info@aneds.org.uk]	(Voice/Text) 01224 315595
Aberdeen: St Machar's Cathedral (H) (01224 485988)	Richard E. Frazer BA BD	1986	1993	18 The Chanonry, Old Aberdeen AB24 1RQ [E-mail: rkfrazer@ukonline.co.uk]	01224 483688
Aberdeen: St Mark's (H) (01224 640672)	John M. Watson LTh	1989		65 Mile-end Avenue, Aberdeen AB15 5PU [E-mail: jomwat@aol.com]	01224 622470
Aberdeen: St Mary's (H) (01224 487227)	Michael S.M. Crawford LTh	1966	1967	456 King Street, Aberdeen AB24 3DE	01224 633778
Aberdeen: St Nicholas Uniting, Kirk of (H) (01224 643494)	J. Ross McLaren MBE	1964	2002	8 Hilton Street, Aberdeen AB24 4QX	01224 491160
Aberdeen: St Nicholas Kincorth, South of	Edward C. McKenna BD DPS	1989	2002	The Manse, Kincorth Circle, Aberdeen AB12 5NX	01224 872820
Aberdeen: St Ninian's (T) (01224 319519)	Alison J. Swindells (Mrs) LLB BD	1998	2000	451 Great Western Road, Aberdeen AB10 6NL [E-mail: alisonswindells@aol.com]	01224 317667

Aberdeen: St Stephen's (H) (01224 624443) James M. Davies BSc BD	1982	1989	6 Belvidere Street, Aberdeen AB25 2QS [E-mail: james.davies85@hotmail.com]	01224 635694
Aberdeen: Summerhill Ian A. McLean BSc BD	1981		36 Stronsay Drive, Aberdeen AB15 6JL [E-mail: iamclean@lineone.net]	01224 324669
Aberdeen: Torry St Fittick's (H) (01224 899183) Iain C. Barclay TD MA BD MTh MPhil PhD	1976	1999	11 Devanha Gardens East, Aberdeen AB11 7UH [E-mail: st.fittick@virgin.net]	01224 588245 07968 131930 (Mbl) 07625 383830 (Pager)
Aberdeen: Woodside (H) (01224 277249) Alistair Murray BD	1984	1990	322 Clifton Road, Aberdeen AB24 4HQ [E-mail: ally.murray@btopenworld.com]	01224 484562
Ann V. Lundie DCS			20 Langdykes Drive, Cove, Aberdeen AB12 3HW	01224 898416
Bucksburn Stoneywood (H) (01224 712411) Nigel Parker BD MTh	1994		25 Gilbert Road, Bucksburn, Aberdeen AB21 9AN [E-mail: nigel@revparker.fsnet.co.uk]	01224 712635
Cults: East (T) (H) (01224 869028) Flora J. Munro (Mrs) BD	1993		Cults, Aberdeen AB15 9TD [E-mail: cults-east.church@breathemail.net]	01224 867587
Cults: West (H) (01224 869566) Thomas C. Richardson LTh ThB	1971	1978	3 Quarry Road, Cults, Aberdeen AB15 9EX [E-mail: tom.richardson2@virgin.net]	01224 867417
Dyce (H) (01224 771295) Russel Moffat BD MTh PhD	1986	1998	144 Victoria Street, Dyce, Aberdeen AB21 7BE [E-mail: russelbrenda@dyce144.freeserve.co.uk]	01224 722380
Kingswells Harvey L. Grainger LTh	1975	1989	Kingswells Manse, Lang Stracht, Aberdeen AB15 8PL [E-mail: harvey.grainger@btinternet.com]	01224 740229 (Tel) 07713 855815 (Mbl)
Newhills (H) (Tel/Fax: 01224 716161) Norman Maciver MA BD	1976		Bucksburn, Aberdeen AB21 9SS [E-mail: newhillsnm@aol.com]	01224 712655
Peterculter (H) (01224 735845) John A. Ferguson BD DipMin	1988	1999	7 Howie Lane, Peterculter, Aberdeen AB14 0LJ [E-mail: jc.ferguson@virgin.net]	01224 735041

Name			Role	Address	Phone
Aitchison, James W. BD	1993		Chaplain: Army	HQ Briton, UNFICUP, BFPO 567	
Ballantyne, Samuel MA BD	1941	1982	(Rutherford)	26 Cairncy Road, Aberdeen AB16 5DP	01224 483049
Beattie, Walter G. MA BD	1956	1995	(Arbroath Old and Abbey)	126 Seafield Road, Aberdeen AB15 7YQ	01224 329259
Blythe, Scott C. BSc BD	1997	1999	Chaplain: Robert Gordon University	19A Whitehouse Street, Aberdeen AB10 1QJ [E-mail: s.blythe@rgu.ac.uk]	01224 636856
Bryden, Agnes Y. (Mrs) DCS			(Deaconess)	9 Rosewell Place, Aberdeen AB15 6HN	01224 315042
Campbell, W.M.M. BD CPS	1970	1986	Hospital Chaplain	43 Murray Terrace, Aberdeen AB11 7SA [E-mail: campbw@ghc-grampian.scot.nhs.uk]	01224 591174
Coutts, Fred MA BD	1973	1989	Hospital Chaplain	9A Millburn Street, Aberdeen AB11 6SS [E-mail: fred.coutts@chaplains.co.uk]	01224 583805
Deans, John Bell	1951	1986	(Hospital Chaplain)	14 Balmoral Avenue, Ellon AB41 9EW	01358 721539
Dickson, John C. MA	1950	1987	(Aberdeen St Fittick's)	56 Countesswells Road, Aberdeen AB15 7YE	01224 314488
Douglas, Andrew M. MA	1957	1995	(High Hilton)	219 Countesswells Road, Aberdeen AB15 7RD	01224 311932
Falconer, James B. BD	1982	1992	Hospital Chaplain	3 Brimmond Walk, Westhill, Skene AB32 6XH [E-mail: james.falconer@virgin.net]	01224 744621
Finlayson, Ena (Miss) DCS			(Deaconess)	16E Denwood, Aberdeen AB15 6JF	01224 321147
Goldie, George D. ALCM	1953	1995	(Greyfriars)	27 Broomhill Avenue, Aberdeen AB10 6JL	01224 322503
Gordon, Laurie Y.	1960	1995	(John Knox)	1 Alder Drive, Portlethen, Aberdeen AB12 4WA	01224 782703
Grubb, Anthony J. MA BD	1937	1986	(Deer)	Ardier House, Oakdale Terrace, Aberdeen AB15 7PT	01224 352177
Haddow, Angus BSc	1963	1999	(Methlick)	25 Lerwick Road, Aberdeen AB16 6RF	01224 696362
Hutchison, A. Scott MA BD DD	1957	1991	(Hospital Chaplain)	Ashfield, Drumoak, Banchory AB31 5AG	01330 811309
Hutchison, Alison M. (Mrs) BD DipMin	1988	1988	Hospital Chaplain	Ashfield, Drumoak, Banchory AB31 5AG [E-mail: amhutch62@aol.com]	01330 811309
Hutchison, David S. BSc BD ThM	1991	1999	(Aberdeen: Torry St Fittick's)	51 Don Street, Aberdeen AB24 1UH	01224 276122
Jack, David LTh	1984	1999	(West Mearns)	7 Cromwell Road, Aberdeen AB15 4UH	01224 325355
Johnstone, William MA BD	1963	1963	(University of Aberdeen)	37 Rubislaw Den South, Aberdeen AB15 6BD	01224 316022
McCallum, Moyra (Miss) MA BD DCS			(Deaconess)	176 Hilton Drive, Aberdeen AB24 4LT [E-mail: moymac@aol.com]	01224 486240
Mackay, Murdoch M. MA	1941	1986	(Hospital Chaplain)	17 Hillview Terrace, Cults, Aberdeen AB15 9HJ	01224 868082
Main, Alan TD MA BD STM PhD	1963	1980	(University of Aberdeen)	Kirkfield, Barthol Chapel, Inverurie AB51 8TD [E-mail: mbed39@dial.pipex.com]	01651 806773
Mirrilees, J.B. MA BD	1937	1977	(High Hilton)	22 King's Gate, Aberdeen AB15 4EJ	01224 638351
Munro, Gillian (Miss) BSc BD	1989	1995	Chaplain's Assistant: Aberdeen Royal Infirmary	685 George Street, Aberdeen AB25 3XP [E-mail: g.munro@talk21.com]	01224 643418
Russell, Andrew M. MA BD	1940	1976	(Woodside North)	3 Hill Place, Alloa FK10 2LP	01259 213115
Sefton, Henry R. MA BD STM PhD	1957	1992	(University of Aberdeen)	25 Albury Place, Aberdeen AB11 6TQ	01224 572305
Skakle, George S. MA	1945	1987	(Aberdeen Powis)	30 Whitehall Terrace, Aberdeen AB25 2RY	01224 646478
Smith, Angus MA LTh	1965	1991	Industrial Chaplain	1 Fa'burn Terrace, Lumphanan AB31 4AG	01339 883395
Stewart, James C. MA BD STM	1960	2000	(Aberdeen: Kirk of St Nicholas)	54 Murray Terrace, Aberdeen AB11 7SB	01224 587071
Strachan, Ian M. MA BD	1959	1994	(Ashkirk with Selkirk)	'Cardenwell', Glen Drive, Dyce, Aberdeen AB21 7EN	01224 772028
Swinton, John BD PhD	1999		University of Aberdeen	4 Whitestairs Close, Bridge of Don, Aberdeen AB22 8WE [E-mail: j.swinton@abdn.ac.uk]	01224 825637

Torrance, Iain R. TD MA BD DPhil	1982	1993	University of Aberdeen (01224 272274)	Concraig Smiddy, Clinterty, Kingswells, Aberdeen AB15 8RN 01224 790902 [E-mail: i.r.torrance@abdn.ac.uk]
Walton, Ainslie MA MEd	1954	1995	(University of Aberdeen)	359 Great Western Road, Aberdeen AB10 6NU 01224 318218
Watt, William G.	1970	1977	(South of St Nicholas Kincorth)	50 Rosewell Gardens, Aberdeen AB15 6HZ 01224 321915
Wilkie, William E. LTh	1978	2001	(Aberdeen: St Nicholas Kincorth, South of)	38 St Anne's Crescent, Newtonhill, Stonehaven AB39 3WZ 01569 731630
Wood, James L.K.	1967	1995	(Ruthrieston West)	1 Glen Drive, Dyce, Aberdeen AB21 7EN 01224 722543

ABERDEEN ADDRESSES

Church	Address
Beechgrove	Beechgrove Avenue
Bridge of Don	Ashwood Park
Old Machar	Loirston Primary School, Loirston Avenue
Cove	
Craigiebuckler	Springfield Road
Cults East	North Deeside Road, Cults
Cults West	Quarry Road, Cults
Denburn	Summer Street
Dyce	Victoria Street, Dyce
Ferryhill	Fonthill Road x Polmuir Road
Garthdee	Ramsay Gardens
Gilcomston South	Union Street x Summer Street
Greyfriars John Knox	Broad Street
High Hilton	Hilton Drive
Holburn	
Central	Holburn Street
West	Great Western Road
Kingswells	Old Skene Road, Kingswells
Mannofield	Great Western Road x Craigton Road
Mastrick	Greenfern Road
Middlefield	Manor Avenue
North Church of St Andrew	
Northfield	Queen Street
Peterculter	Byron Crescent
Queen's Cross	Craigton Crescent
Rosemount	Albyn Place
Rubislaw	Rosemount Place
Ruthrieston	Queen's Gardens
South	Holburn Street
West	Broomhill Road
St Columba's	Braehead Way, Bridge of Don
St George's	Hayton Road, Tillydrone
St John's for the Deaf	Smithfield Road
St Machar's	The Chanonry
St Mark's	Rosemount Viaduct
St Mary's	King Street
St Nicholas Kincorth, South of	
St Nicholas Uniting, Kirk of	Kincorth Circle
St Ninian's	Union Street
St Stephen's	Mid Stocket Road
New Stockethill	Powis Place
Summerhill	Castleton Crescent
Torry St Fittick's	Stronsay Drive
Woodside	Walker Road
	Church Street, Woodside

(32) KINCARDINE AND DEESIDE

Meets at Banchory on the first Tuesday of February, March, November and December, and at Stonehaven, the first Tuesday of May, September and October, and the last Tuesday of June.

Clerk:	REV. J.W.S. BROWN BTh			10 Forestside Road, Banchory AB31 5ZH 01330 824353 [E-mail: akph58@uk.uumail.com]	

Aberluthnott linked with Laurencekirk (H)

Ronald Gall BSc BD	1985	2001	Aberdeen Road, Laurencekirk AB30 1AJ 01561 378838 [E-mail: ronniegall@aol.com]

Aboyne – Dinnet (H)

David J. Devenney BD	1997		49 Charlton Crescent, Charlton Park, Aboyne AB34 5GN 01339 886447 [E-mail: davidjdevenney@freeuk.com]

Arbuthnott linked with Bervie
Alastair McKillop BD DipMin
1995
10 Kirkburn, Inverbervie, Montrose DD10 0RT
[E-mail: alastairmckillop<revicar@revicar.freeserve.co.uk]
01561 362633

Banchory-Devenick and Maryculter/Cookney
Bruce K. Gardner MA BD PhD
1988 2002
The Manse, Kirkton of Maryculter, Aberdeen AB12 5FS
[E-mail: ministerofbdmc@aol.com]
01224 735776

Banchory Ternan: East (H) (Tel: 01330 820380; E-mail: eastchurch@banchory.fsbusiness.co.uk)
Mary M. Haddow (Mrs) BD
2001
East Manse, Station Road, Banchory AB31 5YP
[E-mail: mary_haddow@ntlworld.com]
01330 822481

Banchory Ternan: West (H)
Donald K. Walker BD
1979 1995
2 Wilson Road, Banchory AB31 5UY
[E-mail: walkerdk.exzam@virgin.net]
01330 822811

Bervie See Arbuthnott

Birse and Feughside
Jack Holt BSc BD
1985 1994
Finzean, Banchory AB31 6PB
[E-mail: jack@finzean.freeserve.co.uk]
01330 850237

Braemar linked with Crathie
Robert P. Sloan MA BD
1968 1996
Crathie, Ballater AB35 5UL
01339 742208

Crathie See Braemar

Cromar
Lawrie I. Lennox MA BD DipEd
1991 2001
Aberdeen Road, Tarland, Aboyne AB34 4UA
01339 881464

Drumoak (H) and Durris (H)
James Scott MA BD
1973 1992
The Manse, Durris, Banchory AB31 6BU
[E-mail: jimscott@durrismanse.freeserve.co.uk]
01330 844557

Glenmuick (Ballater) (H)
Anthony Watts BD
1999
The Manse, Craigendarroch Walk, Ballater AB35 5ZB
01339 754014

Kinneff linked with Stonehaven South (H)
David J. Stewart BD MTh DipMin
2000
Cameron Street, Stonehaven AB39 2HE
[E-mail: brjgodon@ifb.co.uk]
01569 762576

Laurencekirk See Aberluthnott

Mearns Coastal
George I. Hastie MA BD   1971 1998   The Manse, Kirkton, St Cyrus, Montrose DD10 0BW   01674 850880 (Tel/Fax)

Mid Deeside
Vacant   01339 882276
(Charge formed by the union of Kincardine O'Neil with Lumphanan and Torphins)
The Manse, Torphins, Banchory AB31 4GQ

Newtonhill
Hugh Conkey BSc BD   1987 2001   39 St Ternans Road, Newtonhill, Stonehaven AB39 3PF   01569 730143
[E-mail: conkey@tesco.net]

Portlethen (H) (01224 782883)
Douglas M. Main BD (Interim Minister)   1986 2002   18 Rowanbank Road, Portlethen, Aberdeen AB12 4QY   01224 780211

Stonehaven: Dunnottar (H)
Gordon Farquharson MA BD DipEd   1998   Dunnottar Manse, Stonehaven AB39 3XL   01569 762874
[E-mail: gfarqu@lineone.net]

Stonehaven: Fetteresso (H) (Tel: 01569 767689; E-mail: office@fetteressokirk.org.uk)
John R. Notman BSc BD   1990 2001   11 South Lodge Drive, Stonehaven AB39 2PN   01569 762876
[E-mail: jr.notman@virgin.net]

Stonehaven: South See Kinneff

West Mearns
Catherine A. Hepburn (Miss) BA BD   1982 2000   West Mearns Parish Church Manse, Fettercairn, Laurencekirk AB30 1YA   01561 340203
[E-mail: chepburn@fish.co.uk]

Name			Charge	Address	Tel
Brown, Alastair BD	1986	1992	(Glenmuick, Ballater)	52 Henderson Drive, Kintore, Inverurie AB51 0FB	01467 632787
Brown, J.W.S. BTh	1960	1995	(Cromar)	10 Forestside Road, Banchory AB31 5ZH	01330 824353
Caie, Albert LTh	1983	1997	(Glenmuick [Ballater])	16 Swann Place, Ballater AB35 5RW	01339 755787
Christie, Andrew C. LTh	1975	2000	(Banchory-Devenick and Maryculter/Cookney)	17 Broadstraik Close, Elrick, Aberdeen AB32 6JP	01224 746888
Forbes, John W.A. BD	1973	1999	(Edzell Lethnot with Fern, Careston and Menmuir with Glenesk)	Mid Clune, Finzean, Banchory AB31 6PL	01330 850283
Gray, Robert MA BD	1942	1982	(Stonehaven Fetteresso)	4 Park Drive, Stonehaven AB39 2NW	01569 767027
Hood, E.C.P. MA	1946	1989	(Methlick)	1 Silver Gardens, Stonehaven AB39 2LH	
Kinniburgh, Elizabeth B.F. (Miss) MA BD	1970	1986	(Birse with Finzean with Strachan)	7 Huntly Cottages, Aboyne AB31 5HD	01339 886757
MacLeod, Kenneth	1950	1986	(Bourtreebush with Portlethen)	30 Woodlands Place, Inverbervie, Montrose DD10 0SL	01561 362414
Nicholson, William	1949	1986	(Banchory Ternan East with Durris)	10 Pantoch Gardens, Banchory AB31 5ZD	01330 823875
Rennie, Donald B. MA	1956	1996	(Industrial Chaplain)	Mernis Howe, Inverurie Street, Auchenblae, Laurencekirk AB30 1XS	01561 320622
Skinner, Silvester MA	1941	1979	(Lumphanan)	29 Silverbank Gardens, Banchory AB31 3YZ	01330 823032
Smith, J.A. Wemyss MA	1947	1983	(Garvock St Cyrus)	30 Greenbank Drive, Edinburgh EH10 5RE	0131-447 2205

Stephen, Anthony MA BD	2001		Assistant Minister and Youth Leader: The Banchory Churches (Torphins)	
Taylor, Peter R. JP BD	1977	2001	(Peterhead West Associate)	42 Beltie Road, Torphins, Banchory AB31 4JT	01339 882780
Tierney, John P. MA	1945	1985	(Kincardine O'Neil)	3 Queenshill Drive, Aboyne AB34 5DG	01339 886741
Urie, D.M.L. MA BD PhD	1940	1980		Cochrane Cottage, North Deeside Road, Kincardine O'Neil AB34 5AA	01339 884204
Watt, William D. LTh	1978	1996	(Aboyne – Dinnet)	2 West Toll Crescent, Aboyne AB34 5GB	01339 886943

(33) GORDON

Meets at various locations on the first Tuesday of February, March, April, May, September, October, November and December, and on the fourth Tuesday of June.

Clerk:	**REV. G. EUAN D. GLEN BSc BD**			**The Manse, 26 St Ninian's, Monymusk, Inverurie AB51 7HF** [E-mail: akph52@uk.uumail.com]	**01467 651470**

Barthol Chapel linked with Tarves

Alan T. McKean BD	1982	1999	8 Murray Avenue, Tarves, Ellon AB41 7LZ	01651 851250

Belhelvie (H)

Daniel Hawthorn MA BD	1965	1998	Balmedie, Aberdeen AB23 8YR [E-mail: donhawthorne@compuserve.com]	01358 742227

Blairdaff linked with Chapel of Garioch

Kim Cran (Mrs) MDiv BA	1993	2000	Chapel of Garioch, Inverurie AB51 9HE [E-mail: blairdaff.chapelofgariochparish@btinternet.com]	01467 681619

Chapel of Garioch See Blairdaff

Cluny linked with Monymusk (H)

G. Euan D. Glen BSc BD	1992		The Manse, 26 St Ninian's, Monymusk, Inverurie AB51 7HF [E-mail: euanglen@aol.com]	01467 651470

Culsalmond and Rayne linked with Daviot (H)

Mary M. Cranfield (Miss) MA BD	1989		The Manse, Daviot, Inverurie AB51 0HZ [E-mail: marymc@ukgateway.net]	01467 671241

Cushnie and Tough (T) (H) Margaret J. Garden (Miss) BD	1993	2000	The Manse, Muir of Fowlis, Alford AB33 8JU [E-mail: m.garden@virgin.net]	01975 581239
Daviot See Culsalmond and Rayne				
Drumblade linked with Huntly Strathbogie Neil I.M. MacGregor BD	1995		Deveron Road, Huntly AB54 5DU	01466 792702
Echt linked with Midmar (T) Vacant			The Manse, Echt, Skene AB32 7AB	01330 860533
Ellon Eleanor E. Macalister (Mrs) BD	1994	1999	The Manse, Ellon AB41 9BA [E-mail: macal1ster@aol.com]	01358 720476
Pauline Steenbergen (Ms) MA BD (Assoc)	1996	1999	1 Landale Road, Peterhead AB42 1QN [E-mail: psteenb@fish.co.uk]	01779 472141
Sheila Craggs (Mrs) (Aux)	2001		7 Morar Court, Ellon AB41 9GG	01358 723055
Fintray and Kinellar linked with Keithhall Vacant			20 Kinmhor Rise, Blackburn, Aberdeen AB21 0LJ	01467 620435
Foveran Neil Gow BSc MEd BD	1996	2001	The Manse, Foveran, Ellon AB41 6AP [E-mail: the-gows@lineone.net]	01358 789288
Howe Trinity John A. Cook MA BD	1986	2000	The Manse, 110 Main Street, Alford AB33 8AD [E-mail: j-a-cook@howe-trinity.freeserve.co.uk]	01975 562282
Huntly Cairnie Glass Thomas R. Calder LLB BD WS	1994		The Manse, Queen Street, Huntly AB54 8EB	01466 792630
Huntly Strathbogie See Drumblade				
Insch-Leslie-Premnay-Oyne (H) Jane C. Taylor (Miss) BD DipMin	1990	2001	Western Road, Insch AB52 6JR	01464 820914
Inverurie: St Andrew's T. Graeme Longmuir MA BEd	1976	2001	1 Ury Dale, Inverurie AB51 3XW [E-mail: standrew@ukonline.co.uk]	01467 620468
Inverurie: West Ian B. Groves BD CPS	1989		West Manse, 42 Westfield Road, Inverurie AB51 3YS [E-mail: igroves@fish.co.uk]	01467 620285

Keithhall See Fintray and Kinellar

Kennay
John P. Renton BA LTh   1976   1990   Kennay, Inverurie AB51 9ND
                                                [E-mail: johnrenton@btinternet.com]   01467 642219

Kintore (H)
Alan Greig BSc BD   1977   1992   6 Forest Road, Kintore, Inverurie AB51 0XG
                                                [E-mail: greig@kincarr.free-online.co.uk]   01467 632219 (Tel/Fax)

Meldrum and Bourtie
Hugh O'Brien CSS MTheol   2001   Oldmeldrum, Inverurie AB51 0EQ
                                                [E-mail: minister@meldrum-bourtiechurch.org]   01651 872250

Methlick
Albert E. Smith BD FSAScot   1983   1999   Methlick, Ellon AB41 0DS
                                                [E-mail: aesmethlick@aol.com]   01651 806215

Midmar See Echt
Monymusk See Cluny

New Machar
Manson C. Merchant BD CPS   1992   2001   The Manse, Disblair Road, Newmachar, Aberdeen AB21 0RD
                                                [E-mail: manson@tinyworld.co.uk]   01651 862278

Noth
John McCallum BD DipPTh   1989   Manse, Kennethmont, Huntly AB54 4NP
                                                [E-mail: jmccallum@talk21.com]   01464 831244

Skene (H)
Iain U. Thomson MA BD   1970   1972   The Manse, Kirkton of Skene, Skene AB32 6XX   01224 743277
Marion G. Stewart (Miss) DCS   Kirk Cottage, Kirkton of Skene, Skene AB32 6XX   01224 743407

Tarves See Barthol Chapel

Udny and Pitmedden
George R. Robertson LTh   1985   Udny, Ellon AB41 0RS   01651 842052

Upper Donside (H)
Richard J.G. Darroch BD MTh   1993   1999   Lumsden, Huntly AB54 4JQ
                                                [E-mail: richdarr@aol.com]   01464 861757

Name			Parish/Role	Address	Telephone
Andrew, John MA BD DipRE DipEd	1961	1995	(Teacher: Religious Education)	Cartar's Croft, Midmar, Inverurie AB51 7NJ	01330 833208
Bowie, Alfred LTh	1974	1998	(Alford with Keig with Tullynessle Forbes)	17 Stewart Road, Alford AB33 8UD	01975 563824
Collie, Jeannie P. (Miss) DCS			(Deaconess)	3 Formartindale, Udny Station, Ellon AB41 6QJ	01651 842575
Collie, Joyce P. (Miss) MA PhD	1966	1994	(Corgarff Strathdon and Glenbuchat Towie)	35 Foudland Court, Insch AB52 6LG	01464 820945
Dryden, Ian MA DipEd	1988	2001	(New Machar)	16 Glenhome Gardens, Dyce, Aberdeen AB21 0FG	01224 722820
Jones, Robert A. LTh CA	1966	1997	(Marnoch)	13 Gordon Terrace, Inverurie AB51 4GT	01467 622691
Ledgard, J. Christopher BA	1969	1998	(Upper Donside)	Streonshalh, South Road, Rhynie, Huntly AB54 4GA	01464 861429
Lister, Douglas	1945	1986	(Largo and Newburn)	Gowanbank, Port Elphinstone, Inverurie AB51 3UN	01467 621262
Macallan, Gerald B.	1954	1992	(Kintore)	82 Angusfield Avenue, Aberdeen AB15 6AT	01224 316125
McLeish, Robert S.	1970	2000	(Insch-Leslie-Premnay-Oyne)	19 Western Road, Insch AB52 6JR	01464 820749
Mack, John C. JP (Aux)	1985	2001	Presbytery Auxiliary Minister	The Willows, Auchleven, Insch AB52 6QD	01464 820387
Mellis, Robert J. BTh CA	1982	1998	(Shapinsay)	81 Western Avenue, Ellon AB41 9EX	01358 721929
Milligan, Rodney	1949	1985	(Culsalmond with Rothienorman)	Cameron House, Culduthel Road, Inverness IV2 4YG	01463 243241
Rodger, Matthew A. BD	1978	1999	(Ellon)	57 Eilean Rise, Ellon AB41 9NF	01358 724556
Scott, Allan D. BD	1977	1989	(Culsalmond with Daviot with Rayne)	20 Barclay Road, Inverurie AB51 9QP	01467 625161
Stewart, George C. MA	1952	1995	(Drumblade with Huntly Strathbogie)	104 Scott Drive, Huntly AB54 5PF	
Stoddart, A. Grainger	1975	2001	(Meldrum and Bourtie)	6 Mayfield Gardens, Insch AB52 6XL	01464 821124
Wallace, R.J. Stuart MA	1947	1986	(Foveran)	Manse View, Manse Road, Methlick, Ellon AB41 7DW	01651 806843

(34) BUCHAN

Meets at the places listed on the first Tuesday of the following months: September (Crimond), October (Peterhead), November and December (Banff), February and March (Fraserburgh), April and June (Turriff).

Acting Clerk:	REV. MRS MARGARET McKAY MA BD MTh	The Smithy, Knowes of Elrick, Aberchirder, Huntly AB54 7PP [E-mail: akph41@uk.uumail.com] [E-mail: buchan@dial.pipex.com]	01466 780208 (Tel) 01466 780015 (Fax)

Aberdour linked with New Pitsligo

Vacant			137 High Street, New Pitsligo, Fraserburgh AB43 6NH	01771 653256

Auchaber United linked with Auchterless

Alison Jaffrey (Mrs) MA BD	1990	1999	The Manse, Auchterless, Turriff AB53 8BA [E-mail: alison.jaffrey@bigfoot.com]	01888 511217
Margaret McKay (Mrs) MA BD MTh	1991	1999	The Smithy, Knowes of Elrick, Aberchirder, Huntly AB54 7PP [E-mail: rev_margaret_mckay@hotmail.com]	01466 780208 (Tel) 01466 780015 (Fax)

Auchterless See Auchaber United

Banff linked with King Edward
Alan Macgregor BA BD — 1992 1998 — 7 Colleonard Road, Banff AB45 1DZ
[E-mail: alan.macgregor@banff98.freeserve.co.uk] — 01261 812107 (Tel) / 01261 818526 (Fax)
James Cook MA MDiv (Assoc) — 1999 1999 — 3B St Catherine Street, Banff AB45 1HT
[E-mail: therev@jimmiecook.freeserve.co.uk] — 01261 815512

Crimond linked with Lonmay linked with St Fergus
Vacant — Crimond, Fraserburgh AB43 8QJ — 01346 532431

Cruden
Rodger Neilson JP BSc BD — 1972 1974 — Hatton, Peterhead AB42 0QQ
[E-mail: buchan@dial.pipex.com] — 01779 841229 (Tel) / 01779 841822 (Fax)

Deer (H)
James Wishart JP BD — 1986 — Old Deer, Peterhead AB42 5JB
[E-mail: jimmy_wishart@lineone.net] — 01771 623582

Fordyce
Iain A. Sutherland BSc BD — 1996 2000 — Portsoy, Banff AB45 2QB
[E-mail: revsuthy@aol.com] — 01261 842272

Fraserburgh: Old
Douglas R. Clyne BD — 1973 — The Old Parish Church Manse, 4 Robbies Road, Fraserburgh AB43 7AF
[E-mail: manse1@supanet.com] — 01346 518536

Fraserburgh: South (H) linked with Inverallochy and Rathen East
Ronald F. Yule — 1982 — 15 Victoria Street, Fraserburgh AB43 9PJ — 01346 518244 (Tel) / 0870 055 4665 (Fax)

Fraserburgh: West (H) linked with Rathen West
B. Andrew Lyon LTh — 1971 1978 — 23 Strichen Road, Fraserburgh AB43 9SA
[E-mail: balyon@tiscali.co.uk] — 01346 513303 (Tel) / 01346 512398 (Fax)

Fyvie linked with Rothienorman
Alexander B. Noble MA BD ThM — 1982 1999 — The Manse, Fyvie, Turriff AB53 8RD
[E-mail: alexbnoble@themanse38.freeserve.co.uk] — 01651 891230

Gardenstown
Donald N. Martin BD — 1996 — The Manse, Fernie Brae, Gardenstown, Banff AB45 3YL
[E-mail: d.n.martin@virgin.net] — 01261 851256 (Tel) / 01261 851022 (Fax)

Inverallochy and Rathen East See Fraserburgh South
King Edward See Banff

Longside
Norman A. Smith MA BD   1997   9 Anderson Drive, Longside, Peterhead AB42 4XG
[E-mail: normsmith@aol.com]   01779 821224

Lonmay See Crimond

Macduff
David J. Randall MA BD ThM   1971   The Manse, Banff AB45 3QL
[E-mail: djrandall@macduff.force9.co.uk]   01261 832316 (Tel)
01261 832301 (Fax)

Marnoch
Vacant   Aberchirder, Huntly AB54 7TS   01466 780276

Maud and Savoch linked with New Deer
Alastair P. Donald MA PhD BD   1999   Fordyce Terrace, New Deer, Turriff AB53 6TD
[E-mail: alistair@donalds99 freeserve.co.uk]   01771 644216

Monquhitter and New Byth
H. Stewart Congdon DMin   1968   2000   10 Teuchar Road, Cuminestown, Turriff AB53 5YD
[E-mail: stewartandjean@congdons.freeserve.co.uk]   01888 544279

New Deer St Kane's See Maud and Savoch
New Pitsligo See Aberdour

Ordiquhill and Cornhill (H) linked with Whitehills
Vacant   6 Craigneen Place, Whitehills, Banff AB45 2NE   01261 861671

Peterhead: Old
David S. Ross MSc PhD BD   1978   1 Hawthorn Road, Peterhead AB42 2DW
[E-mail: dsross@btinternet.com]   01779 472618 (Tel/Fax)

Peterhead: St Andrew's (H)
David G. Pitkeathly LLB BD   1996   1 Landale Road, Peterhead AB42 1QN
[E-mail: dgpitkeathly@aol.com]   01779 472141

Peterhead: Trinity
L. Paul McClenaghan BA   1973   1996   18 Landale Road, Peterhead AB42 1QP
[E-mail: paul.mcclenaghan@virgin.net]   01779 472405

Pitsligo linked with Sandhaven
Vacant   49 Pitsligo Street, Rosehearty, Fraserburgh AB43 7JL   01346 571237

Rathen West See Fraserburgh: West
Rothienorman See Fyvie
St Fergus See Crimond
Sandhaven See Pitsligo

Strichen linked with Tyrie
Vacant   Kingsville, Strichen, Fraserburgh AB43 6SQ   01771 637365

Turriff: St Andrew's
Vacant   Balmellie Road, Turriff AB53 4DP   01888 563240 (Tel)
01888 569071 (Fax)

Turriff: St Ninian's and Forglen
Murdo C. MacDonald   2002   4 Deveronside Drive, Turriff AB53 4SP   01888 563850

Tyrie See Strichen
Whitehills See Ordiquhill and Cornhill

Name				Address	Phone
Bell, Douglas W. MA LLB	1975	1993	(Alexandria: North)	76 Burnside Road, Mintlaw, Peterhead AB42 5PE	01771 623299
Birnie, Charles J. MA	1969	1995	(Aberdour and Tyrie)	'The Dookit', 23 Water Street, Strichen, Fraserburgh AB43 6ST	01771 637775
Blaikie, James BD	1972	1997	(Berwick-on-Tweed: St Andrew's Wallace Green and Lowick)	57 Glenugie View, Peterhead AB42 2BW	01779 490625
Brown, William H.	1953	1990	(Peterhead: St Andrew's)	11 Henderson Park, Peterhead AB42 2WR	01779 472592
Douglas, Ian P. LTh	1974	1998	(Aberdeen: Craigiebuckler)	1 Torterston Drive, Blackhills, Peterhead AB42 7LB	01779 479189
Dunlop, M. William B. LLB BD	1981	1995	(Peterhead: St Andrew's)	18 Iona Avenue, Peterhead AB42 1NZ	01779 841814
Fawkes, G.M. Allan JP BA BSc	1979	2000	(Lonmay with Rathen West)	3 Northfield Gardens, Hatton, Peterhead AB42 0SW	01261 861523
Jeffrey, Stewart D. BSc BD	1962	1997	(Banff with King Edward)	8 West End, Whitehills, Banff AB42 2NL	
Mackenzie, Seoras L. BD	1996	1998	Chaplain: Army	1 RHF, BFPO 38	
Noble, George S. DipTh	1972	2000	(Carfin with Newarthill)	Craigowan, 3 Main Street, Inverallochy, Fraserburgh AB43 8XX	01346 582749
Scott, W.D.	1956	1989	(Maud with Savoch)	2 Thistle Gardens, Mintlaw, Peterhead AB42 5FG	01771 622258
Taylor, William MA MEd	1984	1996	(Buckie North)	23 York Street, Peterhead AB42 6SN	01779 481798
Walker, Colin D.	1977	1982	(Auchindoir and Kildrummy)	The Old Manse, Alvah, Banff AB54 3US	01261 821656

(35) MORAY

Meets at St Andrew's-Lhanbryd and Urquhart on the first Tuesday of February, March, April, May, September, October, November, December, and at the Moderator's Church on the fourth Tuesday of June.

Clerk: REV. G. MELVYN WOOD MA BD   3 Seafield Place, Cullen, Buckie AB56 4UU
[E-mail: akph67@uk.uumail.com]
01542 841851 (Tel)
01542 841991 (Fax)
07974 095840 (Mbl)

Aberlour (H)
Elizabeth M. Curran (Miss) BD   1995 1998   Mary Avenue, Aberlour AB38 9QN
[E-mail: ecurran8@aol.com]
01340 871027

Alves and Burghead linked with Kinloss and Findhorn
John C. Beck BD   1975 1995   Dunbar Street, Burghead, Elgin IV30 5XB
[E-mail: pictkirk@aol.com]
01343 830365

Bellie linked with Speymouth
Gordon Henig BSc BD   1997 2001   11 The Square, Fochabers IV32 7DG
01343 820256

Birnie linked with Pluscarden
Ronald J. Scotland BD   1993   The Manse, Birnie, Elgin IV30 8SU
[E-mail: ronnieandjillscotland@btopenworld.com]
01343 542621

Buckie: North (H)
Robert P. Boyle LTh   1990 1996   14 St Peter's Road, Buckie AB56 1DL
01542 831328

Buckie: South and West (H) linked with Enzie
John D. Hegarty LTh ABSC   1988 2002   East Church Street, Buckie AB56 1ES
[E-mail: j.hegarty@btinternet.com]
01542 832103

Cullen and Deskford
G. Melvyn Wood MA BD   1982 1997   3 Seafield Place, Cullen, Buckie AB56 4UU
[E-mail: melvynwood@cullenmanse.freeserve.co.uk]
01542 841851 (Tel)
01542 841991 (Fax)
07974 095840 (Mbl)

Dallas linked with Forres St Leonard's (H) linked with Rafford
Paul Amed LTh DPS   1992 2000   Nelson Road, Forres IV36 1DR
[E-mail: paulamed@stleonardsmanse.freeserve.co.uk]
01309 672380

Duffus, Spynie and Hopeman (H)
Bruce B. Lawrie BD   1974 2001   The Manse, Duffus, Elgin IV30 5QP
[E-mail: blawrie@zetnet.co.uk]
01343 830276

Andrew F. Graham (Aux)   2001   4 Woodside Park, Forres IV36 2GT
[E-mail: andy@afg1.fsnet.co.uk]
01309 673886

Dyke linked with Edinkillie
Ann McColl Poole (Mrs) DipEd ACE LTh   1983   Manse of Dyke, Brodie, Forres IV36 2TD   01309 641239

Edinkillie See Dyke

Elgin: High
Charles D. McMillan LTh   1979   1991   5 Forteath Avenue, Elgin IV30 1TQ   01343 542449 (Tel/Fax)
[E-mail: revchaselginhigh@btinternet.com]

Elgin: St Giles' (H) and St Columba's South (01343 551501)
George B. Rollo BD   1974   1986   (Office and Church Halls: Greyfriars Street, Elgin IV30 1LF)   01343 547208
18 Reidhaven Street, Elgin IV30 1QH
[E-mail: gbrstgiles@hotmail.com]

Norman R. Whyte BD DipMin (Assoc)   1982   2000   2 Hay Place, Elgin IV30 1LZ   01343 540143
[E-mail: burraman@msn.com]

Enzie See Buckie South and West

Findochty linked with Portknockie linked with Rathven
Graham Austin BD   1997   20 Netherton Terrace, Findochty, Buckie AB56 4QD   01542 833484
[e-mail: gaustin@ntlworld.com]

Forres: St Laurence (H)
Barry J. Boyd LTh DPS   1993   12 Mackenzie Drive, Forres IV36 2JP   01309 672260   07778 731018 (Mbl)

Forres: St Leonard's See Dallas

Keith: North, Newmill, Boharm and Rothiemay (H) (01542 886390)
T. Douglas McRoberts BD   1975   2002   Church Road, Keith AB55 5BR   01542 882559

Keith: St Rufus, Botriphnie and Grange (H)
Ranald S.R. Gauld MA LLB BD   1991   1995   Church Road, Keith AB55 5BR   01542 882799
Kay Gauld (Mrs) BD STM PhD (Assoc)   1999   Church Road, Keith AB55 5BR   01542 882799
[E-mail: kay_gauld@strufus.fsnet.co.uk]

Kinloss and Findhorn See Alves and Burghead

Knockando, Elchies and Archiestown (H) linked with Rothes
Robert J.M. Anderson BD   1993   2000   Manse Brae, Rothes, Aberlour AB38 7AF   01340 831381 (Tel/Fax)
[E-mail: robert@carmanse.freeserve.co.uk]

Lossiemouth: St Gerardine's High (H)
Vacant   The Manse, St Gerardine's Road, Lossiemouth IV31 6RA   01343 813146

Lossiemouth: St James'
Vacant   Prospect Terrace, Lossiemouth IV31 6JS   01343 813135

Mortlach and Cabrach (H)
Hugh M.C. Smith LTh   1973 1982   The Manse, Church Street, Dufftown, Keith AB55 4AR   01340 820380

Pluscarden See Birnie
Portknockie See Findochty
Rafford See Dallas
Rathven See Findochty linked with Portknockie
Rothes See Knockando, Elchies and Archiestown

St Andrew's-Lhanbryd (H) and Urquhart
Rolf H. Billes BD   1996 2001   39 St Andrews Road, Lhanbryde, Elgin IV30 8PU   01343 843995
                                   [E-mail: rolf.billes@lineone.net]

Speymouth See Bellie

Name			Congregation	Address	Phone
Cowie, Gordon S. MA LLB	1986	1992	(Birnie with Pluscarden)	Strathspey, Lower Inchberry, Orton, Fochabers IV32 7QH	01343 880377
Davidson, A.A.B. MA BD	1960	1997	(Grange with Rothiemay)	9 Woodlands Park, Rosemount, Blairgowrie PH10 6UW	01250 875957
Diack, Peter MA	1951	1994	(Elgin South)	3A Gordon Street, Elgin IV30 1JQ	01343 542545
Douglas, Christina A. (Mrs)	1987	1993	(Inveraven and Glenlivet)	6 Cameron Court, Almond Place, Comrie, Crieff PH6 2BB	
Evans, John W. MA BD	1945	1984	(Elgin High)	15 Weaver Place, Elgin IV30 1HB	01343 543607
Ferguson, David J.	1966	2001	(Bellie with Speymouth)	4 Russell Gardens, Ladybank, Cupar KY15 7LT	01337 831406
Macaulay, Alick Hugh MA	1943	1981	(Bellie with Speymouth)	5 Duke Street, Fochabers IV32 7DN	01343 820726
Miller, William B.	1950	1987	(Cawdor with Croy and Dalcross)	10 Kirkhill Drive, Lhanbryde, Elgin IV30 8QA	01343 842368
Murray, Duncan BTh	1986	2002	(Lossiemouth: St Gerardine's High)	6 Golf View, Hopeman, Elgin IV30 5PF	01343 830913
Porter, John C.	1962	1987	(Forres: St Leonard's)	20 Coppice Court, Grantown-on-Spey PH26 3LF	01479 873082
Robertson, John T. FPhS	1961	1993	(Keith: North, Newmill and Boharm)	43 Nelson Terrace, Keith AB55 5EF	01542 886339
Spence, Alexander	1944	1989	(Elgin St Giles': Associate)	16 Inglis Court, Edzell, Brechin DD9 7SR	01356 648502
Stuart, John T. MA	1958	1993	(Duffus, Spynie and Hopeman)	1 Seaview Farm Paddock, Cummingston, Burghead, Elgin IV30 2XY	01343 830890
Wright, David L. MA BD	1957	1998	(Stornoway: St Columba)	84 Wyvis Drive, Nairn IV12 4TP	01667 451613
Thomson, James M. BA	1952	2000	(Elgin: St Giles' and St Columba's South: Associate)	48 Mayne Road, Elgin IV30 1PD	01343 547664

(36) ABERNETHY

Meets at Boat of Garten on the first Tuesday of February, March, April, June, September, October, November and December.

| Clerk: | REV. JAMES A.I. MACEWAN MA BD | The Manse, Nethy Bridge PH25 3DG
[E-mail: akph35@uk.uumail.com] | 01479 821280 |

Abernethy (H) linked with Cromdale (H) and Advie
James A.I. MacEwan MA BD   1973 1980   The Manse, Nethy Bridge PH25 3DG   01479 821280
[E-mail: manse@nethybridge.freeserve.co.uk]

Alvie and Insh (T) (H) linked with Kingussie (H)
Helen Cook (Mrs) BD (Locum)   The Manse, West Terrace, Kingussie PH21 1HA   01540 661311
[E-mail: bhja@cookville.freeserve.co.uk]

Boat of Garten (H) and Kincardine linked with Duthil (H)
David W. Whyte LTh   1993 1999   Deshar Road, Boat of Garten PH24 3BN   01479 831252
[E-mail: djwhyte@fish.co.uk]

Cromdale and Advie See Abernethy

Dulnain Bridge linked with Grantown-on-Spey (H)
Morris Smith BD   1988   Golf Course Road, Grantown-on-Spey PH26 3HY   01479 872084
[E-mail: janmo@tinyworld.co.uk]

Duthil See Boat of Garten and Kincardine
Grantown-on-Spey See Dulnain Bridge
Kingussie (H) See Alvie and Insh

Laggan linked with Newtonmore (H)
Douglas F. Stevenson BD DipMin   1991 2001   The Manse, Fort William Road, Newtonmore PH20 1DG   01540 673238
[E-mail: dfstevenson@lineone.net]

Newtonmore See Laggan

Rothiemurchus and Aviemore (H)
Ron C. Whyte BD CPS   1990   Dalfaber Park, Aviemore PH22 1QF   01479 810280
[E-mail: ron4xst@aol.com]

Tomintoul (H), Glenlivet and Inveraven
Sven S. Bjarnason CandTheol   1975 1992   The Manse, Tomintoul, Ballindalloch AB37 9HA   01807 580254
[E-mail: sven@bjarnason.org.uk]

Stewart, Matthew S. LTh   1981 1998   (Boat of Garten and Kincardine with Duthil)   2 Ruarden Court, Grantown-on-Spey PH26 3DA [E-mail: mattstewart1@tinyworld.co.uk]   01479 872210

(37) INVERNESS

Meets at Inverness, in the Dr Black Memorial Hall, on the first Tuesday of February, March, April, May, September, October, November and December, and at the Moderator's Church on the fourth Tuesday of June.

Clerk: REV. ALASTAIR S. YOUNGER BScEcon ASCC   3 Elm Park, Inverness IV2 4WN [E-mail: akph55@uk.uumail.com] [E-mail: inverness.presbytery@uk.uumail.com]   01463 232462 (Tel/Fax)

Ardclach linked with Auldearn and Dalmore
Vacant   Auldearn, Nairn IV12 5SX   01667 453180

Ardersier (H) linked with Petty
Alexander Whiteford LTh   1996   Ardersier, Inverness IV2 7SX [E-mail: revwhiteford@cs.com]   01667 462224

Auldearn and Dalmore See Ardclach

Cawdor (H) linked with Croy and Dalcross (H)
Vacant   Croy, Inverness IV2 5PH   01667 493217

Croy and Dalcross See Cawdor

Culloden The Barn (H)
James H. Robertson BSc BD   1975 1994   45 Oakdene Court, Culloden IV2 7XL, [E-mail: revjimrobertson@netscape.net]   01463 790504

Daviot and Dunlichity linked with Moy, Dalarossie and Tomatin
Vacant   Daviot, Inverness IV2 5XL   01463 772242

Dores and Boleskine
James Christie LTh   1993   The Manse, Foyers, Inverness IV2 6XU   01456 486206

Inverness: Crown (H) (01463 238929)
Peter H. Donald MA PhD BD   1991 1998   39 Southside Road, Inverness IV2 4XA [E-mail: crownchurch@tesco.net]   01463 231140

Inverness: Dalneigh and Bona (GD) (H) Fergus A. Robertson MA BD	1971	1999	9 St Mungo Road, Inverness IV3 5AS	01463 232339
Inverness: East (H) Aonghas I. MacDonald MA BD	1967	1981	2 Victoria Drive, Inverness IV2 3QD [E-mail: aonghas@online.co.uk]	01463 231269
Inverness: Hilton Duncan MacPherson LLB BD	1994		4 Tomatin Road, Inverness IV2 4UA [E-mail: duncan@hiltonchurch.freeserve.uk]	01463 231417
Inverness: Kinmylies (E) (H) Peter M. Humphris BSc BD	1976	2001	2 Balnafettack Place, Inverness IV3 8TQ [E-mail: peter@humphris.co.uk]	01463 709893
Inverness: Ness Bank (T) (H) S. John Chambers OBE BSc	1972	1998	15 Ballifeary Road, Inverness IV3 5PJ [E-mail: chambers@ballifeary.freeserve.co.uk]	01463 234653
Inverness: St Columba High (H) Alastair S. Younger BScEcon ASCC	1969	1976	3 Elm Park, Inverness IV2 4WN [E-mail: asyounger@aol.com]	01463 232462 (Tel/Fax)
Inverness: St Stephen's linked with The Old High (1st Charge) (T) (H) Colin M. Anderson BA BD STM MPhil	1968	1994	24 Damfield Road, Inverness IV2 3HU	01463 237129
Inverness: The Old High See Inverness: St Stephen's				
Inverness: Trinity (H) Norman I. MacRae LTh	1966		60 Kenneth Street, Inverness IV3 5PZ [E-mail: norman.macrae@tesco.net]	01463 234756
Inverness: West (2nd Charge) (T) (H) Alistair Malcolm BD DPS	1976	1992	48 Redwood Crescent, Milton of Leys, Inverness IV2 6HB {E-mail: alimalcolm@7inverness.freeserve.co.uk}	01463 722402
Kilmorack and Erchless George Duthie BSc MSc PhD BD	1998		'Roselynn', Croyard Road, Beauly IV4 7DJ [E-mail: gduthie@tinyworld.co.uk]	01463 782260
Kiltarlity linked with Kirkhill Vacant			Kirkhill, Inverness IV5 7PX	01463 831662

Kirkhill See Kiltarity
Moy, Dalarossie and Tomatin See Daviot and Dunlichity

Nairn: Old (H)
Ian W.F. Hamilton BD LTh ALCM AVCM | 1978 | 1986 | 3 Manse Road, Nairn IV12 4RN [E-mail: reviwh@btinternet.com] | 01667 452203

Nairn: St Ninian's (H)
William B. Whyte BD | 1973 | 1975 | 7 Queen Street, Nairn IV12 4AA [E-mail: bbuchwhyte@easicom.com] | 01667 452202

Petty See Ardersier

Urquhart and Glenmoriston (H)
Hugh F. Watt BD DPS | 1986 | 1996 | Blairbeg, Drumnadrochit, Inverness IV3 6UG [E-mail: hw@tinyworld.co.uk] | 01456 450231

Name			Charge	Address	Tel
Black, Archibald T. BSc	1964	1997	(Inverness: Ness Bank)	16 Elm Park, Inverness IV2 4WN	01463 230588
Brown, Derek G. BD DipMin DMin	1989	1994	Chaplain: Raigmore Hospital and Highland Hospice	Cathedral Manse, Choc-an-Lobht, Dornoch IV25 3HN [E-mail: revsbrown@aol.com]	01862 810296
Buell, F. Bart BA MDiv	1980	1995	(Urquhart and Glenmoriston)	6 Towerhill Place, Cradlehall, Inverness IV1 2FN [E-mail: bart@tower22.freeserve.co.uk]	01463 794634
Charlton, George W.	1952	1992	(Fort Augustus with Glengarry)	61 Drumfield Road, Inverness IV2 4XL	01463 242802
Chisholm, Archibald F. MA	1957	1997	(Braes of Rannoch with Foss and Rannoch)	32 Seabank Road, Nairn IV12 4EU	01667 452001
Donaldson, Moses	1972	2000	(Fort Augustus with Glengarry)	'Tabgha', 10 Garden Place, Beauly IV4 7AW	(Tel/Fax) 01667 783701
Donn, Thomas M. MA	1932	1969	(Duthil)	6 Cawdor Road, Inverness IV2 3NR	01463 236410
Frizzell, R. Stewart BD	1961	2000	(Wick Old)	98 Boswell Road, Inverness IV2 3EW	01463 231907
Gibbons, Richard BD		1997	Adviser in Mission and Evangelism	3 Holm Burn Place, Inverness IV2 6WT [E-mail: nmadvisernorth@uk.uumail.com]	01463 226889
Gibson, A. Cameron MRCVS	1962	1990	(Eskdalemuir with Hutton and Corrie with Tundergarth)	Langleigh, 10 Rowan Place, Nairn IV12 4TL	01667 455413
Henderson, Roderick B.	1973	1982	(Kingswells)	5 Holm Park, Inverness IV2 4XT	01463 224022
Lacey, Eric R. BD	1971	1992	(Creich with Rosehall)	1 Ross Court, 96/98 Old Edinburgh Road, Inverness IV2 3HT	01463 239906
Livesley, Anthony LTh	1979	1997	(Kiltearn)	87 Beech Avenue, Nairn IV12 5SX	01667 455126
Logan, Robert J.V. MA BD	1962	1998	(Abdie and Dunbog with Newburgh)	Lyndores, 1 Murray Park, Smithton, Inverness IV2 7PX [E-mail: rjvlogan@aol.com]	01463 790226
Macaskill, Duncan	1952	1974	(Lochs-in-Bernera)	71 Smithton Park, Inverness IV2 7PD	01463 791376
Macritchie, Iain A.M. BSc BD STM PhD	1987	1998	Chaplain: Inverness Hospitals	7 Merlin Crescent, Inverness IV2 3TE	01463 235204
Morrison, Hector BSc BD MTh	1981	1994	Lecturer: Highland Theological College	24 Oak Avenue, Inverness IV2 4NX	01463 238561
Prentice, Donald K. BSc BD	1989	1992	Army Chaplain	Fort George, Inverness IV1 2TD	
Rettie, James A. BTh	1981	1999	(Melness and Eriboll with Tongue)	2 Trantham Drive, Westhill, Inverness IV2 5QT	01463 798896
Stirling, G. Alan S. MA	1960	1999	(Leochel Cushnie and Lynturk linked with Tough)	97 Lochlaan Road, Culloden, Inverness IV2 7HS	01463 798313
Waugh, John L. LTh	1973	2002		58 Wyvis Drive, Nairn IV12 4TP [E-mail: jswaugh@care4free.net]	
Wilson, Ian M.	1988	1993	(Cawdor with Croy and Dalcross)	3 Kilravock Crescent, Nairn IV12 4QZ	01667 452977

INVERNESS ADDRESSES

Inverness

Crown	Kingsmills Road x Midmills Road
Dalneigh and Bona	St Mary's Avenue
East	Academy Street x Margaret Street
Hilton	Druid Road x Tomatin Road
Kinmylies	Kinmylies Way
Ness Bank	Ness Bank x Castle Road
St Columba High	
St Stephen's	Bank Street x Fraser Street Old Edinburgh Road x Southside Road
Old High	Church Street x Church Lane
Trinity	Huntly Place x Upper Kessock Street
West	Huntly Street x Greig Street

Nairn

Old	Academy Street x Seabank Road
St Ninian's	High Street x Queen Street

(38) LOCHABER

Meets at Caol, Fort William, in Kilmallie Church Hall, on the first Tuesday of each month, except January, May, July and August, when there is no meeting.

Clerk: REV. DAVID M. ANDERSON MSc FCOptom — 'Mirlos', 1 Dumfries Place, Lochview Estate, Fort William PH33 6UQ   01397 703203
[E-mail: akph62@uk.uumail.com]

Acharacle (H) linked with Ardnamurchan
Ian Pittendreigh   2002   Old Manse, Acharacle, Argyll PH36 4JU   01967 431665

Ardgour linked with Strontian
James A. Carmichael LTh   1976   The Manse, Ardgour, Fort William PH33 7AH   01855 841230

Ardnamurchan See Acharacle

Arisaig and the Small Isles
Alan H.W. Lamb BA MTh (Locum)   1959   1992   The Manse, Mid Road, Arisaig PH39 4NJ   01687 450227

Duror (H) linked with Glencoe St Munda's (H)
Vacant   The Manse, Ballachulish, Argyll PH49 4JG   01855 811998

Fort Augustus linked with Glengarry
Adrian P.J. Varwell BA BD PhD   1983   2001   Church of Scotland Manse, Fort Augustus PH32 4BH   01320 366210

Fort William: Duncansburgh (H) linked with Kilmonivaig
Donald A. MacQuarrie BSc BD   1979   1990   The Manse of Duncansburgh, The Parade, Fort William PH33 6BA   01397 702297

Fort William: MacIntosh Memorial (H)
Alan Ramsay MA — 1967 — 26 Riverside Park, Lochyside, Fort William PH33 7RB — 01397 702054
David M. Anderson MSc FCOptom (Aux) — 1984 2001 — 1 Dumfries Place, Fort William PH33 6UQ — 01397 703203
[E-mail: david@mirlos.co.uk]

Glencoe St Munda's See Duror
Glengarry See Fort Augustus

Kilmallie
Vacant — Kilmallie Manse, Corpach, Fort William PH33 7JS — 01397 772210

Kilmonivaig See Fort William: Duncansburgh

Kinlochleven (H) linked with Nether Lochaber (H)
Vacant — Lochaber Road, Kinlochleven, Argyll PA40 4QW — 01855 831227

Mallaig St Columba and Knoydart
Ben Johnstone MA BD — 1973 1989 — Church of Scotland Manse, Mallaig PH41 4RG — 01687 462256

Morvern
Alicia Ann Winning MA BD — 1984 — Lochaline, Morvern, Oban PA34 5UU — 01967 421267
[E-mail: annw@morvern12.fslife.co.uk]

Nether Lochaber See Kinlochleven
Strontian See Ardgour

(Deaconess)
Beaton, Jamesina (Miss) DCS — 'Fairhills', Fort Augustus PH32 4DS — 01320 366252
Burnside, William A.M. MA BD PGCE — 1990 — Teacher: Religious Education — 14 Roxburgh Place, Fort William PH33 6UJ — 01397 701465
MacLean, Hector A.M. MA — 1937 1978 — (Duror with Glencoe) — Gearra Beag, Duror, Argyll PA38 4BW — 01631 74215
Millar, John L. MA BD — 1981 1990 — (Fort William: Duncansburgh with Kilmonivaig) — 17 Whittingehame Court, 1350 Great Western Road, Glasgow G12 0BH — 0141-339 4098
Rae, Peter C. BSc BD — 1968 2000 — (Beath and Cowdenbeath North) — Rodane, Badabrie, Banavie, Fort William PH33 7LX — 01397 772603

LOCHABER Communion Sundays

Acharacle	1st Mar, Jun, Sep, Dec	
Ardgour	1st Jun, Sep, Dec, Easter	
Ardnamurchan	1st Apr, Aug, Dec.	
Arisaig and Moidart	1st May, Nov	
Duror	2nd Jun, 3rd Nov	
Fort Augustus	2nd May, 4th Oct	
Fort William		
Duncansburgh	1st Apr, Jun, Oct	
M'Intosh Memorial	1st Mar, Jun, Sep, Dec	
Glencoe	1st Apr, Oct	
Glengarry	1st Jan, Apr, Jul, Oct	
Kilmallie	3rd Mar, May, Sep, 1st Dec	
Kilmonivaig	1st May, Nov	
Kinlochleven	1st Feb, Apr, Jun, Oct, Dec	
Mallaig	4th May, 3rd Nov	
Morvern	Easter, 1st Jul, 4th Sep, 1st Dec	
Nether Lochaber	1st Apr, Oct	
Strontian	1st Jun, Sep, Dec	

(39) ROSS

Meets in Dingwall on the first Tuesday of each month, except January, May, July and August.

Clerk: REV. THOMAS M. McWILLIAM MA BD   **The Manse, Contin, Strathpeffer IV14 9ES**   **01997 421380**
[E-mail: akph71@uk.uumail.com]

Alness
Ronald Morrison BD   1996   27 Darroch Brae, Alness IV17 0SD   01349 882238

Avoch linked with Fortrose and Rosemarkie
Samuel Torrens BD   1995   5 Nessway, Fortrose IV10 8SS   01381 620068

Contin
Thomas M. McWilliam MA BD   1964   1997   The Manse, Contin, Strathpeffer IV14 9ES   01997 421380

Cromarty
John Tallach MA MLitt   1970   1999   Denny Road, Cromarty IV11 8YT   01381 600802

Dingwall: Castle Street (H)
Grahame M. Henderson BD   1974   1987   16 Achany Road, Dingwall IV15 9JB   01349 863167

Dingwall: St Clement's (H)
Russel Smith BD   1994   8 Castlehill Road, Dingwall IV15 9PB   01349 861011

Fearn Abbey and Nigg linked with Tarbat
John Macgregor BD   2001   The Manse, Fearn, Tain IV20 1TN   01862 832626

Ferintosh
Daniel J.M. Carmichael MA BD   1994   Ferintosh Manse, Leanaig Road, Conon Bridge,   01349 861275
                                                Dingwall IV7 8BE

Fodderty and Strathpeffer
Ivan C. Warwick MA BD   1980   1999   The Manse, Strathpeffer IV14 9DL   01997 421398

Fortrose and Rosemarkie See Avoch

Invergordon
Kenneth Donald Macleod BD CPS   1989   2000   Cromlet Drive, Invergordon IV18 0BA   01349 852273

Killearnan linked with Knockbain

| Iain Ramsden BTh | 1999 | The Church of Scotland Manse, Coldwell Road, Artafallie, North Kessock, Inverness IV1 3ZE [E-mail: s4rev@hotmail.com] | 01463 731333 |

Kilmuir and Logie Easter

| Kenneth J. Pattison MA BD STM | 1967 1996 | Delny, Invergordon IV18 0NW [E-mail: ken@thepattisons.fsnet.co.uk] | 01862 842280 |

Kiltearn (H)

| Donald A. MacSween BD | 1991 1998 | Kiltearn, Evanton, Dingwall IV16 9UY | 01349 830472 |

Knockbain See Killearnan

Lochbroom and Ullapool (GD)

| James Gemmell BD MTh | 1999 | The Manse, Garve Road, Ullapool IV26 2SX | 01854 612050 |

Resolis and Urquhart (T)

| C.J. Grant Bell | 1983 2002 | The Manse, Culbokie, Conon Bridge, Dingwall IV7 8JN | 01349 877452 |

Rosskeen

| Robert Jones BSc BD | 1990 | Rosskeen Manse, Perrins Road, Alness IV17 0SX | 01349 882265 |

Tain

| Douglas A. Horne BD | 1977 | 14 Kingsway Ave, Tain IV19 1BN | 01862 894140 |

Tarbat (T) See Fearn Abbey and Nigg

Urray and Kilchrist

| J. Alastair Gordon BSc BD | 2000 | The Manse, Corrie Road, Muir of Ord IV6 7TL | 01463 870259 |

Buchan, John BD MTh	1968	1993	(Fodderty and Strathpeffer)	'Faithlie', 45 Swanston Avenue, Inverness IV3 6QW	01463 713114
Dupar, Kenneth W. BA BD PhD	1965	1993	(Christ's College, Aberdeen)	The Old Manse, The Causeway, Cromarty IV11 8XJ	01381 600428
Forsyth, James LTh	1970	2000	(Fearn Abbey with Nigg Chapelhill)	Rhivs Lodge, Golspie, Sutherland KW10 6DD	
Glass, Alexander OBE MA	1998		Auxiliary Minister: Attached to Presbytery Clerk	Craigton, Tulloch Avenue, Dingwall IV15 9TU	01349 863258
Harries, David A.	1950	1990	(British Sailors Society)	17 Chanonry Crescent, Fortrose IV10 8RH	
Holroyd, Gordon BTh FPhS FSAScot	1959	1993	(Dingwall: St Clement's)	22 Stuarthill Drive, Maryburgh, Dingwall IV15 9HU	01349 863379
Howe, Andrew Y. BTh	1957	1989	(Rosskeen)	2 Springfield Terrace, Alness IV17 0SP	01349 882302
Liddell, Margaret (Miss) BD DipTh	1987	1997	(Contin)	20 Wyvis Crescent, Conon Bridge, Dingwall IV7 8BZ	01349 865997
McGowan, Prof. Andrew T.B. BD STM PhD	1979	1994	Highland Theological College	6 Kintail Place, Dingwall IV15 9RL	

Mackenzie, A. Ian	1945	1986	(Glenelg with Glenshiel with Kintail)	4 St Mary's Well, Tain IV19 1LS	01862 89305
Mackinnon, R.M. LTh	1968	1995	(Kilmuir and Logie Easter)	27 Riverford Crescent, Conon Bridge, Dingwall IV7 8HL	01349 866293
MacLennan, Alasdair J. BD DCE	1978	2001	(Resolis and Urquhart)	Airdale, Seaforth Road, Muir of Ord IV6 7TA	01463 870704
MacLennan, William	1952	1981	(Lochbroom and Ullapool)	8 Firthview Road, Inverness IV3 8LZ	01463 225253
MacLeod, John MA	1959	1993	(Resolis and Urquhart)	'Benview', 19 Balvaird, Muir of Ord IV6 7RG	01463 871286
Niven, William W. BTh	1982	1995	(Alness)	4 Obsdale Park, Alness IV17 0TP	01349 882427
Rutherford, Ellon B. (Miss) MBE DCS			(Deaconess)	41 Duncanston, Conon Bridge, Dingwall IV7 8JB	01349 877439

(40) SUTHERLAND

Meets at Lairg on the first Tuesday of March, May, September, November and December, and on the first Tuesday of June at the Moderator's Church.

Clerk: REV. J.L. GOSKIRK LTh

The Manse, Lairg, Sutherland IV27 4EH   01549 402373
[E-mail: akph76@uk.uumail.com]

Altnaharra and Farr
John M. Wilson MA BD   1965   1998   The Manse, Bettyhill, Thurso KW14 7SZ   01641 521208

Assynt and Stoer
Frederick R. Hurst MA   1965   1971   Canisp Road, Lochinver, Lairg IV27 4LH   01571 844342

Clyne (H)
Ian W. McCree BD   1971   1987   Golf Road, Brora KW9 6QS   01408 621239
[E-mail: ian.mccree@lineone.net]

Creich linked with Rosehall
Olsen, Heather C. (Miss) BD   1978   1999   Church of Scotland Manse, Dornoch Road, Bonar Bridge,   01863 766256
Ardgay IV24 3EB

Dornoch Cathedral (H)
Susan M. Brown (Mrs) BD DipMin   1985   1998   Cnoc-an-Lobht, Dornoch IV25 3HN   01862 810296
[E-mail: revsbrown@aol.com]

Durness and Kinlochbervie
John T. Mann BSc BD   1990   1998   Manse Road, Kinlochbervie, Lairg IV27 4RG   01971 521287
[E-mail: jtmklb@aol.com]

Eddrachillis
John MacPherson BSc BD   1993   Church of Scotland Manse, Scourie, Lairg IV27 4TQ   01971 502431

Golspie
Vacant — Fountain Road, Golspie KW10 6TH — 01408 633295

Kildonan and Loth Helmsdale (H)
Melvyn James Griffiths BTh DipTheol — 1978 1996 — Church of Scotland Manse, Helmsdale KW8 6HT [E-mail: thehavyn@tesco.net] — 01431 821674

Kincardine Croick and Edderton
Alan G.N. Watt MTh — 1996 — The Manse, Ardgay IV24 3BG [E-mail: alan@awattardgay.freeserve.co.uk] — 01863 766285

Lairg (H) linked with Rogart (H)
J.L. Goskirk LTh — 1968 — Church of Scotland Manse, Lairg IV27 4EH — 01549 402373

Melness and Tongue (H)
John F. Mackie BD — 1979 2000 — New Manse, Glebelands, Tongue, Lairg IV27 4XL [E-mail: john.mackie1@virgin.net] — 01847 611230

Rogart See Lairg
Rosehall See Creich

Wilson, Mary D. (Mrs) RGN SCM DTM 1990 1998 Auxiliary Minister — The Manse, Bettyhill, Thurso KW14 7SZ — 01641 521208

(41) CAITHNESS

Meets alternately at Wick and Thurso on the first Tuesday of February, March, May, September, November and December, and the third Tuesday of June.

Clerk: **MRS MYRTLE A. GILLIES MBE** — **Ardachadh, Halladale, Forsinard, Sutherland KW13 6YT** [E-mail: akph42@uk.uumail.com] — **01641 571241 / 01641 571288 (Fax)**

Berriedale and Dunbeath linked with Latheron
Vacant — Ross Manse, Dunbeath KW6 6EA — 01593 731228

Bower linked with Watten
Vacant — Station Road, Watten, Wick KW1 5YN — 01955 621220

Canisbay linked with Keiss
Iain Macnee LTh BD MA PhD — 1975 1998 — The Manse, Canisbay, Wick KW1 4YH — 01955 611309

Dunnet linked with Olrig James F. Todd BD CPS	1984	1999	Olrig, Castletown, Thurso KW14 8TP	01847 821221
Halkirk and Westerdale Kenneth Warner BD DA DipTD	1981		Abbey Manse, Halkirk KW12 6UU	01847 831227
Keiss See Canisbay **Latheron** See Berriedale and Dunbeath				
Lybster and Bruan (T) Vacant			Central Manse, Lybster KW3 6BN	01593 721231
Olrig See Dunnet				
Reay linked with Strathy and Halladale (H) Vacant			Church of Scotland Manse, Reay, Thurso KW14 7RE	01847 811272
Strathy and Halladale See Reay				
Thurso: St Peter's and St Andrew's (H) Kenneth S. Borthwick MA BD	1983	1989	46 Rose Street, Thurso KW14 7HN	01847 895186
Thurso: West (H) Ronald Johnstone BD	1977	1984	Thorkel Road, Thurso KW14 7LW	01847 892663
Watten See Bower				
Wick: Bridge Street A.A. Roy MA BD	1955		Mansefield, Miller Avenue, Wick KW1 4DF	01955 602822
Wick: Old (H) (L) Steven Thomson	2001		The Old Manse, Miller Avenue, Wick KW1 4DF [E-mail: stevie.thomson@btinternet.com]	01955 604252
Wick: Pulteneytown (H) and Thrumster William F. Wallace BDS BD	1968	1974	The Manse, Coronation Street, Wick KW1 5LS	01955 603166
Mappin, Michael G. BA	1961	1998	(Bower with Watten) Mundays, Banks Road, Watten, Wick KW1 5YL	01955 621720

CAITHNESS Communion Sundays

Berriedale and Dunbeath	2nd Mar, Jun, Sep, Dec
Bower	1st Jul, Dec
Canisbay	1st Jun, Nov
Dunnet	last May, Nov
Halkirk	Oct, Apr, Jul
Keiss	1st May, 3rd Nov
Latheron	1st Jul, 2nd Sep, 1st Dec, 2nd Mar
Lybster and Bruan	3rd Jun, Nov, Easter
Olrig	last May, Nov
Reay	last Apr, Sep
Strathy and Halladale	1st Jun, last Nov
Thurso	
St Peter's and St Andrew's	1st Feb, Apr, Jun, Sep, Nov
West	4th Mar, Jun, Nov
Watten	1st Jul, Dec
Westerdale	Apr, Oct, 4th Dec
Wick	
Bridge Street	1st Apr, Oct
Old	4th Apr, Sep
Pulteneytown and Thrumster	1st Mar, Jun, Sep, Dec

(42) LOCHCARRON – SKYE

Meets in Kyle on the first Tuesday of each month, except January, May, July and August.

Clerk: REV. ALLAN J. MACARTHUR BD — High Barn, Croft Road, Lochcarron, Strathcarron IV54 8YA [E-mail: akph63@uk.uumail.com] — 01520 722278 (Tel) / 01520 722674 (Fax)

Applecross, Lochcarron and Torridon (GD)
George M. Martin MA BD — 1987
David V. Scott BTh (Assoc) — 1994
The Manse, Lochcarron, Strathcarron IV54 8YD / Camusterrach, Applecross, Strathcarron IV54 8LU — 01520 722829 / 01520 744263

Bracadale and Duirinish (GD)
Gary Wilson BD — 1996 2000
Kinloch Manse, Dunvegan, Isle of Skye IV55 8WQ [E-mail: garyhelen@dunvegan73.fsnet.co.uk] — 01470 521457

Gairloch and Dundonnell
Derek Morrison — 2000
Church of Scotland Manse, The Glebe, Gairloch IV21 2BT [E-mail: derekmorrison@tinyworld.com] — 01445 712053 (Tel/Fax)

Glenelg and Kintail
Donald Beaton MA BD MTh — 1961 1988
Church of Scotland Manse, Inverinate, Kyle IV40 8HE — 01599 511245

Kilmuir and Stenscholl (GD)
Ivor MacDonald BSc MSc BD — 1993 2000
Staffin, Portree, Isle of Skye IV51 9JX [E-mail: ivormacd@aol.com] — 01470 562759 (Tel/Fax)

Lochalsh
John M. Macdonald — 2002
The Church of Scotland Manse, Main Street, Kyle IV40 8DA — 01599 534294

Portree (GD)
Vacant
Viewfield Road, Portree, Isle of Skye IV51 9ES — 01478 612019

Snizort (H) (GD)
Iain M. Greenshields BD DipRS ACMA MTh 1985 2002 The Manse, Kensaleyre, Snizort, Portree, Isle of Skye IV51 9XE 01470 532260

Strath and Sleat (GD)
Vacant Church of Scotland Manse, Broadford, Isle of Skye IV49 9AA 01471 822538
John M. Nicolson BD DipMin (Assoc) 1997 The Manse, The Glebe, Kilmore, Teangue, Isle of Skye IV44 8RG 01471 844469
[E-mail: jnico84967@aol.com]

Ferguson, John LTh BD DD 1973 2002 (Portree) 9 Braeview Park, Beauly, Inverness IV4 7ED
Macarthur, Allan J. BD 1973 1998 (Applecross, Lochcarron and Torridon) High Barn, Croft Road, Lochcarron, Strathcarron IV54 8YA (Tel) 01520 722278 (Fax) 01520 722674
McCulloch, Alen J.R. MA BD 1990 1995 Chaplain: Army Vimy Barracks, Catterick Garrison, North Yorkshire DL9 3PS
MacDonald, Kenneth 1965 1992 (Associate: Applecross l/w Lochcarron) Tigharry, Main Street, Lochcarron, Strathcarron IV54 8YB 01520 722433
MacDougall, Angus 1940 1982 (Sleat) Tigh Ard, Earlish, Portree, Isle of Skye IV51 9XL 01470 542466
Mackinnon, Duncan 1956 1989 (Plockton and Kyle) 7 Garth Road, Inverness IV2 4DA 01463 230971
Macleod, Donald LTh 1988 2000 (Snizort) 20 Caulfield Avenue, Cradlehall, Inverness IV1 2GA 01463 798093
Matheson, James G. MA BD DD 1936 1979 (Portree) The Elms, 148 Whitehouse Loan, Edinburgh EH9 2EZ 0131-446 6211
Ritchie, Walter M. 1973 1999 (Uphall South) Straloch, Bayview Crescent, Broadford, Isle of Skye IV49 9BD 01471 822604 [E-mail: walter.ritchie@virgin.net]
Williamson, Tom MA BD 1941 1982 (Dyke with Edinkillie) 16 Cove, Inverasdale, Poolewe, Achnasheen IV22 2LT 01445 781423

LOCHCARRON – SKYE Communion Sundays

Applecross	1st Jul	Kintail	3rd Apr, Jul	Sleat	2nd Jun, Dec
Bracadale	3rd Mar, Sep	Lochalsh and Stromeferry	4th Jun, Sep, Christmas, Easter	Snizort	1st Jun, Dec
Duirinish	3rd Jan, Easter, 2nd Jun, 3rd Sep	Lochcarron and Shieldaig	Easter, 3rd Jun, 1st Oct	Stenscholl	1st Jun, Dec
Dundonnell	4th Jun	Plockton and Kyle	2nd May, 1st Oct	Strath	1st Mar, Aug
Gairloch	3rd Jun, Nov	Portree	Easter, Pentecost, Christmas, 2nd Mar, Aug, 1st Nov	Torridon and Kinlochewe	2nd May
Glenelg	2nd Jun, Nov				
Glenshiel	1st Jul				
Kilmuir	1st Mar, Sep				

(43) UIST

Meets on the fourth Wednesday of January, March, September and November in Berneray, and the fourth Wednesday of June in Leverburgh.

Clerk:	REV. MURDO SMITH MA BD		Scarista, Isle of Harris HS3 3HX [E-mail: akph77@uk.uumail.com]	01859 550200
Barra (GD) John D. Urquhart BA BD	1998	2000	Cuithir, Castlebay, Isle of Barra HS9 5XD [E-mail: jurquh8218@aol.com]	01871 810230
Benbecula (GD) (H) Kenneth J. Macpherson BD	1988	1998	Griminish, Isle of Benbecula HS7 5QA	01870 602180
Berneray and Lochmaddy (GD) (H) Vacant			Lochmaddy, Isle of North Uist HS6 5BD	01876 500414
Carinish (GD) (H) Thomas J.R. Mackinnon LTh DipMin	1996	1998	Clachan, Isle of North Uist HS6 5HD [E-mail: tmackinnon@aol.com]	01876 580219
Kilmuir and Paible (GE) Vacant			Paible, Isle of North Uist HS6 5ED	01876 510310
Manish-Scarista (GD) (H) Murdo Smith MA BD	1988		Scarista, Isle of Harris HS3 3HX [E-mail: akph77@uk.uumail.com]	01859 550200
South Uist (GD) Vacant			Daliburgh, Isle of South Uist HS8 5SS	01878 700265
Tarbert (GE) (H) Norman MacIver BD	1976	1988	The Manse, Manse Road, Tarbert, Isle of Harris HS3 3DF [E-mail: norman@n-cmaciver.freeserve.co.uk]	01859 502231

MacDonald, Angus J. BSc BD	(Lochmaddy and Trumisgarry)	1995	2001	7 Memorial Avenue, Stornoway, Isle of Lewis HS1 2QR	01851 706634
MacInnes, David MA BD	(Kilmuir and Paible)	1966	1999	9 Golf View Road, Kinmylies, Inverness IV3 8SZ	01463 717377
Macrae, D.A. JP MA	(Tarbert)	1942	1988	5 Leverhulme Road, Tarbert, Isle of Harris HS3 3DD	01859 502310
Macrae, William DCS	(Deacon)			6 Park View Terrace, Isle of Scalpay, Tarbert, Isle of Harris HS4 3XX	01859 540288
Morrison, Donald John	Auxiliary Minister	2001		Lagnam, Brisgean 22, Kyles, Isle of Harris HS3 3BS	01859 502341
Muir, Alexander MA BD	(Carinish)	1982	1996	14 West Mackenzie Park, Inverness IV2 3ST	01463 712096
Smith, John M.	(Lochmaddy)	1956	1992	Hamersay, Clachan, Isle of North Uist HS6 5HD	01876 580332

UIST Communion Sundays

Barra	Easter, Pentecost, Christmas	Kilmuir and Paible	1st Jun, 3rd Nov	South Uist – Iochdar	1st Mar
Benbecula	2nd Mar, Sep	Manish-Scarista	3rd Apr, 1st Oct	Howmore	1st Jun
Berneray and Lochmaddy	4th Jun, 1st Nov			Daliburgh	1st Sep
Carinish	4th Mar, Aug			Tarbert	2nd Mar, 3rd Sep

(44) LEWIS

Meets at Stornoway, in St Columba's Church Hall, on the first Tuesday of February, March, April, September, November and December. It also meets in June on a date to be decided.

Clerk: REV. THOMAS S. SINCLAIR MA BD

Martin's Memorial Manse,
Matheson Road, Stornoway, Isle of Lewis HS1 2LR   01851 702206
[E-mail: akph61@uk.uumail.com]   07729 372728 (Mbl)
[E-mail: thomas@sinclair0438.freeserve.co.uk]

Barvas (GD) (H)
Thomas MacNeil MA BD   2002   Barvas, Isle of Lewis HS2 0QY   01851 840218
[E-mail: tommymacneil@hotmail.com]

Carloway (GD) (H)
Murdo M. Campbell BD DipMin   1997   Carloway, Isle of Lewis HS2 9AU   01851 643255
[E-mail: murdocampbell@hotmail.com]

Cross Ness (GE) (H)
Ian M.M. Macdonald DPA BD   2001   Swainbost, Ness, Isle of Lewis HS2 0TB   01851 810375
[E-mail: ian.murdo@virgin.net]

Kinloch (GE) (H)
Donald Angus MacLennan   1975 1989   Laxay, Lochs, Isle of Lewis HS2 9LA   01851 830218
[E-mail: donaldkinloch@lochs.net]   07799 668270 (Mbl)

Knock (GE) (H)
Fergus J. MacBain — 1999 2002 — Church of Scotland Manse, Garrabost, Point, Isle of Lewis HS2 0PW — 01851 870362

Lochs-Crossbost (GD) (H)
Andrew W.F. Coghill BD DPS — 1993 — Leurbost, Lochs, Isle of Lewis HS2 9NS [E-mail: andcoghill@aol.com] — 01851 860243 (Tel/Fax), 07776 480748 (Mbl)

Lochs-in-Bernera (GD) (H)
Vacant — Bernera, Isle of Lewis HS2 9LU — 01851 612371

Stornoway: High (GD) (H)
William B. Black MA BD — 1972 1998 — 1 Goathill Road, Stornoway, Isle of Lewis HS1 2NJ [E-mail: willieblack@lineone.net] — 01851 703106

Stornoway: Martin's Memorial (H)
Thomas Suter Sinclair MA BD — 1966 1976 — Matheson Road, Stornoway, Isle of Lewis HS1 2LR [E-mail: thomas@sinclair0438.freeserve.co.uk] — 01851 702206, 07729 372728 (Mbl)

Stornoway: St Columba (GD) (H)
Angus Morrison MA BD PhD — 1979 2000 — Lewis Street, Stornoway, Isle of Lewis HS1 2JF [E-mail: akph61@uk.uumail.com] [E-mail: angusmorrison@lineone.net] — 01851 703350

Uig (GE) (H)
William Macleod — 1957 1964 — Miavaig, Uig, Isle of Lewis HS2 9HW — 01851 672216 (Tel/Fax)

Name	Years	(Charge)	Address	Tel
Macaulay, Donald OBE JP	1968 1992	(Park)	6 Kirkibost, Bernera, Isle of Lewis HS2 9RD [E-mail: garymilis@talk21.com]	01851 612341
Macdonald, Alexander	1957 1991	(Cross Ness)	5 Urquhart Gardens, Stornoway, Isle of Lewis HS1 2TX	01851 702825
Macdonald, James LTh CPS	1984 2001	(Knock)	Elim, 8A Lower Bayble, Point, Isle of Lewis HS2 0QA	01851 870173
Maclean, Donald A. DCS		(Deacon)	8 Upper Barvas, Barvas, Isle of Lewis HS2 0QX	01851 840454
MacRitchie, Murdanie	1958 1969	(Acharacle)	15A New Garrabost, Isle of Lewis HS2 0PR	01851 870763
MacSween, Norman	1952 1986	(Kinloch)	7 Balmerino Drive, Stornoway, Isle of Lewis HS1 2TD	01851 703369
Montgomery, Donald J. DCS		(Deacon)	17 Murray Place, Stornoway, Isle of Lewis HS1 2JB	01851 704346
Morrison, Alexander	1952 1973	(Barvas)	Ceol Mara, Marig, Isle of Harris HS3 3AG	01859 502267

LEWIS Communion Sundays

Barvas	3rd Mar, Sep
Carloway	1st Mar, last Sep
Cross, Ness	2nd Mar, Oct
Kinloch	3rd Mar, 2nd Jun, 2nd Sep
Knock	1st Apr, Nov
Lochs-Crossbost	4th Mar, Sep
Lochs-in-Bernera	1st Apr, 2nd Sep
Stornoway	
High	3rd Feb, last Aug
Martin's Memorial	3rd Feb, last Aug, 1st Dec, Easter
Stornoway St Columba	3rd Feb, last Aug, Thurs before Easter, and before Remembrance
Uig	3rd Jun, 1st Sep

(45) ORKNEY

Meets at Kirkwall, in the Town Hall, on the first Tuesday of September and February, on the second Tuesday of October, on the fourth Tuesday of November and April, and on the third Tuesday in June.

Clerk: REV. TREVOR G. HUNT BA BD
The Manse, Finstown, Orkney KW17 2EG
[E-mail: akph68@uk.uumail.com]
[E-mail (personal): trevorghunt@yahoo.co.uk]
01856 761328 (Tel/Fax)
07799 404227 (Mbl)

Birsay, Harray and Sandwick
Andrea E. Price (Mrs)   1997   2001
The Manse, North Biggings Road, Dounby, Orkney KW17 2HZ
[E-mail: andrea-neil@supanet.com]
01856 771803

Deerness linked with Holm linked with St Andrews
Joan H. Craig (Miss) MTheol   1986
Holm, Orkney KW17 2SB
[E-mail: joanhcraig@bigfoot.com]
01856 781422 (Tel/Fax)

Eday linked with Stronsay Moncur Memorial (H)
Joyce A. Keyes (Mrs) BD   1996
Stronsay, Orkney KW17 2AF
01857 616311

Evie linked with Firth linked with Rendall
Trevor G. Hunt BA BD   1986
Finstown, Orkney KW17 2EG
[E-mail: trevorghunt@yahoo.co.uk]
01856 761328 (Tel/Fax)
07799 404227 (Mbl)

Firth See Evie

Flotta linked with Hoy and Walls (T)
Vacant
South Isles Manse, Longhope, Stromness, Orkney KW16 3PG
01856 701325

Holm See Deerness
Hoy and Walls See Flotta

Kirkwall: East
Allan McCafferty BSc BD   1993
Thom Street, Kirkwall, Orkney KW15 1PF
[E-mail: amccafferty@beeb.net]
01856 875469

Kirkwall: St Magnus Cathedral (H)
G. Fraser H. Macnaughton MA BD   1982   2002
Berstane Road, Kirkwall, Orkney KW15 1NA
[E-mail: fmacnaug@fish.co.uk]
01856 873312

North Ronaldsay linked with Sanday (H)
John L. McNab MA BD — 1997 2002 — Sanday, Orkney KW17 2BW — 01857 600429

Orphir (H) linked with Stenness (H)
Thomas L. Clark BD — 1985 — Stenness, Stromness, Orkney KW16 3HH — 01856 761331

Papa Westray linked with Westray
Iain D. MacDonald BD — 1993 — The Manse, Rapness, Westray, Orkney KW17 2DE [E-mail: macdonald@rapnessmanse.freeserve.co.uk] — 01857 677357 (Tel/Fax) / 07710 443780 (Mbl)

Rendall See Evie

Rousay
Vacant

St Andrew's See Deerness
Sanday See North Ronaldsay

Shapinsay
Vacant — Shapinsay, Balfour, Orkney KW17 2EA — 01856 711332

South Ronaldsay and Burray
Graham D.S. Deans MA BD MTh — 1978 2002 — St Margaret's Manse, Church Road, St Margaret's Hope, Orkney KW17 2SR [E-mail: graham.deans@btopenworld.com] — 01856 831288

Stenness See Orphir

Stromness (H)
Fiona L. Lillie (Mrs) BA BD MLitt — 1995 1999 — 5 Manse Lane, Stromness, Orkney KW16 3AP [E-mail: fiona@lilliput23.freeserve.co.uk] — 01856 850203

Stronsay See Eday
Westray See Papa Westray

Brown, R. Graeme BA BD — 1961 1998 — (Birsay with Rousay) — Bring Deeps, Orphir, Orkney KW17 2LX [E-mail: grasibrown@bringdeeps.fsnet.co.uk] — (Tel/Fax) 01856 811707

Cant, H.W.M. MA BD STM — 1951 1990 — (Kirkwall: St Magnus Cathedral) — Quoylobs, Holm, Orkney KW17 2RY — 01856 781300
Ward, Michael J. BSc BD PhD — 1983 1999 — Community Minister — Ploverhall, Deerness, Orkney KW17 2QJ [E-mail: revmw@lineone.net] — 01856 741349 / (Mbl) 07765 598816

(46) SHETLAND

Meets at Lerwick on the first Tuesday of March, April, June, September, October, November and December.

| Clerk: | REV. CHARLES H.M. GREIG MA BD | The Manse, Sandwick, Shetland ZE2 9HW [E-mail: akph72@uk.uumail.com] | 01950 431244 |

Burra Isle linked with Tingwall

| Edgar J. Ogston BSc BD | 1976 | 2001 | Park Neuk, Meadowfield Place, Scalloway, Shetland ZE1 0UE [E-mail: ogston@ntlworld.com] | 01595 880865 |

Delting linked with Northmavine

| Winnie Munson (Ms) BD | 1996 | 2001 | The Manse, Grindwell, Brae, Shetland ZE2 9QJ | 01806 522219 |

Dunrossness and St Ninian's inc. Fair Isle linked with Sandwick Cunningsburgh and Quarff

| Charles H.M. Greig MA BD | 1976 | 1997 | The Manse, Sandwick, Shetland ZE2 9HW [E-mail: chm.greig@btopenworld.com] | 01950 431244 |

Fetlar linked with Yell

| R. Alan Knox MA LTh Alnst AM | 1965 | 2000 | The Manse, Mid Yell, Shetland ZE2 9BN | 01957 702283 |

Lerwick and Bressay

| Gordon Oliver BD | 1979 | 2002 | The Manse, 82 St Olaf Street, Lerwick, Shetland ZE1 0ES [E-mail: gordon@cofslerwick.freeserve.co.uk] | 01595 692125 |

Nesting and Lunnasting linked with Whalsay and Skerries

| Irene A. Charlton (Mrs) BTh | 1994 | 1997 | The Manse, Marrister, Symbister, Whalsay, Shetland ZE2 9AE [E-mail: irene.charlton@virgin.net] | 01806 566767 |
| Richard M. Charlton (Aux) | | 2001 | The Manse, Marrister, Symbister, Whalsay, Shetland ZE2 9AE [E-mail: malcolm.charlton@virgin.net] | 01806 566767 |

Northmavine See Delting

Sandsting and Aithsting linked with Walls and Sandness

| William J. McMillan CA LTh BD | 1969 | 1997 | Westside Manse, Effirth, Bixter, Shetland ZE2 9LY [E-mail: rev-w-mcmillan@btinternet.com] | 01595 810386 (Tel/Fax) |

Sandwick, Cunningsburgh and Quarff See Dunrossness and St Ninian's
Tingwall See Burra Isle

Unst

| Vacant | | | The Manse, Baltasound, Unst, Shetland ZE2 9DZ | 01957 711335 |

Walls and Sandness See Sandsting and Aithsting
Whalsay and Skerries See Nesting and Lunnasting
Yell See Fetlar

Blair, James N.	1962	1986	(Sandsting and Aithsting with Walls)	2 Swinister, Sandwick, Shetland ZE2 9HH	01950 431472
Dowswell, James A.M.	1991	2001	(Lerwick and Bressay)	Mill House, High Street, Staplehurst, Tonbridge, Kent TN12 0AU	01580 891271
Kirkpatrick, Alice H. (Miss) MA BD FSAScot	1987	2000	(Northmavine)	6 Valladale, Urafirth, Shetland ZE2 9RW	
Smith, Catherine (Mrs) DCS	1964	1998	Presbytery Assistant	21 Lingaro, Bixter, Shetland ZE2 9NN	01595 810207
Williamson, Magnus J.C.	1982	1999	(Fetlar with Yell)	Creekhaven, Houll Road, Scalloway, Shetland ZE1 0XA	01595 880023
Wilson, W. Stewart DA	1980	1997	(Kirkcudbright)	Aesterhoull, Fair Isle, Shetland ZE2 9JU	01595 760273

(47) ENGLAND

Meets at London, in Crown Court Church, on the second Tuesday of March and December, and at St Columba's, Pont Street, on the second Tuesday of June and October.

Clerk: REV. W.A. CAIRNS BD 6 Honiton Gardens, Corby, Northants NN18 8BW 01536 203175
[E-mail: akph14@uk.uumail.com]
[E-mail: englandpresbytery@uk.uumail.com]

Corby: St Andrew's (H)
W. Alexander Cairns BD 1978 2001 6 Honiton Gardens, Corby, Northants NN18 8BW 01536 203175
[E-mail: englandpresbytery@uk.uumail.com]
Marjory Burns (Mrs) DCS 25 Barnsley Square, Corby, Northants NN18 0PQ 01536 264819

Corby: St Ninian's (H) (01536 265245)
Vacant 46 Glyndebourne Gardens, Corby, Northants NN18 0PZ 01536 741179
Marjory Burns (Mrs) DCS 25 Barnsley Square, Corby, Northants NN18 0PQ 01536 264819

Guernsey: St Andrew's in the Grange (H)
Vacant The Manse, Le Villocq, Castel, Guernsey GY5 7SB 01481 257345

Jersey: St Columba's (H)
James G. Mackenzie BA BD 1980 1997 18 Claremont Avenue, St Saviour, Jersey 01534 730659
[E-mail: jim@jgmackenzie.softnet.co.uk]

Liverpool: St Andrew's
Continued Vacancy
Session Clerk: E. Graham (Mr) 0151-525 4496

London: Crown Court (H) (020 7836 5643)

Name			Address	Phone
Sigrid Marten	1997	2001	53 Sidmouth Street, London WC1H 8JX	020 7278 5022
			[E-mail: minister@crowncourtchurch.org.uk]	
Timothy Fletcher BA FCMA (Aux)		1998	37 Hareston Valley Road, Caterham, Surrey CR3 6HN	01883 340826

London: St Columba's (H) (020 7584 2321) linked with Newcastle St Andrew's (H)

Name			Address	Phone
Barry W. Dunsmore MA BD	1982	2000	29 Hollywood Road, Chelsea, London SW10 9HT	020 7376 5230
			[E-mail: office@stcolumbas.org.uk]	
Alexander G. Horsburgh MA BD (Assoc)	1996	2001	2 Tedworth Court, 15 Tedworth Square, London SW3 4DR	020 7376 3386
			[E-mail: office@stcolumbas.org.uk]	
Dorothy Lunn (Aux)		2001	14 Bellerby Drive, Ouston, Co. Durham DH2 1TW	0191-492 0647
Patricia Munro (Miss) BSc DCS		2002	St Columba's Church, Pont Street, London SW1X 0BD	020 7584 2321

Name			Position	Address	Phone
Bowie, A. Glen CBE BA BSc	1954	1984	(Principal Chaplain: RAF)	16 Weir Road, Hemingford Grey, Huntingdon PE18 9EH	01480 381425
Brown, Scott J. BD	1993		Chaplain: RN	4 Darwin Close, Lee-on-Solent, Hants PO13 8LS	02392 54116
				[E-mail: leeonsolent@hotmail.com]	
Cameron, R. Neil	1975	1981	Chaplain: Community	The Church Centre, Rhine Area Support Unit, BFPO 40	0049 2161 472770
Coulter, David G. BA BD PhD	1989	1994	Chaplain: Army	3 Park Avenue, Shrivenham, Swindon, Wilts SN6 8HD	01793 783620
				[E-mail: d.g.coulter@rmcs.cranfield.ac.uk]	
Craig, Gordon W. MBE MA BD	1972	2000	(Chaplain: RN)	The Round House, Venterden, Stoke Climsland, Callington, Cornwall PL17 8PD	01579 370195
Davison, Charles F. MA	1947	1987	(Guernsey: St Andrew's in the Grange)	Maryfield, Green Lanes, St Peter Port, Guernsey GY1 1TN	01481 727446
Drummond, J.S. MA	1946	1978	(Corby: St Ninian's)	77 Low Road, Hellesdon, Norwich NR6 5AG	01603 417736
Duncan, Denis M. BD PhD	1944	1986	(Editor: The British Weekly)	80A Woodland Rise, London N10 3UJ	020 8883 1831
Fields, James MA BD STM	1988	1997	School Chaplain	The Bungalow, The Ridgeway, Mill Hill, London NW7 1QX	(Tel) 020 8374 4708
Fyall, Robert S. MA BD	1986	1989	Tutor: St John's College, Durham	7 Briardene, Durham DH1 4QU	(Fax) 020 8201 1397
Hood, Adam J. J. MA BD DPhil	1989		Lecturer	67A Farquhar Road, Edgbaston, Birmingham B15 2QP	0121-452 2606
				[E-mail: adamhood1@hotmail.com]	
Hughes, O. Tudor MBE BA	1934	1976	(Guernsey: St Andrew's in the Grange)	4 Belcher Court, Dorchester on Thames, Oxon	01865 340779
Jolly, Andrew J. BD	1989	1996	Chaplain: RAF	Chaplaincy Centre, RAF Halton, Aylesbury, Bucks HP22 5PG	01296 623535 (ext 6374)
				[E-mail: acjolly@btinternet.com]	
Lugton, George L. MA BD	1955	1997	(Guernsey: St Andrew's in the Grange)	6 Clos de Beauvoir, Rue Cohu, Guernsey GY5 7TE	01481 254285
McEnhill, Peter BD PhD	1992	1996	Lecturer	Westminster College, Madingley Road, Cambridge CB3 0AA	01223 353997
Macfarlane, Peter T. BA LTh	1970	1994	(Chaplain: Army)	2 Grosvenor House, Warwick Square, Carlisle CA1 1LB	01228 521519
McIndoe, John H. MA BD STM DD	1966	2000	(London: St Columba's with Newcastle St Andrew's)	5 Dunlin, Westerlands Park, Glasgow G12 0FE	0141-579 1366
MacLeod, Angus BD	1996		Chaplain: Army	RMA Sandhurst, Camberley, Surrey GU15 4PQ	01276 691498
				[E-mail: padrermas@btconnect.com]	
MacLeod, Rory BA MBA BD	1994	1998	Chaplain: Royal Navy	Royal Marines, Hamworthy Barracks, Poole, Dorset BH15 4NQ	
				[E-mail: annice@eurobell.co.uk]	

MacLeod, R.N. MA BD	1986 1992	Chaplain: Army	St Andrew's Garrison Church, Queen's Avenue, Aldershot, Hants GU11 2BY	01252 331123
Majcher, Philip L. BD	1982 1987	Chaplain: Army	Chaplain HQ ARRC, BFPO 40	0049 2161 565551
Martin, Anthony M. BA BD	1989 1989	Chaplain: Army	Allied Command Europe, Rapid Reaction Corps, BFPO 40 [E-mail: am_km_martin@hotmail.com]	0049 2161 519197
Milloy, A. Miller DPE LTh DipTrMan	1979 1998	Regional Secretary: United Bible Societies	United Bible Societies, Allied Dunbar House, East Park, Crawley, West Sussex RH10 6AS	
Mills, Peter W. BD CPS	1984	Chaplain: RAF	Chaplaincy Services RAF, HQ PTC Innsworth, Gloucs GL3 1EZ	01452 510828
Milton, A. Leslie MA BD PhD	1996 2001	Lecturer	Ripon College, Cuddesdon, Oxford OX4 9HP	01865 877408
Norwood, David W. BA	1948 1980	(Lisbon)	6 Kempton Close, Thundersley, Benfleet, Essex SS7 3SG	01268 747219
Rennie, Alistair M. MA BD	1939 1986	(Kincardine Croick and Edderton)	Noble's Yard, St Mary's Gate, Wirksworth, Derbyshire DE4 4DQ	
Richmond, James MA BD PhD	1956 1994	(Lancaster University)	10 Wallace Lane, Forton, Preston, Lancs PR3 0BA	01524 791705
Shackleton, Scott S.S. BD	1993	Chaplain: Royal Navy	RM Stonehouse, Plymouth, Devon	01752 836397
Stewart, Charles E. BSc BD PhD	1976 2000	(Chaplain of the Fleet)	The Royal Hospital School, Holbrook, Ipswich IP9 2RX	01473 326200
Walker, R. Forbes BSc BD ThM	1987 2000	School Chaplain	2 Holmleigh, Priory Road, Ascot, Berks SL5 8EA	01344 883272
Wallace, Donald S.	1950 1980	(Chaplain: RAF)	7 Dellfield Close, Watford, Herts WD1 3BL	01923 223289
White, Earlsley M. BA	1957 1998	(Uddingston: Park)	27 North Lodge, Epsom Cottage, Epsom, Surrey KT17 4JH	01372 821227
Whitton, John P.	1977 1999	Assistant Chaplain General	115 Sycamore Road, Farnborough, Hants GU14 6RE	01262 674488

ENGLAND – Church Addresses

Corby
St Andrew's — Occupation Road
St Ninian's — Beanfield Avenue

Liverpool — The Western Rooms, Anglican Cathedral

London
Crown Court — Crown Court WC2, Pont Street SW1
St Columba's — Sandyford Road
Newcastle

(48) EUROPE

Clerk: REV. JOHN A. COWIE BSc BD — Jan Willem Brouwersstraat 9, NL-1071 LH Amsterdam
[E-mail: j.cowie2@chello.nl] **Tel: 0031 20 672 2288** **Fax: 0031 20 676 4895**

Amsterdam
John A. Cowie BSc BD | 1983 | 1989 | Jan Willem Brouwersstraat 9, NL-1071 LH Amsterdam, The Netherlands [E-mail: j.cowie2@chello.nl] | 0031 20 672 2288 Fax: 0031 20 676 4895

Brussels
Thomas C. Pitkeathly MA CA BD | 1984 | 1991 | 23 Square des Nations, B-1000 Brussels, Belgium [E-mail: pitkeathly@compuserve.com] | 0032 2 672 40 56

Charge / Minister			Address / E-mail	Telephone
Budapest Kenneth I. Mackenzie BD CPS	1990	1999	St Columba's Scottish Mission, Vorosmarty utca 51, H-1064 Budapest, Hungary Oltvany Arok 25, H-1112 Budapest, Hungary (Manse) [E-mail: mackenzie@mail.datanet.hu]	0036 1 343 8479 0036 1 246 2258
Costa del Sol linked with Gibraltar John R. Page BD DipMin	1988	1996	11 Calle Margarita Blanca, E-29640 Fuengirola, Malaga, Spain [E-mail: rico@maptel.es]	0034 5 258 8394
Geneva Ian A. Manson BA BD	1989	2001	6 Chemin Taverney, CH-1218 Grand Saconnex, Geneva, Switzerland [E-mail: cofsg@pingnet.ch]	0041 22 798 29 09 (Office) 0041 22 788 08 31
Gibraltar linked with Costa del Sol John R. Page BD DipMin	1988	1996	St Andrew's Manse, 29 Scud Hill, Gibraltar [E-mail: billsmith@gibnet.gi]	00350 77040
Lausanne Douglas R. Murray MA BD	1965	1994	26 Avenue de Rumine, CH-1005 Lausanne, Switzerland [E-mail: scotskirklausanne@bluewin.ch]	(Tel/Fax) 0041 21 323 98 28
Lisbon Vacant			The Manse, Rua da Arriaga 11, 1200-608 Lisbon, Portugal [E-mail: st.andrewschurch@clix-pt]	(Tel/Fax) 00351 21 395 7677
Malta Vacant			206/3 Old Bakery Street, Valletta, Malta	(Tel/Fax) 00356 222 643
Paris William M. Reid MA BD	1966	1993	10 Rue Thimmonier, F-75009 Paris, France [E-mail: scotskirk@wanadoo.fr]	0033 1 48 78 47 94
Rome St Andrew's William B. McCulloch BD	1997	2002	Via XX Settembre 7, 00187 Rome, Italy [E-mail: revwbmcculloch@hotmail.com]	(Tel) 0039 06 482 7627 (Fax) 0039 06 487 4370
Rotterdam Robert A. Calvert BSc BD DMin	1983	1995	Gelebrem 59, NL-3068 TJ Rotterdam, The Netherlands [E-mail: scots_international_church@compuserve.com]	0031 10 220 4199
Joost Pot BSc (Aux)	1992		[E-mail: j.pot@wanadoo.nl]	

| | | | | (Tel) | 0032 2 234 6834 |
| | | | | (Fax) | 0032 2 231 1413 |

Turin
Robert A. Mackenzie LLB BD — 1993 — Via Sant Anselmo 6, 10125 Turin, Italy [E-mail: valdese.english@arpnet.it] — 0039 011 650 9467

Conference of European Churches — 2001 — Church and Society Commission, Ecumenical Centre, Rue Joseph II 174, B-1000 Brussels, Belgium

World Alliance of Reformed Churches
Paraic Raemonn BA BD — 1982 — 1993 — WARC, 150 Route de Ferney, CH-1211 Geneva 2, Switzerland [E-mail: par@warc.ch] — 0041 22 791 62 43

World Council Secretariat
Alan D. Falconer MA BD DLitt — 1972 — 1995 — WCC, 150 Route de Ferney, CH-1211 Geneva 2, Switzerland [E-mail: af@wcc-coe.org] — 0041 22 791 63 37

CORRESPONDING MEMBERS

James M. Brown MA BD — 1982 — Neustrasse 15, D-4630 Bochum, Germany [E-mail: j.brown@web.de] — 0049 234 133 65

Dr Virgil Cruz — 1956 — 1996 — (Senior Professor of New Testament: Louisville Presbyterian Theological Seminary)

Nii Teiko Dagadu — Geelvinckstraat 21, NL–1901 AE Castricum, The Netherlands Startenweg 130A, NL-3039 JM Rotterdam, The Netherlands [E-mail: niiteiko.dagadu@12move.nl] — 0031 10 244 0898

R. Graeme Dunphy — 1988 — 1993 — Institut für Anglistik, Universitätsstrasse 31, D-93053 Regensburg, Germany
Rhona Dunphy (Mrs)
Professor A.J.C. Heron BD DTheol — 1975 — 1987 — University of Erlangen, Kochstrasse 6, D-91054 Erlangen, Germany [E-mail: arheron@theologie.uni-erlangen.de] — 0049 9131 852202

Jane M. Howitt (Miss) MA BD — 1996 — Scripture Union, PO Box 476, LV-1050 Riga, Latvia [E-mail: janesu@com.latnet.lv] — 00371 7 220877

Stewart J. Lamont BSc BD — 1972 — 2002 — La Poujade, F-82160 Caylus, France [E-mail: lamonts@wanadoo.fr] — 0033 5 63 67 03 77

Bertalan Tamas — St Columba's Scottish Mission, Vorosmarty utca 51, H-1064 Budapest, Hungary [E-mail: rch@mail.elender.hu] — 0036 1 343 8479

Derek Yarwood — Chaplain's Department, Garrison HQ, Princess Royal Barracks, BFPO 47, Germany — 0044 5241 77924

(Rome) David F. Huie MA BD — 1962 — (2001) — 9 Kennedy Crescent, Alverstoke, Gosport, Hants PO12 2NL — 02392 529310
David V.F. Kingston BD — 1993 — Army Chaplain
(Brussels) A.J. Macleod MA BD — 1943 — (1974) — 72A Cathcart Road, London SW10 9DJ
(Brussels) Charles C. McNeill OBE BD — 1962 — (1991) — 17 All Saints Way, Beachamwell, Swaffham, Norfolk PE37 8BU

(Gibraltar)	D. Stuart Philip MA	1952	(1990)	6 St Bernard's Crescent, Edinburgh EH4 1NP	0131-332 7499
(Paris)	Bruce Robertson MA BD	1953	(1992)	Old Dairy Cottage, School Lane, Winfrith Newburgh,	
				Dorset DT2 8JX	
(Malta)	Colin A. Westmarland MBE BD	1971	(2001)	PO Box 5, Cospicua CSP 01, Malta	01305 852050

(49) JERUSALEM

Jerusalem: St Andrew's
Clarence W. Musgrave BA BD ThM   1966   2000   PO Box 8619, 91086 Jerusalem, Israel   (Tel) 00972 2 673 2401
[E-mail: standjer@netvision.net.il]   (Fax) 00972 2 673 1711

Tiberias: St Andrew's
Frederick W. Hibbert BD   1986   1995   St Andrew's, Galilee, PO Box 104, 14100 Tiberias, Israel   (Tel) 00972 4 672 1165
[E-mail: scottie@netvision.net.il]   (Fax) 00972 4 679 0145

SECTION 6

Additional Lists
of Personnel

Page

A	Auxiliary Ministers	260
B	Chaplains to HM Forces	261
C	Chaplains, Hospital	263
D	Chaplains, Full-time Industrial	272
E	Chaplains, Prison	272
F	Chaplains, University	274
G	Diaconate	274
H	Ministers having Resigned Membership of Presbytery	279
I	Ministers holding Practising Certificates	280
J	Mission and Evangelism Advisers	283
K	Overseas Appointments	283
L	Overseas Locations	284
M	Overseas Resigned and Retired Mission Partners	289
N	Parish Assistants and Project Workers	292
O	Readers	293
P	Representatives on Council Education Committees	302
Q	Retired Lay Agents	303
R	Deceased Ministers	304
S	Ministers Ordained for Sixty Years and Upwards	305

LIST A – AUXILIARY MINISTERS

NAME	ORD	ADDRESS	TEL	PR
Anderson, David M. MSc FBCO	1984	1 Dumfries Place, Fort William PH33 6UQ	01397 702091	38
Birch, Jim PGDip FRSA FIOC	2001	1 Kirkhill Grove, Cambuslang, Glasgow G72 8EH	0141-583 1722	16
Brown, Elizabeth (Mrs) JP RGN	1996	25 Highfield Road, Scone, Perth PH2 6RN	01738 552391	28
Brown, Marina D. (Mrs) MA	2000	Elmbank, 3 Lovers Loan, Dollar FK14 7AB	01259 742870	23
Campbell, Gordon	2001	2 Falkland Place, Kingoodie, Invergowrie, Dundee DD2 5DY	01382 561383	29
Charlton, Richard	2001	The Manse, Symbister, Whalsay, Shetland ZE2 9AE	01806 566767	46
Cloggie, June (Mrs)	1997	8 Trossachs Road, Aberfoyle, Stirling FK8 3SW	01877 382382	23
Craggs, Sheila (Mrs)	2001	7 Morar Court, Ellon AB41 9GG	01358 723055	33
Cruikshank, Alistair A.B. MA	1991	2A Chapel Place, Dollar FK14 7DW	01259 742549	23
Davidson, David W.	1987	Grianail, Glenegedale, Port Ellen, Isle of Islay PA42 7AS	01496 302194	19
Durno, Richard C. DSW CQSW	1989	31 Springfield Road, Bishopbriggs, Glasgow G64 1PJ	0141-772 1052	16
Ferguson, Archibald M. MSc PhD CEng FRINA	1989	The Whins, Barrowfield, Cardross, Dumbarton G82 5NL	01389 841517	18
Fletcher, Timothy E.G. BA FCMA	1998	37 Hareston Valley Road, Caterham, Surrey CR3 6HN	01883 340826	47
Glass, Alexander OBE MA	1998	Craigton, Tulloch Avenue, Dingwall IV15 9TU	01349 863258	39
Graham, Andrew	2001	4 Woodside Park, Forres IV36 2GJ	01309 673886	35
Howie, Marion L.K. (Mrs) MA ARCS	1992	51 High Road, Stevenston KA20 3DY	01294 466571	12
Jenkinson, John J. JP LTCL ALCM DipEd DipSen	1991	8 Rosehall Terrace, Falkirk FK1 1PY	01324 625498	22
Kay, Elizabeth (Miss) Dip YCS	1993	1 Kintail Walk, Inchture, Perth PH14 9RY	01828 686029	29
Lunn, Dorothy	2002	14 Bellerby Drive, Ouston, Co. Durham DH2 1TW	0191-492 0647	47
McAlpine, John BSc	1988	Braeside, 201 Bonkle Road, Newmains, Wishaw ML2 9AA	01698 384610	17
McCann, George McD. BSc ATI	1994	Rosbeg, Parsonage Road, Galashiels TD1 3HS	01896 752055	4
MacDonald, Kenneth MA BA	2001	5 Henderland Road, Bearsden, Glasgow G61 1AH	0141-943 1103	16
Mack, Elizabeth (Miss) Dip PEd	1994	24 Roberts Crescent, Dumfries DG2 7RS	01387 264847	8
Mack, John C. JP	1985	The Willows, Auchleven, Insch AB52 6QD	01464 820387	33
Mailer, Colin	2000	Innis Chonain, Back Row, Polmont, Falkirk FK2 0RD	01324 712401	22
Manson, Eileen (Mrs) DCE	1994	1 Cambridge Avenue, Gourock PA19 1XT	01475 632401	15
Morrison, Donald John	2001	22 Kyles Harris, Isle of Harris HS3 3BS	01859 502341	43
Munro, Mary (Mrs) BA	1993	High Barbeth, Leswalt, Stranraer DG9 0QS	01776 870250	9
Paterson, Andrew E. JP	1994	6 The Willows, Kelty KY4 0FQ	01383 830998	24
Paterson, Maureen (Mrs) BSc	1992	91 Dalmahoy Crescent, Kirkcaldy KY2 6TA	01592 262300	25
Pot, Joost BSc	1992	Rijksstraatweg 12, NL-2988 BJ Ridderkerk, The Netherlands	0031 18 042 0894	48
Ramage, Alistair E. BA	1996	16 Claremont Gardens, Milngavie, Glasgow G62 6PG	0141-956 2897	18
Riddell, Thomas S. BSc CEng FIChemE	1993	4 The Maltings, Linlithgow EH49 6DS	01506 843251	2
Ritchie, Christine (Mrs)	2002	Throughgate, 78 High Street, Dunbar EH42 1JH	01368 863141	3
Shaw, Catherine A.M. MA	1998	40 Merrygreen Place, Stewarton, Kilmarnock KA3 5EP	01560 483352	11
Simpson, James H. BSc	1996	11 Claypotts Place, Broughty Ferry, Dundee DD5 1LG	01382 776520	29
Sutherland, John	2001	6 Cromarty Drive, Dundee DD2 2UQ	01382 621473	29
Thomas, Shirley A. (Mrs) Dip Soc Sci AMIA	1988	14 Kirkgait, Letham, Forfar DD8 2XQ	01307 818084	30

Wandrum, David	1993	5 Cawder View, Carrickstone Meadows, Cumbernauld, Glasgow G68 0BN	01236 723288	22
Watson, Jean S. (Miss) MA	1993	29 Strachan Crescent, Dollar FK14 7HL	01259 742872	23
Wilson, Mary D. (Mrs) RGN SCM DTM	1993	The Manse, Bettyhill, Thurso KW14 7SS	01641 521208	40
Wilson, Roy DA ARIBA ARIAS	1990	20 William Ure Place, Bishopbriggs, Glasgow G64 3BH	0141-563 1829	18
Zambonini, James LIA Dip	1997	100 Old Manse Road, Netherton, Wishaw ML2 0EP	01698 350889	17

LIST B – CHAPLAINS TO HM FORCES

NAME	ORD	COM	BCH	ADDRESS
Abeledo, Benjamin J.A. BTh DipTh PTh	1991	1999	A	1 Highlanders, Redford Barracks, Edinburgh EH13 0PP
Aitchison, James W. BD	1993	1993	A	HQ Britcon, UNFICUP, BFPO 567
Britchfield, Alison E.P. (Mrs) MA BD	1987	1992	RN	Britannia Royal Naval College
Brown, Scott J. BD	1993	1993	RN	HMS *Sultan*, Military Road, Gosport, Hants PO12 3BY
Cameron, Robert N.	1975	1981	A	Church Centre, BFPO 40
Cobain, Alan R. BD	2000		A	Somme Barracks, Catterick Garrison, N Yorks DL9 4LD
Connolly, Daniel BD DipTheol DipMin	1983		A	2CS Regt Royal Logistics Corps, BFPO 47
Coulter, David G. BA BD PhD	1989	1994	RN	RMCS, Shrivenham, Swindon, Wilts SN6 8HD
Craig, Gordon T. BD DipMin	1988	1988	RAF	Room 34, Whittle Hall, RAF Cranwell NG34 8HB
Craig, Gordon W. MBE MA BD	1972	1972	RN	420 CDO RM, Bickleigh Barracks, Plymouth, Devon PL6 7AJ
Dailly, J.R. BD DipPS	1979	1979	A	DACC, HQ15(NW) Bde, Imphal Barracks, Fuller Road, York YO10 4AU
Duncan, John C. BD MPhil	1987		A	35 Regt Royal Engineers, BFPO 31
Jolly, Andrew J. BD CertMin	1983	2001	RAF	Chaplaincy Centre, RAF Akrotiri, BFPO 57
Kellock, Chris N. MA BD	1998	1996	RAF	Chaplaincy Services, HQPTC, RAF Innsworth, Gloucester GL3 1EZ
Kennon, Stan MA BD	1992	2000	RN	Church of Scotland and Free Churches Chaplain, RNAS Culdrose, Cornwall
Kingston, David V.F. BD	1993	1993	A	Senior Chaplain, HQ20, Armoured Brigade, BFPO 31
McCulloch, Alen J.R. MA BD	1990	1995	A	3 Regt Royal Horse Artillery, BFPO 38
McFadzean, Iain MA BD	1989	1999	RN	HMS *Neptune*, Faslane, Helensburgh G84 8HL
Mackenzie, Seoras L. BD	1996	1998	A	1 Bn Royal Scots, BFPO 802
MacLeod, Charles A. MA BD	1996	1996	A	Royal Military Academy, Camberley, Surrey GU15 4PQ
MacLeod, Roderick N. MA BD	1986	1992	A	101 Logistic Brigade, Buller Barracks, Aldershot, Hants GU11 2BX
MacLeod, Rory A.R. BA BD MBA	1994	1998	A	Commando Training Establishment, Lympstone, Exmouth, Devon EX8 5AR
Majcher, Philip L. BD	1982	1987	RN	HQ ARRC, Joint Headquarters, BFPO 40
Martin, Anthony M. BA BD	1989	1989	A	16 Regt Royal Corps of Signals, BFPO 40
Mills, Peter W. BD CPS	1984	1984	RAF	Principal Chaplain, Church of Scotland and Free Churches RAF, Room 86, HQ PTC, RAF Innsworth, Gloucester GL3 1EZ
Prentice, Donald K. BSc BD	1987	1992	A	IRNF, Fort George, Inverness IV2 7TE
Rae, Scott M. MBE BD CPS	1976	1981	RN	HMS *Neptune*, Faslane, Helensburgh G84 8HL
Shackleton, Scott J.S. BA BD	1993	1993	RN	Staff Chaplain Commandant General Royal Navy Marines, RM Barracks, Stonehouse, Plymouth PL1 3QS
Shaw, Duncan LTh CPS	1984	1984	RAF	Chaplains Office, RAF Leuchars, St Andrews KY16 0XJ
Whitton, John P. MA BD	1977	1977	A	Assistant Chaplain General, Headquarters 4th Division, Steele's Road, Aldershot GU11 2DP

CHAPLAINS TO HM FORCES (Territorial Army)

NAME	ORD	COM	ADDRESS
Barclay, Iain C. TD	1976	1982	HQ 2nd Division
Blakey, Stephen A.	1977	1996	32 Sig. R (V)
Forsyth, Alex R. TD	1973	1983	71 (AS) Regt RE (V)
Gibson, James M.	1978	1986	205 (S) Fd Hosp (V)
Kinsey, Louis	1991	1992	205 (S) Fd Hosp (V)
Swindells, Sean	1996	2001	225 (H) Fd Ambulance
Thomson, John M.A.	1978	1992	105 Regt RA (V)
Warwick, Ivan C.	1980	1990	Highland Volunteers

CHAPLAINS TO HM FORCES (Army Cadet Force)

NAME	ORD	COM	ADDRESS
Almond, David M.	1996	1998	West Lowland
Andrews, J. Edward	1985	1998	Lothian & Borders Bn
Barclay, Iain C. TD	1976	1996	BW Bn
Campbell, R.D.M. TD			Highlanders Bn
Charlton, I.A.			Shetland (Indep) Bty
Fisk, E.A.	1996	1999	BW Bn
Goskirk, J. Leslie	1968	1985	1 Hldrs Bn
Homewood, I. Max	1997	1998	Argyll & Sutherland Highlanders Bn
Keys, J.			Orkney (Indep) Bty
Sherratt, Arthur	1994	1999	West Lowland Bn
Sutherland, Iain A.	1996	1999	1 Hldrs Bn
Swindells, Sean	1996	1998	2 Hldrs Bn
Whyte, Margaret A.	1988	1997	Glasgow & Lanarkshire Bn
Wilson, G.N.			Glasgow & Lanarkshire Bn

LIST C – HOSPITAL CHAPLAINS ('Full-time' Chaplains are listed first in each area)

LOTHIAN

EDINBURGH – LOTHIAN UNIVERSITY HOSPITALS NHS TRUST

ROYAL INFIRMARY [0131-536 3085]
Rev. Iain Telfer — 32 Alnwickhill Park, Edinburgh EH16 6UH — 0131-536 3084
Miss Anne Mulligan Chaplain's Assistant — 27A Craigour Avenue, Edinburgh EH17 1NH — 0131-536 3086

WESTERN GENERAL HOSPITAL [0131-537 1000]
Rev. Alexander Young — 19B Craigour Drive, Edinburgh EH17 7NY — 0131-537 1401
Rev. Alistair K. Ridland — 13 Stewart Place, Kirkliston EH29 2BQ — 0131-537 1401

LOTHIAN PRIMARY CARE NHS TRUST

ROYAL EDINBURGH HOSPITAL [0131-537 6734]
Rev. Murray Chalmers — 25 Greenbank Road, Edinburgh EH10 5RX
Rev. Lorna Murray — 5 Comely Bank Place, Edinburgh EH4 1DT
Rev. Patricia Allen Chaplain's Assistant — 1 Westgate, Dunbar EH42 1JL

ROYAL HOSPITAL FOR SICK CHILDREN/LIBERTON [0131-536 0000]
Rev. Caroline Upton — 10 (3FL) Montagu Terrace, Edinburgh EH3 5QX

EDINBURGH COMMUNITY MENTAL HEALTH
Rev. Lorna Murray — 41 George IV Bridge, Edinburgh EH1 1EL — 0131-220 5150
Rev. Iain Whyte — 41 George IV Bridge, Edinburgh EH1 1EL — 0131-220 5150

LIVINGSTON – WEST LOTHIAN HEALTHCARE NHS TRUST [01506 419666]
Rev. Thomas Crichton — 18 Carlton Terrace, Edinburgh EH7 5DD
Rev. Dr Georgina Nelson — 6 Pentland Park, Craigshill, Livingston EH54 5NR

HOSPICES

MARIE CURIE CENTRE
Rev. Tom Gordon — Frogston Road West, Edinburgh EH10 7DR — (Tel) 0131-445 2141 / (Fax) 0131-445 5845

ST COLUMBA'S HOSPICE
Rev. Alison Wagstaff — Challenger Lodge, 15 Boswall Road, Edinburgh EH5 3RW — 0131-551 1381

CORSTORPHINE
Rev. J. William Hill — 23 Belgrave Road, Edinburgh EH12 6NG — 0131-334 3188

EASTERN GENERAL
Rev. John Tait — 52 Pilrig Street, Edinburgh EH6 5AS — 0131-554 1842

ROYAL EDINBURGH HOSPITAL
Rev. John Whitley — 114 Viewforth, Edinburgh EH10 4LN — 0131-229 0133

LINLITHGOW ST MICHAEL'S
Rev. John Paterson — St Michael's Manse, Linlithgow EH49 7AL — 01506 842195

BELHAVEN
Rev. Laurence H. Twaddle — The Manse, Belhaven Road, Dunbar EH42 1NH — 01368 863098

EDENHALL
Rev. Anne M. Jones — 7 North Elphinstone Farm, Tranent EH33 2ND — 01875 614442

HERDMANFLAT
Rev. William C. Thomas — 11 Muirfield Crescent, Gullane EH31 2HN — 01620 842415

LOANHEAD
Mrs Susan Duncan — 35 Kilmaurs Road, Edinburgh EH16 5DB — 0131-667 2995

ROODLANDS
Rev. Kenneth D.F. Walker — The Manse, Athelstaneford, North Berwick EH39 5BE — 01620 880378

ROSSLYNLEE
Rev. John W. Fraser — North Manse, Penicuik EH26 8AG — 01968 672213
Mrs Muriel Willoughby — 32 Marchburn Drive, Penicuik EH26 9HE — 01968 675249

BORDERS

MELROSE –
BORDERS GENERAL HOSPITAL
NHS TRUST [01896 754333]

Location	Name	Address	Tel
	Rev. J. Ronald Dick	Chaplaincy Centre, Borders General Hospital, Melrose TD6 9BS	
DINGLETON	Rev. John Riddell	42 High Street, Jedburgh TD8 6NQ	01835 863223
HAY LODGE, PEEBLES	Rev. James H. Wallace	Innerleithen Road, Peebles EH45 8BD	01721 721749
KNOLL	Rev. Andrew Morrice	The Manse, Castle Street, Duns TD11 3DG	01361 883755
INCH	Rev. Robin McHaffie	Kirk Yetholm, Kelso TD5 8RD	01573 420308

DUMFRIES AND GALLOWAY

DUMFRIES HOSPITALS
[01387 246246]

Location	Name	Address	Tel
	Rev. Alexander E. Strachan	2 Leafield Road, Dumfries DG1 2DS	01387 279460
THOMAS HOPE, LANGHOLM	Rev. Robert Milne	The Manse, Langholm DG13 0BL	01896 668577
LOCHMABEN	Rev. Alexander Stoddart	The Manse, Hightae, Lockerbie DG11 1JL	01387 811499
MOFFAT	Rev. David McKay	The Manse, Moffat DG10 9LR	01683 220128
NEW ANNAN	Rev. Mairi Byers	Meadowbank, Plumdon Road, Annan DG12 6SJ	01461 206512
CASTLE DOUGLAS	Rev. Robert Malloch	1 Castle View, Castle Douglas DG7 1BG	01556 502171
CRESSWELL	Rev. Mary Hutchison (Mrs)	25 Twiname Way, Heathhall, Dumfries DG1 3ST	01387 250610
DUMFRIES AND GALLOWAY ROYAL INFIRMARY	Rev. Mary Hutchison (Mrs)	25 Twiname Way, Heathhall, Dumfries DG1 3ST	01387 250610
	Rev. D.K.P. Bennett	Irongray Manse, Dumfries DG2 9TR	01387 720227
KIRKCUDBRIGHT	Rev. Douglas R. Irving	6 Bourtree Avenue, Kirkcudbright DG6 4AU	01557 330489
THORNHILL			
DALRYMPLE			
GARRICK	Rev. Samuel McC. Harris	Linden, Leswalt Road, Stranraer DG9 0AA	01776 706387
NEWTON STEWART	Rev. Neil G. Campbell	The Manse, Newton Stewart DG8 6HH	01671 402259

AYRSHIRE AND ARRAN

AYRSHIRE AND ARRAN PRIMARY CARE
NHS TRUST [01292 513023]

Location	Name	Address	Tel
AILSA HOSPITAL, AYR	Rev. Sheila Mitchell	Chaplaincy Centre, Dalmellington Road, Ayr KA6 6AB	

AYRSHIRE AND ARRAN ACUTE HOSPITALS NHS TRUST [01563 521133]

Hospital	Chaplain	Address	Tel.
CROSSHOUSE HOSPITAL KILMARNOCK	Rev. Judith Huggett	4 Westmoor Crescent, Kilmarnock KA1 1TX	01292 442554
AYR/BIGGART HOSPITALS [01292 610555]	Rev. Roderick H. McNidder	6 Hollow Park, Alloway, Ayr KA7 4SR	
ARROL PARK	Mrs Norma Livingstone	31 Victoria Drive, Troon KA10 6JF	01292 269161
BALLOCHMYLE	Rev. A.M. McPhail	87 Forehill Road, Ayr KA7 3JR	01465 831282
DAVIDSON	Rev. Robert Bell	The Manse, Ballantrae, Girvan KA26 0UH	01290 420769
HOLMHEAD	Rev. John Paterson	33 Barrhill Road, Cumnock KA18 1PJ	01563 521665
CROSSHOUSE	Mrs Norma Livingstone	31 Victoria Drive, Troon KA10 6JF	01863 538289
KIRKLANDSIDE	Rev. James McNaughtan	35 South Gargieston Drive, Kilmarnock KA1 1TB	01863 538289
STRATHLEA	Mrs Barbara Urquhart	Manse of Kilmaurs, 9 Standalane, Kilmaurs KA3 2NB	01294 279916
	Mrs Barbara Urquhart	Manse of Kilmaurs, 9 Standalane, Kilmaurs KA3 2NB	
AYRSHIRE CENTRAL	Rev. Hugh M. Adamson	Mure Church Manse, West Road, Irvine KA12 8RE	01475 672370
	Rev. Scott Robertson	31 Milgarholm Avenue, Irvine KA12 0EL	01770 700289
	Mrs Norma Livingstone	31 Victoria Drive, Troon KA10 6JF	01475 530460
BROOKSBY HOUSE, LARGS	Rev. Stephen J. Smith	31 Douglas Street, Largs KA30 8PT	
WAR MEMORIAL, ARRAN	Rev. Elizabeth Watson	The Manse, Whiting Bay, Isle of Arran KA27 8RE	
LADY MARGARET, MILLPORT	Rev. Marjory MacKay	The Manse, Millport, Isle of Cumbrae KA28 0EE	

LANARKSHIRE

Hospital	Chaplain	Address	Tel.
LOCKHART	Rev. Catherine Collins	2 Friarsdene, Lanark ML11 9EJ	01555 663363
CLELAND	Rev. Bruce Gordon	The Rectory, Cleghorn Road, Lanark ML11 7QT	01698 860260
KELLO	Rev. John Jackson	The Manse, Bellside Road, Cleland, Motherwell ML1 5NP	01899 220227
LADY HOME	Rev. Gavin Elliott	61 High Street, Biggar ML12 6DA	01698 882238
ROADMEETINGS	Rev. Geoff McKee	Kirkstyle Manse, Church Street, Carluke ML8 4BA	01555 892409
WISHAW GENERAL	Rev. James S.G. Hastie	Chalmers Manse, Quarry Road, Larkhall ML9 1HH	01698 372657
	Rev. David A. Young	The Manse, 2 Lanark Road, Kirkmuirhill, Lanark ML11 9RB	01355 663363
	Rev. J. Allardyce	6 Ryde Road, Wishaw ML2 7DU	01236 763154
	Rev. David Collins	Greyfriars Manse, Friarsdene, Lanark ML11 9EJ	01698 263472
	Rev. Sharon Colvin	48 Dunrobin Road, Airdrie ML6 8LR	
	Rev. David W. Doyle	19 Orchard Street, Motherwell ML1 3JE	
STRATHCLYDE	Rev. John Brewster	21 Turnberry Place, East Kilbride, Glasgow G75 8TB	01355 242564
BIRKWOOD	Rev. Dr John McPake	30 Eden Grove, East Kilbride, Glasgow G75 8XY	01355 234196
HAIRMYRES	Rev. Marjorie Taylor	1 Kirkhill Road, Strathaven ML10 6HN	01357 520643
	Rev. James S.G. Hastie	Chalmers Manse, Quarry Road, Larkhall ML9 1HH	01698 882238
KIRKLANDS	Rev. Rosemary Smith	Blantyre Old Manse, High Blantyre, Glasgow G72 9UA	01357 522758
STONEHOUSE	Rev. James P. Fraser	26 Hamilton Road, Strathaven ML10 6JA	

UDSTON	Rev. J. Stanley Cook	137A Old Manse Road, Netherton, Wishaw ML2 0EW	01698 299600
	Rev. William Beattie	33 Dungavel Gardens, Hamilton ML3 7PE	01698 423804
COATHILL	Rev. James Munton	Old Monkland Manse, Coatbridge ML5 5QT	01236 423788
MONKLANDS GENERAL	Rev. James S. Salmond	Manse of Holytown, Motherwell ML1 5RU	01698 832622
	Rev. Andrew Thomson	38 Commonhead Street, Airdrie ML6 6NS	01236 602538
	Rev. James Grier	47 Blair Road, Coatbridge ML5 1JQ	01236 43427
WESTER MOFFAT	Rev. Thomas Pollock	Clarkston Manse, Forrest Street, Airdrie ML6 7BE	01236 769676
HARTWOODHILL	Rev. Henry J.W. Findlay	St Mark's Manse, Coltness Road, Wishaw ML2 7EX	01698 384596
	Rev. Colin Cuthbert	Yieldshields Farm, Carluke ML8 4QB	
HATTONLEA	Rev. Agnes Moore	16 Croftpark Street, Bellshill ML4 1EY	01698 842877
MOTHERWELL –			
PSYCHIATRIC	Rev. John Handley	12 Airbles Crescent Motherwell ML1 3AR	01698 262733
COMMUNITY MENTAL HEALTH CARE	Rev. J. Stanley Cook	137A Old Manse Road, Netherton, Wishaw ML2 0EW	01698 299600
	Rev. Sharon Colvin	48 Dunrobin Road, Airdrie ML6 8LR	01236 763154
	Rev. Rosemary Smith	Blantyre Old Manse, High Blantyre, Glasgow G72 9UA	01698 823130

GREATER GLASGOW

NORTH GLASGOW UNIVERSITY HOSPITALS NHS TRUST			
GLASGOW ROYAL INFIRMARY [0141-211 4000/4661]	Rev. Patricia McDonald	4 Whithope Terrace, Glasgow G53 7LT	
	Rev. Anne J.M. Harper	122 Greenock Road, Bishopton PA7 5AS	
WESTERN INFIRMARY [0141-211 2000]	Rev. Keith Saunders	1 Beckfield Drive, Robroyston, Glasgow G33 1SR	0141-211 2000/2812
GARTNAVEL GENERAL [0141-211 3000]	Rev. Keith Saunders	1 Beckfield Drive, Robroyston, Glasgow G33 1SR	0141-211 3000/3026
GLASGOW HOMEOPATHIC [0141-211 1600]	Rev. Keith Saunders	1 Beckfield Drive, Robroyston, Glasgow G33 1SR	0141-211 1600
GREATER GLASGOW PRIMARY CARE NHS TRUST	Rev. Cameron H. Langlands: Co-ordinator		
GARTNAVEL ROYAL HOSPITAL [0141-211 3686]	Rev. Gordon B. Armstrong: North/East Sector		
	Ms Anne MacDonald: South Sector		
SOUTH GLASGOW UNIVERSITY HOSPITALS NHS TRUST			
SOUTHERN GENERAL HOSPITAL [0141-201 2156]	Rev. Janet P.H. Macmahon	6 Jubilee Gardens, Bearsden, Glasgow G61 2RT	
	Rev. Blair Robertson	14 Crosbie Street, Glasgow G20 0BD	
VICTORIA INFIRMARY	Rev. Iain Reid	Chaplain's Office, Langside Road, Glasgow G42 9TT	0141-201 5164
YORKHILL NHS TRUST [0141-201 0595]	Rev. Alistair Bull	Royal Hospital for Sick Children, Glasgow G3 8SG	
	Rev. Hilda Smith	Royal Hospital for Sick Children, Glasgow G3 8SG	

LIGHTBURN GERIATRIC			
ROYAL INFIRMARY	Rev. Patricia McDonald	4 Whithope Terrace, Glasgow G53 7LT	0141-876 1408
	Mrs Sandra Bell	62 Loganswell Road, Thornliebank, Glasgow G46 8AX	
STOBHILL	Rev. Norma Stewart	127 Nether Auldhouse Road, Glasgow G43 2YS	0141-637 6956
	Rev. Elizabeth W. Sutherland	54 Etive Crescent, Bishopbriggs, Glasgow G54 1ES	0141-772 1453
	Rev. John Beaton	33 North Birbiston Road, Lennoxtown, Glasgow G65 7LZ	
CANNIESBURN	Rev. Kenneth Coulter	8 Abbotsford Avenue, Rutherglen, Glasgow G73 3NX	0141-647 6250
LEVERNDALE	Rev. Margaret Yule	Radnor Park Manse, Spencer Street, Clydebank G81 3AS	0141-951 1007
DARNLEY COURT	Miss Anne MacDonald	62 Berwick Drive, Glasgow G52 3JA	0141-883 5618
VICTORIA INFIRMARY/MEARNSKIRK	Rev. Colin Brown	2 Waukglen Drive, Southpark Village, Glasgow G43 7UG	
GARTNAVEL GENERAL/WESTERN	Rev. Alan Raeburn	110 Mount Annan Drive, Glasgow G44 4RZ	0141-632 1514
	Rev. Stuart Macdonald	28 Kessington Road, Bearsden, Glasgow G61 2HL	0141-942 1313
BLAWARTHILL	Mrs Deirdre Lyon	14 Melfort Avenue, Clydebank, Glasgow G81 2HX	
COWGLEN	Mrs Deirdre Lyon	14 Melfort Avenue, Clydebank, Glasgow G81 2HX	
GREENFIELD PARK	Rev. Patricia McDonald	4 Whithope Terrace, Glasgow G53 7LT	0141-876 1408
KNIGHTSWOOD/DRUMCHAPEL	Rev. Andrew McMillan	1 Swallow Gardens, Glasgow G13 4QD	0141-959 7158
LENZIE	Rev. James Ferguson	The Manse, Larch Avenue, Lenzie, Glasgow G66 4HX	0141-776 3831
RUTHERGLEN TAKARE	Rev. J.W. Drummond	21 Albert Drive, Rutherglen, Glasgow G73 3RT	0141-643 0234
	Rev. Alexander Thomson	31 Highburgh Drive, Rutherglen, Glasgow G73 3RR	0141-647 6178
PRINCE AND PRINCESS OF WALES HOSPICE	Rev. Alan Donald	71 Carlton Place, Glasgow G5 9TD	0141-429 5599
FOURHILLS NURSING HOME	Rev. W.G. Ramsay	3 Tofthill Avenue, Bishopbriggs, Glasgow G64 3PN	0141-762 1844
HUNTERS HILL MARIE CURIE CENTRE	Rev. David Mitchell	1 Belmont Road, Glasgow G21 3AY	0141-558 2555

ARGYLL AND CLYDE

INVERCLYDE ROYAL HOSPITAL			
GREENOCK [01475 633777]			
DYKEBAR	Mrs Joyce Nicol	93 Brisbane Street, Greenock PA16 8NY	01475 723235
	Rev. Alistair Morrison	36 Newtyle Road, Paisley PA1 3JX	0141-889 4279
	Rev. Alexander MacDonald	The Manse, Neilston, Glasgow G78 3NP	0141-881 1958
	Rev. Brian L. Farmer	27 Oakwood Avenue, Paisley PA2 9NG	0141-884 4502
	Miss Margaret McBain	33 Quarry Road, Paisley PA2 7RD	0141-854 2920
HAWKHEAD	Rev. Georgina Baxendale	The Manse, Main Street, Houston, Johnstone PA6 7EL	01505 612569
MERCHISTON HOUSE	Rev. Thomas Cant	18 Oldhall Road, Paisley PA1 3HL	0141-882 2277
JOHNSTONE	Rev. Thomas Cant	18 Oldhall Road, Paisley PA1 3HL	0141-882 2277
ROYAL ALEXANDRA	Rev. Arthur Sherratt	West Manse, Kilbarchan, Johnstone PA10 2JR	01805 702669
	Rev. Robin Allison	1 Station Rise, Lochwinnoch PA12 4NA	01505 843484
	Rev. Douglas Ralph	24 Kinpurnie Road, Paisley PA1 3HH	0141-883 3505
	Rev. Ian S. Currie	9 Hawkhead Road, Paisley PA1 3ND	0141-887 0884
	Rev. Alexander Wark	31 Gibson Road, Renfrew PA4 0RH	0141-886 2005
	Rev. Ritchie Gillon	31 Southfield Avenue, Paisley PA2 8BX	0141-884 6215
	Rev. E. Lorna Hood (Mrs)	North Manse, 1 Alexandra Drive, Renfrew PA4 8UB	0141-886 2074

Institution	Chaplain	Address	Phone
RAVENSCRAIG	Rev. James H. Simpson	76 Finnart Street, Greenock PA16 8HJ	01475 722338
DUMBARTON JOINT	Rev. Douglas Cranston	6 Churchill Road, Kilmacolm PA13 4LH	01505 873271
VALE OF LEVEN GENERAL	Rev. Christine Liddell	3 Havoc Road, Dumbarton G82 4JW	01389 604840
VALE OF LEVEN GERIATRIC	Rev. Ian Miller	1 Glebe Gardens, Bonhill, Alexandria G83 9HB	01389 753039
CAMPBELTOWN	Rev. Ian Wilkie	38 Main Street, Renton, Dumbarton G82 4PU	01389 752017
	Mrs Janice Forrest	The Manse, Southend, Campbeltown PA28 6RQ	01586 830274
LOCHGILPHEAD	Rev. Alison Ross	Kilmichael Glassary, Lochgilphead PA31 8QA	01546 606926
	Mrs Margaret Sinclair	2 Quarry Park, Furnace, Inveraray PA32 8XW	01499 500633
ISLAY	Rev. Anne McIvor	The Manse, Bowmore, Isle of Islay PA43 7LH	01496 810271
DUNOON	Rev. Patricia Lang	1 Royal Crescent, Dunoon PA23 7AH	01369 701291
DUNOON ARGYLL UNIT	Rev. Austin Erskine	99 Sandhaven, Sandbank, Dunoon PA23 8QW	01369 701295
ROTHESAY	Rev. Ronald Samuel	9 Bishop Terrace, Rothesay PA20 9HF	01700 504378
LORN AND THE ISLANDS DISTRICT GENERAL	Rev. William Gray	Lochnagar, Longsdale Road, Oban PA34 5DZ	01631 567471

FORTH VALLEY

Institution	Chaplain	Address	Phone
BELLSDYKE	Rev. Ann Smith	16 Mannerston Holdings, Linlithgow EH49 7ND	01506 834350
	Rev. Henry Munroe	Viewforth, High Road, Maddiston, Falkirk FK2 0BL	01324 712446
	Rev. Robert MacLeod	13 Cannons Way, Falkirk FK2 7QG	01324 631008
BO'NESS	Rev. James Marshall	Craigmailen Manse, Braehead, Bo'ness EH51 0BZ	01506 823784
BONNYBRIDGE	Rev. Alisdair MacLeod-Mair	133 Falkirk Road, Bonnybridge FK4 1BA	01324 812621
FALKIRK ROYAL INFIRMARY	Rev. Joanne Finlay	6 Herd Green, Livingston EH54 8PU	01324 813786
	Rev. Helen Christie	5 Watson Place, Dennyloanhead, Bonnybridge FK4 2BG	0131-337 7153
RSNH LARBERT	Rev. Margery Collin	2 Saughtonhall Crescent, Edinburgh EH12 5RF	01324 861252
BANNOCKBURN	Rev. Robert Philip	Congregational Church Manse, Avonbridge, Falkirk FK1 2LU	01786 814692
CLACKMANNAN COUNTY	Rev. James Landels	Allan Manse, Bogend Road, Bannockburn, Stirling FK7 8NP	01259 212836
KILDEAN	Rev. Eleanor Forgan	18 Alexandra Drive, Alloa FK10 2DQ	01786 823902
SAUCHIE	Rev. Robert Symington	3 Belmont House, The Crescent, Dunblane FK15 0DW	01786 465547
STIRLING ROYAL INFIRMARY	Rev. Malcolm MacRae	10b Victoria Place, Stirling FK8 2QU	01786 831026
	Rev. Stuart Pryce	36 Forth Park, Bridge of Allan FK9 5NT	01786 474421
	Rev. Gary McIntyre	7 Randolph Road, Stirling FK8 2AJ	01786 475802
	Rev. Kenneth Russell	5 Clifford Road, Stirling FK8 2QU	

FIFE

FIFE ACUTE HOSPITALS NHS TRUST
QUEEN MARGARET HOSPITAL, DUNFERMLINE [01383 674136]
VICTORIA HOSPITAL, KIRKCALDY [01592 643355]

Chaplain	Address	Phone
Rev. Isabel Whyte		
Rev. Iain J.M. McDonald	11 James Grove, Kirkcaldy KY1 1TN	01592 253775

LYNEBANK	Rev. Elizabeth Fisk	51 St John's Drive, Dunfermline FK12 7TL	01383 720256
MILESMARK	Rev. Isabel Whyte		01383 674136
CAMERON	Rev. James L. Templeton	Innerleven Manse, McDonald Street, Methil, Leven KY8 3AJ	01333 426310
	Rev. Kenneth Donald	33 Main Road, East Wemyss, Kirkcaldy KY1 4RE	01592 713260
GLENROTHES	Rev. Ian D. Gordon	7 Guthrie Crescent, Markinch, Glenrothes KY7 6AY	01592 758264
RANDOLPH WEMYSS	Rev. Elizabeth Cranfield	9 Chemiss Road, Methilhill, Leven KY8 2BS	01592 713142
ADAMSON, CUPAR	Rev. Colin Dempster	27 Bell Street, Tayport DD6 9AP	01382 552861
NETHERLEA, NEWPORT	Rev. Dr Henry Gibson	4 Comerton Place, Drumoig, St Andrews KY16 0NQ	01382 542199
STRATHEDEN, CUPAR	Rev. Alan Roy	14 Comerton Place, Drumoig, St Andrews KY16 0NQ	01382 542225
	Miss Margaret Browning	4 Wellpark Terrace, Newport-on-Tay DD6 8HT	01382 542140
ST ANDREWS MEMORIAL	Rev. David Arnott	20 Priory Gardens, St Andrews KY16 8XX	01334 472912

TAYSIDE

TAYSIDE UNIVERSITY HOSPITALS NHS TRUST DUNDEE NINEWELLS HOSPITAL [01382 660111]	Rev. David J. Gordon		
PERTH ROYAL INFIRMARY [01738 473896]	Rev. John M. Birrell	Rhynd Road, Perth PH2 8TP	01738 552237
	Rev. Anne Findlay	Balcraig Manse, Scone, Perth PH2 7PG	01887 820656
ABERFELDY	Rev. Alexander M. Gunn	The Manse, Taybridge Terrace, Aberfeldy PH15 2BS	01828 640731
BLAIRGOWRIE RATTRAY	Rev. Ian Knox	Heatherlea, Manse Road, Ardler, Blairgowrie PH12 8SR	01796 472719
IRVINE MEMORIAL	Rev. Christopher Brown	8 Tom-na-Moan Road, Pitlochry PH16 5HN	01764 652325
CRIEFF COTTAGE	Rev. Henry A.G. Tait	14 Shieling Hill Place, Crieff PH7 4ER	01738 624167
MACMILLAN HOSPICE	Rev. Anne Stewart	35 Rose Crescent, Perth PH1 1NT	01334 656991
MURRAY ROYAL	Rev. Peter Meager	7 Lorraine Drive, Cupar KY15 5DY	01738 625694
	Rev. Isobel Birrell	Rhynd Road, Perth PH2 8TP	01764 662525
ST MARGARET'S COTTAGE	Rev. Randal MacAlister	St Kessog's Rectory, High Street, Auchterarder PH3 1AD	01382 532607
ASHLUDIE	Rev. Roy Massie	St Rule's Manse, 8 Church Street, Monifieth, Dundee DD5 4JP	
	Rev. David Jamieson	Panmure Manse, 8A Albert Street, Monifieth, Dundee DD5 4JS	01382 532772
TAYSIDE ORTHOPAEDIC AND REHAB. CENTRE	Rev. Thomas P. Robertson	20 Kilnburn, Newport-on-Tay DD6 8DE	01382 542422
DUNDEE, ROYAL LIFF			
ROYAL VICTORIA	Mr Ian Gray	15 Rossie Island Road, Montrose DD10 9NH	01674 677126
NINEWELLS	Rev. Tom Milroy	9 Long Row, Westhaven, Carnoustie DD7 6BE	01241 856654
STRATHMARTINE			
ARBROATH INFIRMARY	Rev. Alasdair G. Graham	1 Charles Avenue, Arbroath DD11 2EZ	01241 872244
BRECHIN INFIRMARY	Rev. James P.R. Drysdale	36 Park Road, Brechin DD9 7AP	01356 622789
FORFAR INFIRMARY	Rev. Graham Norrie	East Manse, Lour Road, Forfar DD8 2BB	01307 464303
WHITEHILLS	Rev. Brian Ramsay	The Manse, Guthrie, Forfar DD8 2TP	01241 828243

LITTLE CAIRNIE	Rev. Ian G. Gough	St Vigeans Manse, Arbroath DD11 4RD	01241 873206
MONTROSE ROYAL	Rev. Iain M. Douglas	49 North Esk Road, Montrose DD10 8TQ	01674 672060
STRACATHRO	Rev. James Drysdale	51 Airlie Street, Brechin DD9 6JX	01356 625201
SUNNYSIDE ROYAL	Mr Gordon Anderson	33 Grampian View, Montrose DD10 9SU	01674 674915

GRAMPIAN

GRAMPIAN UNIVERSITY HOSPITALS NHS TRUST
ABERDEEN ROYAL INFIRMARY
[01224 681818 and 01224 840747]

Rev. Fred Coutts	9a Millburn Street, Aberdeen AB11 6SS	
Rev. James Falconer	3 Brimmond Walk, Westhill, Skene AB32 6XH	
Rev. Gillian Munro	685 George Street, Aberdeen AB25 3XP	
Rev. Muriel Knox (Chaplain's Assistant)	35 Valentine Drive, Aberdeen AB22 8YF	
Miss Monica Stewart (Chaplain's Assistant)	9 Craigton Avenue, Aberdeen AB15 7RD	
Rev. Alison Hutchison	'Ashfield', Drumoak, Banchory AB31 3AA	

GRAMPIAN PRIMARY CARE NHS TRUST
ROYAL CORNHILL and WOODLANDS HOSPITAL
[01224 663123]

Rev. William Campbell	43 Murray Terrace, Aberdeen AB1 2SA
Mr Donald Meston (Chaplain's Assistant)	20 Rosehill Place, Aberdeen AB2 2LE
Miss Pamela Adam (Chaplain's Assistant)	409 Holburn Street, Aberdeen AB10 7GS

ABERDEEN CITY	Rev. Marian Cowie	6 St Swithin Street, Aberdeen AB10 6XE	01224 593302
ABOYNE			
KINCARDINE COMMUNITY	Rev. Gordon Farquharson	Dunnottar Manse, Stonehaven AB39 3XL	01569 762874
	Rev. David Stewart	South Church Manse, Cameron Street, Stonehaven AB39 2HE	01569 762576
GLEN O' DEE	Rev. Donald Walker	2 Wilson Road, Banchory AB31 3UY	01330 822811
KINCARDINE O'NEIL	Rev. Peter R. Taylor	The Manse, Torphins, Banchory AB31 4JS	01339 882276
INVERURIE	Rev. Ian B. Groves	West Manse, Inverurie AB51 9YS	01467 620285
INSCH			
JUBILEE	Rev. Thomas Calder	The Manse, Queen Street, Huntly AB54 5EB	01466 792630
CAMPBELL	Rev. Iain Sutherland	The Manse, Portsoy, Banff AB45 2QB	01261 842272
CHALMERS	Rev. Alan Macgregor	7 Colleonard Road, Banff AB45 1DZ	01261 812107
FRASERBURGH	Rev. Douglas R. Clyne	97 Saltoun Place, Fraserburgh AB43 5RY	01346 518536
LADYSBRIDGE	Rev. Stewart Jeffrey	8 West End, Whitehills, Banff AB42 2NL	01261 861523

Institution	Chaplain	Address	Telephone
MAUD	Rev. Alastair Donald	New Deer Manse, Turriff AB53 6TG	01771 644216
PETERHEAD COTTAGE	Rev. David S. Ross	1 Hawthorn Road, Peterhead AB42 6DW	01779 472618
TURRIFF	Rev. Sylvia Dyer	The Shieling, Westfield Road, Turriff AB53 4AF	01888 562530
UGIE	Rev. David Pitkeathly	1 Landale Road, Peterhead AB42 1QN	01779 472141
BILBOHALL	Rev. George B. Rollo	18 Reidhaven Street, Elgin IV30 1QH	01343 547208
DR GRAY'S	Rev. George B. Rollo	18 Reidhaven Street, Elgin IV30 1QH	01343 547208
FLEMING COTTAGE	Rev. Ruth Tait	30 Mayne Road, Elgin IV30 1PB	
LEANCHOIL	Rev. John Beck	The Manse, Dunbar Street, Burghead, Elgin IV30 2XB	01343 830365
SPYNIE	Rev. Ray Hall	21 St Peter's Road, Duffus, Elgin IV30 5QL	01343 830985
SEAFIELD	Mrs Sandra Welch	16 Mid Street, Findochty, Buckie AB45 4QU	01542 832189
STEPHEN AND COUNTY HOSPITALS	Rev. Hugh M.C. Smith	The Manse, Church Street, Dufftown, Keith AB55 4AR	01340 820380
TURNER MEMORIAL	Rev. Dr Kay Gauld	The Manse, Church Road, Keith AB55 5BR	01542 882799

HIGHLAND

Institution	Chaplain	Address	Telephone
HIGHLAND ACUTE HOSPITALS NHS TRUST			
THE RAIGMORE HOSPITAL [01463 704000]	Rev. Iain MacRitchie	7 Merlin Crescent, Inverness IV2 3TE	
	Rev. Derek Brown	Cathedral Manse, Dornoch IV25 3HV	
IAN CHARLES	Rev. Morris Smith	Golfcourse Road, Grantown-on-Spey PH26 3HY	01479 872084
ST VINCENT	Dr John Berkeley	Drumbeg, Coylumbridge, Aviemore PH22 1QY	01479 811055
CRAIG DUNAIN	Rev. William J. Campbell	20 Birchview Court, Inverness IV22 5WA	01463 791690
NAIRN TOWN AND COUNTY	Rev. William B. Whyte	St Ninian's Manse, Queen Street, Nairn IV12 4AA	01667 452202
BELFORD AND BELHAVEN	Rev. Donald A. MacQuarrie	Manse of Duncansburgh, Fort William PH33 6BA	01397 702297
GLENCOE	Rev. Alison Burnside	14 Roxburgh Place, Fort William PH33 6UJ	01397 701465
ROSS MEMORIAL, DINGWALL	Rev. Russel Smith	8 Castlehill Road, Dingwall IV15 9PB	01349 861011
	Rev. Grahame M. Henderson	16 Achany Road, Dingwall IV15 9JB	01349 863167
INVERGORDON COUNTY	Rev. Kenneth D. Macleod	The Manse, Cromlet Drive, Invergordon IV18 0BA	01349 852273
LAWSON MEMORIAL	Rev. Iain McCree	The Manse, Golf Road, Brora KW9 6QS	01408 621239
MIGDALE	Rev. Heather Olsen	The Manse, Bonar Bridge, Ardgay IV24 3EB	01863 766256
CAITHNESS GENERAL	Rev. A.A. Roy	Mansefield, Miller Avenue, Wick KW1 4DF	01955 602822
	Rev. Steven Thomson	The Manse, Miller Avenue, Wick KW1 4DF	01955 604252
DUNBAR	Rev. Kenneth Borthwick	46 Rose Street, Thurso KW14 7HN	01847 895186
BROADFORD MACKINNON MEMORIAL	Rev. John Nicolson	The Manse, The Glebe, Kilmore, Sleat, Isle of Skye IV44 8RG	01471 844469
GESTO	Rev. Iain Greenshields	Snizort, Kensaleyre, Isle of Skye IV51 9XE	01470 532260

WESTERN ISLES HEALTH BOARD

Institution	Chaplain	Address	Telephone
UIST AND BARRA HOSPITAL	Rev. Thomas MacKinnon	The Manse, Clachan, Isle of North Uist HS6 5HD	01876 580219
WESTERN ISLES, STORNOWAY	Rev. Alexander MacDonald	5 Urquhart Gardens, Stornoway HS1 2TX	01851 702825

ORKNEY HEALTH BOARD

Institution	Chaplain	Address	Telephone
BALFOUR AND EASTBANK	Rev. Michael J. Ward	Ploverhall, Deerness, Orkney KW17 2QJ	01856 741349

LIST D – FULL-TIME INDUSTRIAL CHAPLAINS

EDINBURGH (Edinburgh City Mission Appointment)	Mr John Hopper	26 Mulberry Drive, Dunfermline KY11 5BZ		01383 737189
EDINBURGH (Methodist Appointment)	Rev. Bill Rayne	5 Dudley Terrace, Edinburgh EH6 6QQ		0131-554 1636
EDINBURGH (part-time)	Mrs Dorothy Robertson	15/1 Meadowhouse Road, Edinburgh EH12 7HW		0131-334 5440
GLASGOW	Rev. Elisabeth Spence	45 Selvieland Road, Glasgow G52 4ES		0141-883 8973
(part-time)	Mr William Shirlaw	194 Redpath Drive, Glasgow G52 2ER		0141-883 1714
			(Office)	0141-332 4458
WEST OF SCOTLAND	Rev. Alister Goss	79 Weymouth Crescent, Gourock PA19 1HR		01475 638944
			(Office)	01475 629383
NORTH-EAST	Rev. Angus Smith	1 Fa'burn Terrace, Lumphanan, Banchory AB31 4AG		01339 883395
			(Office)	01224 297532
NORTH OF SCOTLAND	Mr Lewis Rose DCS	16 Gean Drive, Blackburn, Aberdeen AB21 0YN		01224 790145
TAYSIDE and NATIONAL CO-ORDINATOR	Rev. Erik M. Cramb	65 Clepington Road, Dundee DD4 7BQ		01382 458764

LIST E – PRISON CHAPLAINS

CONTRACT CO-ORDINATOR (NATIONAL)	Rev. R. Stuart M. Fulton	HMP Edinburgh EH11 3LN	07855 314034
ABERDEEN CRAIGINCHES	Rev. Harvey Grainger	Kingswells Manse, Lang Stracht, Aberdeen AB15 8PL	01224 740229
CASTLE HUNTLY	Rev. David MacLeod	6 Carseview Gardens, Dundee DD2 1NE	01382 641371
CORNTON VALE	Rev. Elaine MacRae	The Manse, Kippen, Stirling FK8 3DN	01786 870229
DUMFRIES	Rev. Dennis S. Rose	The Manse, Kirkmahoe, Dumfries DG1 1ST	01387 710572
	Rev. Dr W.C. Campbell-Jack	4 Georgetown Crescent, Dumfries DG1 4EQ	01387 257045

Prison	Chaplain	Address	Telephone
EDINBURGH: SAUGHTON	Rev. Colin Reed	Chaplaincy Centre, HMP Edinburgh EH11 3LN	0131-444 3115
	Rev. Jennifer Booth	39 Lilyhill Terrace, Edinburgh EH8 7DR	0131-661 3813
	Miss Norma Ronald	43/26 Gillespie Crescent, Edinburgh EH10 4HY	0131-228 1008
GLASGOW: BARLINNIE	Rev. Edward V. Simpson	5 Langtree Avenue, Glasgow G46 7LN	0141-638 8767
	Rev. C. Blair Gillon	3 Dargarvel Avenue, Glasgow G41 5LD	0141-427 1282
	Rev. Russell McLarty	38 Lochview Drive, Glasgow G33 1QF	0141-770 9611
	Rev. Ian McInnes	46 Earlbank Avenue, Glasgow G14 9HL	0141-954 0328
LOW MOSS	Rev. William B. Moore	Chaplaincy Centre, HMP Low Moss, Glasgow G64 2QB	0141-762 4848
	Rev. David Cameron	122 Broomfield Avenue, Newton Mearns, Glasgow G77 5JR	0141-616 0642
GLENOCHIL	Rev. George Sherry	The Manse, Menstrie FK11 7EA	01259 761461
	Rev. Malcolm MacRae	10B Victoria Place, Stirling FK8 2QU	01786 465547
	Rev. Alan F.M. Downie	37A Claremont, Alloa FK10 2DG	01259 213872
GREENOCK	Rev. Kenneth Fisher	33 Halfway Street, West Kilbride KA23 9EQ	01294 829973
INVERNESS	Rev. Colin Anderson	24 Damfield Road, Inverness IV2 3HU	01463 237129
	Rev. George Charlton	61 Drumfield Road, Inverness IV2 4XL	01463 242802
KILMARNOCK	Rev. Andrew A. Downie	HMP Bowhouse, Mauchline Road, Kilmarnock KA1 5AA	01563 548928
	Rev. Morag Dawson	206 Bank Street, Irvine KA12 0YB	01294 211403
NORANSIDE			
PERTH INCLUDING FRIARTON	Rev. Graham Matthews	Chaplaincy Centre, HMP Perth PH2 8AT	01738 622293
	Mrs Deirdre Yellowlees	Ringmill House, Gannochy Farm, Perth PH2 7JH	01738 633773
	Rev. Isobel Birrell	Wester Tarsappie, Rhynd, Perth PH2 8QL	01738 625694
PETERHEAD	Rev. G.M. Allan Fawkes	3 Northfield Gardens, Hatton, Peterhead AB42 0SW	01779 841814
POLMONT	Rev. Donald H. Scott	Chaplaincy Centre HMYOI Polmont, Falkirk FK2 0AB	01324 711558
	Rev. Daniel L. Mathers	36 Thistle Avenue, Grangemouth FK3 8YQ	01324 474511
	Rev. James Drysdale	The Manse, Shieldhill, Falkirk FK1 2EG	01324 621938
SHOTTS	Rev. Andrew Campbell	70 Baron's Road, Motherwell ML1 2NB	01698 263803
	Rev. James Seath	1 Allan Avenue, Carluke ML8 5UA	01555 771644

LIST F – UNIVERSITY CHAPLAINS

ABERDEEN	Easter Smart MDiv	01224 484271
ABERTAY, DUNDEE	Leslie M. Barrett BD FRICS	01382 308447
CALEDONIAN	Rev. J. Owain Jones MA BD FSAScot (Visiting)	0141-637 0797
DUNDEE	Fiona C. Douglas BD PhD	01382 344157
EDINBURGH	Diane Williams	0131-650 2596
GLASGOW	Stuart D. MacQuarrie JP BD BSc	0141-330 5419
HERIOT-WATT	Howard G. Taylor BSc BD	0131-449 5111 (ext 4508)
NAPIER	Deryck Collingwood	0131-455 4694
PAISLEY		
ROBERT GORDON	Scott Blythe BSc BD	01224 262000 (ext 3506)
ST ANDREWS	James B. Walker MA BD DPhil	01334 462866
STIRLING	Regine U. Cheyne MA BSc BD (Honorary)	01786 463060
STRATHCLYDE	Marjory Macaskill LLB BD	0141-553 4144

LIST G – THE DIACONATE

NAME	COM	APP	ADDRESS	TEL	PRES
Allan, Jean (Mrs)	1989	1988	12C Hindmarsh Avenue, Dundee DD3 7LW	01382 827299	29
Anderson, Janet (Miss)	1979	1982	322 Gartcraig Road, Glasgow G33 2TB	0141-774 5329	16
Beaton, Margaret (Miss)	1989	1988	64 Gardenside Grove, Carmyle, Glasgow G32 8EZ	0141-646 2297	16
Bell, Sandra (Mrs)	2001		62 Loganswell Road, Thornliebank, Glasgow G46 8AX	0141-638 5884	16
Black, Linda (Miss) BSc	1993	1994	378 Alwyn Green, Glenrothes KY7 6TS		25
Buchanan, John (Mr)	1988	1994	22 Brora Court, North Muirton, Perth PH1 3DQ	01738 631697	28
Buchanan, Marion (Mrs)	1983	1997	6 Hamilton Terrace, Edinburgh EH15 1NB	0131-669 5312	1
Burns, Marjorie (Mrs)	1997	1998	25 Barnsley Square, Corby, Northants NN18 0PQ	01536 264819	47
			[E-mail: mburns8069@aol.com]	(Mbl) 07989 148464	
Carson, Christine (Miss) MA	1992	2000	7 Kirkwood Street, Cessnock, Glasgow G51 1QQ	0141-427 2349	16
Cathcart, John Paul (Mr)	1998		5A Atholl Gardens, Springhall, Rutherglen, Glasgow G73 5HF	0141-569 6865	17
Corrie, Margaret (Miss)	1989	1988	44 Sunnyside Street, Camelon, Falkirk FK1 4BH	01324 670656	22
Crawford, Morag (Miss)	1977	1998	118 Wester Drylaw Place, Edinburgh EH4 2TG	(Tel/Fax) 0131-332 2253	24
			[E-mail: morag.crawford@virgin.net]	(Mbl) 07970 982563	

Name			Address / E-mail		Telephone	No.
Crocker, Elizabeth (Mrs)	1985		77C Craigcrook Road, Edinburgh EH4 3PH [E-mail: crock@crook77c.freeserve.co.uk]		0131-332 0227	1
Cunningham, Ian (Mr)	1994	1997	5 Forth Court, Dalgety Bay, Dunfermline KY11 5SF		01383 823339	24
Deans, Raymond (Mr)	1994	1998	22 Garrowhill Drive, Garrowhill, Glasgow G69 6HL [E-mail: dean@fish.co.uk]		0141-771 6847	17
Dickson, Carol (Miss)	1991	1996	South Lodge, Walkerton Drive, Leslie, Glenrothes KY5 3BT		01592 743272	25
Douglas, Marilyn (Miss)	1988	1987	201 Almond Road, Abronhill, Cumbernauld, Glasgow G67 3LS		01236 732136	22
Dunnett, Linda (Mrs)	1976	2000	17 Munro Road, Glasgow G13 1SQ	(Office)	0141-959 3732 0141-552 4040	[16]
Erskine, Morag (Miss)	1979	1986	111 Mains Drive, Park Mains, Erskine PA8 7JJ		0141-812 6096	14
Evans, Mark (Mr)	1988	2000	13 Easter Drylaw Drive, Edinburgh EH4 2QA [E-mail: mevansdcs@aol.com]	(Mbl)	0131-343 3089 07808 444609	1
Gargrave, Mary (Mrs)	1989	1998	229/2 Calder Road, Edinburgh EH11 4RG	(Office)	0131-476 3493 0131-443 9452	1
Gordon, Margaret (Mrs)	1998	2001	92 Lanark Road West, Currie EH14 5LA		0131-449 2554	1
Gray, Greta (Miss)	1992	1998	67 Crags Avenue, Paisley PA2 6SG		0141-884 6178	14
Hamilton, James (Mr)	1997	2000	6 Beckfield Gate, Glasgow G33 1SW [E-mail: kg@hamilton692.freeserve.co.uk]		0141-558 3195	16
Hamilton, Karen (Mrs)	1995	1998	6 Beckfield Gate, Glasgow G33 1SW		0141-558 3195	16
Hankey, Sarah (Miss)	1991	1990	9 Earn Crescent, Menzieshill, Dundee DD2 4BS		01382 641549	29
Hughes, Helen (Miss)	1977	1980	Flat 2/2, 43 Burnbank Terrace, Glasgow G20 6UQ		0141-333 9459	16
Johnston, Mary (Miss)	1988	1987	19 Lounsdale Drive, Paisley PA2 9ED		0141-849 1615	14
King, Chris (Mrs)	2002		28 Kilnford, Dundonald, Kilmarnock KA2 9ET		01563 851197	10
King, Margaret (Miss)	2002		56 Murrayfield, Fochabers, Moray IV32 7EZ		01343 820937	35
Love, Joanna (Ms) BSc	1992	2000	92 Everard Drive, Glasgow G21 1XQ		0141-563 5859	16
Lundie, Ann V. (Miss)	1972	1992	20 Langdykes Drive, Cove, Aberdeen AB12 3HW		01224 898416	31
Lyall, Ann (Miss)	1980	1979	117 Barfia Drive, Glasgow G45 0AY		0141-631 3643	16
MacDonald, Anne (Miss) BA	1980	1998	62 Berwick Drive, Glasgow G52 3JA	(Mbl)	0141-883 5618 07976 786174	16
McIntosh, Kay (Mrs)	1990	1995	4 Jacklin Green, Livingston EH54 8PZ		01506 495472	3
MacKay, Kenneth (Mr)	1996		11F Balgowan Road, Letham, Perth PH1 2JG [E-mail: kennydandcs@hotmail.com]		01738 621169	28
MacKinnon, Ronald (Mr)	1996	1995	70 Eildon Road, Hawick TD9 8ES	(Mbl)	01450 374816 07808 117538	6
McLellan, Margaret (Mrs)	1986	1997	18 Broom Road East, Newton Mearns, Glasgow G77 5SD		0141-639 6853	16
McNaughton, Janette (Miss)	1982	1997	4 Dunellan Avenue, Moodiesburn, Glasgow G69 0GB		01236 870180	22
McPheat, Elspeth (Miss)	1985	1997	11/5 New Orchardfield, Edinburgh EH6 5ET		0131-554 4143/01224 486240	1
McVean, M. Christine (Miss)	1969	1987	38 Cruachan Street, Glasgow G46 8LQ		0141-638 9035	16
Martin, Jane (Miss)	1979	1979	12A Carnoustie Court, Ardler, Dundee DD2 3RB [E-mail: janemar@aol.com]		01382 813786	29
Merrilees, Ann (Miss)	1994	2000	15 Crookston Grove, Glasgow G52 3PN [E-mail: ann@merrilees.freeserve.co.uk]		0141-883 2488	16
Mitchell, Joyce (Mrs)	1994	1993	16/4 Murrayburn Place, Edinburgh EH14 2RR [E-mail: joyce@mitchell71.freeserve.co.uk]		0131-453 6548	1

Name			Address	Telephone	
Morrison, Jean (Mrs)	1964	1994	45 Corslet Road, Currie EH14 5LZ	0131-449 6859	1
Mulligan, Anne (Miss)	1974	1986	27A Craigour Avenue, Edinburgh EH17 7NH [E-mail: mulliganne@aol.com]	0131-664 3426	
Munro, Patricia (Miss) BSc	1986	2002	St Columba's Church, Pont Street, London SW1X 0BD [E-mail: patm@totalise.co.uk]	(Office) 0131-536 3086 / 020 7584 2321	47
Nicholson, David (Mr)	1994	1993	2D Doonside, Kildrum, Cumbernauld, Glasgow G67 2HX	01236 732260 / (Mbl) 07703 332270	22
Nicol, Joyce (Mrs)	1974	1998	93 Brisbane Street, Greenock PA16 8NY	01475 723235 / (Mbl) 07957 642709	15
Nicol, Senga (Miss)	1993	2000	Flat 2/1, 160 Tollcross Road, Glasgow G31 4UX	0141-554 3028	14
Ogilvie, Colin (Mr)	1998	1998	6 Ranfurly Drive, Cumbernauld, Glasgow G68 0DS	01236 728301	22
Rennie, Agnes M. (Miss)	1974	1979	3/1 Craigmillar Court, Edinburgh EH16 4AD	0131-661 8475	1
Rose, Lewis (Mr)	1993	1998	16 Gean Drive, Blackburn, Aberdeen AB21 0YN [E-mail: scimnorth@dial.pipex.com]	01224 790145	31
Ross, Duncan (Mr)	1996	1996	64 Stewart Crescent, Aberdeen AB16 5SR	01224 692519	31
Smith, Catherine (Mrs)	1964	1998	21 Lingaro, Bixter, Shetland ZE2 9NN	01595 810207	46
Steele, Marilynn J. (Mrs) BD			2 Northfield Gardens, Prestonpans EH32 9LQ	01875 811497	1
Steven, Gordon BD	1997		51 Nantwich Drive, Edinburgh EH7 6RB	0131-669 2054 / (Mbl) 07094 385256	3
Stewart, Marion (Miss)	1991	1994	Kirk Cottage, Kirkton of Skene, Westhill, Skene AB32 6XE	01224 743407	33
Tait, Agnes (Mrs)	1995	1994	2 Lennox Drive, Faifley, Clydebank G81 5JU	01389 873196	18
Teague, Yvonne (Mrs)	1965	1998	46 Craigcrook Avenue, Edinburgh EH4 3PX [E-mail: y.teague.1@blueyonder.co.uk]	0131-336 3113 / (Office) 0131-225 5722 ext 304	1
Urquhart, Barbara (Mrs)	1986	1994	9 Standalane, Kilmaurs, Kilmarnock KA3 2NB	01563 538289	11
Wilson, Glenda (Mrs)	1990	2000	118 Old Rows, Seafield, Bathgate EH47 7AW	01506 655298	2
Wilson, Muriel (Miss)	1997	2001	23 Jellieston Terrace, Patna, Ayr KA6 7JZ	01292 532492	10
Wishart, William (Mr)	1994	1993	17 Swift Bank, Earnock, Hamilton ML3 8PX	01698 429371 / (Mbl) 07971 422201	17
Wright, Lynda (Miss) BEd	1979	1992	6 Key Cottage, High Street, Falkland, Cupar KY15 7BD	01337 857705	26

THE DIACONATE (Retired List)

NAME	COM	ADDRESS	TEL	PRES
Anderson, Catherine B. (Mrs)	1975	13 Mosshill Road, Bellshill, Motherwell ML4 1NQ	01698 745907	17
Anderson, Mary (Miss)	1955	33 Ryehill Terrace, Edinburgh EH6 8EN	0131-553 2818	1
Bayes, Muriel C. (Mrs)	1963	Flat 6, Carleton Court, 10 Fenwick Road, Glasgow G46 4AN	0141-633 0865	16
Beaton, Jamesina (Miss)	1953	Fairhills, Fort Augustus PH32 4DS	01320 366252	38
Bryden, Agnes Y. (Mrs)	1963	9 Rosewell Place, Aberdeen AB15 6HN	01224 315042	31
Cameron, Margaret (Miss)	1961	2 Rowans Gate, Paisley PA2 6RD	0141-840 2479	14
Campbell, Margaret M.M. (Miss)	1958	Tigh-na-Rudha, Port Ellen, Isle of Islay PA42 7DJ	01496 302006	19
Collie, Jeannie P. (Miss)	1950	3 Fortmartindale, Udny Station, Ellon AB41 6QJ	01651 842515	33
Copland, Agnes M. (Mrs) MBE	1950	3 Craigmuschat Road, Gourock PA19 1SE	01475 631870	15
Cunningham, Alison G. (Miss)	1961	23 Strathblane Road, Milngavie, Glasgow G62 8DL	0141-563 9232	18
Drummond, Rhoda (Miss)	1960	23 Grange Loan, Edinburgh EH9 2ER	0131-668 3631	1
Finlayson, Ellena B. (Miss)	1963	16E Denwood, Summerhill, Aberdeen AB15 6JF	01224 321147	31
Flockhart, Andrew (Mr)	1988	31 Castle Street, Rutherglen, Glasgow G73 1DY	0141-569 0716	16
Gillespie, Ann M. (Miss)	1969	Barlochan House, Palnackie, Castle Douglas DG7 1PF	01556 600378	8
Gillon, Phyllis (Miss)	1957	The Hermitage Home, 15 Hermitage Drive, Edinburgh EH10 6BX	0131-447 0664	1
Glass, Irene (Miss)	1976	3E Falcon Road West, Edinburgh EH10 4AA	0131-447 6554	1
Gordon, Fiona S. (Mrs) MA	1958	Machrie, 3 Cupar Road, Cuparmuir, Cupar KY15 5RH [E-mail: machrie@madasafish.com]	01334 652341	26
Gray, Catherine (Miss)	1969	10C Eastern View, Gourock PA19 1RJ	01475 637479	15
Howden, Margaret (Miss)	1954	38 Munro Street, Kirkcaldy KY1 1PY	01592 205913	25
Hutchison, Alan E.W. (Mr)	1988	132 Lochbridge Road, North Berwick EH39 4DR	01620 894077	3
Hutchison, Maureen (Mrs)	1961	23 Drylaw Crescent, Edinburgh EH4 2AU	0131-332 8020	1
McBain, Margaret (Miss)	1974	33 Quarry Road, Paisley PA2 7RD	0141-884 2920	14
McCallum, Moyra (Miss) MA BD	1965	176 Hilton Drive, Aberdeen AB24 4LT [E-mail: moymac@aol.com]	01224 486240	31
McCully, M. Isobel (Miss)	1974	10 Broadstone Avenue, Port Glasgow PA14 5BB	01475 742240	15
McGarva, Sadie (Miss)	1954	87 Hunter Drive, Irvine KA12 9BS	01294 271257	11
MacLean, Donald A. (Mr)	1988	8 Upper Barvas, Isle of Lewis HS2 0QX	01851 840454	44
MacPherson, James B. (Mr)	1988	13 Leslie Street, Glasgow G41 2LQ	0141-423 6868	16
MacQuien, Duncan (Mr)	1988	2 Manor Crescent, Gourock PA19 1VY	01475 633407	15
Macrae, William (Mr)	1988	6 Park View Terrace, Isle of Scalpay, Isle of Harris HS4 3XX	01859 540288	43
MacSween, Helen (Miss)	1960	4 Craig Aonaich, Isle of Scalpay, Isle of Harris PA85 3DH		
Malvenan, Dorothy (Miss)	1955	Flat 19, 6 Craigie Street, Dundee DD4 6PF	01382 462495	29
Martin, Neil (Mr)	1988	3 Strathmiglo Place, Stenhousemuir, Larbert FK5 4UQ	01324 551362	22
Miller, Elsie M. (Miss)	1974	30 Swinton Avenue, Rowanbank, Baillieston, Glasgow G69 6JR	0141-771 0857	22
Montgomery, Donald (Mr)	1992	17 Murray Place, Stornoway, Isle of Lewis HS1 2JB	01859 561201	44

Name	Year	Address	Phone	
Mortimer, Aileen (Miss)	1976	38 Sinclair Way, Knightsridge, Livingston EH54 8HW	01506 430504	2
Moyes, Sheila (Miss)	1957	158 Pilton Avenue, Edinburgh EH5 2JZ	0131-551 1731	1
Nicoll, Janet M. (Miss)	1968	74 Brucefield Avenue, Dunfermline KY11 4SY	01383 725734	24
Potts, Jean M. (Miss)	1973	28B East Claremont Street, Edinburgh EH7 4JP	0131-557 2144	1
Ramsay, Katherine (Miss) MA	1958	25 Homeroyal House, 2 Chalmers Crescent, Edinburgh EH9 1TP	0131-667 4791	1
Ronald, Norma A. (Miss) MBE	1961	43/26 Gillespie Crescent, Edinburgh EH10 4HY	0131-228 1008	39
Rutherford, Ellen B. (Miss) MBE	1962	41 Duncanston, Conon Bridge, Dingwall IV7 8JB	01349 877439	16
Scrimgeour, Alice M. (Miss)	1950	265 Golfhill Drive, Glasgow G31 2PB	0141-564 9602	1
Sloan, Elma C. (Miss)	1957	Ferryfield House, Willowsuite, Pilton Drive, Edinburgh EH5 2HX	0131-537 6246	29
Smith, Lillian (Miss)	1977	6 Fintry Mains, Dundee DD4 9HF	01382 500052	14
Steele, Jean (Miss)	1952	93 George Street, Paisley PA1 2JX	0141-889 9512	24
Stuart, Anne (Miss)	1966	19 St Colme Crescent, Aberdour, Burntisland KY3 0ST	01383 860049	1
Thom, Helen (Miss) BA DipEd	1959	84 Great King Street, Edinburgh EH3 6QU	0131-556 5687	2
Trimble, Robert	1988	5 Templar Rise, Livingston EH54 6PJ	01506 412504	25
Webster, Elspeth H. (Miss)	1950	82 Broomhill Avenue, Burntisland KY3 0BP	01592 873616	
Weir, Minnie Mullo (Miss) MA	1934	37 Strathearn Court, Strathearn Terrace, Crieff PH7 3DS		
White, Elizabeth (Miss)	1950	Rodger Park Nursing Home, Rutherglen, Glasgow G73 3QZ	01764 654189	16

SUPPLEMENTARY LIST

Name	Year	Address
Forrest, Janice (Mrs)	1990	The Manse, Southend, Campbeltown, Argyll PA28 6RQ
Gilroy, Lorraine (Mrs)	1988	5 Bluebell Drive, Cheverel Court, Bedward CV12 0GE
Guthrie, Jennifer (Miss)		2 Fairfield Crescent, Selkirk TD7 4HY
Harris, Judith (Mrs)	1993	243 Western Avenue, Sandfields, Port Talbot, West Glamorgan SA12 7NF
Hood, Katrina (Mrs)	1988	67C Farquhar Road, Edgbaston, Birmingham B18 2QP
Hudson, Sandra (Mrs)	1982	10 Albany Drive, Rutherglen, Glasgow G73 3QN
Muir, Alison M. (Mrs)	1969	77 Arthur Street, Dunfermline KY12 0JJ
Ramsden, Christine (Miss)	1978	52 Noel Street, Nottingham NG7 6AW
Walker, Wikje (Mrs)	1970	24 Brodie's Yard, Queen Street, Coupar Angus PH13 9RA
Wallace, Catherine (Mrs)		4 Thornwood Court, Setauket, NY 11733, USA

LIST H – MINISTERS HAVING RESIGNED MEMBERSHIP OF PRESBYTERY
(in Terms of Act III 1992)

NAME	ORD	ADDRESS	TEL	PRES
Bailey, W. Grahame MA BD	1939	148 Craiglea Drive, Edinburgh EH10 5PU	0131-447 1663	1
Balfour, Thomas MA BD	1945	1 Dean Court, Longniddry EH32 0QT	01875 852694	3
Bogle, Michael M. MA	1936	30 Woodburn Terrace, Edinburgh EH10 4SS	0131-447 3231	1
Chirnside, Charles	1950	11 Stevenson Grove, Edinburgh EH11 2SE	0131-337 2957	23
Cooper, George MA BD	1943	69 Montpelier Park, Edinburgh EH10 4ND	0131-228 2435	1
Craig, Eric MA BD	1959	5 West Relugas Road, Edinburgh EH9 2PW	0131-667 8210	1
Craig, John W. MA BD	1951	83 Milton Road East, Edinburgh EH15 2NL	0131-657 2309	1
Ferguson, Ronald MA BD ThM	1972	Vinbreck, Orphir, Orkney KW17 2RE	01856 811378	45
Finlayson, Duncan	1943	Flat 3, Nicholson Court, Kinnettas Road, Strathpeffer IV14 9BG	01997 420014	39
Forrester-Paton, Colin MA BD	1944	Acharn, Glen Road, Peebles EH45 9AY	01721 720136	4
Gordon, Alasdair B. BD LLB	1970	31 Binghill Park, Milltimber, Aberdeen AB13 0EE	01224 571633	31
Greig, James C.G. MA BD STM	1955	44 Rockmount Avenue, Glasgow G46 7DW [E-mail: jcggreig@netcomuk.co.uk]	0141-621 1302	16
Hosie, James MA BD MTh	1959	Hilbre, Strachur, Cairndow, Dunoon, Argyll PA27 8BY	01369 860634	19
Howie, William MA BD STM	1964	26 Morgan Road, Aberdeen AB2 5JY	01224 483669	31
Lambie, Andrew BD	1957	1 Mercat Loan, Biggar ML12 6DG	01899 221352	13
Levison, Mary I. (Mrs) BA BD DD	1978	2 Gillsland Road, Edinburgh EH10 5BW	0131-228 3118	1
Lynn, Joyce (Mrs) MIPM BD	1995	Hill Park, Sanday, Orkney KW17 2BW	01857 600448	45
McCaskill, George I.L. MA BD	1953	3/5 Dun-ard Garden, Edinburgh EH9 2HZ	0131-668 2721	1
Macfarlane, Alwyn J.C. MA	1957	4/9 Belhaven Place, Edinburgh EH10 5JN	0131-447 9564	1
Macfarlane, Donald MA	1940	8 Muirfield Gardens, Inverness IV2 4HF	01463 231977	37
Macfarlane, Kenneth	1963	9 Bonnington Road, Peebles EH45 9HF	01721 723609	4
McLuskey, J. Fraser MC DD	1938	54/5 Eildon Terrace, Edinburgh EH3 5LU	0131-652 3950	47
Malcolm, John W. MA BD PhD	1939	16 Abbotsford Court, Edinburgh EH10 5EH	0131-447 0326	1
Marshall, James S. MA PhD	1939	25 St Mary's Street, St Andrews KY16 8AZ	01334 476136	26
Millar, Jennifer M. (Mrs) BD DipMin	1986	17 Mapledene Road, Scone, Perth PH2 6NX	01738 550270	28
Miller, Irene B. (Mrs) MA BD	1984	5 Braeside Park, Aberfeldy PH15 2DT	01887 829396	27
Monro, George D. TD MA	1935	Flat 79, 303 Colinton Road, Edinburgh EH13 0HS	0131-441 7303	1
Morris, Gordon C. MA BD	1941	Belleville Lodge, 5 Blacket Avenue, Edinburgh EH9 1RR		1
Nelson, John MA BD	1941	7 Manse Road, Roslin EH25 9LF	0131-440 3321	3
Ogilvie, Kenneth G. MA	1953	124 Comiston Drive, Edinburgh EH10 5QU	0131-447 8909	1
Petty, P.W.P.	1962	7 Marchbank Place, Balerno EH14 7EU	0131-449 2123	1
Robertson, Crichton MA	1938	Robin Hill, Ludlow Road, Church Stretton SY6 6AD	01694 722046	26
Ross, John H.G. OBE MA BD	1940	43 Arden Street, Edinburgh EH9 1BS	0131-447 2027	3

			TEL	PRES
Scott, J. Leonard MA BD	1957	13 Cornwall Street (1FL), Edinburgh EH1 2EQ	0131-229 0395	1
Shaw, Duncan JP PhD ThD Drhc	1951	4 Sydney Terrace, Edinburgh EH7 6SL	0131-669 1089	1
Stobie, Charles I.G.	1942	18 Market Street, St Andrews KY16 9NS	01334 476806	26
Sutherland, Douglas G.	1946	4 Mount Melville Crescent, Strathkinness, St Andrews KY16 9XS	01334 850338	26
Swan, Andrew MA	1941	11 The Terrace, Ardbeg, Rothesay, Isle of Bute PA20 0NP	01700 502138	15
Taylor, Alexander T.H. MA BD	1938	4 The Pleasance, Strathkinness, St Andrews KY16 9SD	01334 850585	26
Wilkie, George D. OBE BL	1948	2/37 Barnton Avenue West, Edinburgh EH4 6EB	0131-339 3973	1
Wylie, W. Andrew	1953	Well Rose Cottage, Peat Inn, Cupar KY15 5LH	01334 840600	26

LIST I – MINISTERS HOLDING PRACTISING CERTIFICATES (UNDER ACT II, AS AMENDED BY ACT VIII, 2000)

NAME	ORD	ADDRESS	TEL	PRES
Alexander, Helen J.R. (Miss) BD	1981	7 Polwarth Place, Edinburgh EH11 1LG	0131-346 0685	1
Anderson, David MA BD	1975	1A Sanquhar Road, Forres IV36 1DG	01309 672426	35
Arbuthnott, Joan (Mrs) MA BD	1993	139/1 New Street, Musselburgh EH21 6DH	0131-665 6736	1
Archer, Nicholas D.C. BA BD	1971	Hillview, Edderton, Tain IV19 4AJ	01862 821494	47
Atkins, Yvonne E.S. (Mrs) BD	1997	13 Grange Crescent East, Prestonpans EH32 9LS	01875 815137	3
Beattie, Warren R. BSc BD	1991	33A Chancery Lane, Singapore 908854	0065 256 3208	1
Beautyman, Paul H. MA BD	1993	G/R, 149 Stanmore Road, Glasgow G42 9AN	0141-649 5203	16
Black, James S. BD DPS	1976	7 Breck Terrace, Penicuik EH26 0RJ	01968 677559	3
Black, Janette M.K. (Mrs) BD	1993	5 Craigiehall Avenue, Erskine PA8 7DB	0141-812 0794	16
Black, Sandra (Mrs) BSc BD	1988	36 Glencairn Drive, Glasgow G41 4PW	0141-423 4000	16
Black, W. Graham MA BD	1983	19 Laurel Braes, Bridge of Don, Aberdeen AB22 8XY	01224 820333	31
Blair, Shirley (Miss) BD DipMin	1990			
Blane, Quintin A. BSc BD MSc	1979	18D Kirkhill Road, Penicuik EH26 8HZ	01968 670017	3
Bowman, Norman M. MA BD	1940	18 Eglinton Court, Eglinton Street, Saltcoats KA21 5DN	01294 463453	12
Boyd, Ian R. MA BD PhD	1989	33 Castleton Drive, Newton Mearns, Glasgow G77 3LE		16
Boyd, Kenneth M. MA BD PhD	1970	1 Doune Terrace, Edinburgh EH3 6DY	0131-225 6485	1
Buchanan-Smith, Robin D. BA ThM	1962	Isle of Eriska, Ledaig, Oban, Argyll PA37 1SD		
Burnside, Alison H. (Mrs) MA BD	1991	14 Roxburgh Place, Fort William PH33 6UJ	01397 701465	38
Campbell, Roderick D.M. TD BD FSAScot	1975	22 Greenlaw Road, Newton Mearns, Glasgow G77 6ND	0141-639 7328	16
Campbell, Thomas R. MA BD	1986	17 Falside Avenue, Paisley PA2 6JY	0141-884 8291	14
Chilton, R. Michael L. BD BA(Open) BA(Hull) MA DipEurHum	1972	69 Hill Rise, Market Weighton, East Yorkshire YO43 3JX	01430 871147	33
Cowie, Marion (Mrs) MA BD	1990	6 St Swithin Street, Aberdeen AB10 6XE	01224 593302	31

Name	Ord.	Address	Tel	No.
Currie, Gordon C.M. MA BD	1975	43 Deanburn Park, Linlithgow EH49 6HA	01506 842722	2
Davidson, John F. BSc	1970	49 Craigmill Gardens, Carnoustie DD7 6HX [E-mail: jfdavid@breathemail.net]	01241 855412	30
Davies, Gareth W. BA BD	1979	8 Inchcolme Drive, North Queensferry KY11 1LD	01383 418863	24
Donaldson, George M. MA BD	1984	Suilven, Victoria Road, Brora, Sutherland KW9 6LN	01408 621257	40
Drummond, Norman W. MA BD	1976	c/o Columba 1400 Ltd, Staffin, Isle of Skye IV51 9JY	01478 611400	42
Dutch, Morris M. BD	1998	41 Baronald Drive, Kelvindale, Glasgow G12 0HN	0141-357 2286	16
Ellis, David W. GIMechE GIProdE	1962	26 Prospect Road, Sevenoaks, Kent TN13 3UA		16
Finlay, Joanne G. (Mrs) DipMusEd	1996	6 Herd Green, Livingston EH54 8PU	01324 552004	22
Fleming, Thomas G.	1961	5 Glenbervie Drive, Larbert FK5 4NP	01875 833208	22
Flockhart, D. Ross OBE MA BD DUniv	1955	Longwood, Humbie EH36 5PN		3
Fowler, Richard C.A. BSc MSc BD	1978	4 Gardentown, Whalsay, Shetland ZE2 9AB	01806 566538	46
Fraser, Ian M. MA BD PhD	1946	Ferndale, Gargunnock, Stirling FK8 3BW	01786 860612	23
Frew, John M. MA BD	1946	17 The Furrows, Walton-on-Thames KT12 3JQ		16
Galloway, Kathy (Mrs) BD	1977	20 Hamilton Park Avenue, Glasgow G12 8UU	0141-357 4079	16
Gilmour, Robert M. MA BD	1942	'Bellevue', Station Road, Watten, Wick KW1 5YN	01955 621317	37
Gunn, F. Derek BD	1986	6 Yardley Place, Falkirk FK2 7FH	01324 624938	22
Hendrie, Yvonne (Mrs)	1995	98 Duncansby Way, Perth PH1 5XF	01738 441029	28
Higgins, G.K.	1957	150 Broughty Ferry Road, Dundee DD4 6JJ	01382 461288	29
Howitt, Jane M. (Miss) MA BD	1996	4 Sycamore Gardens, Edinburgh EH12 7JJ	0131-334 8882	16
Inglis, Ann (Mrs) LLB BD	1986	48 Jubilee Court, St Margaret's Street, Dunfermline KY12 7PE	01383 732223	1
Ireland, Andrew BA BTh DipRD	1963	Glenallan, Doune Road, Dunblane FK15 9AT	01786 823241	24
Jack, Alison M. (Mrs) MA BD PhD	1998	1 Redburn, Bayview, Stornoway HS1 2UV	01851 704789	23
Jamieson, Esther M.M. (Mrs) BD	1984	22 Glenhove Road, Cumbernauld, Glasgow G67 2JZ	01236 612479	16
Johnstone, Donald B.	1969	59 Cliffburn Road, Arbroath DD11 5BA	01241 439292	22
Johnstone, Robert MTheol	1973	7 North Elphinstone Farm, Tranent EH33 2ND	01875 614442	32
Jones, Anne M. (Mrs) BD	1998	78 Victoria Park Drive South, Glasgow G14 9NX	0141-954 8786	3
Kirkwood, Gordon BSc BD	1987	Flat 2, 1 Trafalgar Terrace, New St John's Road, St Helier, Jersey JE2 3LE	01534 625825	16
Kirby, Paul S. BD	1976	West Benview, Main Road, Langbank, Port Glasgow PA14 6XP	01475 540240	47
Lawrie, Robert M. BD MSc DipMin LLCM(TD)	1994			15
Liddiard, F.G.B. MA	1957	34 Trinity Fields Crescent, Brechin DD9 6YF	01356 622966	30
Logan, Thomas M. LTh	1971	3 Duncan Court, Kilmarnock KA3 7TF	01563 524398	11
MacArthur, Alexander MA	1946	Luath, St Barchan's Road, Kilbarchan, Johnstone PA10 2AR	01505 702598	14
McKean, Martin J. BD DipMin	1984	14 Morriston Drive, Murieston, Livingston EH54 9HT	01506 418150	2
MacPherson, Gordon C.	1963	203 Capelrig Road, Patterton, Newton Mearns, Glasgow G77 6ND		11
Main, Arthur W.A. BD	1954	13/3 Eildon Terrace, Edinburgh EH3 5NL	0131-556 1344	16
Mair, John BSc	1965	21 Kenilworth Avenue, Helensburgh G84 7JR	01436 671744	18
Marr, Ian MA BD	1984	116 Jeanfield Road, Perth PH1 1LP	01738 629883	28
Masson, John D.	1984	5 Wheatlands, Wigton Road, Carlisle CA2 7ER	ex-directory	7
Matheson, Iain G. BD BMus	1985	16 New Street, Musselburgh EH21 6JP	0131-665 2128	3
Meredith, Ian BA MTh	1980	'Skedholm', Greenhill, Lockerbie DG11 1GB	01387 810843	47
Mill, John Stuart MA BD MBA DipEd	1974	11 Somersford Place, Beaconsfield, Bucks HA9 1AZ	01494 681906	47

NAME	ORD	ADDRESS	TEL.	PRES
Millar, Peter W. MA BD PhD	1971	Iona Cottage, Laggan, Newtonmore PH20 1AN	01528 544337	36
Mills, Archibald MA PhD	1953	32 High Street, South Queensferry EH30 9PP	0131-331 3906	1
Morrice, Alexander M. MA BD	1968	5 Brechin Road, Kirriemuir DD8 4BX		30
Munro, Alexander W. MA BD	1978	Clevedon House, Ben Rhydding Drive, Ilkley, West Yorks LS29 8BJ	01943 608515	47
O'Donnell, Callum T. MA BD	1984	45 Queens Drive, Troon KA10 6SE	01292 514065	10
Ostler, John H. MA LTh	1975	52E Middleshot Square, Prestonpans EH32 9RJ	01875 814358	3
Owen, Catherine W. (Mrs) MTheol	1984	The Vicarage, St Mary's Road, Worcester Park, Surrey KT4 7JL	020 8337 5025	47
Parker, Andrew H. BSc BD	1967	25 Canton Street, London E14 8JG	020 7538 8505	47
Peat, S. William BSc BD PhD	1977	27/320 West Savile Terrace, Edinburgh EH9 3DS	0131-662 9319	1
Provan, Iain W. MA BA PhD	1991	Regent College, 5800 University Boulevard, Vancouver BC V6T 2E4, Canada	001 604 224 3245	1
Quigley, Barbara D. (Mrs) MTheol ThM DPS	1979	7 Albany Terrace, Dundee DD3 6HQ	01382 223059	29
Ross, Alison J. (Mrs) BD	1995			19
Ross, Robin A. MA BD	1977	Yarrow Feus, Selkirk TD7 5BL	01750 82236	4
Sawers, Hugh BA	1968	2 Rosemount Meadows, Castlepark, Bothwell, Glasgow G71 8EL	01698 853960	17
Scouller, Hugh BSc BD	1985	39 Melbourne Place, North Berwick EH39 4JS	01620 893021	3
Shaw, Alistair N. MA BD	1982	The Beeches, 7 Bargany Road, Crookston, Glasgow G53 7JB	0141-882 5921	16
Speirs, Archibald BD	1995	Ground Flat, 27 Brabloch Crescent, Paisley PA3 4RG	0141-587 4980	14
Squires, J. Finlay R. MA BD	1964	16 Bath Street, Stonehaven AB39 2DH	01569 762458	32
Stewart, Margaret L. (Mrs) BSc MB ChB BD	1985	28 Inch Crescent, Bathgate EH48 1EU	01506 653428	2
Strachan, David G. BD DPS	1978	1 Deeside Park, Aberdeen AB15 7PQ	01224 324101	31
Strachan, Gordon MA BD PhD	1963	59 Merchiston Crescent, Edinburgh EH10 5AH	0131-229 3654	1
Thomas, W. Colville BTh BPhil DPS DSc	1964	11 Muirfield Crescent, Gullane EH31 2HN	01620 842415	3
Tollick, Frank BSc DipEd	1958	3 Bellhouse Road, Aberdour, Burntisland KY3 0TL	01383 860559	24
Turnbull, Julian S.	1980	25 Hamilton Road, Gullane EH31 2HP [E-mail: jules-turnbull@zetnet.co.uk]	01620 842958	3
Watt, John H.I. MA BD	1960	Lyndale, 24 Bank Street, Wigtown DG8 9HP	01546 602143	20
Weir, Mary K. (Mrs) BD PhD	1968	1249 Millar Road RR1, SITEH-46, BC V0N 1G0, Canada	001 604 947 0636	1
Welsh, Alex M. BD	1979	134 Onslow Drive, Glasgow G31 2PZ	0141-550 0229	16
Williams, Linda J. (Mrs) BD	1993	The Manse, Kirtlebridge, Lockerbie DG11 3LY	01461 500378	7
Wilson, Thomas F. BD	1984	55 Allison Close, Cove, Aberdeen AB12 3WG	01224 873501	31
Winn, Fiona M.M. MA BD RGN	1994	35 Ashwood Avenue, Melbourne 3190, Australia	0061 3 9555 2038	1
Wood, Peter J. MA BD	1993	97 Broad Street, Cambourne, Cambridgeshire CB3 6DH	01954 715558	47

LIST J – MISSION AND EVANGELISM ADVISERS

Position	Name	Address	Telephone
SENIOR ADVISER with South Region	Rev. David Currie BSc BD	21 Rosa Burn Avenue, Lindsayfield, East Kilbride, Glasgow G75 9DE [E-mail: nmsenioradviser@uk.uumail.com] Office: contact via the Church of Scotland Offices	01355 248510 07775 515594 (Mbl)
CONGREGATIONAL DEVELOPMENT ADVISER	Mr Brian Burden	'Edinbane', Mid Road, Northmuir, Kirriemuir DD8 4QX [E-mail: nmadviscred@uk.uumail.com]	01575 575280 (Tel/Fax)
MISSIONS CO-ORDINATOR	Mr Philip Wray BSc Msc	59 Elmbank Street, Glasgow G2 4PQ (Office) [E-mail: missionco-ordinator@uk.uumail.com]	0141-352 6946 (Tel/Fax) 07900 900776 (Mbl)
REGIONAL ADVISER (EAST)	Rev. Robin J. McAlpine BDS BD	10 Seton Place, Kirkcaldy KY2 6UX [E-mail: nmkirkcaldy@uk.uumail.com] St Bryce Kirk Centre, St Brycedale Avenue, Kirkcaldy KY1 1ET (Office)	01592 643518 (Tel) 01592 646406 (Tel/Fax)
REGIONAL ADVISER (NORTH)	Rev. Richard J. Gibbons BD	3 Holm Burn Place, Inverness IV2 6WT [E-mail: nmadvisernorth@uk.uumail.com] National Mission Highland Office, Main Street, North Kessock, Inverness IV1 3XN [E-mail: nminverness@uk.uumail.com]	01463 226889 01463 731712
URBAN PRIORITY AREAS ADVISER	Rev. Martin Johnstone MA BD	3 Herries Road, Glasgow G41 4DE [E-mail: upadviser@uk.uumail.com] 59 Elmbank Street, Glasgow G2 4PQ (Office) [E-mail: nmglasgow@uk.uumail.com]	0141-423 3760 (Tel/Fax) 0141-333 1948 (Tel/Fax)

LIST K – OVERSEAS APPOINTMENTS

The Board of World Mission has decided to discontinue the separate printing of this list. The information it contained is all to be found in the other lists. In particular, List L gives details of the various Overseas Locations currently applicable.

LIST L – OVERSEAS LOCATIONS

EUROPE

AMSTERDAM
Rev. John A. Cowie and Mrs Gillian Cowie
Jan Willem Brouwersstraat 9, NL-1071 LH Amsterdam, The Netherlands
[E-mail: j.cowie2@chello.nl]
The English Reformed Church, The Begijnhof (off the Spui). Service each Sunday at 10.30am.
(Tel) 0031 20 672 2288
(Fax) 0031 20 676 4895

BRUSSELS
Rev. Thomas C. Pitkeathly
23 Square des Nations, B-1000 Brussels, Belgium
[E-mail: pitkeathly@compuserve.com]
St Andrew's Church, Chaussée de Vleurgat 181 (off Ave. Louise). Service each Sunday at 11.00am.
(Tel/Fax) 0032 2 672 40 56

BUDAPEST
Rev. Kenneth I. Mackenzie and Mrs Jayne Mackenzie, Oltvany Arok 25, H-1112 Budapest
St Columbia's Scottish Mission, Vorosmarty utca 51, H-1064 Budapest, Hungary
[E-mail: mackenzie@mail.datanet.hu]
Service in English and Sunday School each Sunday at 11.00am.
Rev. Bertalan Tamas (1976, held previous appointment) and Mrs Elizabeth Tamas
[E-mail: zsinatko@matavnet.hu]
(Tel/Fax) 0036 1 246 2258
(Church Tel) 0036 1 343 8479
(Fax) 0036 1 460 0708

COSTA DEL SOL
Vacant
11 Calle Margarita Blanca, E-29640 Fuengirola, Malaga, Spain.
Services at Lux Mundi Ecumenical Centre, Calle Nueva 7, Fuengirola. Service each Sunday at 10.30am.
(Tel) 0034 95 258 8394

GENEVA
Rev. Ian A. Manson and Mrs Roberta Manson
[E-mail: cofsg@pingnet.ch]
6 Chemin Tavernay, CH-1218 Grand Saconnex, Geneva, Switzerland
The Calvin Auditoire, Place de la Taconnerie (beside Cathedral of St Pierre). Service each Sunday at 11.00am.
(Tel/Fax) 0041 22 798 29 09

GIBRALTAR
Vacant
St Andrew's Manse, 29 Scud Hill, Gibraltar
St Andrew's Church, Governor's Parade. Service each Sunday at 6.00pm.
[E-mail: billsmth@gibnet.gi]
(Tel) 00350 77040
(Fax) 00350 40852

LAUSANNE
Rev. Douglas R. Murray and Mrs Sheila Murray
26 Avenue de Rumine, CH-1005 Lausanne, Switzerland
[E-mail: scotskirklausanne@bluewin.ch]
Service each Sunday at 10.30am.
(Tel/Fax) 0041 21 323 98 28

LISBON
Vacant
The Manse, Rua da Arriaga 11, 1200-608, Lisbon, Portugal
[E-mail: st.andrewschurch@clix.pt]
St Andrew's Church, Rua da Arriaga 13–15, Lisbon. Service each Sunday at 11.00am.
(Tel/Fax) 00351 21 395 7677

MALTA

Rev. David Morris
210 Old Bakery Street, Valletta, Malta
St Andrew's Church, 210 Old Bakery Street, Valletta. Service each Sunday at 10.30am.

(Tel/Fax) 00356 222 643

PARIS

Rev. William M. Reid and Mrs Esther Reid
10 Rue Thimonnier, F-75009 Paris, France
[E-mail: scotskirk@wanadoo.fr]
The Scots Kirk, c/o L'Eglise Reformée du Saint-Esprit
5 Rue de Roquepine (nearest Metros Madeline and St Augustin) Service each Sunday at 11.30am.

(Tel/Fax) 0033 1 48 78 47 94

ROME

Rev. William B. McCulloch and Mrs Jean McCulloch
Via XX Settembre 7, 00187 Rome, Italy. Service each Sunday at 11.00am.

(Tel) 0039 06 482 7627
(Fax) 0039 06 487 4370

ROTTERDAM

Rev. Robert A. Calvert and Mrs Lesley-Ann Calvert
Gelebrem 59, NL-3068 TJ Rotterdam, The Netherlands
[E-mail: scots_international_church@compuserve.com]
The Scots Kirk, Schiedamsevest 121, Rotterdam. Service each Sunday at 10.30 am.
Informal Service at 9.15 am.

(Tel/Fax) 0031 10 220 4199
(Tel) 0031 10 412 4779

TURIN

Rev. Robert A. Mackenzie and Mrs Anne Mackenzie
Via Sante Anselmo 6, 10125 Turin, Italy
[E-mail: valdese.english@arpnet.it]
The English-Speaking Church in Turin
Via 5. Plov, 15 (first floor), 10125 Turin, Italy

(Church office Tel) 0039 11 650 9467

AFRICA

KENYA

Presbyterian Church of East Africa
Dr Elizabeth Borlase (1992) and Kevin Borlase
Rev. Elaine W. McKinnon (1992)

PCEA Kikuyu Hospital, PO Box 45, Kikuyu, Kenya   (Fax) 00254 2501626
Presbyterian College, PO Box 387, Kikuyu, Kenya
[E-mail: ewmck@wananchi.com]

Dr Alison Wilkinson (1992)

PCEA Chogoria Hospital, PO Box 35, Chogoria, Kenya   (Fax) 00254 166 22122
[E-mail: alisonjwilkinson@doctors.org.uk]

MALAWI

Church of Central Africa Presbyterian
Synod of Blantyre
Rev. Bruce Ritchie (2001)

Zomba Theological College, PO Box 130, Zomba, Malawi

Synod of Livingstonia
Dr Andrew and Mrs Felicity Gaston (1997)
(on study leave in UK)

CCAP Ekwendeni Hospital, PO Box 19, Ekwendeni, Malawi

Miss Helen Scott (2000, held previous appointment)
Dr Alex Maclean (2001) and Mrs Carolyn Maclean

CCAP Girls' Secondary School, PO Box 2, Ekwendeni, Malawi
Embangweni Hospital, PO Box 7, Embangweni,
Mzimba District, Malawi

SOUTH AFRICA	Rev. Graham Duncan (1998, held previous appointment) and Mrs Sandra Duncan (1998)	56 Daphne Road, Maroelana 00081, Pretoria, South Africa	
UGANDA/SUDAN	Rev. Roderick D.M. Campbell (2001)	PO Box 975, Arua, Uganda [E-mail: rdmcampbell@bushnet.net]	
ZAMBIA	**United Church of Zambia** Rev. Colin D. Johnston (1994)	Trinity UCZ, PO Box 30079, Lusaka, Zambia [E-mail: trinity@zamnet.zm]	
	Ms Jane Petty (2000)	Mwandi Mission Hospital, PO Box 60693, Livingstone, Zambia [E-mail: pettyjane@hotmail.com]	
	Mr Brian Payne (2002) and Mrs Georgina Payne (2002)	United Church of Zambia Synod Office, Lusaka, Zambia [E-mail: uczsynod@zamnet.zm]	(Tel) 00260 1 250 641 (Fax) 00260 1 252 198

THE CARIBBEAN, CENTRAL AND SOUTH AMERICA

BAHAMAS	Rev. John Fraser (2002) and Mrs Jillian Fraser	St Andrew's Manse, PO Box N1099, Nassau	(Tel) 001 242 322 5475 (Fax) 001 242 323 1960
		Lucaya Presbyterian Kirk, PO Box F-40777, Freeport	(Tel) 001 242 373 2568 (Fax) 001 242 373 4961
BERMUDA	Rev. T. Alan W. Garrity (1999) and Mrs Elizabeth Garrity	The Manse, PO Box PG88, Paget PGBX, Bermuda [E-mail: revtawg@ibl.bm *and* christchurch@ibl.bm]	(Tel) 001 441 236 0400 and (Tel) 001 441 236 1882 (Fax) 001 441 232 0552
JAMAICA	**United Church of Jamaica and Grand Cayman** Rev. Roy A. Dodman and Mrs Jane Dodman (1983)	8 Wishaw Drive, Kingston 8, Jamaica [E-mail: rdodman@cwjamaica.com]	(Tel) 001 876 925 8491 (Fax) 001 876 931 5004
	Rev. Margaret Fowler (1988)	PO Box 3097, Negril, Westmoreland, Jamaica [E-mail: revm@cwjamaica.com]	(Tel) 001 876 640 0846
	Ms Maureen Burke (1998)	1B Woodley Drive, Meadowbrook, Kingston 19, Jamaica [E-mail: moburke@cwjamaica.com]	(Tel/Fax) 001 876 905 3206
TRINIDAD	Rev. Harold Sitahal (2000) and Mrs Ruth Sitahal	Church of Scotland Greyfriars St Ann's, 50 Frederick Street, Port of Spain, Trinidad	(Tel/Fax) 001 868 622 1757

ASIA

Ecumenical Appointments

BANGLADESH	**Church of Bangladesh**	
	Ms Gillian Rose (1996)	Bollobhpur Hospital, PC Kedargonj, DR Meherpur, Bangladesh
	Mr Andrew and Mrs Rosemary Symonds (1999)	St Andrew's College, Dhaka, Bangladesh
		[E-mail: ajsymond@bd.drik.net]
	Ms Ann Tuesley (2000)	Rajshahi Hospital, Kushtia, Bangladesh
CHINA	**Together with Scottish Churches China Group**	
	Mr Ian Groves (1996)	Amity Foundation, Overseas Office, 4 Jordan Road, Kowloon, Hong Kong
	Ms Julie Chrystal (1997)	Ganzholl Teachers' College, Ganzholl, Jiang-xi Province, China
	Mr Mick and Mrs Anne Kavanagh (1997)	Nanping Teachers' College, 45 Guanshatian, Nanping, Fujian 353000, China
	Ms Jane Thompson (1997)	Changshu Teachers' College, 98 Yuanhe Road, Changshu, Jiangsu 2185009, China
	Mr Richard Brunt (1998)	Tai'an Teachers' College, 56 Wenhua Road, Tai'an, Shandong 271000, China
	Mr David Conkey (1998)	Tai'an Teachers' College, 56 Wenhua Road, Tai'an, Shandong 271000, China
	Mrs Valerie King (1999)	Jiujiang Teachers' College, Jiujiang 332000, Jiangxi Province, China
	Mr Jason Waller (1999)	Fuzhou Teachers' College, Fuzhou, Fujian 350011, China
	Sara Ker (2000)	Jiujiang Teachers' College, Jilljiang 332000, Jiangxi Province, China
	Mark McLeister (2000)	Changwie Teachers' College, 65 Shangjie East Road, Weifang, Shangdong, 261043, China
INDIA	**Church of South India**	
	Rev. Eileen Thompson	c/o CSI Diocesan Office, Melukavumattom PO, Kerala 686 652
NEPAL	**United Mission to Nepal**	
	Mr John Ross (1995)	PO Box 126, Kathmandu, Nepal (Fax) 00977 1 225 559
		[E-mail: jross@wlink.com.np]
	Mrs Moira and Alasdair Murray (1999)	Kathmandu International Study Centre, Kathmandu, Nepal (Fax) 00977 1 225 559
		[E-mail: amurray@wlink.com.np]
	Mrs Marianne Karsgaard (2001)	PO Box 126, Kathmandu, Nepal (Fax) 00977 1 225 559
		[E-mail: marianne@wlink.com.np]
KOREA	Rev. Elinor Gordon (2002)	Flat 202, Ichon Apartments, Ichon, I-Dong, Yongsan-gu, Seoul, Korea
		[E-mail: elinorgordon@aol.com]

PAKISTAN

Church of Pakistan

Mrs Elizabeth M. McKee (1989)
Murree Christian School, Jhika Gali, Murree Hills, Pakistan
[E-mail: stewart@bob.isb.sdnpk.org]
(Fax) 0092 593 411 668

Miss Helen F. McMillan (1981)
United Bible Training Centre, PO Box 14, Gujranwala, Pakistan
[E-mail: chris@guj.brain.net.pk]
(Fax) 0092 431 257 539

Mr Alexander M. Sneddon (1986) and Mrs S. Marie Sneddon
Diocesan Office, Peshawar, Church of Pakistan, 1 Sir Syed Road, Peshawar 25000, Pakistan

Rev. Paul Burgess (1994) and Mrs Cathie Burgess
Gujranwala Theological Seminary, PO Box 13, Gujranwala, Pakistan
[E-mail: burgess@brain.net.pk]
(Fax) 0092 431 258 345

SRI LANKA

Presbytery of Lanka

Rev. Anthony McLean-Foreman (1995)
Theological College of Lanka, Nandana Uyana, Pilimatalawa, Sri Lanka
[E-mail: tony@slt.lk]
(Fax) 00948 232 343

THAILAND

Church of Christ in Thailand

Mr Michael D. Fucella and Mrs E. Jane Fucella (1990)
2, MU3, Tambon Nongloo, Sangklaburi, Kanchanaburi 71240, Thailand
[E-mail: jfucella@loxinfo.co.th]

MIDDLE EAST AND NORTH AFRICA

EGYPT

Dr Keith Russell (2000) and Mrs Lai Fun Russell
The Joint Relief Ministry of All Saints' Anglican Cathedral, Michael Lutfallah Street Zamalek 11211, Cairo, Egypt
[E-mail: russell@link.net]
(Tel) 00202 738 0821
(Fax) 00202 735 8941

[NOTE: Church Services are held in St Andrew's Scots Memorial Church, Jerusalem, each Sunday at 10.00am, and at St Andrew's, Galilee (contact minister for worship time)]

ISRAEL

Jerusalem
Rev. Clarence W. Musgrave (2000) and Mrs Joan Musgrave
St Andrew's Scots Memorial Church, PO Box 8619, Jerusalem 91086, Israel
(Tel: 00972 2 6732401; Fax: 00972 2 673 1711)
[E-mail: standjer@netvision.net.il] [Private E-mail: stachjer@netvision.net.il]

Tiberias
Rev. Fred Hibbert (1996) and Mrs Diane Hibbert
St Andrew's, Galilee, PO Box 104, Tiberias, Israel
[E-mail: scottie@netvision.net.il] (Tel: 00972 4 6721165; Fax: 00972 4 6790145)
[Private E-mail: scotdir@netvision.net.il]

Jaffa
Mr Christopher Mottershead (2000) and Mrs Sue Mottershead
Tabeetha School, PO Box 8170, 21 Yeffet Street, Jaffa, Israel
(Tel: 00972 3 6821581; Fax: 00972 3 6819357)
[E-mail: costab@netvision.net.il]
Tabeetha School

Mrs Karen Anderson (1992)
Ms Irene Wilson (1993)
Tabeetha School

Ibillin
Rev. Dr Bryson Arthur and Mrs May Arthur (2001)
Mar Elias University College, Mar Elias Educational Institutions, PO Box 102, Ibillin 30012, Galilee, Israel
(Tel: 00972 4 986 6848; Fax: 00972 4 986 9573)
[E-mail: arthurz@netvision.net.il]

LEBANON
Mr David Kerry (1999)
Near East School of Theology, Sourati Street, PO Box 13-5780, Chouran, Beirut, Lebanon
[E-mail: nest.lib@inco.lb]
(Tel) 00961 1346 708
(Fax) 00961 1347 129

LIST M – OVERSEAS RESIGNED AND RETIRED MISSION PARTNERS (10 or more years' service)

NAME	APP	RET	AREA	ADDRESS
Archibald, Mary L. (Miss)	1964	1982	Nigeria/Ghana	490 Low Main Street, Wishaw ML2 7PL
Bailey, Winifred (Miss)	1949	1979	Kolhapur	22 Mardale Crescent, Edinburgh EH10 5AG
Barbour, Edith R. (Miss)	1952	1983	North India	13/11 Pratik Nagar, Yerwada, Pune 411006, Maharashta, India
Bogle, Rev. Michael M.	1936	1961	Lovedale	30 Woodburn Terrace, Edinburgh EH10 4SS
Boyle, Lexa (Miss)	1959	1992	Aden/Yemen/Sudan	7 Maxwell Grove, Glasgow G41 5JP
Burnett, Dr Fiona	1988	1998	Zambia	The Glenholm Centre, Broughton, Biggar ML12 6JF
Burt, M.R.C. (Miss)	1940	1975	Kenya	22 The Loaning, Chirnside, Duns TD11 3YE
Campbell, George H.	1957	1971	Livingstonia	27 Avenue Street, Stewarton, Kilmarnock KA3 5AP
Coltart, Rev. Ian O.	1967	1985	North India	161 Kirk Road, Wishaw ML2 7BZ

Name			Country	Address
Conacher, Marion (Miss)	1963	1993	India	41 Magdalene Drive, Edinburgh EH15 3BG
Conn, A. (Mr)	1937	1960	Blantyre	90 Endbutt Lane, Great Crosby, Liverpool L23
Cooper, Rev. George	1966	1986	Kenya	69 Montpelier Park, Edinburgh EH10 4WD
Cowan, Dr Betty	1969	1988	North India	2 Sunningdale Square, Kilwinning KA13 6PH
Dabb, Dr R. Gwen	1943	1971	Blantyre	14/44 Ethel Terrace, Edinburgh EH10 5NA
Dawson, Miss Anne	1976	2000	Malawi	5 Cattle Market, Clackmannan FK10 4EH
Dougall, Ian C.	1960	1990	Kenya	60B Craigmillar Park, Edinburgh EH16 5PU
Drever, Dr Bryan	1962	1982	Aden/Yemen/Pakistan	188 Addison Road, King's Head, Birmingham
Dunlop, Walter T. (Mr)	1979	1994	Malawi/Israel	50 Oxgangs Road, Edinburgh EH13 9DR
Fauchelle, Rev. Don and Mrs Margaret	1971 and 1991	1979 and 1999	Zambia, Malawi, Zimbabwe	Flat 3, 22 North Avenue, Devonport, Auckland 1309, New Zealand
Ferguson, John K.P. (Mr) and Mrs Margaret	1977	1989	Pakistan	12 Bencleuch Place, Bourtreehill South, Irvine KA11 1EL
Finlay, Carol (Ms)	1990	2001	Malawi	96 Broomfield Crescent, Edinburgh EH12 7LX
Fischbacher, Dr Colin M. and Mrs Sally	1984	1998	Malawi	11 Barclay Square, Gosforth, Newcastle-upon-Tyne NE3 2JB
Forrester-Paton, Rev. Colin	1946	1972	Ghana	Acharn, Glen Road, Peebles EH45 9AY
Gall, E.G. (Miss)	1940	1962	Blantyre	151 Raeburn Heights, Glenrothes KY16 1BW
Glass, Irene (Miss)	1945	1976	Delhi	3E Falcon Road West, Edinburgh EH10 4AA
Hutchison, C.M. (Mr)	1951	1972	Calabar	75 Grampian Road, Torry, Aberdeen AB11 8ED
Irvine, Mr Clive and Mrs Su	1984	1999	Nepal	McGregor Flat, 92 Blackford Avenue, Edinburgh EH9 3ES
Irvine, Dr Geoffrey C. and Mrs Dorothy	1952	1989	Kenya	Lakeside, PO Box 1356 Naivasha, Kenya
Kreuger, Dr Hendrikje	1957	1982	Western India	Rm 418, Nellestein Lopikhof 1, NL-1108 Amsterdam, The Netherlands
Lamont, Rev. A. Donald	1941	1975	Kenya	36 St Clair Terrace, Edinburgh EH10 5PS
Liddell, Margaret (Miss)	1964	1980	Zambia	20 Wyvis Place, Conon Bridge, Dingwall IV7 8BZ
Lyon, Rev. D.H.S.	1952	1972	Nagpur	30 Mansfield Road, Balerno EH14 7JZ
McArthur, G. (Mr)	1956	1972	South Africa	3 Craigcrook Road, Edinburgh EH4 3NQ
McCulloch, Lesley (Mrs)	1982	1992	Malawi/Pakistan	c/o 19 North Approach Road, Kincardine, Alloa FK10 4NW
McCutcheon, Agnes W.F. (Miss)	1957	1989	India	10A Hugh Murray Grove, Cambuslang, Glasgow G72 7NG
Macdonald, Rev. R.M.	1929	1968	Calabar	Pinewood Nursing Home, Leny Road, Callander FK17 8AP
McDougall, Rev. John N.	1935	1960	West Pakistan	2/58 Allendale Road, Mount Albert, Auckland 3, New Zealand
McGoff, A.W. (Miss)	1954	1974	Kolhapur	6 Mossvale Walk, Craigend, Glasgow G33 5PF
MacGregor, Rev. Margaret	1959	1994	India	Gordon Flat, 16 Learmonth Court, Edinburgh EH4 1PB
McKenzie, Rev. Robert	1938	1951	India	23 Foulis Crescent, Edinburgh EH14 5BN
McKenzie, Rev. W.M.	1958	1974	Zambia	Troqueer Road, Dumfries DG2 7DF
MacKinnon, E.L. (Miss)	1952	1972	Nigeria	142 Glencairn Street, Stevenston KA20 3BU
McNeel, M.S.H. (Miss)	1938	1975	Seoni	47/5 Gillespie Grescent, Edinburgh EH10 4JB
Malley, Beryl Stevenson (Miss)	1982	1992	Malawi	272/2 Craigcrook Road, Edinburgh EH4 7TF

Name			Place	Address
Marshall, Rev. Fred J.	1946	1992	Bermuda	Flat 3, 31 Oswald Road, Edinburgh EH9 2HT
Millar, Rev. Margaret R.M.	1967	1996	Malawi/Zambia	The Manse, Taynuilt, Argyll PA35 1HW
Millar, Rev. Peter	1976	1989	South India	
Morrice, Rev. Dr Charles and Mrs Margaret	1971	1998	Buenos Aires/Kenya	104 Baron's Hill Avenue, Linlithgow EH49 7JG
Morris, Rev. Gordon C.	1948	1983	Zambia, Argentina	42 Regent Street, Edinburgh EH5 2AY
Morton, Rev. Alasdair J.	1960	1973	Zambia	8 Ormiston Grove, Melrose TD6 9SR
Morton, Rev. Colin	1988	1998	Israel	313 Lanark Road West, Currie EH14 5RS
Murison, Rev. W.G.	1951	1971	Santalia	21 Hailes Gardens, Edinburgh EH13 0JL
Murray, Mr Ian and Mrs Isabel	1962	2000	Pakistan	17 Piershill Terrace, Edinburgh EH8 7EY
Nicholson, Rev. Thomas S.	1981	1995	Taiwan	Todholes, Greenlaw, Duns TD10 6XD
Nicol, Catherine (Miss)	1960	2000	Pakistan	St Columba Christian Girls' RTC, Barah Patthar, Sialkot 2, Pakistan
Nicoll, J.M. (Miss)	1950	1967	Rajasthan	74 Brucefield Avenue, Dunfermline KY11 4SY
Pacitti, Rev. Stephen A.	1977	1996	Taiwan	157 Nithsdale Road, Pollokshields, Glasgow G41 5RD
Philip, Rev. David Stuart	1978	1991	Gibraltar	6 St Bernard's Crescent, Edinburgh EH4 1NP
Philpot, Rev. David	1981	1995	WCC Geneva	2/27 Pentland Drive, Edinburgh EH10 6PX
Rae, Rev. David	1953	1989	India	29 Falcon Avenue, Edinburgh EH10 4AL
Reid, Margaret I. (Miss)	1964	1982	Malawi	26A Angle Park Terrace, Edinburgh EH11 2JT
Rennie, Rev. Alistair M.	1939	1976	Malawi	13 Tullich Terrace, Tillicoultry FK13 6RD
Rhodes, Rev. William S.	1954	1981	North India	22 Hamilton Place, Edinburgh EH3 5AU
Ritchie, Ishbel M. (Miss)	1955	1996	Eastern Himalaya	8 Ross Street, Dunfermline KY12 0AN
Ritchie, Rev. J.M.	1974	1977	Yemen	46 St James' Gardens, Penicuik EH26 9DU
Ritchie, Mary Scott (Miss)	1968	1991	Malawi/Israel	Afton Villa, 1 Afton Bridgend, New Cumnock KA18 4AX
Ross, Rev. Prof. Kenneth and Mrs Hester	1988	1998	Malawi	35 Madeira Street, Edinburgh EH6 4AJ
Rough, Mary E. (Miss)	1966	1987	Blantyre	6 Glebe Street, Dumfries DG1 2LF
Roy, Rev. Alan J.	1960	1972	Zambia	14 Comerton Place, Drumoig, St Andrews KY16 0NQ
Russell, M.M. (Miss)	1946	1969	Nigeria	14 Hozier Street, Carluke ML8 5DW
Samuel, Lynda (Mrs)	1974	1990	Madras	c/o Balgownie, 1 Argyll Street, Brechin DD9 6JL
Scrimgeour, Elizabeth (Miss)	1946	1976	Darjeeling	73 Novar Drive, Glasgow G12 9SS
Smith, M.I. (Miss)	1956	1973	Madras	6 Fintry Mains, Dundee DD4 9HF
Smith, Dr R.B.	1939	1958	Yemen	Flat G4, 21 Queen's Bay Crescent, Edinburgh EH15 2NA
Smith, Rev. W. Ewing	1962	1978	Delhi	1 Hardy Gardens, Bathgate EH48 1NH
Stewart, Marion G. (Miss)	1976	1989	Malawi/Israel	Kirk Cottage, Kirkton of Skene, Westhill, Skene AB32 6XX
Stone, W. Vernon MA BD	1949	1966	Zambia	36 Woodrow Court, Port Glasgow Road, Kilmacolm PA13 4QA
Taylor, Rev. A.T.H.	1938	1972	Nigeria/Jamaica	4 The Pleasance, Strathkinness, St Andrews KY16 9SD
Wallace, A. Dorothy (Miss)	1953	1991	North India	7 Bynack Place, Nethy Bridge PH25 3DU
Westmarland, Rev. Colin	1975	2001	Malta	PO Box 5, Cospicua, CSPO1, Malta
Wilkie, Rev. James L.	1959	1976	Zambia	7 Comely Bank Avenue, Edinburgh EH4 1EW
Wilkinson, Rev. John	1946	1975	Kenya	70 Craigleith Hill Gardens, Edinburgh EH4 2JH
Wilson, M.H. (Miss)	1946	1977	Nasik	7 Lady's Well, Moat Road, Annan DG12 5AD
Wilson, Rev. Mark	1953	1978	Nagpur	37 Kings Avenue, Longniddry EH32 0QN

LIST N – PARISH ASSISTANTS and PROJECT WORKERS

NAME	APP	ADDRESS	APPOINTMENT	TEL	PRES
Adam, Dougie	2001	Flat D, 89 Western Road, Aberdeen AB24 4DR	Aberdeen: Bridge of Don		31
Anderson, Gordon	2002	33 Grampian View, Ferryden, Montrose DD10 9SU	Angus Presbytery	01674 674915	30
Black, Colm	2001	2B Mason Road, Inverness IV2 3SZ	Inverness: Hilton	01463 717208	37
Campbell, Alasdair	2000	3 Gellatly Road, Dunfermline KY11 4BH	Dunfermline: St Ninian's	01383 726238	24
Carmichael, Colin	1999	60 Glenview Road, Gorebridge EH23 4BW	Newbattle	01875 820229	3
Close, David	2001	2/2 156 Garrioch Road, Glasgow G20 8RN	The Star Project: Paisley North	0141-945 1022	14
Conlin, Melodie	2000	427 Carmunnock Road, Glasgow G45 9DG	Glasgow East End	0141-583 0790	16
Cowie, Marjorie	2002	35 Balbirnie Avenue, Markinch, Glenrothes KY7 6BS	Glenrothes: St Margaret's	01592 758402	25
Craw, John	1998	21 Redburn Avenue, Culloden, Inverness IV2 7AZ	Inverness: Culloden: The Barn	01463 798753	37
Douglas, Jessie (Mrs)	1999	24 Niddrie Marischal Crescent, Edinburgh EH16 4LA	Edinburgh: Richmond Craigmillar	0131-669 6848	1
Falconer, Alexander J.	1996	59 Waldegrave Road, Carlisle CA2 6EW	Carlisle Chapel Street/Longtown	01228 544757	7
Finch, John	2002	6 Balmuildy Road, Glasgow G64 3BS	Glasgow: St Francis in the East	0141-772 1363	16
Fraser, Lesley (Ms)	2001	40 Muir Wood Road, Currie EH14 5JN	Edinburgh: North Leith	0131-451 5628	1
Geddes, David	2002	108 Maxwelton Avenue, East Kilbride, Glasgow G74 3DU	Hamilton Presbytery	01355 235998	17
Govan, Alec	1999	1 School Road, Sandford, Strathaven ML10 6BF	Hamilton: Trinity	01357 523815	17
Hutchison, John	2001	30/4 West Pilton Gardens, Edinburgh EH4 4EA	Edinburgh: The Old Kirk	0131-538 1622	1
Lydall, Alex (Miss)	2001	2/1 3 Springfield Road, Glasgow G64 1PD	Linwood	0141-772 6298	14
Ma, Lyn	2000	G/R 4 Doune Quadrant, Glasgow G20 6DL	Glasgow: Gorbals	0141-946 1658	16
McBean, Archie	1999	28 Taransay Crescent, Aberdeen AB16 6UG	Aberdeen: Mastrick	01224 789784	31
McCorkindale, Yvonne (Mrs)	1997	118 Ardfin Road, Prestwick KA9 2LE	Kilmarnock: Shortlees	01292 678874	11
McLaren, Kirsty Ann (Ms)	2002	37 West Main Street, Blackburn, Bathgate EH47 7LU	Edinburgh: Kaimes Lockhart Meml	01505 650819	1
McLauchlan, Dorothy Jean	2001	114 Brownside Road, Glasgow G72 8AF	Glasgow: Cranhill	0141-641 3171	16
Morrison, Rosie (Mrs)	2000	12 Hailes Place, Dunfermline KY12 7XJ	Cowdenbeath: Trinity	01383 621353	24
Muir, Graeme	2001	2 Nithsdale Place, Noblehill, Dumfries DG1 3HT	Dumfries: St George's	01387 267470	8
Philip, Elizabeth MA BA	2001	43 Smithycroft Road, Glasgow G33 2RH [E-mail: elizabethphilip@cheerful.com]	Glasgow: Garthamlock/Craigend East	0141-770 7593	16
Redford, Susan	2001	45 Kirknethan, Wishaw ML2 0BU	East Kilbride: Claremont	01698 357432	17

Scrimgeour, Anne-Marie (Miss)	2000	34 Mallaig Avenue, Dundee DD2 4TW	Dundee: Craigiebank with Douglas and Angus	01382 642465	29
White, Ken	2002	97 Howes Drive, Aberdeen AB16 7FH		01224 686592	31
Young, Neil James	2001	33 Alexandra Park Street, Glasgow G31 2UB			16

LIST O – READERS

1. EDINBURGH

Beasley, Ronald E.	37 Warrender Park Terrace, Edinburgh EH9 1EB	0131-229 8383
Davies, Ruth (Mrs) (attached to Liberton)	4 Hawkhead Grove, Edinburgh EH16 6LS	0131-664 3608
Farrant, Yvonne (Mrs) (attached to Kirk o' Field)	Flat 7, 14 Duddingston Mills, Edinburgh EH8 7NF	0131-661 1026
Farrell, William J.	50 Ulster Crescent, Edinburgh EH8 7JS	0131-558 8210
Farrow, Edmund	14 Brunswick Terrace, Edinburgh EH7 5PG	0131-660 3007
Kerrigan, Herbert A. MA LLB QC	Airdene, 20 Edinburgh Road, Dalkeith EH22 1JY	0131-441 3150
Kinnear, M.A.	25 Thorburn Road, Edinburgh EH13 0BH	0131-337 7711
Morrison, Peter K.	65 Balgreen Road, Edinburgh EH12 5UA	0131-335 3427
Scott, May (Miss)	34/2 Station Road, Kirkliston EH29 9BE	0131-447 9035
Wyllie, Anne (Miss)	46 Jordan Lane, Edinburgh EH10 4QX	

2. WEST LOTHIAN

Coyle, Charlotte (Mrs)	28 The Avenue, Whitburn EH47 0DA	01501 740687
Davidson, Sheila (Mrs)	12 Slamannan Road, Avonbridge, Falkirk FK1 2LW	01324 861554
Elliott, Sarah (Miss)	105 Seafield, Bathgate EH47 7AW	01506 654950
Notman, Jean G.S. (Miss)	31 South Loch Park, Bathgate EH48 2QZ	01506 633820
Smith, George	15 Manse Avenue, Armadale EH48 3HS	01501 732025

3. LOTHIAN

Booth, Sidney J. IEng CCME	6 Winton Court, Cockenzie, Prestonpans EH32 0JW	01875 813978
Cannon, S. Christopher MA	Briarwood, Winterfield Place, Belhaven, Dunbar EH42 1QQ	01368 864991
Evans, W. John IEng MIIE(Elec)	Edenwood, 29 Smileyknowes Court, North Berwick EH39 4RG [E-mail: jevans7@compuserve.com]	01620 894309
Gibson, C.B. Stewart	27 King's Avenue, Longniddry EH32 0QN	01875 853464
Hogg, David MA	82 Eskhill, Penicuik EH26 8DQ	01968 676350
Lyall, George JP	Mossgiel, 13 Park Road, Bonnyrigg EH19 2AW [E-mail: george.lyall@bigfoot.com]	0131-663 9343
Trevor, A. Hugh MA	29A Fidra Road, North Berwick EH39 4NE [E-mail: hughtrevor@compuserve.com]	01620 894924
Yeoman, Edward T.N. FSA(Scot)	75 Newhailes Crescent, Musselburgh EH21 6ES	0131-653 2291

4. MELROSE AND PEEBLES

Butcher, John W. — 'Sandal', 11 Ormiston Grove, Melrose TD6 9SR — 01896 822339
Cashman, Margaret (Mrs) — 38 Abbotsford Road, Galashiels TD1 3HR — 01896 752711

5. DUNS

Deans, M. (Mrs) BA — The Lodge, Edrington House, Mordington, Berwick-on-Tweed TD15 1UF — 01289 386222
Elphinston, Enid (Mrs) — Edrington House, Berwick-on-Tweed TD15 1UF — 01289 386359
Landale, William — Cranshaws House, Cranshaws, Duns TD11 3SJ — 01361 890242

6. JEDBURGH

Finlay, Elizabeth (Mrs) — 10 Inch Park, Kelso TD5 7EQ — 01573 226641
Knox, Dagmar (Mrs) — 3 Stichill Road, Ednam, Kelso TD5 7QQ — 01573 224883
Thomson, Robert R. — 34/36 Fisher Avenue, Hawick TD9 9NB — 01450 373851

7. ANNANDALE AND ESKDALE

Boncey, David — Redbrae, Beattock, Moffat DG10 9RF [E-mail: bonceyofredbrae@yahoo.co.uk] — 01683 300243
Brown, S. Jeffrey BA — Skara Brae, 8 Ballplay Road, Moffat DG10 9AR — 01683 220475
Chisholm, Dennis A.G. MA BSc — Moss-side, Hightae, Lockerbie DG11 1JR — 01387 811803
Dodds, Alan — Trinco, Battlehill, Annan DG12 6SN — 01461 201235
Jackson, Sue (Mrs) — Lauries Close Cottage, Waterbeck, Lockerbie DG11 3HD — 01461 600685
Morton, Andrew A. BSc — 19 Sherwood Park, Lockerbie DG11 2DX [E-mail: thecroft@appleonline.net] — 01576 203164

8. DUMFRIES AND KIRKCUDBRIGHT

Archer, Morven (Mrs) — 1 Grilloch Drive, Dumfries DG1 4DP — 01387 263946
Carroll, J. Scott — 17 Downs Place, Heathhall, Dumfries DG1 3RF — 01387 265350
Greer, Kathleen (Mrs) — 10 Watling Street, Dumfries DG1 1HF — 01387 256113
Marsh, Sally (Mrs) BTh — 32 Queen Street, Castle Douglas DG7 1HS — 01556 503706
Ogilvie, D.W. MA FSAScot — Lingerwood, 2 Nelson Street, Dumfries DG2 9AY — 01387 264267
Paterson, Ronald M. (Dr) — Mirkwood, Ringford, Castle Douglas DG7 2AL — 01557 820202
Piggins, Janette (Mrs) — Cleugh Wood, Dalbeattie DG5 4PF — 01387 780655

9. WIGTOWN AND STRANRAER

Clough, Alan — Dowiesbank, Whauphill, Newton Stewart DG8 9PN — 01988 700824
Connery, Graham — Skellies Knowe, West Ervie, Stranraer DG9 — 01776 854277
Rankin, Stuart — Villa Cree, Cree Bridge, Minnigaff, Newton Stewart DG8 6NR — 01671 403914
Robinson, J.J. — Kirwaugh, Wigtown, Newton Stewart DG8 9AY — 01988 403244
Williams, Roy — 120 Belmont Road, Stranraer DG9 7BG

10. AYR

Coghlan, Tony	'Hawthorns', Auchendoon, Hollybush, Ayr KA6 6HA	01242 560307
Fleming, William H.	35 Briar Grove, Ayr KA7 3PD	01292 268599
Jamieson, I.	2 Whinfield Avenue, Prestwick KA9 2BH	01242 476898
McNally, David BEd MEd ThDip ACP	50 Kenmore, Troon KA10 6PT	01292 312015
Murphy, I.	56 Lamont Crescent, Cumnock KA18 3DU	01290 423675
Riome, Elizabeth (Mrs)	Monkwood Mains, Minishant, Maybole KA19 8EY	01292 443440
Todd, Joy M. (Mrs) BD	15 Firth Road, Troon KA10 6TF	01292 312995
Todd, S.J.	15 Firth Road, Troon KA10 6TF	01292 312995
Wallace, D.	4 Holmston Crescent, Ayr KA7 3JJ	01292 261620

11. IRVINE AND KILMARNOCK

Bircham, James	8 Holmlea Place, Kilmarnock KA1 1UU	01563 532287
Cuthbert, Helen (Miss) MA MSc	63 Haining Avenue, Kilmarnock KA1 3QN	01563 550403
Crosbie, Shona (Mrs)	4 Campbell Street, Darvel KA17 0PA	01560 322229
Findlay, Elizabeth (Mrs)	19 Keith Place, Kilmarnock KA3 7NS	01563 528084
Hamilton, Margaret A. (Mrs)	59 South Hamilton Street, Kilmarnock KA1 2DT	01563 534431
Jamieson, John BSc(Hons) DEP AFBPSS	22 Moorfield Avenue, Kilmarnock KA1 1TS	01563 534065
Lightbody, Hunter B.	36 Rannoch Place, Irvine KA12 9NQ	01294 273955
McAllister, Anne C. (Mrs)	39 Bowes Rigg, Stewarton KA3 5EN	01560 483191
McLean, Donald	1 Four Acres Drive, Kilmaurs, Kilmarnock KA3 2ND	01563 381475
MacTaggart, Elspeth (Miss)	21 Scargie Road, Kilmarnock KA3 1QR	01563 527713
Scott, William BA DipEd	6 Elgin Avenue, Stewarton, Kilmarnock KA3 3HJ	01560 484273
Storm, Iain	17 Kilwinning Road, Irvine KA12 8RR	01294 277647
Wilson, Robert L.S. MA BD	57 Woodstock Street, Kilmarnock KA1 2JH	01563 526658

12. ARDROSSAN

Allan, J.H.	Creag Dhubh, Golf Course Road, Whiting Bay, Brodick, Isle of Arran KA27 8RE	01770 700462
Barclay, Elizabeth (Mrs)	2 Jacks Road, Saltcoats KA21 5NT	01294 471855
Hunter, Jean C.Q. (Mrs)	The Manse, Shiskine, Isle of Arran KA27 8EP	01770 860380
Mackay, Brenda H. (Mrs)	19 Eglinton Square, Ardrossan KA22 8LN	01294 464491
Mills, Colin J.	Roadend Christian Guesthouse, Shiskine, Brodick, Isle of Arran KA27 8EW	01770 860448
Price, James	Dunjara, The Orchard, West Kilbride KA23 9AE	01294 822247

13. LANARK

Allan, Robert	59 Jennie Lee Drive, Overtown, Wishaw ML2 0EE	01698 376738
Grant, Alan	25 Moss-side Avenue, Carluke ML8 5UG	01555 771419
Kerr, Sheilagh I. (Mrs)	Dunvegan, 29 Wilsontown Road, Forth, Lanark ML11 8ER	01555 812214

14. PAISLEY

Campbell, Tom BA FRICS DipCPC	100 Craigielea Road, Renfrew PA4 8NJ	0141-886 2503
McHugh, Jack	'Earlshaugh', Earl Place, Bridge of Weir PA11 3HA	01505 612789
Maxwell, Margaret (Mrs) BD	2 Grants Avenue, Paisley PA2 6AZ	0141-884 3710

15. GREENOCK

Davey, Charles L.	16 Divert Road, Gourock PA19 1DT	01475 631544
	[E-mail: charles@davey2.freeserve.co.uk]	
Geddes, Douglas S.	167 South Street, Greenock PA16 8TE	01475 723601
	[E-mail: do.flo@virgin.net]	
Glenny, John C.	49 Cloch Road, Gourock PA19 1AT	01475 636415
Jamieson, J.A.	148 Finnart Street, Greenock PA16 8HY	01475 729531
Mackenzie, Elizabeth (Miss)	35 Forsyth Street, Greenock PA16 8DH	01475 722446
Marshall, Leon M.	Glenisla, Gryffe Road, Kilmacolm PA13 4BA	01505 872417

16. GLASGOW

Armstrong, J.	44 Eckford Street, Glasgow G32 7AJ	0141-778 4745
Birchall, Edwin R.	11 Sunnybank Grove, Clarkston, Glasgow G76 7SU	0141-638 4332
Calder, William	111 Muirside Avenue, Kirkintilloch, Glasgow G66 3PP	0141-776 5495
Callander, Thomas M.S.	31 Dalkeith Avenue, Bishopbriggs, Glasgow G64 2HQ	0141-563 6955
Campbell, Jack T. BD BEd	1 Springfield Road, Bishopbriggs, Glasgow G64 1PJ	0141-563 5837
Clarke, Samuel	'Gola', 142 Shelley Road, Glasgow G12 0XN	0141-337 2238
Dickson, Hector	'Guito', 61 Whitton Drive, Giffnock, Glasgow G46 6EF	0141-637 0080
Findlay, William	36 Firpark Road, Bishopbriggs, Glasgow G64 1SP	0141-772 7253
Gibson, James N.	153 Peveril Avenue, Glasgow G41 3SF	0141-632 4162
Horner, David J.	32 Burnside Road, Rutherglen, Glasgow G73 4RS	0141-634 2178
Lennie, Henry	14 Clyde Place, Cambuslang, Glasgow G72 7QT	0141-641 1410
Lockhart, James C.	56 Springfield Road, Bishopbriggs, Glasgow G64 1PN	0141-772 1852
MacColl, Duncan N.	14 Mosspark Avenue, Glasgow G52 1JX	0141-427 2395
McFarlane, Robert	25 Avenel Road, Glasgow G13 2PB	0141-954 5540
McLaughlin, C.	8 Lamlash Place, Glasgow G33 3XH	0141-774 2483
McLellan, Duncan	138 King's Park Avenue, Glasgow G44 4HS	0141-632 8433
Middleton, W.G.	20 Rannoch Avenue, Bishopbriggs, Glasgow G64 1BU	0141-772 6240
Montgomery, Hamish	13 Avon Avenue, Kessington, Bearsden, Glasgow G61 2PS	0141-942 3640
Nairne, Elizabeth (Mrs)	229 Southbrae Drive, Glasgow G13 1TT	0141-959 5066
Philips, John B.	6/63, 200 Sandiefield Road, Glasgow G5 0DW	0141-429 7716
Robertson, Adam	423 Amulree Street, Glasgow G32 7SS	0141-778 1563
Shirlaw, William	77 Southpark Avenue, Glasgow G12 8LE	0141-339 0454
Tindall, Margaret (Mrs)	23 Ashcroft Avenue, Lennoxtown, Glasgow G65 7EN	01360 310911
Williamson, John G.	34 King Edward Road, Glasgow G13 1QW	0141-959 1300
Wilson, George A.	46 Maxwell Drive, Garrowhill, Baillieston, Glasgow G69 6LS	0141-771 3862

17. HAMILTON

Bell, Sheena	2 Langdale, East Kilbride, Glasgow G74 4RP	01355 248217
Black, Gavin	11 Torrance Road, West Mains, East Kilbride, Glasgow G74 1AR	01355 224600
Clemenson, Anne	25 Dempsey Road, Lochview, Bellshill ML4 2UF	01698 747032
Cruickshanks, William	63 Progress Drive, Caldercruix, Airdrie ML6 7PU	01236 843352
Falconer, Leslie D.	48 Fraser River Tower, East Kilbride, Glasgow G75 8AD	01355 230133
Haggarty, Frank	46 Glen Road, Caldercruix, Airdrie ML6 7PZ	01236 842182
Hawthorne, William	172 Main Street, Plains, Airdrie ML6 7JH	01236 842230
Hewitt, Samuel	3 Corrie Court, Earnock, Hamilton ML3 9XE	01698 457403
Hislop, Eric	3 Kellie Grove, East Kilbride, Glasgow G74 4DN	01355 231600
Leckie, Elizabeth	41 Church Street, Larkhall ML9 1EZ	01698 308933
McCleary, Isaac	719 Coatbridge Road, Bargeddie, Glasgow G69 7PH	0141-236 0158
McRae, James	36 Crosshill Road, Strathaven ML10 6DS	01357 520053
Queen, Leslie	60 Loch Assynt, East Kilbride, Glasgow G74 2DW	01355 233932
Robertson, Rowan	68 Townhead Road, Coatbridge, ML5 2HU	01236 425703
Smith, Alexander	6 Coronation Street, Wishaw ML2 8LF	01698 385797
White, Ian	21 Muirhead, Stonehouse ML9 3HG	01698 792772
Wilson, William	115 Chatelherault Crescent, Low Waters Estate, Hamilton ML3 9PL	01698 421856

18. DUMBARTON

Galbraith, Iain B.	Beechwood, Overton Road, Alexandria G83 0LJ	01389 753563
Hart, R.J.M. BSc	7 Kidston Drive, Helensburgh G84 8QA	01436 672039
McFarlane, Andrew L.	9 Smugglers Way, Rhu, Helensburgh G84 8HX	01436 820058
Neville, Robert	4 Glen Drive, Helensburgh G84 9BJ	01436 671481

19. SOUTH ARGYLL

Holden, Robert	Orsay, West Bank Road, Ardrishaig, Lochgilphead PA30 8HG	01546 603327
Mitchell, James S.	4 Main Street, Port Charlotte, Islay PA48 7TX	01496 850650
Ramsay, Matthew M.	Portnastorm, Carradale, Campbeltown PA28 6SB	01583 431381
Stewart, Agnes	Creagdhu Mansions, New Quay Street, Campbeltown PA28 6BB	01586 552805
Stewart, John Y.S.	9 Foulis Road, Inveraray PA32 8UW	01499 302077

20. DUNOON

Challis, John O.	Bay Villa, Strachur, Cairndow PA27 8DE	01369 860436

21. LORN AND MULL

Binner, Aileen	'Ailand', Connel, Oban PA37 1QX	01631 710264
Elwis, Michael	Erray Farm Cottage, Tobermory, Mull PA75 6PS	01688 302331
Simpson, J.	Ardmhullean, Longsdale Road, Oban PA34 5JW	01631 562022

22. FALKIRK

Duncan, Lorna (Mrs) BA	Richmond, 28 Solway Drive, Head of Muir, Denny FK5 5NS	01324 813020
Stewart, Arthur MA	34 Raith Drive, Blackwood, Cumbernauld, Glasgow G68 9PF	01236 732532
Struthers, I.	169 The Auld Road, Cumbernauld, Glasgow G67 2RQ	01236 733879

23. STIRLING

- Brown, Kathryn (Mrs) — The Manse, Tullibody, Alloa FK10 2RG — 01259 213236
- Durie, Alastair — 25 Forth Place, Stirling FK8 1UD — 01786 451029
- Kimmitt, Alan — 111 Glasgow Road, Bannockburn, Stirling FK7 0PF
- Lamont, John — 'Serendipity', Wardpark, Gartmore, Stirling FK8 3RN — 01360 850313
- Tilly, Patricia — 4 Innerdownie Place, Dollar FK14 7BY — 01259 742094

24. DUNFERMLINE

- Arnott, Robert G.K. — 25 Sealstrand, Dalgety Bay, Dunfermline KY11 5GH — 01383 822293
- Conway, Bernard — 4 Centre Street, Kelty KY4 0DU — 01383 830442
- McCaffery, Joyce (Mrs) — 79 Union Street, Cowdenbeath KY4 9SA — ex-directory

25. KIRKCALDY

- Biernat, Ian — 13 Westpark Avenue, Leslie, Glenrothes KY6 3BX — 01592 741487
- Biernat, Margaret (Mrs) — 13 Westpark Avenue, Leslie, Glenrothes KY6 3BX — 01592 741487

26. ST ANDREWS

- Allan, Angus J. — Craigmore, The Barony, Cupar KY15 5ER — 01334 653369
- Browning, Margaret (Miss) — 4 Wellpark Terrace, Newport-on-Tay DD6 8HT — 01382 542140
- Elder, Morag (Mrs) — 5 Provost Road, Tayport DD6 9JE — 01382 552218
- King, C.M. (Mrs) — 8 Bankwell Road, Anstruther KY10 3DA — 01333 310017
- Kinnis, W.K.B. (Dr) — 4 Dempster Court, St Andrews KY16 9EU — 01334 476959
- Smith, Elspeth (Mrs) — Whinstead, Dalgairn, Cupar KY15 4PH — 01334 653269

27. DUNKELD AND MEIGLE

- Carr, Graham — St Helen's, Meigle Road, Alyth PH11 8EU — 01828 632474
- Davidson, Margaret (Mrs) — 9 Woodlands Park, Blairgowrie PH10 6UW — 01250 875957
- Howat, David — Lilybank Cottage, Newton Street, Blairgowrie, Blairgowrie PH10 6MZ — 01250 874715
- Macmartin, Duncan M. — Teallach, Old Crieff Road, Aberfeldy PH15 2DG — 01887 820693
- Saunders, Grace (Ms) — 40 Perth Street, Blairgowrie PH10 6DQ — 01250 873981
- Templeton, Elizabeth (Mrs) — Tenandry Manse, Killiecrankie, Pitlochry PH16 5LH — 01796 472360

28. PERTH

- Begg, J. — Benholm, 12 Commissioner Street, Crieff PH7 3AY [E-mail: begg1@supanet.com] — 01764 655907
- Brown, Stanley — 14 Buchan Drive, Perth PH1 1NQ — 01738 628818
- Buchan, J.S. — 47 Dunkeld Road, Perth PH1 5RP — 01738 621814
- Chappell, E. (Mrs) — Strathdon, 2 Acharn, Perth PH1 2SR — 01738 634640
- Coulter, Hamish — 95 Cedar Drive, Perth PH1 1RW [E-mail: hamish@coulter9530.freeserve.co.uk] — 01738 636761
- Hastings, W.P. — 5 Craigroyston Road, Scone, Perth PH2 6NB — 01738 560498
- Johnstone, David — 92 Duncansby Way, Perth PH1 5XF — 01738 442051
- Laing, John — Flat 1, Middle Church, 6 Tay Street, Perth PH1 5LQ — 01738 623888
- Michie, M. (Mrs) — 3 Loch Leven Court, Wester Balgedie, Kinross KY13 7NE — 01592 840602
- Packer, Joan (Miss) — 11 Moredun Terrace, Perth PH2 0DA — 01821 623873
- Thorburn, Susan (Mrs) — 3 Daleally Cottages, St Madoes Road, Errol, Perth PH2 7TJ — 01821 642681
- Wilkie, R. — 24 Huntingtower Road, Perth PH1 2JS — 01738 628301
- Yellowlees, Deirdre (Mrs) — Ringmill House, Gannochy Farm, Perth PH2 7JH — 01738 633773

29. DUNDEE

Baxter, John T.G.	2 Garten Street, Broughty Ferry, Dundee DD5 3HH	01382 739997
Bell, S. (Dr)	10 Victoria Street, Newport-on-Tay DD6 8DJ	01382 542315
Doig, Andrew	6 Lyndhurst Terrace, Dundee DD2 3HP	01382 610596
Johnston, William	62 Forthill Road, Broughty Ferry, Dundee DD5 3TJ	01382 739704
Owler, Harry G.	43 Brownhill Road, Dundee DD2 4LH	01382 622902
Ramsay, Thomas A.	Inchcape Place, Broughty Ferry, Dundee DD5 2LP	01382 778915
Rodgers, Mary (Mrs)	12 Balmerino Road, Dundee DD4 8RN	01382 500291
Shepherd, E.	34 Dalmahoy Drive, Dundee DD2 3UT	01382 815825
Simpson, Webster	51 Wemyss Crescent, Monifieth, Dundee DD5 4RA	01382 535218
Webster, Charles A.	16 Bath Street, Broughty Ferry, Dundee DD5 2BY	01382 739520
Woodley, A.G. (Dr)	67 Marlee Road, Broughty Ferry, Dundee DD5 3EU	01382 739820

30. ANGUS

Anderson, Gordon	33 Grampian View, Ferryden, Montrose DD10 9SU	01674 674915
Beedie, A.W.	62 Newton Crescent, Arbroath DD11 3JZ	01241 875001
Davidson, P.I.	27 Dorward Road, Montrose DD10 8SB	01674 674098
Edwards, Dougal	25 Mackenzie Street, Carnoustie DD7 6HD	01241 852666
Gray, Ian	15 Rossie Island Road, Montrose DD10 9NH	01674 677126
Gray, Linda (Mrs)	8 Inchgarth Street, Forfar DD8 3LY	01307 464039
Ironside, C.T. PhD	21 Tailyour Crescent, Montrose DD10 9BL	01674 673959
Leslie Melville, Ruth (Hon. Mrs)	Little Deuchar, Fern, Forfar DD8 3RA	01356 650279
Nicol, Douglas C.	Edenbank, 16 New Road, Forfar DD8 2AE	01307 463264
Stevens, Peter J. BSc BA	7 Union Street, Montrose DD10 8PZ	01674 673710
Thompson, Anne	22 Braehead Drive, Carnoustie DD7 7SX	01241 852084
Wade, Nan (Mrs)	Lea-Rig, Charleston, Forfar DD8 1UF	01307 840204
Wheat, M.	16A South Esk Street, Montrose DD10 8BJ	01674 676083

31. ABERDEEN

Forrester, Arthur A.	158 Lee Crescent North, Bridge of Don AB22 8FR	01224 822783
Gray, Peter PhD	165 Countesswells Road, Aberdeen AB15 7RA	01224 318172
Sinton, George P. FIMLS	12 North Donside Road, Bridge of Don, Aberdeen AB23 8PA	01224 702273

32. KINCARDINE AND DEESIDE

Bell, Peter D. BA	63 St Nicholas Drive, Banchory AB31 5YE	01330 823661
Cameron, Ann (Mrs)	30 Wilson Road, Banchory AB31 5UY	01330 825953
Grant, Prof. Raymond MA PhD	Ballochbrock, Braemar, Ballater AB35 5YQ	01339 741340
Haddow, Steven	East Manse, Station Road, Banchory AB31 5YP	01330 822481
McCafferty, W. John	East Crossley, Netherley, Stonehaven AB39 3QY	01569 730281
Middleton, Robbie (Capt.)	7 St Ternan's Road, Newtonhill, Stonehaven AB39 2PF	01569 730852
Mitchell, D. Ronald BDS	4 Durris Stables, Durris, Banchory AB31 6BD	01330 811899
Sedgwick, Sheila (Dr) BA BD MEd PhD	Girnock Shiel, Glengirnock, Ballater AB35 5SS	01339 755292
Woods, Julie (Mrs)	23 St Aidan Crescent, Banchory AB31 5YX	01330 824184

33. GORDON

Findlay, Patricia (Mrs)	Douglas View, Tullynessle, Alford AB33 8QR	01975 562379
Hart, Elsie (Mrs)	The Knoll, Craigearn, Kemnay AB51 9LN	01467 642105
Rennie, Lyall	5 Urydale, Inverurie AB51 3XW	01467 624636
Robb, Margaret (Mrs)	Chrislouan, Keithhall, Inverurie AB51 0LN	01651 882310
Robertson, James Y.	1 Nicol Road, Kintore, Inverurie AB51 0QA	01467 633001

34. BUCHAN

Brown, Lillian (Mrs)	Bank House, 45 Main Street, Aberchirder, Huntly AB54 7ST	01466 780100
Davidson, James	19 Great Stuart Street, Peterhead AB42 1JX	01779 470234
Lumsden, Vera (Mrs)	8 Queen's Crescent, Portsoy, Banff AB45 2PX	01261 842712
McColl, John	6 Bracoden Terrace, Gardenstown, Banff AB45 3ZF	01261 851390
Mair, Dorothy (Miss)	53 Dennyduff Road, Fraserburgh AB43 9LY	01346 513879
Michie, William	Rosebank, 9 Seafield Street, Whitehills, Banff AB45 2NA	01261 861439
Noble, John	44 Henderson Park, Peterhead AB42 2WR	01779 472522
Ogston, Norman	Sunnybrae Christian Centre, Woodhead, Fyvie AB53 8LS	01651 891734
Simpson, Andrew C.	10 Wood Street, Banff AB45 1JX	01261 812538
Smith, Ian M.G. MA	Chomriach, 2 Hill Street, Cruden Bay, Peterhead AB42 0HF	01779 812698
Smith, Jenny (Mrs)	5 Seatown Place, Cairnbulg, Fraserburgh AB43 5YN	01346 582980
Sneddon, Richard	8 School Road, Peterhead AB42 2BE	01779 474492

35. MORAY

Benson, F. Stuart	8 Springfield Court, Forres IV36 3WY	01309 671525
Carson, John	2 Woodside Drive, Forres IV36 2UF	01309 674541
Forbes, Jean (Mrs)	Greenmoss, Drybridge, Buckie AB56 5JB	01542 831646
MacKenzie, Stuart G. MA	Woodend Cottage, Blackburn, Fochabers IV32 7LN	01343 843248
Middleton, Alex	Coral Cottage, Pilmuir Road, Forres IV36 2HU	01309 676912

36. ABERNETHY

Berkeley, John S. (Dr)	Drumbeg, Coylumbridge, Aviemore PH22 1QU	01479 811055

37. INVERNESS

Cook, Arnett D.	128 Laurel Avenue, Inverness IV3 5RS	01463 242586
Maclean, Hamish	63 Ashton Road, Inverness IV2 3UY	01463 239030
Robertson, Hendry	'Park House', 51 Glenurquhart Road, Inverness IV3 5PB	01463 231858

38. LOCHABER

Fraser, John A.	26 Clunes Avenue, Caol, Fort William PH33 7BJ	01397 703467
Maitland, John	St Monance, Ardgour, Fort William PH33 7AA	01855 841267
Thomas, Geoff	Drumcannach, Station Road, Arisaig PH39 4NJ	01687 450230

39. ROSS

Finlayson, Michael R.	Amberlea, Evanton IV16 9UY	01349 830598
Gilbertson, Ian	Firth View, Craigrory, North Kessock, Inverness IV1 1XH	01463 73538
Galbraith, Hamish	Kinnettas House, Strathpeffer IV14 9AJ	01997 421832
McCredie, Frederick	Highfield, Highfield Park, Conon Bridge, Inverness IV7 8AP	01349 862171
Robertson, John (Dr)	East Wing, Kincurdie House, Rosemarkie IV10 8SJ	01381 621388
Woodham, Maisey F. (Mrs)	Scardroy, Greenhill, Dingwall IV15 9JQ	01349 862116

40. SUTHERLAND

Betts-Brown, Andrew	54 Muirfield Road, Brora KW9 6QY	01408 621610
Burnett, Michael	16 The Meadows, Dornoch IV25 3SF	01862 810972
Mackay, Donald F.	The Retreat, Lillieshall Street, Helmsdale KW8 6JF	01431 821469
Stobo, Mary (Mrs)	Druim-an-Sgairnich, Lower Gledfield, Ardgay IV24 3BG	01863 766529

41. CAITHNESS

Duncan, Esme (Miss)	Avalon, Upper Warse, Canisbay, Wick KW1 4YD	01955 611455
Macnee, Anthea (Mrs)	The Manse, Canisbay, Wick KW1 4YH	01955 611309

42. LOCHCARRON – SKYE

Mackenzie, Hector	53 Strath, Gairloch IV21 2DB	01445 712433
Macrae, D.E.	Nethania, 52 Strath, Gairloch IV21 2DB	01445 712235
Murray, John W.	Totescore, Kilmuir, Portree, Skye IV51 9YW	01470 522297
Ross, R. Ian	St Conal's, Inverinate, Kyle of Lochalsh IV40 8HB	01599 511371

43. UIST

Lines, Charles	79 Ullswater Road, Southmead, Bristol BS10 6DP	01779 593105
MacAuley, John	Fernhaven, Flodabay, Isle of Harris HS3 3HA	01859 530340
MacNab, Ann (Mrs)	Druim Skillivat, Scolpaig, Lochmaddy, Isle of North Uist HS6 5DH	01876 510701
MacSween, John	5 Scott Road, Tarbert, Isle of Harris HS3 3DL	01859 502338
Taylor, Hamish	Tigh na Tobair, Flodabay, Isle of Harris HS3 3HA	01859 530310

44. LEWIS

Forsyth, William	1 Berisay Place, Stornoway, Isle of Lewis HS1 2TF	01851 702332
McAlpin, Robert J.G. MA FEIS	42A Upper Coll, Back, Isle of Lewis HS2 0LS	01851 820288
Murray, Angus	4 Ceann Chilleagraidh, Stornoway, Isle of Lewis HS1 2UJ	01851 703550

45. ORKNEY

Alexander, Malcolm	Copwillo', Button Road, Stenness, Stromness, Orkney KW16 3HA	01856 850444
Kent, Reginald F.	Greenfield, Stronsay, Orkney KW17 2AG	01857 616351
Steer, John	Beckington, Hillside Road, Stromness, Orkney KW16 3AH	01856 850815

46. SHETLAND

Christie, William C.	11 Fullaburn, Bressay, Shetland ZE2 9ET	01595 820244
Greig, Diane (Mrs) MA	The Manse, Sandwick, Shetland ZE2 9HW	01950 431244
Jamieson, Ian MA	Linksview, Ringesta, Quendale, Shetland ZE2 9JD	01950 460477
Laidlay, Una (Mrs)	5 Bells Road, Lerwick, Shetland ZE1 0QB	01595 695147
Macdonald, Michael	8 Roebrek, Brae, Shetland ZE2 9QY	01806 522318
MacGregor, Robert	Olna Cottage, Brae, Shetland ZE2 9QS	01806 522773

47. ENGLAND

Green, Peter (Dr)	Samburu Cottage, Russells Green Road, Ninfield, East Sussex	01424 892033
Mackay, Donald	90 Hallgarth Street, Elvet, Durham DH1 3AS	0191-383 2110
Munro, William H.	35 Stour Road, Corby NN17 2HX	01536 504864
Goodbourne, David (Dr)	145 Westcombe Hill, Blackheath, London SE3 7DP	020 8305 0126

48. EUROPE

Ross, David	9 Cormorant Wharf, Gibraltar	(Tel/Fax) 00350 46780
	[E-mail: macross@gibnynex.gi]	
Sharp, James	102 Rue des Eaux-Vives, CH-1207 Geneva, Switzerland	0041 22 786 48 47
	[E-mail: jsharp@world.scout.org]	

LIST P – REPRESENTATIVES ON COUNCIL EDUCATION COMMITTEES

COUNCIL	NAME	ADDRESS
ABERDEEN CITY	Mr Ronald Riddell	66 Hammersmith Road, Aberdeen AB10 6ND
ABERDEENSHIRE	Mr William Michie	34 Seafield Street, Whitehills, Banff AB45 2NP
ANGUS	Rev. Allan Webster	7 Braehead Road, Letham, Forfar DD8 2PG
ARGYLL and BUTE	Miss Alexandra Montgomery	Fairfield, 47 Crichton Road, Craigmore, Rothesay PA20 9JT
BORDERS	Rev. Alan C.D. Cartwright	The Manse, Swinton, Duns TD11 3JJ
CLACKMANNAN	Mrs Elizabeth J. Smith	The Manse, Menstrie FK11 7EA
DUMFRIES and GALLOWAY	Mr K.D. Anderson	Keltere, Rhonehouse, Castle Douglas DG7 1SL
DUNDEE	Rev. John W. Paterson	10 Douglas Terrace, Broughty Ferry, Dundee DD5 1EA
EAST AYRSHIRE	Mrs Barbara Jarvie	The Manse, 33 Barrhill Road, Cumnock KA18 1PJ
EAST DUNBARTONSHIRE	Rev. Cameron Mackenzie	18 Cannerton Crescent, Milton of Campsie, Glasgow G66 8DR
EAST LOTHIAN	Rev. Angus Kerr	15 West Road, Haddington EH41 3RD
EAST RENFREWSHIRE	Mr Henry L. Philip	28 Waterside Road, Newton Mearns, Glasgow G77 6TJ
EDINBURGH CITY	Dr Andrew Prentice	Lauder Grange, 69/2 Grange Loan, Edinburgh EH9 2EG
FALKIRK	Mrs Rosemary Stewart	18 Chestnut Grove, Stenhousemuir, Larbert FK5 4DU
FIFE	Rev. Andrew J. Philip	Muirhead House, Freuchie, Cupar KY15 7JG
GLASGOW CITY	Rev. Alexander Glass	The Manse, 43 Smithycroft Road, Riddrie, Glasgow G33 2RH
HIGHLAND	Rev. John Miller	Craigton, Tulloch Avenue, Dingwall IV15 9LH
INVERCLYDE	Rev. P.M. Gardner	Clunebraehead, Clune Brae, Port Glasgow PA14 5SL
MIDLOTHIAN	Mrs Mhairi Dick	Cranstoun Cottage, Ford, Pathhead EH37 5RE
MORAY	Mrs Christine Welch	22 West High Street, Portgordon, Buckie AB56 2QS
NORTH AYRSHIRE		6 Brodick Close, Kilwinning KA13 6KN

NORTH LANARKSHIRE	Mr George Paton	24 Low Quarry Gardens, Hamilton ML3 6RH
ORKNEY	Mrs Jenny Deans	Kenmore, Tankerness, Orkney KW17 2QT
PERTH and KINROSS	Mr A. Dunlop	3 Auchmore Drive, Rosemount, Blairgowrie PH10 6LZ
RENFREWSHIRE	Mr Edward Smith	82 Main Street, Elderslie, Johnstone PA5 9AX
SHETLAND	Rev. Winnie Munson	The Manse, Grindwell, Brae, Shetland ZE2 9QJ
SOUTH AYRSHIRE	Rev. Roger M. Hollins	Smithy Cottage, Dunure, Ayr KA7 4LH
SOUTH LANARKSHIRE	Mrs M. Dickie	2 Murchison Drive, East Kilbride G75 8PR
STIRLING	Rev. Moira MacCormick	8 Culbowie Crescent, Buchlyvie, Stirling FK8 3NH
WEST DUNBARTONSHIRE	Miss Sheila Rennie	128 Dumbuie Avenue, Dumbarton G82 2JW
WEST LOTHIAN	Rev. John Povey	The Manse, 19 Maryfield Park, Mid Calder, Livingston EH53 0SB
WESTERN ISLES	Rev. Andrew W.F. Coghill	Leurbost, Lochs, Isle of Lewis HS2 9NS

LIST Q – RETIRED LAY AGENTS

Forrester, Arthur A.	158 Lee Crescent North, Bridge of Don, Aberdeen AB22 8FR
Lamont, Donald	Staffin House Nursing Home, Portree, Isle of Skye IV51 9JS
MacNaughtan, Winifred H. (Mrs)	15 Carlyle Court, Haddington EH41 3EZ
Scott, John W.	15 Manor Court, Forfar DD8 1BR
Shepherd, Dennis	Mission House, Norby, Sandness, Shetland ZE2 9PL

LIST R – DECEASED MINISTERS

The Editor has been made aware of the following ministers who have died since the publication of the previous volume of the *Year Book*.

Allsop, Thomas Douglas	(Aberdeen: Beechgrove)
Anderson, David John Boyd	General Secretary: Evangelical Alliance Scotland
Angus, James Alexander Keith	(Braemar with Crathie)
Baird, William Gordon Glen	(Inverkeithing: St John's with North Queensferry)
Bell, William	(Law)
Carmont, Robert	(Glasgow: Sandyhills)
Cooke, John Mackay	(Fowlis Wester with Monzie)
Davidson, James Meldrum	(Inverurie: St Andrew's)
Douglas, Andrew McNeil	(Hamilton: Cadzow)
Dunn, James Frederick	(Coatbridge: Dunbeth)
Dunnett, William Gavin	(Foulden and Mordington with Hutton and Fishwick and Paxton)
Edgar, William Murray Galbraith	(Auchindoir and Kildrummy)
Gilchrist, George Rorison	(Dalrymple)
Goring, John McCormick	(Dunfermline: Gillespie Memorial)
Grant, Alexander Rae	(Cults West)
Grant, George Victor Rowland	(Urray and Kilchrist)
Gray, John Anderson	(Baillieston: Mure Memorial)
Greig, James	(Irvine: Old)
Henderson, Charlotte McKenzie (Mrs)	(Hospital Chaplain)
Heron, John	(Ochiltree)
Hill, Robert Stitt	(Glenshee and Glenericht)
Inglis, Charles George	(Glasgow: St Bride's)
Johnstone, David	(Glasgow: Belhaven Westbourne)
Jones, John David	(Kirkconnel: St Mark's)
Kennedy, David Alexander	(Lanark: Cairns)
Kennedy, Hamish Miller	(Glasgow: North Kelvinside)
Leckie, Joseph Logan	(Fowlis Wester with Madderty with Monzie)
Lindsay, James Adam	(Glasgow: Burnside)
Lyall, James Edward	Crimond with St Fergus
MacAlpine, Alexander Gillon	(Tain)
McCutcheon, George Alexander	(Clackmannan)
Macdonald, Donald Macaulay	(Kippen)
Macdonald, John	(Lochee Old)
Macdonald, Robert Malcolm	(Calabar)
McIlroy, Alexander Matthews	(Darvel: Irvine Bank and Easton Memorial)
McKean, David	(Paris)
MacNab, Samuel Gillies	(Broughty Ferry: St Luke's and Queen Street)

Macpherson, Fergus (British Council of Churches)
McWilliam, Stuart Wilson (Killearn)
Mechie, Lindsay M. Licentiate
Mechie, William Muir (Kirknewton and East Calder)
Miller, Ian David (Prison Chaplain and Edinburgh: St Margaret's)
Mitchell, Andrew Scotland (Kilmaronock Gartocharn)
Murray, Douglas Millar University of Glasgow
Peterkin, Welsh Neilson (Broom)
Reid, John Kelman Sutherland (University of Aberdeen)
Shaw, Andrew (Gardenstown)
Stevenson, Alexander (Greenock: St Andrew's)
Stewart, Finlay John (Lochgelly: Churchmount)
Turner, Duncan McMillan (Innerwick with Spott)
Urquhart, John Macneill (Kilspindie and Rait with Kinfauns)
Warnock, John (Biggar: Gillespie Moat Park)
Weir, David Gordon (Saltcoats: Landsborough and Trinity)
Whitelaw, William Dickie (Bothkennar and Carronshore)
Young, Henry James (Edinburgh: Dean)

LIST S – MINISTERS ORDAINED FOR SIXTY YEARS AND UPWARDS

Until 1992, the *Year Book* contained each year a list of those ministers who had been ordained 'for fifty years and upwards'. For a number of reasons, that list was there-after discontinued. During this past year, the suggestion was made that the Editor might consider restoring it – and indeed, possibly with a mix of anticipation, expectation and misgiving, comment has been made in *Life & Work* and in *Ministers' Forum* as to who the current Father of the Kirk is.

It is perhaps interesting to note that, in 1992, the Rev. A. Rae Grant, who was ordained in 1923 and who retired from Cults West in December 1966, was the second most senior on the list; only the Rev. Robert Robertson, who was ordained in 1922 and who retired from Collace in May 1965, had been ordained longer. Mr Robertson died in 1992, and as a result Mr Grant was 'Father of the Kirk' until his death on 7 August 2001. His successor in that role was the Rev. Robert M. Macdonald, formerly of Calabar. His 'reign', however, was all too brief, as he in fact died just one day later.

The list below is offered following the best enquiries that could be made. The date of ordination is given in full where this is known. With ministers, no less than the rest of society, living longer, the list is restricted now to those ordained for sixty years and upwards.

1929	26 June	Norman Walker Porteous (Professor of Hebrew and Semitic Languages: Edinburgh University)
1930	4 June	James Clarence Finlayson (Edinburgh: Grange)
		James Ferguson Macdonald (Bendochy with Kinclaven)
1931	18 December	Robert Law Kinnis (Baillieston: Mure Memorial)
1932	14 August	Thomas Mackenzie Donn (Duthil)

1933	1 January	Robert Crawford (Annan: Erskine)
	20 October	The Very Rev. William Roy Sanderson (Stenton with Whittingehame)
	16 November	Edward Rankine Marr (Buittle)
1934	5 May	John Steven Thomson (Covington and Thankerton with Libberton and Quothquan)
	20 May	The Very Rev. Andrew Herron (Presbytery Clerk of Glasgow)
	10 July	Walter Macfarlane Calderwood (Leven: Forman)
	31 July	Thomas Roberts Robertson (Broughton, Glenholm and Kilbucho with Skirling)
	3 November	Owain Tudor Hughes (Guernsey: St Andrew's in the Grange)
1935	10 April	George Douglas Monro (Yester)
	30 October	David Stevens (Glenesk)
	6 November	Joseph Blair Gillon (Borthwick with Heriot)
1936	5 April	George Thomas Jamieson (Stirling: Viewfield)
	29 April	Robert Paterson Mackenzie (Dunfermline: St Leonard's)
	13 May	Norman Birnie (Monquhitter)
	12 July	Michael McCulloch Bogle (Banton)
	25 August	Ronald Stewart Wallace (Edinburgh: Lothian Road)
	September	The Very Rev. James Gunn Matheson (Portree)
	17 November	The Very Rev. David Steel (Linlithgow: St Michael's)
1937	14 February	Robert Allan Howieson (Newport-on-Tay: St Thomas's)
	4 March	Tom Sidney Senior Adamson (Musselburgh: St Michael's Inveresk)
	31 March	James Brown Mirrilees (Aberdeen: High Hilton)
	14 April	Anthony James Grubb (Deer)
	19 August	Hector Angus Macintosh MacLean (Duror with Glencoe)
	15 October	Robert Anderson Philp (Stepps: St Andrew's)
1938	26 February	John Macgregor MacKechnie (Kilchrenan and Dalavich)
	31 March	David Cecil Henderson (Glamis)
	8 June	Crichton Robertson (Cockpen and Carrington with Lasswade)
	29 June	George Alestair Alison Bennett (Strathkinness)
	1 July	Alexander Thomas Hain Taylor (Dunoon Old and St Cuthbert's)
	28 September	David Nairn McLeish (Fisherton)

	13 October	Robert Hamilton (Kelso Old)
	8 November	Archibald Alexander Orrock (Teacher: Religious Instruction)
	15 November	The Very Rev. James Fraser McLuskey (London St Columba's with Newcastle)
1939	23 February	William Uist McDonald (Aberdalgie and Dupplin with Forteviot)
	6 April	Charles Armour: St Andrews: Holy Trinity
	2 June	David Noel Fisher (Glasgow: Sherbrooke St Gilbert's)
	7 June	Murdo Ewen Macdonald (Professor of Practical Theology: Glasgow University)
	28 June	James Hamilton (Auchterhouse)
	7 July	John Welsh Malcolm (Uddingston: Park)
	27 October	James Scott Marshall (Associate Minister: Leith South)
	12 November	Alexander McRae Houston (Tibbermore)
	18 November	David Sloan Walker (Makerstoun with Smailholm with Stichill, Hume and Nethorn)
	10 December	Wellesley Grahame Bailey (Ladykirk with Whitsome)
	22 December	Alastair McRae Rennie (Kincardine Croick and Edderton)
1940	24 February	James Johnstone Turnbull (Arbirlot with Colliston)
	20 March	The Very Rev. Thomas Forsyth Torrance (Professor of Christian Dogmatics: Edinburgh University)
	22 March	Donald MacKellar Leitch Urie (Kincardine O'Neil)
	24 April	Robert Russell Brown (Perth: Kinnoull)
	25 April	Angus MacDougall (Sleat)
	29 May	Norman McGathan Bowman (Edinburgh: St Mary's)
	23 June	Andrew Montgomery Russell (Aberdeen: Woodside North)
	14 July	Nigel Ross MacLean (Perth: St Paul's)
	8 August	Robert James Fenton (Glasgow: St Kiaran's Dean Park)
	21 August	Donald MacFarlane (Inverness: East)
	3 September	Arthur Thomas Hill (Ormiston with Prestonpans: Grange)
	6 September	Peter McPhail (Creich, Flisk and Kilmany)
	29 September	John Hugh Gunn Ross (Dundurn)
	18 December	Colin Campbell (Glasgow: Williamwood)
1941	26 January	Samuel Ballantyne (Aberdeen: Rutherford)
	29 May	Harry Galbraith Miller (Iona and Ross of Mull)
	1 June	The Very Rev. John McIntyre (Professor of Divinity: Edinburgh University)
	1 June	Robert Bernard William Walker (Lesmahagow: Abbeygreen)
	6 June	Thomas Williamson (Dyke with Edinkillie)
	3 July	Donald William MacKenzie (Auchterarder: The Barony)
	13 July	Murdoch Macbeth Mackay (Hospital Chaplain)

20 July	Allan Donald Lamont (Nakuru)
21 September	Silvester Skinner (Lumphanan)
21 September	Andrew Swan (Greenock: St Margaret's)
31 October	Gordon Cumming Morris (Buenos Aires)
9 December	John Nelson (Crawford and Elvanfoot with Leadhills and Wanlockhead)

SECTION 7

Congregational
Statistics
2001

CHURCH OF SCOTLAND STATISTICS
FOR 2001

```
Congregations  ......................................1,543
Communicants  ................................590,824
Elders .........................................43,499
Charges ........................................1,256
Ministers serving charges .........................1,090
Chaplains to HM Forces ............................30
Students completing their courses .....................20
```

NOTES ON CONGREGATIONAL STATISTICS

Com   Number of communicants at 31 December 2001.

Eld   Number of elders at 31 December 2001.

G   Membership of the Guild including Young Woman's Group. The letter 'j' beside a figure indicates that the figure is a joint figure for all the congregations making up the charge.

In 01   Ordinary General Income for 2001. Ordinary General Income consists of members' offerings, contributions from congregational organisations, regular fund-raising events, income from investments, deposits and so on. This figure does not include extraordinary or special income, or income from special collections and fund-raising for other charities.

Ass   Amount allocated to congregations for the Mission and Aid Fund in 2001.

Gvn   Amount contributed by congregations to the Mission and Aid Fund in 2001. The amount shown includes contributions to allocation and voluntary extra contributions. The figures do not take into account late payments made in 2002 for 2001 but may contain late payments made in 2001 for 2000 and prior years.

(NB Figures may not be available for new charges created or for congregations which have entered into readjustment late in 2001 or during 2002.)

The Board of Parish Education has again confirmed that current figures for young people receiving Christian Education are not available.

Congregation	Com	Eld	G	In 01	Ass	Gvn
1. Edinburgh						
Dalmeny 142	9	12	9222	625	625
Albany Deaf Church of Edinburgh 144	12	–	1365	–	–
Balerno 849	66	57	116427	27000	32310
Barclay 382	43	24	100817	15760	15760
Blackhall St Columba 1134	91	50	140354	40480	42341
Bristo Memorial Craigmillar 189	7	25	15123	–	–
Broughton St Mary's 332	38	36	50072	8160	8205
Canongate 464	43	–	62562	12960	12960
Carrick Knowe 685	42	86	64041	12000	12205
Cluny 668	69	19	91031	22110	22110
Colinton 1175	97	–	167851	33680	34846
Colinton Mains 257	18	22	42800	3420	3640
Corstorphine Craigsbank 885	31	–	86259	21870	25370
Corstorphine Old 704	63	62	80887	17790	18941
Corstorphine St Anne's 548	51	46	73103	16590	17690
Corstorphine St Ninian's 1153	91	63	118214	35600	36479
Craigentinny St Christopher's 182	17	–	35100	–	2250
Craiglockhart 603	61	48	114511	25640	25640
Craigmillar Park 340	27	35	83159	18850	20350
Cramond 1372	104	25	168167	45300	45300
Currie 1436	72	94	164864	38430	40930
Davidson's Mains 863	71	56	138458	33340	33340
Dean 250	25	22	66535	9910	9910
Drylaw 236	16	–	20067	–	–
Duddingston 867	65	55	83076	15500	15800
Fairmilehead 1040	71	41	94642	18700	18700
Gilmerton 188	9	–	7305	–	–
Gorgie 371	41	22	61447	12540	12690
Granton 402	37	–	31307	4560	–
Greenbank 1018	101	109	177906	48190	48190
Greenside 282	24	–	38186	9190	9190
Greyfriars Tolbooth and Highland 410	46	19	88058	18360	18360
High (St Giles') 707	50	–	195236	36050	33000
Holyrood Abbey 284	34	16	140349	30890	30890
Holy Trinity 233	24	–	66684	6000	6000
Inverleith 411	44	–	76817	15140	15140
Juniper Green 452	36	–	73180	19400	19400
Kaimes Lockhart Memorial 103	9	15	16952	–	–
Kirkliston 364	37	43	43731	5370	5370
Kirk o' Field 259	33	–	52275	7170	7170
Leith North 531	50	25	67358	14600	14600
Leith St Andrew's 343	35	–	48111	7920	8025
Leith St Serf's 326	34	25	49815	6590	6590
Leith St Thomas' Junction Road 329	28	–	45586	6240	6314
Leith South 783	82	–	93364	26780	26880
Leith Wardie 642	80	64	105580	25510	25778
Liberton 1049	80	73	111905	24540	24540
Liberton Northfield 280	11	29	43764	–	–
London Road 431	30	33	51028	7960	7960
Marchmont St Giles' 359	45	37	73088	15560	15560

Congregation	Com	Eld	G	In 01	Ass	Gvn
Mayfield Salisbury	839	72	35	189552	45800	45800
Morningside Braid	301	49	25	43717	7510	8102
Morningside United	220	21	–	52481	9100	10100
Muirhouse St Andrew's	133	10	–	8194	–	–
Murrayfield	609	68	7	117774	33300	33300
Newhaven	280	16	56	59456	11390	11390
New Restalrig	457	17	33	107842	15120	15120
Old Kirk	204	14	–	18872	–	–
Palmerston Place	546	78	–	134133	35310	36011
Pilrig St. Paul's	396	33	40	53531	1000	1000
Polwarth	384	38	22	65887	11370	11370
Portobello Old	442	60	40	43098	7640	7640
Portobello St James'	431	40	18	52824	7760	8092
Portobello St Philip's Joppa	754	70	122	155541	31600	32500
Priestfield	263	28	31	58666	8390	7779
Queensferry	849	50	86	53376	10760	10760
Ratho	259	24	19	39372	–	85
Reid Memorial	468	26	–	83100	18980	19430
Richmond Craigmillar	128	11	9	14435	–	–
St Andrew's and St George's	407	51	20	152166	32790	33040
St Andrew's Clermiston	367	27	–	40889	–	163
St Catherine's Argyle	360	31	27	116737	24300	24300
St Colm's	208	23	33	43010	3370	3370
St Cuthbert's	579	69	–	151131	38350	38350
St David's Broomhouse	204	17	–	46681	5810	5810
St George's West	215	42	–	82858	25570	25850
St John's Oxgangs	352	25	34	27190	–	874
St Margaret's	473	45	24	49633	7710	7710
St Martin's	265	20	12	18028	–	–
St Michael's	542	37	–	62707	11810	11810
St Nicholas' Sighthill	624	40	21	50657	7490	7715
St Stephen's Comely Bank	558	25	40	109429	21830	21830
Slateford Longstone	355	27	50	46248	7400	3500
Stenhouse St Aidan's	303	20	–	21850	–	442
Stockbridge	395	38	38	48204	7990	7990
Tron Moredun	171	12	–	7551	–	–
Viewforth	283	37	21	55067	12540	12540

2. West Lothian

Congregation	Com	Eld	G	In 01	Ass	Gvn
Abercorn	90	9	12	10402	875	875
Pardovan, Kingscavil and Winchburgh	309	23	21	39296	–	–
Armadale	715	46	32	60007	9860	9860
Avonbridge	91	10	12	12230	320	320
Torphichen	293	21	–	36108	3060	3060
Bathgate Boghall	295	38	20	57072	9560	9560
Bathgate High	666	41	44	64447	11390	11390
Bathgate St David's	325	14	18	53821	6990	7200
Bathgate St John's	408	27	35	52805	7260	7260
Blackburn and Seafield	561	34	–	45566	4950	4950
Blackridge	127	7	15	14135	1720	1720
Harthill – St Andrew's	272	22	37	42924	6050	6050

Congregation	Com	Eld	G	In 01	Ass	Gvn
Breich Valley	248	11	19	21878		
Broxburn	555	29	44	53639	7790	7790
Fauldhouse St Andrew's	381	16	18	36202	4470	4470
Kirknewton and East Calder	558	38	27	64686	10970	10970
Kirk of Calder	824	39	29	60162	13100	13100
Linlithgow St Michael's	1579	114	61	212275	41300	43516
Linlithgow St Ninian's Craigmailen	640	64	79	60817	11050	11599
Livingston Ecumenical	857	52	–	69677	–	–
Livingston Old	516	29	28	61366	10410	10549
Polbeth Harwood	298	36	–	25009	–	–
Strathbrock	435	42	25	71706	18650	18650
Uphall South	240	18	–	34032	–	–
West Kirk of Calder	372	29	42	39657	5910	5910
Whitburn – Brucefield	477	25	30	63320	10190	10190
Whitburn – South	406	35	33	63769	10190	10190
3. Lothian						
Aberlady	329	28	–	32717	5970	6003
Gullane	497	37	50	46523	9040	9040
Athelstaneford	220	18	15	20205	2515	2515
Whitekirk and Tyninghame	187	18	–	24043	5420	5420
Belhaven	796	33	71	52534	9740	9740
Spott	105	8	–	11643	1330	1330
Bolton and Saltoun	223	16	19	20009	3980	3980
Humbie	112	8	12	12543	3460	3460
Yester	330	27	31	23413	3710	3710
Bonnyrigg	899	67	84	75311	15560	15699
Borthwick	88	5	17	11343	–	1765
Newtongrange	276	9	24	29367	–	1720
Cockenzie & Port Seton Chalmers M'rl	322	31	60	61709	9030	9030
Cockenzie and Port Seton Old	443	10	25	27036	–	–
Cockpen and Carrington	368	26	37	19523	2700	2841
Lasswade	370	25	25	23146	3950	3950
Rosewell	217	11	–	10079	2070	570
Cranstoun, Crichton and Ford	286	14	–	33875	4470	4353
Fala and Soutra	84	6	12	8293	1125	1125
Dalkeith St John's and King's Park	596	41	27	57257	12580	12580
Dalkeith St Nicholas' Buccleuch	632	21	29	35932	7670	7670
Dirleton	276	19	20	29892	5070	5070
North Berwick Abbey	357	26	43	65449	11250	11250
Dunbar	866	37	72	62948	8260	8363
Dunglass	371	26	20	24719	–	300
Garvald and Morham	44	8	–	11853	1562	1562
Haddington West	479	37	54	57676	8352	8352
Gladsmuir	257	13	15	17626	2970	2970
Longniddry	479	40	56	66373	14550	16062
Glencorse	374	10	–	24560	4810	4810
Roslin	412	9	–	28381	3040	3040
Gorebridge	499	22	44	51938	3350	3350
Haddington St Mary's	823	64	–	82414	21490	21884
Howgate	46	5	8	11688	1770	1770

Congregation	Com	Eld	G	In 01	Ass	Gvn
Penicuik South	342	19	–	98584	16460	16460
Loanhead	584	30	41	38217	4310	4437
Musselburgh Northesk	492	40	15	58231	8300	8446
Musselburgh St Andrew's High	500	42	36	38131	6410	6651
Musselburgh St Clement's & St Ninian's	394	42	9	29833	–	–
Musselburgh St Michael's Inveresk	569	36	41	58323	9670	9670
Newbattle	576	41	25	37984	5750	5750
Newton	321	15	19	16505	–	–
North Berwick St Andrew Blackadder	799	53	30	78150	17370	19051
Ormiston	194	14	31	27315	3480	3688
Pencaitland	274	17	13	45965	7840	7840
Penicuik North	666	42	–	66088	12120	12621
Penicuik St Mungo's	563	37	31	46083	8730	8730
Prestonpans: Prestongrange	441	60	27	36103	4530	4530
Tranent	420	18	41	45141	5370	5370
Traprain	593	36	34	45863	10400	10400

4. Melrose and Peebles

Congregation	Com	Eld	G	In 01	Ass	Gvn
Ashkirk	81	7	11	9642	1230	1230
Selkirk	662	27	43	56758	10320	10320
Bowden	105	13	12	14281	2450	2450
Newtown	220	15	–	15805	2710	2710
Broughton Glenholm and Kilbucho	175	15	30j	12367	–	960
Skirling	91	8	j	6732	–	360
Stobo and Drumelzier	115	7	j	6252	–	720
Tweedsmuir	46	7	j	11852	–	360
Caddonfoot	202	13	–	10011	1490	1490
Galashiels St Ninian's	603	49	39	49286	9900	9900
Carlops	74	12	–	11635	1400	1400
Kirkurd and Newlands	120	9	10	11623	1718	1718
West Linton St Andrew's	269	18	42	31994	4015	4015
Channelkirk	84	5	8	6752	731	731
Lauder Old	367	17	32	26614	2670	2670
Earlston	610	17	37	39620	4600	4600
Eddleston	120	7	14	7348	760	–
Peebles Old	723	48	–	65205	13130	13130
Ettrick	–	8	–	8269	–	–
Yarrow	–	11	8	11305	–	83
Galashiels Old and St Paul's	446	28	39	57814	7500	7500
Galashiels St Aidan's	527	25	24	39565	4970	4970
Galashiels St John's	279	18	–	32537	–	700
Innerleithen, Traquair and Walkerburn	686	43	67	54611	10270	10529
Lyne and Manor	110	9	–	17989	250	250
Maxton and Mertoun	157	15	13	16543	2460	2560
St Boswells	353	24	25	31358	4880	4880
Melrose	918	54	48	82825	15380	16412
Peebles: St Andrew's Leckie	739	44	47	79046	12750	13175
Stow St Mary of Wedale and Heriot	210	16	–	15005	–	–

5. Duns

Congregation	Com	Eld	G	In 01	Ass	Gvn
Ayton and Burnmouth	222	14	–	14338	–	219

Congregation	Com	Eld	G	In 01	Ass	Gvn
Grantshouse and Houndwood and Reston . 148		5	12	9781	–	306
Berwick on Tweed St Andrew's						
Wallace Green & Lowick. 522		30	37	48799	2335	2385
Bonkyl and Preston 103		7	–	7457	1200	1200
Chirnside. 437		23	–	23217	2440	2440
Edrom Allanton. 88		9		6535	530	530
Coldingham and St. Abb's 119		8	19	13794	1222	1222
Eyemouth 292		25	64	34077	5150	5810
Coldstream 448		23	26	33058	4260	4260
Eccles 111		8	21	6727	890	890
Duns 535		23	61	40342	2290	2290
Fogo and Swinton 184		4	–	6721	1273	1660
Ladykirk 48		7	12	6554	1060	1060
Leitholm 117		9	–	9291	1283	1283
Whitsome 56		4	11	3249	620	620
Foulden and Mordington 99		11	12	6912	–	–
Hutton and Fishwick and Paxton 110		10	11	9829	–	–
Gordon St Michael's 82		6	18j	8458	1050	–
Greenlaw. 158		13	23	16681	3720	3720
Legerwood 69		8	–	5927	430	430
Westruther. 60		6	j	5384	830	830
Kirk of Lammermuir 66		9	–	13439	–	–
Langton and Polwarth 94		8	23	11359	–	–
6. Jedburgh						
Ancrum. 223		17	15	16507	250	250
Crailing and Eckford 115		9	–	5139	200	300
Lilliesleaf 161		10	11	11832	250	250
Bedrule 44		4	29j	7954	250	250
Denholm 208		15	j	16372	250	250
Minto 89		7	j	8676	250	450
Cavers and Kirkton 162		11	–	9068	781	781
Hawick St Mary's and Old 681		29	40	41260	7200	7200
Hawick Burnfoot. 236		15	16	21887	–	–
Hawick Teviot and Roberton 429		15	13	38666	5910	6510
Hawick Trinity 949		35	53	53296	7990	7087
Hawick Wilton 459		26	36	35244	2843	6490
Teviothead. 76		4	12	6430	1137	2047
Hobkirk and Southdean 187		13	12	8055	672	689
Jedburgh Old and Edgerston 816		25	24	44617	8490	8490
Jedburgh Trinity 274		10	39	39281	4770	4993
Kelso North and Ednam 1568		78	75	90682	20350	20350
Kelso Old and Sprouston. 689		42	44	44641	6340	6476
Liddesdale. 205		7	22	32607	250	452
Linton 94		7	–	8138	760	760
Morebattle and Hownam 219		11	29	20189	2350	2350
Yetholm. 215		12	20	20319	2690	2421
Makerstoun and Smailholm. 71		5	–	8287	–	–
Roxburgh 75		6	–	5072	–	–
Stichill, Hume and Nenthorn 79		7	14	2847	–	–
Oxnam 103		6	–	6197	467	467

Congregation	Com	Eld	G	In 01	Ass	Gvn
7. Annandale and Eskdale						
Annan Old	465	40	55	56029	10940	10940
Annan St Andrew's	830	38	86	56322	7010	7566
Applegarth and Sibbaldbie	187	8	19	8246	1000	1000
Lochmaben	582	24	48	33566	5070	5670
Brydekirk	73	7	–	6829	–	–
Hoddam	164	8	–	9129	–	–
Canonbie	188	13	–	17199	1720	1720
Carlisle: Chapel Street	431	34	46	55513	10060	10060
Longtown: St. Andrew's	52	8	15	5076	640	640
Dalton	124	8	7	10623	1920	1920
Hightae	106	6	15	10711	1170	1170
St Mungo	139	8	14	7923	1260	420
Dornock	238	13	–	12648	–	–
Eskdalemuir	37	2	–	2757	–	–
Hutton and Corrie	110	6	–	7878	–	–
Tundergarth	77	8	9	5415	–	–
Gretna Old, St Andrew's & Half Morton & Kirkpatrick Fleming	442	30	25	32920	1420	1400
Johnstone	136	7	–	3984	–	–
Kirkpatrick Juxta	190	9	–	11351	–	–
Kirtle – Eaglesfield	138	12	23	11581	884	884
Middlebie	108	9	17	5378	165	–
Waterbeck	74	6	–	4761	176	–
Langholm, Ewes and Westerkirk	590	33	61	38455	4780	3752
Lockerbie Dryfesdale	991	49	51	45655	7460	7460
Moffat St. Andrew's	507	43	39	54902	7830	7830
Wamphray	61	7	–	6200	968	968
8. Dumfries and Kirkcudbright						
Anwoth and Girthon	427	26	25	44830	9800	10183
Borgue	62	6	9	3752	160	160
Auchencairn and Rerrick	155	11	20	8822	1390	1112
Buittle and Kelton	251	21	25	21136	2230	2230
Balmaclellan and Kells	162	12	18	13756	–	–
Carsphairn	114	9	10	6499	–	600
Dalry	193	12	32	10814	–	–
Balmaghie	160	6	14	11998	1598	1598
Tarff and Twynholm	215	18	38	23168	4375	4375
Caerlaverock	176	7	–	5071	–	200
Castle Douglas	614	33	59	39581	4440	4656
Closeburn	274	12	–	19250	1327	1327
Durisdeer	182	6	30	14265	1336	1336
Colvend, Southwick and Kirkbean	396	28	43	45700	8840	8840
Corsock and Kirkpatrick Durham	215	18	27	18443	1810	1810
Crossmichael and Parton	204	15	17	20538	2762	2762
Cummertrees	65	5	9	6477	416	333
Mouswald	95	7	18	6109	560	–
Ruthwell	147	9	16	11082	1130	1130
Dalbeattie	710	43	55j	41273	8940	9616
Urr	256	13	j	12706	2250	2315

Congregation	Com	Eld	G	In 01	Ass	Gvn
Dumfries Greyfriars.	455	24	28	57319	12170	12170
Dumfries Lincluden.	151	12	–	13542	1065	336
Holywood	193	13	–	16558	800	800
Dumfries Lochside	423	18	27	22921	–	–
Dumfries Maxwelltown West.	779	50	59	58616	11390	11390
Dumfries St George's	549	44	52	68056	9710	9710
Dumfries St Mary's	824	47	45	49929	9470	9470
Dumfries St Michael's and South	972	40	46	68817	8180	15684
Dumfries Troqueer	501	30	22	55000	10500	10500
Dunscore	283	18	10	24220	3470	4375
Glencairn and Moniaive	233	11	7	22755	2940	2940
Irongray, Lochrutton and Terregles	535	35	22	24375	2861	2861
Kirkconnel	394	11	19	43319	5320	5520
Kirkcudbright	950	49	–	64956	11600	11600
Kirkgunzeon	63	8	–	7112	–	92
Kirkmahoe	433	16	35	25642	950	950
Kirkmichael and Tinwald and Torthorwald	612	34	35	43575	7000	7000
Lochend	59	4	8	3272	–	–
New Abbey	238	14	10	19105	–	–
Penpont, Keir and Tynron	204	8	–	20171	–	–
Sanquhar St Bride's	580	26	50	34697	6250	6250
Thornhill	326	14	26	23961	1327	1327

9. Wigtown and Stranraer

Congregation	Com	Eld	G	In 01	Ass	Gvn
Ervie Kirkcolm	264	22	–	19176	2050	2050
Leswalt	309	13	18	19191	2300	2300
Glasserton and Isle of Whithorn	140	8	–	10189	2000	2081
Whithorn St Ninian's Priory	344	8	25	21340	2780	2884
Inch	277	22	12	10070	1940	1940
Stranraer St Andrew's	511	28	–	34941	6830	6830
Kirkcowan	215	10	14	20798	2280	2280
Wigtown	291	13	14	30095	4620	4620
Kirkinner	180	7	14	11384	–	–
Sorbie	178	8	11	13235	–	–
Kirkmabreck	197	12	23	17089	1787	1787
Monigaff	470	32	19	29936	5750	5750
Kirkmaiden	252	21	23	21586	3850	3964
Stoneykirk	415	26	15	28194	3590	3590
Mochrum	309	20	47	26339	–	–
New Luce	117	10	51j	9703	1960	1960
Old Luce	341	22	j	34100	4280	4280
Penninghame	672	34	33	54317	14210	14210
Portpatrick	270	10	30	16694	2500	2601
Stranraer St Ninian's	526	28	31	40477	8530	8530
Stranraer High Kirk	670	36	30	48636	8000	8000
Stranraer Old	398	27	40	44154	7050	7050

10. Ayr

Congregation	Com	Eld	G	In 01	Ass	Gvn
Alloway	1435	98	46	164390	40030	47534
Annbank	340	17	23	29661	–	–

Congregation	Com	Eld	G	In 01	Ass	Gvn
Arnsheen Barrhill	114	4	15	8964	–	–
Colmonell	220	15	10	15122	–	100
Auchinleck	414	24	46	n/a	7660	11250
Ayr Auld Kirk of Ayr						
(St John the Baptist)	751	83	64	91124	20300	20450
Ayr Castlehill	892	62	79	78122	16590	16590
Ayr Newton – on – Ayr	494	49	51	77174	15590	17091
Ayr St Andrew's	658	59	28	74772	16090	18504
Ayr St Columba	1807	122	72	169487	38440	39503
Ayr St James'	549	36	51	54473	7700	7700
Ayr St Leonard's	689	59	43	71765	14510	14510
Ayr St Quivox	433	35	19	45176	6610	6610
Ayr Wallacetown	502	26	42	46118	6910	7200
Ballantrae	300	20	34	34540	3110	3110
Barr	80	3	15	5643	–	–
Dailly	197	15	22	17646	–	–
Girvan South	346	22	33	41831	990	1790
Catrine	186	20	35	27096	2031	2031
Sorn	191	16	19	24974	2112	2112
Coylton	373	23	–	21490	–	–
Drongan The Schaw Kirk	307	23	19	16286	–	600
Craigie	128	7	–	10929	1375	1375
Symington	400	23	27	51500	8937	8937
Crosshill	203	10	30	13953	718	718
Dalrymple	372	17	–	17905	2240	2240
Dalmellington	373	26	96	42530	2480	2480
Dundonald	614	54	69	62373	8070	10329
Fisherton	168	12	13	12313	563	563
Maybole West	290	14	25	19411	3100	3213
Girvan North (Old and St Andrew's)	1154	74	46	65234	14350	14850
Kirkmichael	244	18	22	21623	–	2000
Straiton St Cuthbert's	172	13	16	10782	–	50
Kirkoswald	293	15	16	37696	3050	3050
Lugar	186	7	21	15635	2031	2031
Old Cumnock Old	446	21	48	44518	8593	8593
Mauchline	633	29	71	61174	12530	12965
Maybole Old	447	27	30	43745	5000	5143
Monkton and Prestwick North	639	50	59	60169	11200	11200
Muirkirk	269	19	26	19687	–	239
New Cumnock	620	35	54	39340	5660	5660
Ochiltree	286	21	21	21180	3790	4178
Stair	220	14	24	19713	3920	4120
Old Cumnock Crichton West						
and St Ninian's	473	35	56	36943	5620	5820
Patna Waterside	164	17	20	11707	–	–
Prestwick Kingcase	1175	104	60	97231	15340	15340
Prestwick St Nicholas'	885	72	77	88626	18470	18470
Prestwick South	440	40	86	66020	12820	12820
Tarbolton	603	36	47	35963	7370	7730
Troon Old	1309	78	–	129414	25990	25990
Troon Portland	796	55	52	97314	21180	21180

Congregation	Com	Eld	G	In 01	Ass	Gvn
Troon St Meddan's	1222	136	88	147390	25580	25580
11. Irvine and Kilmarnock						
Crosshouse	384	33	34	28966	1137	1304
Darvel	649	35	45	38540	5690	5690
Dreghorn and Springside	701	61	42	72385	14410	14410
Dunlop	453	38	38	51017	8140	8440
Fenwick	456	24	49	53575	9500	9500
Galston	847	61	88	99426	12840	14342
Hurlford	748	28	35	41578	4236	4436
Irvine Fullarton	545	38	38	85735	16970	17377
Irvine Girdle Toll..................	235	23	26	33484	–	–
Irvine Mure.......................	480	30	33	70548	13460	14714
Irvine Old	649	44	34	84540	20800	20800
Irvine Relief Bourtreehill.............	430	38	40	49008	1625	1625
Irvine St Andrew's.................	499	26	56	45023	5320	7935
Kilmarnock Grange.................	495	33	51	63455	9440	9440
Kilmarnock Henderson	842	81	65	100134	18640	18640
Kilmarnock Howard St Andrew's	485	42	45	70103	13522	13522
Kilmarnock Laigh West High	1004	70	98	128701	26600	26600
Kilmarnock Old High Kirk	342	19	25	41829	5120	5220
Kilmarnock Riccarton	403	33	27	60992	8320	8320
Kilmarnock St Andrew's Glencairn	190	15	16	18815	1620	–
Kilmarnock St John's Onthank	317	24	30	40662	3687	3587
Kilmarnock St Kentigern's	298	29	–	49537	5380	5880
Kilmarnock St Marnock's	738	78	–	118200	15570	15570
Kilmarnock St Ninian's Bellfield........	243	21	15	28807	1935	5060
Kilmarnock Shortlees	173	15	28	29577	–	250
Kilmaurs St Maur's Glencairn	385	22	25	47170	7580	7580
Newmilns Loudoun..................	447	14	–	63125	10500	10900
Stewarton John Knox	419	41	28	59302	12090	13512
Stewarton St Columba's	647	40	66	60298	8960	10680
12. Ardrossan						
Ardrossan Barony St John's...........	365	21	40	47288	6770	6770
Ardrossan Park	515	38	42	53906	6140	6246
Beith High........................	1012	93	42	66938	14420	14895
Beith Trinity	268	38	38	45810	6410	6420
Brodick	215	21	–	33646	–	1227
Corrie	62	8	–	11458	–	198
Cumbrae	367	28	49	34911	–	300
Dalry St Margaret's	1120	64	48	95029	19540	19540
Dalry Trinity	353	22	32	71051	14410	14410
Fairlie	304	27	50	51732	6980	6980
Fergushill	54	5	–	6519	–	–
Kilwinning Erskine	132	15	19	27182	–	2100
Kilbirnie Auld Kirk	558	37	30	37489	4280	4280
Kilbirnie St Columba's	641	38	32	49514	7410	7672
Kilmory..........................	42	4	–	6948	–	–
Lamlash	150	14	47	23601	–	1000
Kilwinning Abbey..................	938	65	62	73810	17590	17590

Congregation	Com	Eld	G	In 01	Ass	Gvn
Kilwinning Mansefield Trinity......... 224	17	22	29564	–	–
Largs Clark Memorial 1024	97	88	92878	21560	21560
Largs St Columba's 680	59	67	60078	12590	12590
Largs St John's 901	52	69	106753	21560	23810
Lochranza and Pirnmill 78	7	33	10770	–	–
Shiskine 65	5	20	15573	–	–
Saltcoats New Trinity 405	44	38	51486	7490	7490
Saltcoats North 432	24	26	44372	6190	7704
Saltcoats St Cuthbert's.............. 557	56	30	78737	16520	16520
Stevenston Ardeer 383	28	39	39509	6010	6010
Stevenston High 276	28	50	55265	11170	11770
Stevenston Livingstone 416	35	36	52409	7230	8613
West Kilbride Overton............... 390	27	36	46550	6640	6640
West Kilbride St Andrew's 749	53	46	72269	16910	16910
Whiting Bay and Kildonan 133	14	–	36720	–	4299

13. Lanark

Biggar............................ 781	47	69	62883	13880	13880
Black Mount 112	7	15	13140	–	30
Culter 99	7	–	10988	–	–
Libberton and Quothquan 91	8	–	7962	–	–
Cairngryffe 293	20	17	22040	3710	3710
Symington......................... 265	16	26	23272	4600	4600
Carluke Kirkton.................... 851	43	25	81055	17820	18263
Carluke St Andrew's 423	20	27	44293	5500	4990
Carluke St John's.................. 911	66	56	72962	15730	15730
Carnwath.......................... 427	17	31	35688	1800	1800
Carstairs 245	13	35	24479	2480	2631
Carstairs Junction 147	6	24	15807	2187	2187
Coalburn 186	6	16	22367	262	382
Lesmahagow Old.................... 728	35	27	41901	5850	6590
Crossford.......................... 213	7	16	26816	3830	3830
Kirkfieldbank 141	6	17	16050	1030	1040
Douglas St Bride's.................. 359	28	24	28124	3470	3780
Douglas Water and Rigside 96	10	17	11254	1520	1795
Forth St Paul's..................... 505	32	57	41371	3200	5402
Glencaple 276	24	15	20005	805	874
Lowther............................ 50	5	–	6154	413	441
Kirkmuirhill 321	19	61	85304	15740	18240
Lanark Greyfriars 947	59	42	67611	11480	11480
Lanark St Nicholas'................. 645	45	45	68602	12500	13000
Law............................... 170	21	30	27943	–	–
Lesmahagow Abbeygreen 241	17	26	64050	9980	9980

14. Paisley

Barrhead Arthurlie.................. 431	32	25	66224	13580	13580
Barrhead Bourock 580	51	77	69267	11550	11550
Barrhead South and Levern 515	36	38	66214	11990	12990
Bishopton 913	56	–	73592	12690	12690
Bridge of Weir Freeland 457	53	–	95345	18100	18100
Bridge of Weir St Machar's Ranfurly..... 553	47	54	72800	16470	15098

Congregation	Com	Eld	G	In 01	Ass	Gvn
Caldwell	279	20	–	51808	7400	7400
Elderslie Kirk	676	62	73	98875	21310	21717
Erskine	470	35	50	90829	11625	11625
Houston and Killellan	769	54	50	95387	19470	19470
Howwood	236	19	32	43285	7670	7670
Inchinnan	467	38	26	50082	6500	4000
Johnstone High	480	42	65	72135	10442	10442
Johnstone St Andrew's Trinity	274	29	45	41493	5770	5770
Johnstone St Paul's	716	84	33	67254	13740	13740
Kilbarchan East	413	39	44	56589	8030	8030
Kilbarchan West	513	48	40	92112	17050	17050
Linwood	537	40	38	53844	9260	9260
Lochwinnoch	168	12	–	29365	–	203
Neilston	795	41	42	66934	15860	20860
Paisley Abbey	843	62	–	100522	21180	21180
Paisley Castlehead	323	38	17	52419	7080	7080
Paisley Glenburn	344	21	23	44989	4960	4960
Paisley Laigh Kirk	618	81	65	70317	13210	13210
Paisley Lylesland	522	55	60	67670	13980	13980
Paisley Martyrs'	606	65	25	69170	13433	13433
Paisley Oakshaw Trinity	910	118	63	114271	23095	23095
Paisley St Columba Foxbar	321	32	31	42185	4475	4623
Paisley St James'	403	36	36	49853	7653	7653
Paisley St Luke's	323	31	38	48003	8260	8260
Paisley St Mark's Oldhall	677	63	123	94049	19370	19370
Paisley St Ninian's Ferguslie	65	13	11	8256	–	–
Paisley Sandyford (Thread Street)	435	27	24	47954	9100	9100
Paisley Sherwood Greenlaw	808	90	68	109841	24050	24050
Paisley Wallneuk North	594	66	38	57936	13320	10000
Renfrew North	738	73	48	80932	14420	14420
Renfrew Old	755	43	70	71391	16470	16470
Renfrew Trinity	443	44	88	61046	9780	9780

15. Greenock

Gourock: Old Gourock and Ashton	1101	72	90	116616	24310	30313
Gourock St John's	733	66	25	81522	20262	20262
Greenock Ardgowan	501	50	34	64497	11690	11690
Greenock Cartsdyke	334	35	–	25439	725	725
Greenock Finnart St Paul's	388	36	20	75711	13745	13745
Greenock Mount Kirk	408	47	30	61346	9700	9700
Greenock Old West Kirk	373	35	42	70612	14670	14670
Greenock St George's North	499	36	–	62442	11165	11165
Greenock St Luke's	798	75	60	107978	27020	27020
Greenock St Margaret's	320	36	32	34509	2850	–
Greenock St Ninian's	285	21	17	28092	–	–
Greenock Wellpark Mid Kirk	722	53	30	61008	12445	12445
Inverkip	431	25	46	41974	9020	9020
Kilmacolm Old	879	67	52	117724	32920	33706
Kilmacolm St Columba	608	48	22	94643	17667	17667
Langbank	169	12	–	33393	1210	1210
Port Glasgow Hamilton Bardrainney	543	26	12	38610	4700	4700

Congregation	Com	Eld	G	In 01	Ass	Gvn
Port Glasgow St Andrew's............773	65	69	83802	15050	28118
Port Glasgow St Martin's 201	15	–	17146	–	–
Skelmorlie and Wemyss Bay..........425	28	–	53700	8233	8863

16. Glasgow

Congregation	Com	Eld	G	In 01	Ass	Gvn
Banton 83	11	–	11833	–	–
Twechar...........................113	12	–	9199	–	–
Bishopbriggs Kenmure 381	21	58	65252	11250	12850
Bishopbriggs Springfield............1025	58	73	83516	18710	18710
Blairbeth: Rodger Memorial 69	8	22	10896	–	–
Broom.........................1005	66	70	140383	42240	42781
Burnside 745	44	86	163636	43910	46758
Busby 439	46	45	62075	12500	12500
Cadder..........................1002	89	72	132022	33500	33750
Cambuslang Flemington H'side.........264	16	20	31664	–	–
Cambuslang Old 502	64	32	70467	17000	19480
Cambuslang St Andrew's..............507	39	22	74195	15000	10377
Cambuslang Trinity St Paul's..........351	21	–	64219	12900	13529
Campsie 346	26	26	44654	2600	2067
Chryston 851	46	42	155641	26410	26410
Eaglesham........................755	61	65	101769	27130	27130
Fernhill and Cathkin 352	24	43	40365	2500	3234
Gartcosh 167	9	19	18099	–	–
Glenboig 171	9	14	10546	–	–
Giffnock Orchardhill 593	59	34	145137	38550	40050
Giffnock South 1032	86	55	161011	41580	43580
Giffnock The Park...................366	37	–	45173	6200	6200
Greenbank.......................1236	89	64	200677	59400	59400
Kilsyth Anderson....................479	26	50	67604	9570	10620
Kilsyth Burns and Old................683	36	45	61574	6500	6500
Kirkintilloch Hillhead 177	14	18	16491–	–	–
Kirkintilloch St Columba's 676	52	39	83739	16860	16960
Kirkintilloch St David's Memorial Park...844	61	55	99622	23800	23800
Kirkintilloch St Mary's 767	63	71	92128	20650	20650
Lenzie Old 514	48	–	69080	14060	14060
Lenzie Union......................998	92	108	152419	29200	29939
Maxwell Mearns Castle...............361	34	–	129251	22540	22540
Mearns 809	51	–	124796	30140	30140
Milton of Campsie...................402	40	34	40297	3050	3050
Netherlee.........................929	79	73	163733	44790	47761
Newton Mearns....................812	76	32	116117	30000	30000
Rutherglen Old 470	37	–	49110	1500	2226
Rutherglen Stonelaw 499	52	68	99242	25290	25290
Rutherglen Wardlawhill...............431	40	68	46805	9320	9445
Rutherglen West 530	28	29	59345	10190	10190
Stamperland 490	45	36	80803	15240	15240
Stepps...........................416	30	27	44729	5370	5870
Thornliebank......................288	20	54	47198	2500	2500
Torrance 272	16	–	65904	2000	2000
Williamwood......................591	74	48	115798	27710	27710
Glasgow Anderston Kelvingrove........198	24	18	20497	–	–

Congregation	Com	Eld	G	In 01	Ass	Gvn
Glasgow Baillieston Mure Memorial	657	45	137	79410	17090	17450
Glasgow Baillieston St Andrew's	441	37	56	58735	10590	10590
Glasgow Balshagray Victoria Park	334	34	28	67769	17530	17730
Glasgow Barlanark Greyfriars	158	17	30	26045	–	100
Glasgow Battlefield East	227	14	39	41155	3500	3500
Glasgow Blawarthill	253	30	55	28558	–	–
Glasgow Bridgeton St Francis in the East	122	17	14	27572	–	132
Glasgow Broomhill	700	66	90	124996	28540	28540
Glasgow Calton Parkhead	198	17	14	19903	–	–
Glasgow Cardonald	577	62	110	115645	25390	27118
Glasgow Carmunnock	398	29	45	56432	11560	11560
Glasgow Carmyle	132	7	30	19444	1860	1860
Glasgow Kenmuir Mount Vernon	164	9	38	30415	4740	4740
Glasgow Carntyne Old	177	19	21	33991	5560	5560
Glasgow Eastbank	186	19	25	30952	4550	4550
Glasgow Carnwadric	166	20	30	22630	–	100
Glasgow Castlemilk East	178	13	18	n/a	–	–
Glasgow Castlemilk West	160	23	32	22611	–	–
Glasgow Cathcart Old	398	47	40	62584	12550	11025
Glasgow Cathcart South	472	52	65	105971	24470	25617
Glasgow Cathedral (High or St. Mungo's)	453	54	–	80718	14900	14903
Glasgow Colston Milton	161	18	–	25007	–	–
Glasgow Colston Wellpark	223	19	–	30139	–	–
Glasgow Cranhill	65	10	–	12018	–	–
Glasgow Croftfoot	410	46	39	66833	12190	12350
Glasgow Dennistoun Blackfriars	164	28	23	37470	2570	2570
Glasgow Dennistoun Central	288	29	30	49492	4000	4000
Glasgow Drumchapel Drumry St Mary's	157	13	–	11062	–	–
Glasgow Drumchapel St Andrew's	514	43	–	55361	6700	6700
Glasgow Drumchapel St Mark's	82	12	15	7975	–	–
Glasgow Easterhouse St George's and St Peter's	52	8	–	6303	–	–
Glasgow Eastwood	445	59	75	80816	12440	12670
Glasgow Gairbraid	258	21	29	36560	–	644
Glasgow Gardner Street	50	8	–	45143	4700	4700
Glasgow Garthamlock and Craigend East	88	11	–	n/a	–	–
Glasgow Gorbals	129	14	12	23272	–	–
Glasgow Govan Old	237	36	18	38679	4850	4850
Glasgow Govanhill Trinity	169	25	47	33072	3820	3856
Glasgow High Carntyne	697	35	85	72882	14500	15108
Glasgow Hillington Park	471	34	64	–	11900	11900
Glasgow Househillwood St Christopher's	118	10	26	16628	–	–
Glasgow Hyndland	310	48	47	81159	17940	18300
Glasgow Ibrox	256	23	34	48605	6120	4120
Glasgow John Ross Memorial for Deaf People	76	7	–	–	–	–
Glasgow Jordanhill	715	86	36	151268	34210	36010
Glasgow Kelvin Stevenson Memorial	200	38	23	39657	4710	4710
Glasgow Kelvinside Hillhead	204	26	–	65920	12690	12690
Glasgow King's Park	916	81	78	136499	33000	34000
Glasgow Kinning Park	202	18	16	35294	4000	4000

Congregation	Com	Eld	G	In 01	Ass	Gvn
Glasgow Knightswood St Margaret's	703	37	57	54475	11130	11130
Glasgow Langside	288	44	47	52540	1950	2150
Glasgow Lansdowne	164	15	–	25084	–	–
Glasgow Linthouse St Kenneth's	175	18	21	22788	–	–
Glasgow Lochwood	79	6	10	10741	–	–
Glasgow Martyrs' The	132	6	–	25723	–	–
Glasgow Maryhill	247	20	16	33333	3080	3545
Glasgow Merrylea	567	66	45	81382	18830	18830
Glasgow Mosspark	270	37	49	62696	13010	3592
Glasgow Mount Florida	381	39	65	89174	17000	21950
Glasgow New Cathcart	277	31	35	n/a	5500	5500
Glasgow New Govan	152	21	15	43533	6120	6120
Glasgow Newlands South	766	88	45	151205	44660	39160
Glasgow North Kelvinside	86	3	28	30840	3500	3500
Glasgow Partick South	289	40	37	49735	3550	3550
Glasgow Partick Trinity	231	29	–	45564	8690	8776
Glasgow Penilee St Andrew's	185	28	–	38885	2500	2686
Glasgow Pollokshaws	206	23	34	34905	2000	2000
Glasgow Pollokshields	385	46	76	102053	22500	22500
Glasgow Possilpark	205	21	35	33204	1041	1378
Glasgow Priesthill and Nitshill	196	19	19	28158	–	–
Glasgow Queen's Park	345	34	50	70688	9000	9000
Glasgow Renfield St Stephen's	216	29	35	76663	11010	11870
Glasgow Robroyston				1080		
Glasgow Ruchazie	84	10	–	16990	–	–
Glasgow Ruchill	128	28	–	37726	3280	3280
Glasgow St Andrew's East	177	23	30	26813	–	100
Glasgow St Columba	136	15	16	33376	–	–
Glasgow St David's Knightswood	727	31	63	90084	15210	15460
Glasgow St Enoch's Hogganfield	241	14	62	45381	3500	3500
Glasgow St George's Tron	460	49	–	195633	52410	52410
Glasgow St James' (Pollok)	283	29	25	44978	1875	1900
Glasgow St John's Renfield	496	62	–	127851	23970	23970
Glasgow St Luke's and St Andrew's	93	8	14	7844	–	–
Glasgow St Margaret's Tollcross	167	7	–	32740	–	150
Glasgow St Nicholas' Cardonald	451	41	26	49198	7640	7354
Glasgow St Paul's	78	7	–	11514	–	–
Glasgow St Rollox	115	10	–	24951	–	–
Glasgow St Thomas' Gallowgate	79	8	8	11398	–	250
Glasgow Sandyford Henderson Memorial	204	23	17	100715	16040	16040
Glasgow Sandyhills	400	37	56	68208	10990	10990
Glasgow Scotstoun	307	24	–	53121	11000	9783
Glasgow Shawlands	570	39	67	117794	24500	24500
Glasgow Sherbrooke St Gilbert's	600	47	42	110868	24270	24270
Glasgow Shettleston Old	329	31	34	45365	5000	5000
Glasgow South Carntyne	157	12	13	25975	–	202
Glasgow South Shawlands	245	24	–	51518	10660	10660
Glasgow Springburn	353	41	29	42004	11820	11820
Glasgow Temple Anniesland	545	43	50	81512	15600	15936
Glasgow Toryglen	124	12	36	17919	–	–

Congregation	Com	Eld	G	In 01	Ass	Gvn
Glasgow Trinity Possil						
and Henry Drummond 142	7	–	41244	1410	1410
Glasgow Tron St Mary's 149	16	16	31068	–	–
Glasgow Victoria Tollcross 170	12	36	31017	–	1000
Glasgow Wallacewell 198	18	28	31769	–	319
Glasgow Wellington 312	41	–	78478	17770	18800
Glasgow Whiteinch 30	–	–	30896	–	–
Glasgow Yoker 135	11	13	25890	–	–
17. Hamilton						
Airdrie Broomknoll 433	41	57	54079	10170	10170
Calderbank 181	13	29	15735	2660	2660
Airdrie Clarkston 500	44	27	60797	11940	11160
Airdrie Flowerhill 835	65	41	90831	18860	18860
Airdrie High 450	31	–	45066	4900	4900
Airdrie Jackson 366	50	34	53777	9260	9260
Airdrie New Monkland 479	39	31	40753	7250	10271
Greengairs 212	8	9	14712	2130	2130
Airdrie St Columba's 253	15	11	20217	–	–
Airdrie The New Wellwynd 768	81	46	80484	17820	17820
Bargeddie 187	16	–	43584	9610	1876
Bellshill Macdonald Memorial 331	30	28	39792	5780	5780
Bellshill Orbiston 288	21	19	15823	2640	2640
Bellshill West 851	65	41	62399	12940	13024
Blantyre Livingstone Memorial 299	17	33	32034	4987	4987
Blantyre Old 413	23	50	63345	12910	13210
Blantyre St Andrew's 312	26	30	61851	8480	8490
Bothwell 662	44	46	96240	22370	22370
Caldercruix and Longriggend 245	13	24	50422	6240	6440
Carfin 64	5	–	5552	1330	1330
Newarthill 611	21	30	45659	8150	8150
Chapelhall 312	25	39	34825	2170	2170
Chapelton 212	16	32	21120	3630	3630
Strathaven Rankin 604	58	30	71937	15440	15440
Cleland 328	16	20	27541	–	–
Coatbridge Blairhill-Dundyvan 464	40	36	57140	7220	7220
Coatbridge Calder 499	32	61	51680	9680	9680
Coatbridge Clifton 285	25	29	36885	6290	11802
Coatbridge Middle 431	32	48	45239	5820	6625
Coatbridge Old Monkland 406	22	44	36124	2950	2655
Coatbridge St Andrew's 751	60	52	77681	18290	18290
Coatbridge Townhead 371	22	34	44905	4970	4970
Dalserf 275	24	19	54397	9210	9210
East Kilbride Claremont 854	88	52	94242	17630	18049
East Kilbride Greenhills 272	21	30	20752	–	–
East Kilbride Moncrieff 1147	75	59	99853	21110	21110
East Kilbride Mossneuk 269	23	–	30843	–	–
East Kilbride Old 718	64	91	72915	14660	14660
East Kilbride South 430	43	55	78350	16420	16420
East Kilbride Stewartfield					
East Kilbride West 756	39	78	56416	11820	11820

Congregation	Com	Eld	G	In 01	Ass	Gvn
East Kilbride Westwood	834	53	141	72846	12450	12450
Glasford	200	13	22	12279	2780	2780
Strathaven East	326	35	35	42680	7130	7130
Hamilton Burnbank	150	17	–	22664	4470	4470
Hamilton North	184	32	30	32108	6480	6480
Hamilton Cadzow	820	66	75	91232	18380	18380
Hamilton Gilmour and Whitehill	231	27	–	35064	4210	4210
Hamilton Hillhouse	518	44	28	58729	13250	9392
Hamilton Old	758	64	41	109634	27290	27290
Hamilton St Andrew's	385	34	48	55497	10620	10720
Hamilton St John's	649	59	66	95460	19960	19960
Hamilton South	340	33	33	42157	7530	8240
Quarter	120	11	22	13943	2680	2680
Hamilton Trinity	335	25	–	36033	4140	5711
Hamilton West	409	32	–	62031	11810	11810
Holytown	381	23	28	44958	4630	4630
Kirk o' Shotts	236	11	11	19821	–	–
Larkhall Chalmers	249	18	31	34974	3760	3760
Larkhall St Machan's	751	65	54	81167	19190	19190
Larkhall Trinity	360	26	46	43243	6080	6480
Motherwell Crosshill	564	60	61	70447	13621	13870
Motherwell Dalziel St Andrew's	676	67	61	94104	22470	10968
Motherwell Manse Road	284	32	25	44406	10140	10140
Motherwell North	234	30	42	41438	4990	4990
Motherwell St Margaret's	408	20	28	34906	3420	1660
Motherwell St Mary's	1051	99	92	91208	19760	19760
Motherwell South Dalziel	477	60	77	67938	15020	15940
Newmains Bonkle	205	18	29	31488	6330	6330
Newmains Coltness Memorial	240	31	31	40472	8100	8100
New Stevenston: Wrangholm Kirk	199	14	30	30354	4830	5135
Overtown	295	27	46	33372	4600	3107
Shotts Calderhead Erskine	646	38	44	60995	7240	7240
Stonehouse St Ninian's	541	42	43	55036	10010	10079
Strathaven Avendale Old and Drumclog	843	70	60	97384	281110	28110
Strathaven West	276	21	40	38354	5800	5800
Uddingston Burnhead	291	28	17	31822	4230	9565
Uddingston Old	717	60	82	87187	16670	18718
Uddingston Park	244	21	30	54070	9340	9540
Uddingston Viewpark	483	37	37	60763	11470	12022
Wishaw Cambusnethan North	589	44	33	75220	13290	13290
Wishaw Cambusnethan Old and Morningside	612	57	18	64469	13310	13314
Wishaw Chalmers	531	33	42	57202	9440	9440
Wishaw Craigneuk and Belhaven	242	31	33	49003	8110	8110
Wishaw Old	416	43	–	44218	5415	5415
Wishaw St Mark's	536	39	59	60678	10000	10000
Wishaw Thornlie	285	27	40	41525	5090	5171

18. Dumbarton

Congregation	Com	Eld	G	In 01	Ass	Gvn
Alexandria	494	36	31	59050	12240	12240
Arrochar	61	10	16	14195	–	–

Congregation	Com	Eld	G	In 01	Ass	Gvn
Luss	82	9	16	14635	–	–
Baldernock	238	21	16	35802	5790	6303
Bearsden Killermont	685	58	66	120121	28440	32474
Bearsden New Kilpatrick	1873	139	139	273025	80820	81070
Bearsden North	721	78	90	106467	23610	23910
Bearsden South	1012	85	47	142136	35560	48161
Bearsden Westerton Fairlie Memorial	519	49	53	81399	19450	19450
Bonhill	934	63	–	56793	15260	15260
Cardross	515	36	28	90316	21070	21070
Clydebank Abbotsford	392	27	33	51691	7730	7730
Clydebank Faifley	249	22	52	35619	–	–
Clydebank Kilbowie St Andrew's	352	24	45	41528	5570	5570
Clydebank Radnor Park	304	38	44	43485	6190	6190
Clydebank St Cuthbert's	148	18	28	19296	–	500
Craigrownie	253	24	22	30443	5850	5850
Rosneath St Modan's	234	14	23	24548	2580	2580
Dalmuir Barclay	394	22	62	39539	7320	7320
Dumbarton Riverside	839	89	94	87335	19030	19030
Dumbarton St Andrew's	297	24	20	31071	–	–
Dumbarton West Kirk	396	44	25	49764	7990	5353
Duntocher	377	28	25	37223	850	1006
Garelochhead	195	20	–	46852	5240	5240
Helensburgh Park	522	59	41	83361	18820	19308
Helensburgh St Columba	653	52	47	79333	18340	18473
Helensburgh: The West Kirk	698	57	70	112498	23780	23780
Jamestown	484	23	30	50152	10220	10220
Kilmaronock Gartocharn	285	12	–	27396	–	–
Milngavie Cairns	797	56	–	97909	25400	25600
Milngavie St Luke's	453	37	49	68853	13220	13220
Milngavie St Paul's	1216	96	126	184575	41450	41450
Old Kilpatrick Bowling	314	23	31	33723	8350	11350
Renton Trinity	353	29	–	32490	1935	1935
Rhu and Shandon	334	33	56	67843	17160	18389

19. South Argyll

Ardrishaig	196	29	37	33986	3880	3880
South Knapdale	38	6	–	6494	507	792
Campbeltown Highland	504	36	31	47488	4937	4937
Campbeltown Lorne and Lowland	996	53	72	71388	13770	13770
Craignish	43	6	–	17119	–	–
Kilninver and Kilmelford	55	5	–	8706	–	–
Cumlodden Lochfyneside and Lochgair	112	13	14	21705	–	–
Gigha and Cara	44	7	–	8983	–	500
Glassary and Kilmartin and Ford	138	13	14	22252	–	–
Glenaray and Inveraray	139	13	14	19669	–	–
Jura	42	6	–	9633	–	–
Kilarrow	107	12	19	23245	–	–
Kilmeny	51	6	–	10141	–	–
Kilberry	16	4	–	1537	–	–
Tarbert	175	17	30	26052	–	–
Kilcalmonell	72	10	19	7709	–	–

Congregation	Com	Eld	G	In 01	Ass	Gvn
Skipness	31	2	–	7225	–	–
Kilchoman	87	5	–	8323	610	610
Portnahaven	16	3	11	4585	562	562
Kildalton and Oa	129	14	13	24233	–	400
Killean and Kilchenzie	199	14	26	26594	–	–
Lochgilphead	238	20	16	24488	–	–
North Knapdale	79	11	–	21221	–	–
Saddell and Carradale	243	13	32	25759	–	400
Southend	247	11	29	22331	–	75

20. Dunoon

	Com	Eld	G	In 01	Ass	Gvn
Bute United	776	42	78	80763	12500	12759
Dunoon Old and St Cuthbert's	451	41	40	45992	6531	6531
Dunoon St John's	270	30	30	38687	6340	6340
Sandbank	162	11	–	12751	1690	1890
Innellan	152	10	20	17120	–	2400
Inverchaolain and Toward	115	10	–	14303	–	–
Kilfinan	29	5	7	4496	560	560
Kyles	198	16	31	24475	900	720
Kilmodan and Colintraive	133	12	10	19528	–	250
Kilmun (St Munn's)	118	11	20	14578	–	400
Strone and Ardentinny	139	13	13	18515	–	350
Kirn	381	29	30	49046	7730	7730
Lochgoilhead and Kilmorich	120	18	17	21192	–	100
Rothesay Trinity	531	46	49	61846	7380	7380
Strachur and Strathlachlan	173	18	19	23294	–	148

21. Lorn and Mull

	Com	Eld	G	In 01	Ass	Gvn
Appin	94	13	22	13745	–	–
Lismore	55	6	13	5909	–	–
Ardchattan	172	14	12	21835	–	–
Coll	14	3	–	2732	–	–
Colonsay and Oronsay	16	2	–	3740	–	–
Kilbrandon and Kilchattan	111	13	–	22743	–	401
Connel	162	19	29	28024	–	–
Glenorchy and Innishael	88	6	–	8871	–	–
Strathfillan	62	4	–	8348	–	–
Iona	18	3	–	4889	–	–
Kilfinichen and Kilvickeon and The Ross Of Mull	36	8	–	12510	–	80
Kilchrenan and Dalavich	37	5	10	8279	–	–
Muckairn	152	13	16	19744	–	500
Kilmore and Oban	789	78	70	94834	19910	19910
Mull (Isle of), Kilninian and Kilmore	41	5	9	10705	–	–
Salen and Ulva	33	6	–	8333	–	–
Tobermory	89	17	12	11909	–	200
Torosay and Kinlochspelvie	30	6	–	4639	–	–
Tiree	123	10	20	23839	–	–

22. Falkirk

	Com	Eld	G	In 01	Ass	Gvn
Airth	196	11	27	37824	2200	2275

Congregation	Com	Eld	G	In 01	Ass	Gvn
Blackbraes and Shieldhill	194	17	18	24168	–	–
Bo'ness Old	764	52	43	59043	8100	8175
Bo'ness St Andrew's	591	30	–	62060	9600	9675
Bonnybridge St Helen's	676	30	36	41656	5960	5960
Bothkennar and Carronshore	342	31	10	36044	–	–
Brightons	772	45	64	93092	17010	18030
Carriden	737	54	22	49993	7600	7600
Cumbernauld Abronhill	320	27	34	41881	–	1100
Cumbernauld Condorrat	540	38	45	54394	8150	8250
Cumbernauld Kildrum	489	43	–	39299	4800	4800
Cumbernauld Old	487	34	–	51912	9010	9159
Cumbernauld St Mungo's	397	34	–	54664	1000	2075
Denny Dunipace	464	35	27	46613	7010	7085
Denny Old	510	52	24	61065	10260	10260
Denny Westpark	782	71	45	69617	15820	15820
Falkirk Bainsford	402	22	–	40982	5510	5560
Falkirk Camelon: Irving	320	16	16	28360	–	–
Falkirk Camelon St John's	384	25	30	52778	7870	7945
Falkirk Erskine	610	56	45	71960	14900	16625
Falkirk Grahamston United	567	61	42	72210	15400	15500
Falkirk Laurieston	289	20	38	30931	6190	6265
Redding and Westquarter	148	14	38	17282	2320	2320
Falkirk Old and St Modan's	1098	70	24	108286	17280	17280
Falkirk St Andrew's West	642	45	40	101271	21410	21410
Falkirk St James'	415	30	13	39459	4480	4862
Grangemouth Charing Cross and West	270	17	–	25390	1125	1125
Grangemouth Dundas	366	26	–	38652	2600	2675
Grangemouth Kerse	606	58	29	43659	6380	6455
Grangemouth Kirk of the Holy Rood	717	53	–	53967	9870	9970
Grangemouth Zetland	960	69	71	85220	16960	17035
Haggs	335	31	14	38414	4200	5081
Larbert East	667	47	50	66867	11060	11390
Larbert Old	768	48	25	79160	17120	17195
Larbert West	599	48	36	64156	13130	13130
Muiravonside	266	23	24	29456	–	1275
Polmont Old	583	34	47	68414	12330	12405
Slamannan	271	10	9	27486	–	–
Stenhouse and Carron	659	50	35	57969	9680	9780

23. Stirling

Congregation	Com	Eld	G	In 01	Ass	Gvn
Aberfoyle	149	12	18	19153	–	–
Port of Menteith	69	6	9	10190	–	–
Alloa North	293	18	24	41480	4930	4930
Alloa St Mungo's	772	50	50	60269	14510	14510
Alloa West	241	19	42	38973	6210	6210
Alva	637	46	49	56916	8580	9103
Balfron	243	21	23	47507	10070	10070
Fintry	176	12	21	18093	3510	3860
Balquhidder	96	5	–	16043	1625	1625
Killin and Ardeonaig	179	9	19	17874	1540	1180
Bannockburn Allan	542	39	29	51961	6980	6971

Congregation	Com	Eld	G	In 01	Ass	Gvn
Bannockburn Ladywell	717	36	36	36660	4320	3512
Bridge of Allan Chalmers	295	23	20	40286	6510	6510
Bridge of Allan Holy Trinity	631	42	57	88160	16370	16920
Buchanan	107	10	29j	14670	3950	3950
Drymen	297	20	j	38126	5250	5250
Buchlyvie	246	19	27	22693	2790	2790
Gartmore	80	13	–	15953	2260	2260
Callander	718	44	55	90134	18990	19140
Cambusbarron The Bruce Memorial	425	20	–	42845	2160	2660
Clackmannan	629	42	36	71550	16460	16860
Cowie	163	12	12	12443	720	764
Plean	299	8	–	16546	608	608
Dollar	708	50	45	96467	16580	16580
Glendevon	54	4	–	5522	640	640
Muckhart	157	15	8	22357	4230	4230
Dunblane Cathedral	1122	92	92	179600	44630	45060
Dunblane St Blane's	453	47	38	75525	17090	17273
Fallin	269	6	–	29317	–	–
Gargunnock	248	17	–	19540	2380	2380
Kincardine-in-Menteith	125	9	–	9917	760	760
Killearn	630	48	60	67222	16400	16400
Kilmadock	250	11	–	10965	–	–
Kippen	340	24	30	28132	5050	5200
Norrieston	164	11	16	15422	1108	1358
Lecropt	280	15	28	44149	4020	4020
Logie	702	60	63	79062	20200	20200
Menstrie	446	34	35	60522	8680	8680
Sauchie and Coalsnaughton	951	39	34	62587	10860	10860
Stirling Allan Park South	288	46	47	35943	5890	5890
Stirling Church of The Holy Rude	270	43	–	39737	5850	5850
Stirling North	578	44	29	62202	9770	10012
Stirling St Columba's	605	68	–	83273	15990	15990
Stirling St Mark's	358	14	–	35717	2850	2850
Stirling St Ninian's Old	833	49	–	71793	12120	12120
Stirling Viewfield	550	30	34	67927	10520	10744
Strathblane	386	26	47	51819	7520	7600
Tillicoultry	942	63	46	76500	16860	17039
Tullibody St Serf's	644	29	18	61833	7480	7521

24. Dunfermline

Congregation	Com	Eld	G	In 01	Ass	Gvn
Aberdour St Fillan's	424	29	–	55971	11580	14080
Ballingry and Lochcraig	131	19	8	16094		
Beath and Cowdenbeath North	213	13	17	38775	–	400
Cairneyhill	228	28	–	24526	4150	4150
Limekilns	371	49	–	58599	10460	10460
Carnock and Oakley	249	22	26	48221	3250	3400
Cowdenbeath Trinity	439	25	30	48604	1250	1250
Culross and Torryburn	317	24	37	34489	4200	750
Dalgety	680	41	41	96423	14750	15425
Dunfermline Abbey	806	59	–	106135	17840	17840
Dunfermline Gillespie Memorial	415	73	23	87990	16650	16650

Congregation	Com	Eld	G	In 01	Ass	Gvn
Dunfermline North 236	14	–	30840	–	–
Dunfermline St Andrew's Erskine 318	27	15	34701	2020	2020
Dunfermline St Leonard's 557	46	54	64524	11430	11430
Dunfermline St Margaret's 470	52	39	54039	7380	9380
Dunfermline St Ninian's 391	36	53	35698	–	–
Dunfermline Townhill and Kingseat 460	31	45	53576	7210	7210
Inverkeithing St John's 210	22	20	32738	3730	4010
North Queensferry. 93	7	–	14472	2010	2520
Inverkeithing St Peter's 343	14	–	25331	2910	2910
Kelty. 407	26	59	45447	4570	4570
Lochgelly Macainsh 415	37	–	33200	3360	3360
Lochgelly St Andrew's 371	26	27	40001	4200	4200
Rosyth. 369	23	–	32526	–	–
Saline and Blairingone 267	12	17	47182	6590	6590
Tulliallan and Kincardine 672	50	80	38575	7070	6995

25. Kirkcaldy

Congregation	Com	Eld	G	In 01	Ass	Gvn
Auchterderran St Fothad's 449	28	21	30083	4500	4500
Kinglassie 203	13	16	15854	2540	2735
Auchtertool 86	7	11	7043	1262	1262
Kirkcaldy Linktown. 457	39	41	45180	7670	7670
Buckhaven 265	32	25	31267	3510	3213
Burntisland 706	50	64	45967	9690	9790
Denbeath. 106	7	21	8294	–	–
Methilhill 195	16	32	17102	–	200
Dysart 415	36	18	49197	7640	7640
Glenrothes Christ's Kirk 375	24	59	44696	–	–
Glenrothes St Columba's 694	30	27	50351	9690	13493
Glenrothes St Margaret's 502	34	32	51785	9010	10354
Glenrothes St Ninian's. 327	35	18	52037	6250	6250
Innerleven East 308	8	24	21921	–	597
Kennoway, Windygates					
and Balgonie St Kenneth's. 833	48	85	76945	14280	14280
Kinghorn. 504	33	43	43750	9600	9600
Kirkcaldy Abbotshall. 795	66	–	70058	14910	23360
Kirkcaldy Pathhead 618	54	62	65667	12180	14880
Kirkcaldy St Andrew's 342	27	34	42050	7260	7260
Kirkcaldy St Bryce Kirk 904	72	58	90581	20040	20040
Kirkcaldy St John's 446	53	64	62470	10520	10779
Kirkcaldy Templehall 395	22	20	48984	6780	6780
Kirkcaldy Torbain 286	37	32	32053	–	–
Kirkcaldy Viewforth 407	18	–	28099	5580	5580
Thornton 268	10	–	17679	1560	1570
Leslie Trinity. 410	29	46	25810	1065	–
Leven 971	63	17	89238	6443	6443
Markinch. 691	33	45	55422	8200	8200
Methil 420	25	36	31129	2453	2453
Wemyss. 302	16	41	25991	870	870

26. St Andrews

Congregation	Com	Eld	G	In 01	Ass	Gvn
Abdie and Dunbog 179	19	–	10091	1730	1730

Congregation	Com	Eld	G	In 01	Ass	Gvn
Newburgh	352	16	–	14842	2990	2990
Anstruther	491	39	–	35413	4900	6584
Auchtermuchty	343	26	18	38442	1800	1800
Balmerino	202	21	15	23530	3500	3500
Wormit	308	24	67	29163	6370	6370
Boarhills and Dunino	189	10	j	11633	2994	2994
St Andrews Martyrs'	423	34	45j	36071	7250	7250
Cameron	107	12	13	13351	2390	3141
St Andrews St Leonard's	693	54	38	105448	18760	20250
Carnbee	107	10	21	13660	1770	1770
Pittenweem	321	20	42	25207	4210	4494
Cellardyke	405	29	46	32819	5000	5000
Kilrenny	133	10	18	16349	3270	3270
Ceres and Springfield	560	30	44	27185	7870	7870
Crail	483	32	37	34036	7670	7961
Kingsbarns	107	11	–	12035	2300	2300
Creich, Flisk and Kilmany	113	9	17	19557	2450	2450
Monimail	138	14	–	18659	3220	3220
Cupar Old and St Michael of Tarvit	660	49	30	73136	16100	16100
Cupar St John's	871	43	61	65220	11390	11390
Dairsie	143	10	25	14244	2070	2070
Kemback	117	7	20	10913	2350	2350
Strathkinness	155	14	16	17896	2670	2670
Edenshead and Strathmiglo	256	14	21	26287	1400	1400
Elie	384	28	69	62846	12270	12270
Kilconquhar and Colinsburgh	202	20	11	21799	3720	3720
Falkland	366	22	10	30448	5950	5950
Freuchie	259	16	23	26441	5210	5362
Howe of Fife	884	46	–	55624	9100	9100
Largo and Newburn	304	16	–	30306	6810	6810
Largo St David's	204	15	53	22160	4680	4778
Largoward	82	5	15	6454	625	625
St Monans	272	13	63	37867	5820	6978
Leuchars: St Athernase	570	33	34	45533	4210	4210
Newport-on-Tay	456	36	–	59946	12790	12790
St Andrews Holy Trinity	725	29	64	42325	10770	10770
St Andrews Hope Park	909	98	62	111990	29770	29770
Tayport	477	27	26	35323	5500	5500
27. Dunkeld and Meigle						
Aberfeldy	374	25	27	58652	6240	6325
Amulree and Strathbraan	23	3	–	2375	820	820
Dull and Weem	95	9	16	10309	1357	1357
Alyth	835	42	40	54747	9670	9670
Ardler Kettins and Meigle	512	25	37	37956	6290	6290
Bendochy	89	10	8	10626	1790	1790
Blairgowrie St Mary's South	322	15	24	25182	3282	3282
Blair Atholl and Struan	191	17	22	16216	–	–
Tenandry	71	8	12	17825	1230	1644
Blairgowrie St Andrew's	694	41	38	65495	10530	10530
Braes of Rannoch	31	5	j	12775	–	900

Congregation	Com	Eld	G	In 01	Ass	Gvn
Foss and Rannoch	144	16	18j	24835	–	400
Caputh and Clunie	222	27	15	19568	2106	2106
Kinclaven	175	21	12	16755	2145	2145
Coupar Angus Abbey	420	33	34	47437	3580	3580
Dunkeld	478	36	33	74528	14900	15809
Fortingall and Glenlyon	57	6	–	11096	800	800
Kenmore and Lawers	105	7	19	19379	1422	1433
Grantully Logierait and Strathtay	168	16	16	33321	920	920
Kirkmichael Straloch and Glenshee	157	11	15	13860	650	1150
Rattray	565	25	35	34268	4490	4490
Pitlochry	552	53	39	68242	10490	10629

28. Perth

Congregation	Com	Eld	G	In 01	Ass	Gvn
Abernethy and Dron	285	16	16	22394	2240	2240
Arngask	163	12	19	15938	2570	2570
Almondbank Tibbermore	347	21	43	27844	–	800
Ardoch	167	10	28	25059	–	2400
Blackford	93	10	–	14231	–	–
Auchterarder	905	45	62	73853	13170	13170
Auchtergaven and Moneydie	553	26	42	36378	3530	3530
Cargill Burrelton	381	20	49	33043	2258	2258
Collace	142	11	18	19403	3093	3093
Cleish	254	17	18	42091	9610	9610
Fossoway St Serf's and Devonside	233	22	–	27346	6680	6680
Comrie	525	33	48j	49077	10440	11905
Dundurn	60	7	j	9578	1710	1859
Crieff	1106	52	51	76558	17190	17190
Dunbarney	585	33	62	55283	9240	9240
Forgandenny	94	7	9	10481	1710	1710
Errol	346	17	19	36783	5620	5620
Kilspindie and Rait	75	5	–	7203	1020	1020
Fowlis Wester	125	13	8	14660	893	893
Madderty	107	9	13	14037	730	750
Monzie	109	12	8	13404	730	730
Gask	125	9	15	9369	–	500
Methven and Logiealmond	387	34	26	24524	–	800
Kinross	742	34	24	68892	11490	11490
Muthill	351	21	15j	23231	3230	–
Trinity Gask and Kinkell	60	5	j	5534	7737	737
Orwell	369	30	29	32355	4340	4959
Portmoak	163	15	–	16673	4430	4430
Perth Craigie	786	38	45	60112	11990	11990
Perth Kinnoull	431	31	35	53705	10700	10700
Perth Letham St Mark's	726	48	45	63695	11170	11170
Perth Moncrieffe	204	16	–	11176	–	200
Perth North	1502	117	26	194720	44400	44400
Perth Riverside	44	–	–	23880	–	–
Perth St John the Baptist's	938	70	–	71397	14690	14696
Perth St Leonard's-in-the-Fields and Trinity	645	80	43	83619	20730	20730
Perth St Matthew's	990	72	47	64526	17710	18020

Congregation	Com	Eld	G	In 01	Ass	Gvn
Redgorton	159	13	19	13744	920	920
Stanley	305	22	30	27692	4990	4990
St Madoes and Kinfauns	329	20	28	25250	–	–
St Martin's	215	11	18	10882	1600	1600
Scone New	637	52	68	55665	11450	11450
Scone Old	779	60	34	51707	9420	10420
The Stewartry of Strathearn	568	39	33	40641	2000	1600

29. Dundee

Congregation	Com	Eld	G	In 01	Ass	Gvn
Abernyte	100	9	–	8741	1406	1406
Inchture and Kinnaird	253	25	14	18596	3762	3762
Longforgan	260	23	25	26956	5780	5780
Auchterhouse	158	17	20	19769	3800	3800
Murroes and Tealing	324	17	32	22679	1737	1823
Dundee Albany – Butterburn	222	9	9	5990	–	–
Dundee St David's North	120	8	26	11517	–	–
Dundee Balgay	568	46	33	55280	10100	10106
Dundee Barnhill St Margaret's	903	70	48	105879	22500	25000
Dundee Broughty Ferry East	628	52	32	75561	14020	14020
Dundee Broughty Ferry St Aidan's	680	51	69	66018	11870	11870
Dundee Broughty Ferry St James'	269	16	34	45251	5630	5630
Dundee Broughty Ferry St Luke's and Queen Street	542	48	51	78894	14190	14813
Dundee Broughty Ferry St Stephen's and West	401	24	–	38943	5630	5630
Dundee Camperdown	230	24	20	27891	–	250
Dundee Chalmers Ardler	277	23	27	65503	9300	9301
Dundee Clepington	495	26	–	27170	5920	5920
Dundee Fairmuir	288	12	16	25748	2812	2812
Dundee Craigiebank	434	12	25	45742	7440	7440
Dundee Douglas and Angus	368	21	25	24624	2500	2500
Dundee Downfield South	461	31	30	60757	7462	7724
Dundee – Dundee (St Mary's)	723	77	36	94037	22500	25750
Dundee Lochee Old and St Luke's	283	27	29	29576	3906	3906
Dundee Lochee West	608	35	25	33851	5100	72
Dundee Logie and St John's Cross	478	27	35	75109	16680	16680
Dundee Mains	257	13	–	22885	–	–
Dundee Mains of Fintry	168	12	–	43747	6240	6240
Dundee Meadowside St Paul's	588	54	33	66987	14990	15030
Dundee Menzieshill	480	30	–	46433	500	1191
Dundee Mid Craigie	56	6	–	8772	–	–
Dundee St Andrew's	878	82	46	68677	12080	12180
Dundee Steeple	354	32	14	70230	16140	16140
Dundee Stobswell	676	48	–	62056	11640	11640
Dundee Strathmartine	597	44	40	51264	7740	8743
Dundee The High Kirk	534	56	61	44515	8750	8750
Dundee Trinity	749	48	42	38565	5940	5940
Dundee West	561	34	26	55357	14400	14400
Dundee Whitfield	208	25	–	13325	–	–
Fowlis and Liff	165	11	5	11726	2580	2580
Lundie and Muirhead of Liff	373	27	–	32223	4460	4534

Congregation	Com	Eld	G	In 01	Ass	Gvn
Invergowrie	475	43	57	49280	7190	7290
Monifieth Panmure	475	39	37	46818	7760	8510
Monifieth St Rule's	814	34	65	52228	7777	8702
Monifieth South	433	20	33	41579	3710	4004
Monikie and Newbigging	291	15	9	26867	517	2392

30. Angus

Congregation	Com	Eld	G	In 01	Ass	Gvn
Aberlemno	203	11	–	16681	1630	1430
Guthrie and Rescobie	224	8	20	17920	1650	230
Airlie Ruthven Kingoldrum	174	13	–	12037	990	–
Glenisla Kilry Lintrathen	173	20	13	31467	2832	2832
Arbirlot	304	15	–	17152	4380	4380
Carmyllie	143	8	5	18556	3020	3020
Colliston	230	11	12	17029	3140	3140
Arbroath Knox's	449	28	39	27872	5730	5914
Arbroath St Vigeans	679	49	38	47162	10830	11105
Arbroath Old and Abbey	917	47	46	62462	9350	12850
Arbroath St Andrew's	793	55	24	70108	13240	14468
Arbroath West Kirk	1175	99	47	65555	12940	12940
Barry	405	19	13	29283	2830	2330
Brechin Cathedral	1191	39	21	49769	6350	6350
Brechin Gardner Memorial	620	30	21	48088	7170	7170
Carnoustie	695	50	39	67562	11800	12110
Carnoustie Panbride	819	39	–	52918	8370	8370
Dun	93	10	j	8416	870	870
Hillside	446	28	52j	37262	2583	2583
Dunnichen, Letham and Kirkden	483	21	32	33224	–	317
Eassie and Nevay	65	9	10	6726	720	–
Newtyle	316	16	22	23333	2620	5610
Edzell Lethnot	443	28	58	30569	9050	9050
Fern, Careston and Menmuir	146	10	–	11933	1521	1521
Glenesk	61	6	–	3021	1406	1406
Farnell	109	9	–	8209	1080	1080
Montrose St Andrew's	575	25	30	35809	5140	5240
Forfar East and Old	1593	55	58	67827	17870	19604
Forfar Lowson Memorial	1114	42	36	61579	10820	10820
Forfar St Margaret's	1103	46	33	68244	13850	14050
Friockheim and Kinnell	246	15	22	19926	983	1234
Inverkeillor and Lunan	211	10	15	20404	2690	2950
Glamis, Inverarity and Kinettles	528	31	31	36220	5720	5720
Glens, The and Kirriemuir Old	1234	107	50	124310	21810	21810
Inchbrayock	238	11	–	27826	5520	6520
Montrose Melville South	402	22	–	30833	8550	8550
Kirriemuir St Andrew's	485	28	56j	43693	6830	6830
Oathlaw Tannadice	184	8	j	10068	1212	1489
Montrose Old	812	41	45	63248	16840	16840

31. Aberdeen

Congregation	Com	Eld	G	In 01	Ass	Gvn
Aberdeen Beechgrove	666	84	57	104858	26310	27306
Aberdeen Bridge of Don Oldmachar	221	12	–	47030	–	–
Aberdeen Cove	81	8	–	8639	–	–

Congregation	Com	Eld	G	In 01	Ass	Gvn
Aberdeen Craigiebuckler 900	68	69	82872	17070	18070
Aberdeen Denburn 436	45	25	31502	5710	5710
Aberdeen Ferryhill 586	61	32	61750	11810	11810
Aberdeen Garthdee 332	21	25	32473	–	2000
Aberdeen Gilcomston South 277	26	–	109449	17150	17150
Aberdeen Greyfriars John Knox 629	44	38	48137	7880	8457
Aberdeen High Hilton 659	53	46	94986	12650	12650
Aberdeen Holburn Central 582	54	17	52054	10060	10060
Aberdeen Holburn West. 638	52	32	116031	25850	25850
Aberdeen Mannofield 1827	124	93	161325	39850	50928
Aberdeen Mastrick 692	29	28	46676	5720	6088
Aberdeen Middlefield 210	13	–	15223	–	–
Aberdeen New Stockethill.		–	4548		60
Aberdeen North of St Andrew 559	63	34	64855	16390	16390
Aberdeen Northfield 395	19	21	39667	3530	2100
Aberdeen Queen's Cross 697	56	38	132335	30630	33630
Aberdeen Rosemount 189	21	14	22861	1154	1222
Aberdeen Rubislaw 724	84	45	125625	32460	33542
Aberdeen Ruthrieston South 712	51	61	57135	9880	9880
Aberdeen Ruthrieston West 446	52	32	53063	6680	6847
Aberdeen St Columba's Bridge of Don . . . 478	27	–	67624	12187	12187
Aberdeen St George's Tillydrone 191	10	20	14492	–	–
Aberdeen St John's Church for Deaf					
People 109	6	–	–	–	–
Aberdeen St Machar's Cathedral 667	53	–	94366	17810	17810
Aberdeen St Mark's. 589	72	26	68519	13420	12302
Aberdeen St Mary's. 556	53	25	46108	11170	1862
Aberdeen St Nicholas, Kirk of. 509	46	26	44174	10970	10970
Aberdeen St Nicholas South of Kincorth . . 525	38	37	45408	7590	7590
Aberdeen St Ninian's. 359	24	24	42337	5780	5780
Aberdeen St Stephen's. 308	29	19	49234	8180	8180
Aberdeen Summerhill 221	23	–	27023	–	242
Aberdeen Torry St Fittick's 603	30	33	42739	4190	4190
Aberdeen Woodside. 445	36	45	42840	5040	5160
Bucksburn Stoneywood 646	26	31	45518	6740	6800
Cults East 360	33	22	45913	6864	6864
Cults West. 655	46	25	96683	22680	22680
Dyce 1449	79	58	67182	11980	12344
Kingswells 500	40	26	41799	4090	4090
Newhills 1015	46	80	83627	17400	17400
Peterculter. 863	53	36	60649	12360	12360

32. Kincardine and Deeside

Aberluthnott 243	8	18	13842	2840	2840
Laurencekirk 549	13	56	21072	4330	4330
Aboyne – Dinnet 493	22	35	45198	8190	8190
Arbuthnott. 128	8	9	8462	1660	1660
Bervie 572	26	28	41326	4820	4820
Banchory-Devenick, Maryculter/						
Cookney 413	18	10	21357	3900	3900
Banchory Ternan East 1236	68	50	83214	15060	15060

Congregation	Com	Eld	G	In 01	Ass	Gvn
Banchory Ternan West...............	677	55	45	74429	11520	12668
Birse and Feughside	318	26	–	26395	5350	4833
Braemar..........................	110	10	21j	19140	2370	2370
Crathie	167	18	j	39904	6290	6290
Cromar...........................	265	13	–	14281	–	–
Drumoak..........................	277	11	33	28592	–	224
Durris	211	13	16	13602	–	–
Glenmuick (Ballater)................	409	24	33	35963	5440	5440
Kincardine O'Neil..................	228	10	10	7715	–	–
Lumphanan	284	15	14	13411	–	–
Kinneff..........................	188	9	6	6414	1000	1000
Stonehaven South	349	26	20	35253	5910	5910
Mearns Coastal	395	18	43	28795	3265	3265
Newtonhill	422	21	23	25575	1981	1981
Portlethen	549	18	–	42087	11260	10276
Stonehaven Dunnottar	1045	36	44	61273	11240	11240
Stonehaven Fetteresso	935	46	45	79150	18850	18850
Torphins	471	34	21	42899	4670	4670
West Mearns	633	29	73	37329	8030	8030

33. Gordon

Barthol Chapel	108	9	10	9928	1080	1176
Tarves...........................	542	37	41	34366	7800	7800
Belhelvie.........................	606	31	19	50828	4400	4400
Blairdaff	107	13	–	10035	1290	1290
Chapel of Garioch	296	22	17	26615	3140	3140
Cluny	228	12	13	17445	2310	2310
Monymusk	146	5	8	11550	1765	1765
Culsalmond and Rayne	258	9	7	9390	996	360
Daviot...........................	177	10	10	16012	2280	2280
Cushnie and Tough	301	19	10	26235	–	–
Drumblade	133	9	10	7640	2230	2230
Huntly Strathbogie	855	44	38	48001	10500	11630
Echt.............................	313	18	15	18486	2187	2187
Midmar..........................	184	13	–	15358	1680	1680
Ellon............................	2127	102	41	127797	22790	23048
Fintray and Kinellar................	198	12	15j	12718	533	533
Keithhall.........................	80	8	j	5128	1327	1327
Foveran..........................	413	24	–	33966	2670	2670
Howe Trinity......................	735	34	42	40614	7570	7570
Huntly Cairnie Glass	882	35	40	36797	6220	6220
Insch-Leslie-Premnay-Oyne	621	46	42	42188	8110	8930
Inverurie St Andrew's	1902	55	72	84425	18620	18620
Inverurie West.....................	775	50	40	46501	8200	4100
Kemnay..........................	675	37	–	42793	7360	7360
Kintore	871	54	46	64756	17800	22145
Meldrum and Bourtie	582	34	45	48784	5430	5430
Methlick	385	26	30	41212	4370	4370
New Machar	581	34	28	34155	6610	2280
Noth	395	16	–	14526	–	–
Skene	1630	101	61	113302	18830	19207

Congregation	Com	Eld	G	In 01	Ass	Gvn
Udny and Pitmedden	553	32	14	47938	7370	7370
Upper Donside	496	22	–	35148	390	420
34. Buchan						
Aberdour	169	9	12	8203	650	650
New Pitsligo	371	11	–	18739	810	810
Auchaber United	207	15	13	13321	653	630
Auchterless	257	22	20	17820	3030	3374
Banff	948	47	38	84731	17230	18034
King Edward	184	15	15	13717	2760	2760
Crimond	309	10	10	18743	–	–
St Fergus	223	9	16	14355	–	–
Cruden	514	32	24	43836	6550	6831
Deer	966	32	33	40624	5270	5464
Fordyce	552	33	22	39550	7180	8401
Fraserburgh Old	964	59	87	118924	26660	26660
Fraserburgh South	360	22	26	42035	4050	4228
Inverallochy and Rathen: East	97	10	–	14968	2720	2779
Fraserburgh West	728	45	–	52423	9180	9180
Fyvie	437	26	48	45771	7350	7350
Rothienorman	201	10	15	9957	990	990
Gardenstown	69	10	32	40781	2670	2670
Longside	614	33	–	41340	5200	5332
Lonmay	185	14	11	11471	1330	1330
Rathen West	119	8	–	11316	730	730
Macduff	923	39	60	68155	13260	14601
Marnoch	426	28	16	33508	3915	3970
Maud and Savoch	325	17	19	20601	562	772
New Deer St Kane's	499	22	19	35947	5780	5780
Monquhitter and New Byth	418	22	26	23247	–	–
Ordiquhill and Cornhill	182	12	15	8419	290	–
Whitehills	362	18	34	26210	3850	4038
Peterhead Old	566	44	39	47415	9030	9031
Peterhead St Andrew's	639	35	35	48895	7740	7740
Peterhead Trinity	406	30	22	82245	17690	17690
Pitsligo	200	14	–	20323	2350	2370
Sandhaven	98	6	–	6264	990	1027
Strichen	494	16	35	24072	3220	3220
Tyrie	179	8	14	6668	781	781
Turriff St Andrew's	587	27	16	31300	4350	4350
Turriff St Ninian's and Forglen	1063	53	61	49802	14490	14490
35. Moray						
Aberlour	480	21	35	36394	2610	2549
Alves and Burghead	175	17	36	21137	–	–
Kinloss and Findhorn	98	15	11	11547	–	300
Bellie	419	17	31	36429	8790	8790
Speymouth	253	14	25	17324	2230	2230
Birnie	236	16	24	17181	1830	1830
Pluscarden	138	13	15	17122	2420	2420
Buckie North	653	44	73	53241	9210	9543

Congregation	Com	Eld	G	In 01	Ass	Gvn
Buckie South and West 364	23	32	31312	7010	7010
Enzie. 121	10	13	11360	662	662
Cullen and Deskford 445	37	65	31382	6940	7110
Dallas 60	7	16	9222	2080	2080
Forres St Leonard's 366	26	43	46915	8046	8046
Rafford 90	6	16	9501	1525	1525
Duffus, Spynie and Hopeman 436	41	39	49250	5760	5760
Dyke. 187	14	19	22059	3490	3490
Edinkillie 95	14	–	14729	2702	2702
Elgin High. 818	54	47	79619	13560	13560
Elgin St Giles' and St. Columba's South . 1692	99	67	115135	21150	21150
Findochty 68	10	24	19113	350	486
Portknockie. 107	10	37	14699	510	510
Rathven. 146	14	30	12897	781	781
Forres St Laurence 673	43	43	63157	11580	12318
Keith North, Newmill and Boharm 535	46	30	67994	11520	11820
Keith St Rufus, Botriphnie and Grange . . 1128	55	33	58176	10430	10590
Knockando, Elchies and Archiestown 279	13	17	17880	1400	1400
Rothes. 322	16	25	23751	3410	3410
Lossiemouth St Gerardine's High 411	22	40	43376	8970	10635
Lossiemouth St James' 357	22	32	36484	6280	6280
Mortlach and Cabrach 500	35	47	23964	–	–
Rothiemay. 231	11	15	9080	200	200
St Andrew's-Lhanbryd and Urquhart 520	40	25	47729	6120	6120

36. Abernethy

Abernethy 166	16	–	34678	3020	3020
Cromdale and Advie 106	3	–	8506	710	811
Alvie and Insh. 79	7	–	23336	2700	5594
Boat of Garten and Kincardine 105	11	20	19194	–	–
Duthil 72	8	14	7789	–	–
Dulnain Bridge 46	6	–	10177	643	643
Grantown-on-Spey 306	18	24	31630	6280	6280
Inveraven and Glenlivet. 92	6	9	9491	–	–
Kingussie. 115	15	–	17587	1000	1000
Kirkmichael and Tomintoul 84	7	–	9338	–	–
Laggan 37	6	–	11183	–	–
Newtonmore 95	11	–	16882	–	–
Rothiemurchus and Aviemore 103	6	–	15920	–	–

37. Inverness

Ardclach 41	3	–	2731	–	–
Auldearn and Dalmore 86	8	17	14217	–	–
Ardersier. 76	11	13	18634	–	215
Petty 72	9	12	22155	–	90
Cawdor 172	15	22	24783	–	2000
Croy and Dalcross 61	13	19	8613	–	200
Culloden The Barn 374	37	38	64657	10850	10850
Daviot and Dunlichity 63	8	–	12440	–	–
Moy, Dalarossie and Tomatin 38	4	10	7301	–	–
Dores and Boleskine 103	9	9	14155	–	346

Congregation	Com	Eld	G	In 01	Ass	Gvn
Inverness Crown 817	89	87	102845	20560	20560
Inverness Dalneigh and Bona 295	21	30	69025	10030	10030
Inverness East 321	43	25	103658	25120	25120
Inverness Hilton 255	13	31	46040	–	–
Inverness Kinmylies 219	16	–	32361	–	–
Inverness Ness Bank 601	62	31	78249	13420	13420
Inverness St Columba High 265	32	24	61006	10480	10630
Inverness St Stephen's 424	38	–	53590	12820	13161
Inverness The Old High 196	29	–	30110	10090	10089
Inverness Trinity 392	40	36	56943	13270	13270
Inverness West 185	18	–	68380	13780	13780
Kilmorack and Erchless 144	17	25	34415	–	–
Kiltarlity 54	7	–	12127	–	–
Kirkhill 78	8	15	12438	–	–
Nairn Old 961	61	32	90105	15990	15990
Nairn St Ninian's 315	19	32	31123	3623	3623
Urquhart and Glenmoriston 141	8	–	46367	5500	5606

38. Lochaber

Congregation	Com	Eld	G	In 01	Ass	Gvn
Acharacle 32	1	–	11905	–	–
Ardnamurchan 19	4	–	5128	–	–
Ardgour 52	8	14	11803	–	180
Strontian 23	3	9	6939	–	62
Arisaig and The Small Isles 62	7	18	10863	–	567
Duror 48	10	14	12232	–	1000
Glencoe St. Munda's 78	9	17	14188	–	–
Fort Augustus 83	7	15	17555	–	–
Glengarry 44	8	12	9697	–	72
Fort William Duncansburgh 319	23	21	45586	7480	7780
Kilmonivaig 76	8	12	19900	4760	9090
Fort William MacIntosh Memorial 226	27	19	42772	5660	5660
Kilmallie 164	17	25	37254	7490	6477
Kinlochleven 81	7	22	19785	–	–
Nether Lochaber 72	7	–	12216	–	–
Mallaig St Columba and Knoydart 96	5	–	28503	–	–
Morvern 56	5	10	11647	–	–

39. Ross

Congregation	Com	Eld	G	In 01	Ass	Gvn
Alness 133	14	–	31079	–	–
Avoch 29	5	12	14094	2020	2020
Fortrose and Rosemarkie 143	11	–	29290	5260	5260
Contin 55	12	–	16120	–	–
Cromarty 72	6	17	17993	–	500
Dingwall Castle Street 148	18	24	43053	5210	5361
Dingwall St Clement's 254	25	23	40934	5960	2904
Fearn Abbey and Nigg 118	16	29	49330 .	–	–
Tarbat 70	11	13	17205	–	200
Ferintosh 202	25	44	47965	1700	1970
Fodderty and Strathpeffer 159	22	27	29271	–	346
Invergordon 244	15	30	44267	6370	6370
Killearnan 150	17	–	29260	1000	1000

Congregation	Com	Eld	G	In 01	Ass	Gvn
Knockbain	80	10	8	17614	500	500
Kilmuir and Logie Easter	74	12	17	23603	–	–
Kiltearn	86	5	5	27750	–	–
Lochbroom and Ullapool	62	7	12	25087	–	2
Resolis and Urquhart	101	10	–	26145	–	–
Rosskeen	144	12	27	36092	–	643
Tain	189	13	33	47564	7310	7310
Urray and Kilchrist	122	19	27	33960	–	312

40. Sutherland

Congregation	Com	Eld	G	In 01	Ass	Gvn
Altnaharra and Farr	32	1	–	10652	–	–
Assynt and Stoer	28	2	–	14906	–	–
Clyne	102	12	–	20408	–	–
Creich	50	4	–	10328	–	–
Rosehall	27	1	–	7554	–	140
Dornoch Cathedral	411	35	57	71073	13250	13250
Durness and Kinlochbervie	45	4	14	16863	–	722
Eddrachillis	19	2	–	15065	–	–
Golspie	101	24	18	23129	–	–
Kildonan and Loth Helmsdale	40	4	19	14567	–	–
Kincardine Croick and Edderton	79	11	14	23855	–	–
Lairg	54	6	27	18708	–	–
Rogart	28	3	11	9654	–	–
Melness and Tongue	56	8	8	13254	–	–

41. Caithness

Congregation	Com	Eld	G	In 01	Ass	Gvn
Berriedale and Dunbeath	18	3	–	6593	–	–
Latheron	23	3	–	7325	–	–
Bower	32	5	12	10234	–	138
Watten	46	5	–	10741	–	63
Canisbay	46	4	12	11170	–	–
Keiss	30	2	11	8968	–	–
Dunnet	23	2	9	3913	–	–
Olrig	55	5	11	6911	–	–
Halkirk and Westerdale	89	6	19	15638	–	–
Lybster and Bruan	42	8	29	15540	–	–
Reay	35	5	8	11031	–	–
Strathy and Halladale	26	5	16	9041	–	151
Thurso St Peter's and St Andrew's	253	25	49	49984	5000	5000
Thurso West	299	29	43	43964	4620	4620
Wick Bridge Street	190	14	13	32379	3062	2459
Wick Old	239	40	31	47431	5960	6360
Wick Pulteneytown and Thrumster	250	15	30	51041	8560	2733

42. Lochcarron – Skye

Congregation	Com	Eld	G	In 01	Ass	Gvn
Applecross, Lochcarron and Torridon	87	5	21	30055	–	300
Bracadale and Duirinish	104	10	12	26215	–	350
Gairloch and Dundonnell	93	5	–	43999	4740	4740
Glenelg and Kintail	60	11	–	24513	–	627
Kilmuir and Stenscholl	78	11	–	30769	–	600
Lochalsh	93	7	31	32228	–	2000

Congregation	Com	Eld	G	In 01	Ass	Gvn
Portree	144	10	–	49628	3953	–
Snizort	82	6	–	40301	1562	1562
Strath and Sleat	186	14	24	61686	7410	7410
43. Uist						
Barra	35	5	–	10996	–	–
Benbecula	78	11	16	28503	–	–
Berneray and Lochmaddy	69	4	11	19443	–	–
Carinish	75	8	22	40114	–	–
Kilmuir and Paible	32	8	–	27273	–	–
Manish – Scarista	50	4	–	25062	–	–
South Uist	60	12	12	18540	–	–
Tarbert	157	12	–	65221	10510	10510
44. Lewis						
Barvas	88	11	–	37666	3150	3150
Carloway	40	1	–	23623	–	700
Cross Ness	57	9	–	31297	–	–
Kinloch	47	9	–	26675	–	–
Knock	82	6	–	31353	–	–
Lochs-in-Bernera	34	6	–	13969	–	–
Lochs – Crossbost	18	2	–	16958	–	–
Stornoway High	277	16	–	97147	17470	17470
Stornoway Martin's Memorial	115	9	19	47578	5420	5420
Stornoway St Columba	137	14	37	58614	11610	11610
Uig	49	7	–	20219	–	–
45. Orkney						
Birsay, Harray and Sandwick	396	32	54	27724	1883	1883
Deerness	102	9	–	6253	690	115
Holm	144	11	15	10739	1070	1116
St Andrew's	87	10	8	6995	750	–
Eday	7	2	6	2383	–	–
Stronsay Moncur Memorial	75	10	26	11378	–	585
Evie	52	4	–	4693	937	937
Firth	124	7	21	19168	3780	3780
Rendall	58	4	13	7803	680	680
Flotta	30	4	–	2759	–	–
Hoy and Walls	78	11	12	5137	–	–
Kirkwall East	529	47	43	55404	11600	11600
Kirkwall St Magnus Cathedral	842	75	24	70791	17010	17713
North Ronaldsay	17	2	–	1529	–	–
Sanday	110	10	17	9782	–	–
Orphir	135	11	18	17549	–	53
Stenness	94	9	13	16214	–	85
Papa Westray	12	3	–	2894	–	–
Westray	73	14	24	18083	–	–
Rousay	30	4	10	2083	–	–
Shapinsay	71	8	–	5743	–	–
South Ronaldsay and Burray	198	11	13	15118	–	–
Stromness	416	25	33	55436	5410	11790

Congregation	Com	Eld	G	In 01	Ass	Gvn
46. Shetland						
Burra Isle	49	7	25	7481	–	–
Tingwall	174	17	29	22979	–	–
Delting	117	9	–	20470	–	–
Nesting and Lunnasting	47	5	20	7946	–	–
Dunrossness and St Ninian's	73	17	–	12102	–	200
Sandwick Cunningsburgh and Quarff	157	11	36	23083	–	500
Fetlar	23	3	–	1695	–	–
Yell	146	11	36	10749	–	–
Lerwick and Bressay	5836	41	–	55206	11220	11220
Northmavine	91	10	–	7796	–	–
Sandsting and Aithsting	56	11	7	8484	–	50
Walls and Sandness	52	11	14	6785	–	50
Unst	132	10	26	16316	–	–
Whalsay and Skerries	254	18	20	24095	–	100
47. England						
Corby St Andrew's	349	25	32	37273	2160	2160
Corby St Ninian's	374	25	12	44411	5220	5220
Guernsey St Andrew's in the Grange	245	21	–	48414	5440	5440
Jersey St Columba's	143	24	–	48234	3460	3460
Liverpool St Andrew's	53	6	7	9414	2560	2560
London Crown Court	311	40	10	82272	16870	16870
London St Columba's	1490	54	–	205096	50400	50400
Newcastle St Andrew's	124	21	9	–	3080	3080

INDEX OF MINISTERS

NOTE: Ministers who are members of a Presbytery are designated 'A' if holding a parochial appointment in that Presbytery, or 'B' if otherwise qualifying for membership.
'A-1, A-2' etc. indicate the numerical order of congregations in the Presbyteries of Edinburgh, Glasgow and Hamilton.
Also included are:
(1) Ministers who have resigned their seat in Presbytery (List 6-H)
(2) Ministers who hold a Practising Certificate (List 6-I)
(3) Ministers serving overseas (List 6-L)
(4) Auxiliary Ministers (List 6-A)
(5) Ministers who have died since the publication of the last *Year Book* (List 6-R)
(6) Ministers ordained for sixty years and upwards (List 6-S)
NB *For a List of the Diaconate, see List 6-G.*

Abeledo, B.J.	Paisley 14B	Angus, J.A.K.	List 6-R	Beaton, D.	Lochcarron/Skye 42A
Acklam, C.R.	West Lothian 2A	Annand, J.M.	Annandale/Eskdale 7B	Beattie, J.A.	Glasgow 16B
Adams, D.G.	Dunfermline 24A	Arbuthnott, Mrs J.	List 6-I	Beattie, W.R.	List 6-I
Adamson, H.	Irvine/K'marnock 11A	Archer, N.D.C.	List 6-I	Beattie, W.G.	Hamilton 17B
Adamson, S.	Lothian 3B	Archibald, D.Y.	Dunfermline 24B	Beattie, W.G.	Aberdeen 31B
Aitchison, J.W.	Aberdeen 31B	Armitage, W.L.	Edinburgh 1A-49	Beautyman, P.H.	List 6-I
Aitken, A.J.	Glasgow 16B	Armour, C.	St Andrews 26A	Beck, J.C.	Moray 35A
Aitken, A.R.	Edinburgh 1B	Armstrong, W.R.	Greenock 15A	Beckett, D.M.	Edinburgh 1B
Aitken, E.D.	Stirling 23B	Arnott, A.D.K.	St Andrews 26A	Beebee, G.W.	St Andrews 26A
Aitken, E.R.	Edinburgh 1A-79	Atkins, Mrs Y.E.S.	List 6-I	Bell, C.J.G.	Ross 39A
Aitken, F.R.	Ayr 10A	Auld, A.G.	Edinburgh 1B	Bell, D.W.	Buchan 34B
Aitken, I.M.	Aberdeen 31A	Austin, G.	Moray 35A	Bell, G.K.	Glasgow 16A-60
Alexander, D.N.	Paisley 14B			Bell, I.W.	Paisley 14A
Alexander, E.J.	Glasgow 16B	Baigrie, R.A.	Edinburgh 1B	Bell, J.L.	Glasgow 16B
Alexander, Miss H.J.R.	List 6-I	Bailey, W.G.	List 6-H	Bell, Mrs M.	Paisley 14A
Alexander, I.W.	Edinburgh 1B	Baillie, D.	Annandale/Eskdale 7B	Bell, R.P.	Ayr 10A
Alexander, J.S.	St Andrews 26B	Bain, B.	Perth 28A	Bell, W.	List 6-R
Alexander, W.M.	Perth 28B	Bain, J.	Edinburgh 1A-13	Bennett, A.	St Andrews 26B
Allan, A.G.	Glasgow 16B	Baird, G.W.	Hamilton 17B	Bennett, A.G.	Melrose/Peebles 4A
Allan, J.B.	Hamilton 17B	Baird, K.S.	Glasgow 16A-41	Bennett, D.K.P.	Dum'/K'cudbright 8B
Allan, R.T.	Falkirk 22B	Baird, W.G.G.	List 6-R	Benson, J.W.	Stirling 23B
Allen, M.A.W.	Glasgow 16A-14	Baker, Mrs C.	Ayr 10A	Benzie, I.W.	Ardrossan 12A
Allen, Miss V.L.	Angus 30A	Balfour, T.	List 6-H	Berrill, P.A.D.	Kincard'/Dee' 32A
Allison, Mrs A.	Dunfermline 24A	Ballantyne, S.	Aberdeen 31B	Bertram, T.A.	Perth 28B
Allison, Mrs M.M.	Glasgow 16A-86	Ballentine, Miss A.M.	W' Lothian 2A	Best, E.	St Andrews 26B
Allison, R.N.	Paisley 14A	Banks, J	Ayr 10B	Beveridge, S.E.P.	Annan'/Eskdale 7A
Allsop, T.D.	List 6-R	Barber, P.I.	Edinburgh 1A-28	Bews, J.	St Andrews 26B
Almond, D.	Annan'/Eskdale 7A	Barbour, R.A.	Dunkeld/Meigle 27B	Bezuidenhout, L.C.	Dum'/K'cudbright
Alston, W.G.	Glasgow 16A-109	Barclay, I.C.	Aberdeen 31A		8A
Amed, P.	Moray 35A	Barclay, N.W.	Falkirk 22A	Bicket, M.S.	Angus 30A
Anderson, A.F.	Edinburgh 1A-31	Barclay, S.G.	Irvine/Kilmarnock 11A	Billes, R.H.	Moray 35A
Anderson, C.M.	Inverness 37A	Bardgett, F.D.	Edinburgh 1B	Birch, J.	Glasgow 16A-11
Anderson, D.	List 6-I	Barge, N.L.	Glasgow 16A-43	Bircham, M.F.	Perth 28A
Anderson, D.J.B.	List 6-R	Barr, A.C	Glasgow 16B	Bird, J.W.	Ayr 10B
Anderson, D.M.	Lochaber 38B	Barr, G.K.	Perth 28B	Birnie, C.J.	Buchan 34B
Anderson, H.	Edinburgh 1B	Barr, G.R.	Edinburgh 1A-19	Birrell, Mrs I.	Perth 28A
Anderson, J.F.	Aberdeen 31A	Barr, J.	Ayr 10B	Birrell, J.M.	Perth 28B
Anderson, J.W.	Angus 30B	Barr, T.L.	Perth 28B	Birse, G.S.	Ayr 10A
Anderson, K.G.	Perth 28A	Barrett, L.	Dundee 29B	Birss, A.D.	Paisley 14A
Anderson, R.	Glasgow 16A-55	Barrie, A.	Falkirk 22A	Bjarnason, S.	Abernethy 36A
Anderson, R.A.	West Lothian 2A	Barrie, A.P.	Hamilton 17A-43	Black, A.G.	Lothian 3A
Anderson, R.J.M.	Moray 35A	Barrington, C.W.H.	Edinburgh 1A-2	Black, A.R.	Ardrossan 12A
Anderson, R.S.	Edinburgh 1B	Barron, Mrs J.L.	Dundee 29A	Black, A.T.	Inverness 37B
Anderson, Mrs S.M.	Irv'/K'nock 11A	Bartholomew, D.S.	Dum/Kirk 8A	Black, D.R.	Glasgow 16A-114
Andrew, I.	Lothian 3A	Baxendale, Mrs G.M.	Paisley 14A	Black, D.W.	West Lothian 2A
Andrew, J.	Gordon 33A	Baxter, R.	Kirkcaldy 25A	Black, I.W.	Falkirk 22A
Andrew, R.J.M.	Ayr 10B	Baxter, R.F.	Edinburgh 1B	Black, J.M.	Hamilton 17A-23
Andrews, J.E.	Ayr 10A	Bayne, A.L.	Edinburgh 1A-5	Black, Mrs J.M.K.	List 6-I

Black, J.S.	List 6-I	Brough, R.	West Lothian 2B	Caie, A.	Kincard'/Deeside 32B
Black, Mrs S.	List 6-I	Brown, A.	Kincard/Deeside 32B	Cairns, A.B.	Wigtown/Stranraer 9B
Black, W.B.	Lewis 44A	Brown, A.B.	Kirkcaldy 25A	Cairns, J.B.	Lothian 3A
Black, W.G.	List 6-I	Brown, D.G.	Inverness 37B	Cairns, Miss W.	Angus 30
Blackley, Mrs J.R.M.	Stirling 23B	Brown, Mrs E.	Perth 28A	Cairns, W.A.	England 47A
Blackwood, K.T.	Dumbarton 18A	Brown, H.J.	Dundee 29A	Calder, B.	Glasgow 16A-27
Blaikie, J.	Buchan 34B	Brown, H.T.	Falkirk 22A	Calder, T.R.	Gordon 33A
Blair, D.B.	Falkirk 22A	Brown, J.	Falkirk 22B	Calderwood, W.	Dum'/K'cud 8B
Blair, F.	Aberdeen 31A	Brown, J.	Jedburgh 6B	Calvert, R.A.	Europe 48A
Blair, J.N.	Shetland 46B	Brown, J.	Stirling 23A	Cameron, A.F.	Paisley 14A
Blair, Miss S.	List 6-I	Brown, J.H.	Dumbarton 18A	Cameron, C.M.	Irv'/K'marnock 11A
Blair, T.J.L.	Irvine/Kilmarnock 11A	Brown, J.M.	Annan'/Eskdale 7A	Cameron, D.C.	Glasgow 16A-31
Blakey, R.S.	Edinburgh 1B	(Brown, J.M.	Europe 48)	Cameron, D.J.R.	Glasgow 16A-128
Blakey, S.A.	Dundee 29A	Brown, J.W.S.	Kincard'/Deeside 32B	Cameron, D.S.	Irv'/K'marnock 11A
Blane, Q.A.	List 6-I	Brown, L.R.	St Andrews 26B	Cameron, G.G.	Edinburgh 1B
Blount, Mrs A.S.	Falkirk 22A	Brown, Mrs M.	Stirling 23A	Cameron, I.	West Lothian 2B
Blount, G.K.	Falkirk 22B	Brown, P.	Dunfermline 24B	Cameron, J.K.	St Andrews 26B
Blyth, J.G.S.	Ayr 10B	Brown, R.	Melrose/Peebles 4B	Cameron, J.U.	Dundee 29A
Blythe, S.C.	Aberdeen 31B	Brown, R.F.	Aberdeen 31A	Cameron, J.W.M.	Edinburgh 1B
Boag, J.A.S.	Paisley 14A	Brown, R.G.	Orkney 45B	Cameron, R.	Glasgow 16A-137
Boath, G.K.	Irvine/Kilmarnock 11B	Brown, R.H.	Lothian 3B	Cameron, R.N.	England 47B
Bogie, A.P.	St Andrews 26B	Brown, R.R.	Perth 28B	Cameron, M.S.	Ardrossan 12A
Bogle, A.O.	Falkirk 22A	Brown, S.J.	England 47B	Campbell, A.B.	Lorn/Mull 21A
Bogle, M.M.	List 6-H	Brown, Mrs S.M.	Sutherland 40A	Campbell, A.I.	Glasgow 16B
Bogle, T.C.	Ayr 10A	Brown, W.	Lothian 3B	Campbell, A.M.	Hamilton 17A-62
Bonar, A.F.	Perth 28A	Brown, W.D.	Edinburgh 1B	Campbell, C.	Glasgow 16B
Bond, M.S.	Dum'/K'cudbright 8A	Brown, W.D.	Edinburgh 1A-55	Campbell, D.	Dum'/K'cudbright 8A
Bonomy, W.	Perth 28B	Brown, W.H.	Buchan 34B	Campbell, D.	Perth 28A
Booth, F.M.	Dumbarton 18A	Browning, D.	Edinburgh 1A-9	Campbell, Mrs E.C.	Ayr 10B
Booth, Mrs J.	Edinburgh 1A-45	Brownlie, G.D.	Angus 30B	Campbell, G.	Dundee 29A
Borthwick, K.S.	Caithness 41A	Bruce, A.W.	Greenock 15B	Campbell, G.H.	Irv'/K'marnock 11B
Boswell G.	Falkirk 22A	Bruce, Miss L.M.	Edinburgh 1B	Campbell, J.	Paisley 14A
Bowie, A.	Gordon 33B	Bruce, W.C.	Angus 30B	Campbell, J.	Dunfermline 24B
Bowie, A.G.	England 47B	Bryden, W.A.	Glasgow 16B	Campbell, J.A.	Irv'/Kilmarnock 11B
Bowie, A.McC.	Jedburgh 6B	Bryson, T.M.	Dum'/K'cudbright 8A	Campbell, J.E.R.	Kirkcaldy 25A
Bowman, N.	List 6-I	Buchan, A.	St Andrews 26B	Campbell, J.W.	Melrose/Peebles 4A
Boyd, B.	Moray 35A	Buchan, C.	Melrose/Peebles 4A	Campbell, M.M.	Lewis 44A
Boyd, I.R.	List 6-I	Buchan, Mrs I.C.	St Andrews 26B	Campbell, N.G.	Wigtown/Stranraer 9A
Boyd, K.M.	List 6-I	Buchan, J.	Ross 39B	Campbell, P.D.G.	Stirling 23B
Boyd, R.M.H.	Ayr 10A	Buchan, W.	Perth 28B	Campbell, R.	Stirling 23A
Boyle, R.P.	Moray 35A	Buchanan, F.C.	Dumbarton 18A	Campbell, R.D.M.	List 6-I
Bradley, A.W.	Paisley 14A	Buchanan, N.	Edinburgh 1A-62	Campbell, T.R.	List 6-I
Bradley, I.	St Andrews 26B	Buchanan-Smith, R.D.	List 6-I	Campbell, W.F.	Jedburgh 6A
Brady, I.D.	Edinburgh 1B	Buckley, R.G.	Glasgow 16A-146	Campbell, W.M.M.	Aberdeen 31B
Brady, Miss L.	St Andrews 26A	Buell, F.B.	Inverness 37B	Campbell-Jack, W.C.	Dum'/K'cud 8A
Brain, E.J.	Glasgow 16B	Bull, A.W.	Glasgow 16B	Cant, H.W.M.	Orkney 45B
Brain, Mrs I.J.	Glasgow 16B	Burgess, P.	List 6-L	Cant, T.M.	Paisley 14A
Brennan, Mrs A.J.	D'keld/Meigle 27A	Burnett, J.B.	Stirling 23B	(Capstick, D.	South Argyll 19A)
Brewster, J.	Hamilton 17A-32	Burns, J.H.	Wigtown/Stranraer 9A	Carmichael, D.J.M.	Ross 39A
Brice, D.G.	Glasgow 16B	Burnside, Mrs A.H.	List 6-I	Carmichael, D.S.	Lanark 13A
Bristow, Mrs I.A.	Glasgow 16A-134	Burnside, W.A.M.	Lochaber 38B	Carmichael, J.A.	Lochaber 38A
Bristow, W.H.G.	South Argyll 19B	Burt, D.W.G.	Hamilton 17A-45	Carmichael, R.C.M.	South Argyll 19B
Britchfield, Mrs A.E.P.	Dunf'line 24B	Burt, T.W.	Melrose/Peebles 4A	Carmont, R.	List 6-R
Broadley, Mrs L.J.	D'keld/Meigle 27A	Burton, W.	Dunfermline 24A	Carr, W.S.	Perth 28B
Brockie, C.G.F.	Irv'/K'marnock 11A	Butters, D.	Angus 30B	Carrie, J.G.	Edinburgh 1A-66
Brodie, J.	Angus 30B	Buwert, K.O.F.	Hamilton 17A-87	Carruth, Mrs P.A.	Falkirk 22A
Brook, S.A.	Edinburgh 1A-35	Byers, A.J.	Annan'/Eskdale 7B	Carruthers, D.	South Argyll 19A
Broster, D.	Ardrossan 12A	Byers, Mrs M.	Annan'/Eskdale 7B	Cartlidge, G.	Glasgow 16B
Brough, C.H.	Hamilton 17A-59			Cartwright, A.C.D.	Duns 5A

Casebow, B.C.	St Andrews 26B	(Cook, Mrs H.)	Abernethy 36A	Cumming, D.P.L.	Dunoon 20B
Cashman, P.H.	Melrose/Peebles 4B	Cook, J.	Edinburgh 1A-42	Cunningham, A.	Glasgow 16B
Caskie, J.C.	Dumbarton 18A	Cook, J.A.	Gordon 33A	Cunningham, I.D.	Lanark 13A
Cassells, A.K.	Dunkeld/Meigle 27B	Cook, J.M.	Buchan 34A	Cunningham, J.S.A.	Glasgow 16B
Cathcart, I.	St Andrews 26A	Cook, J.S.	Hamilton 17B	Curran, Mrs E.M.	Moray 35A
Cattanach, W.D.	Edinburgh 1B	Cook, J.W.	Edinburgh 1A-65	Currie, A.I.	Wigtown/Stranraer 9A
Chalmers, G.A.	Falkirk 22B	Cooke, J.M.	List 6-R	Currie, D.E.P.	Edinburgh 1B
Chalmers, J.P.	Edinburgh 1B	Cooper, G.	List 6-H	Currie, G.C.M.	List 6-I
Chalmers, M.	Edinburgh 1B	Cooper, M.W.	Kirkcaldy 25B	Currie, I.S.	Paisley 14A
Chalmers, W.R.	Lothian 3B	Corbett, R.T.	West Lothian 2A	Currie, Ms M.F.	Hamilton 17A-7
Chambers, S.J.	Inverness 37A	Cordiner, J.	Wigtown/Stranraer 9B	Currie, R.	Glasgow 16B
Chapman, E.	Aberdeen 31A	Coull, M.C.	Stirling 23A	Currie, R.D.	Glasgow 16A-9
Charlton, G.W.	Inverness 37B	Coulter, D.	England 47B	Cuthbertson, M.	Glasgow 16A-76
Charlton, Mrs I.A.	Shetland 46A	Court, D.L.	Edinburgh 1A 57	Cuthell, T.C.	Edinburgh 1A-74
Charlton, R.	Shetland 46A	Coutts, F.	Aberdeen 31B	Cutler, J.S.H.	Duns 5A
Cherry, A.J.	Glasgow 16A-40	Cowan, J.S.A.	Paisley 14A		
Chester, S.J.	Glasgow 16B	Cowell, Miss S.G.	Lanark 13B	Dailly, J.R.	Ardrossan 12B
Chestnut, A.	Greenock 15B	Cowie, G.S.	Aberdeen 31A	Darroch, R.J.G.	Gordon 33A
Cheyne, A.C.	Edinburgh 1B	Cowie, G.S.	Moray 35B	Davidge, Mrs A.	Paisley 14A
Cheyne, M.	Stirling 23B	Cowie, J.A.	Europe 48A	Davidson, A.A.B.	Moray 35B
Cheyne, Mrs R.U.	Stirling 23A	Cowie, J.L.	Perth 28B	Davidson, D.H.	Edinburgh 1A-36
Chilton, R.M.L.	List 6-I	Cowie, J.M.	Lothian 3A	Davidson, D.W.	South Argyll 19B
Chirnside, C.	List 6-H	Cowie, Mrs M.	List 6-I	Davidson, I.M.P.	Edinburgh 1B
Chisholm, A.F.	Inverness 37B	Cowper, M.C.	Hamilton 17B	Davidson, J.	Hamilton 17B
Chisholm, W.D.	Dundee 29B	Craggs, Mrs S.	Gordon 33A	Davidson, J.F.	List 6-I
Christie, A.A.	Ayr 10A	Craig, A.J.D.	Glasgow 16A-102	Davidson, J.M.	List 6-R
Christie, A.C.	Kincard'/Deeside 32B	Craig, E.	List 6-H	Davidson, R.	Dumbarton 18B
Christie, Mrs H.F.	Falkirk 22A	Craig, G.T.	Moray 35B	Davies, G.W.	List 6-I
Christie, J.	Inverness 37A	Craig, G.W.	England 47B	Davies, J.M.	Aberdeen 31A
Christie, J.C.	Glasgow 16A-87	Craig, I.R.	Dundee 29B	Davison, C.F.	England 47B
Christie, R.S.	Irv'/K'marnock 11B	Craig, Miss J.H.	Orkney 45A	Dawson, M.A.	Irv'/K'marnock 11A
Clancy, Mrs P.J.	Greenock 15A	Craig, J.W.	List 6-H	Dawson, M.S.	Edinburgh 1A-35
Clark, D.M.	Dundee 29A	Craig, M.D.	Stirling 23A	Day, C.T.	Lothian 3B
Clark, D.W.	Glasgow 16A-29	Craig, N.D.	Dum'/K'cudbright 8B	Dean, R.A.F.	Wigtown/Stranraer 9A
Clark, D.W.	Dumbarton 18A	Craig, R.A.S.	Glasgow 16A-59	Deans, G.D.S.	Orkney 45A
Clark, T.L.	Orkney 45A	Craig, W.	Lanark 13B	Deans, J.B.	Aberdeen 31B
Clarkson, R.G.	Dundee 29B	Craik, Mrs S.	Dundee 29B	Dempsey, B.	Dunkeld/Meigle 27A
Clelland, Mrs E.	Stirling 23A	Cramb, E.M.	Dundee 29B	Dempster, C.J.	St Andrews 26A
Clinkenbeard, W.W.	Edinburgh 1B	Cran, Mrs K.	Gordon 33A	Denniston, D.W.	Perth 28A
Clipston, S.F.	Melrose/Peebles 4A	Cranfield, Miss E.F.	Kirkcaldy 25A	Devenney, D.J.	Kincard'/Deeside 32A
Cloggie, Mrs J.	Stirling 23A	Cranfield, Miss M.M.	Gordon 33A	Devenny, R.P.	Mel'/Peebles 4B
Clyne, D.R.	Buchan 34A	Cranston, G.	Ayr 10B	Dewar, J.S.	Edinburgh 1A-37
Cobain, A.R.	Edinburgh 1B	Cranston, R.D.	Greenock 15A	Diack, P.	Moray 35B
Cochrane, J.	Stirling 23A	Crawford, J.F.	Mel'/Peebles 4A	Dick, A.B.	Lothian 3A
Coghill, A.W.F.	Lewis 44A	Crawford, M.S.M.	Aberdeen 31A	Dick, J.H.A.	Aberdeen 31A
Coleman, S.H.	Glasgow 16B	Crawford, R.	Irv'/K'marnock 11B	Dick, J.R.	Melrose/Peebles 4B
Coley, R.	Glasgow 16A-148	Crawford, S.G.V.	Kirkcaldy 25B	Dick, J.S.	Kirkcaldy 25B
Collard, J.K.	Hamilton 17A-31	Creegan, Mrs C.M.	D'keld/Meigle 27A	Dick, T.	Dunkeld/Meigle 25B
Collie, Miss J.P.	Gordon 33B	Crichton, J.	Ayr 10A	Dickie, M.M.	Ayr 10B
Collins, Mrs C.E.E.	Lanark 13A	Crichton, T.	West Lothian 2B	Dickson, A.P.	Aberdeen 31A
Collins, D.A.	Lanark 13A	Cringles, G.G.	Stirling 23A	Dickson, A.S.	West Lothian 2B
Collins, M.	St Andrews 26A	Crombie, W.D.	Dumbarton 18B	Dickson, G.T.	Edinburgh 1A-82
Coltart, I.O.	Hamilton 17A-83	Cross, B.F.	Edinburgh 1B	Dickson, J.C.	Aberdeen 31B
Colvin, Mrs S.E.F.	Hamilton 17A-5	Crosthwaite, M.D.	Falkirk 22A	Dilbey, Miss M.D.	Edinburgh 1B
Combe, N.R.	Jedburgh 6A	Cruickshank, A.A.B.	Stirling 23B	Dixon, D.S.	Angus 30A
Congdon, H.S.	Buchan 34A	Cruickshank, N.	Ardrossan 12A	Dobie, Mrs R.J.W.	Mel'/Peebles 4A
Conkey, H.	Kin'/Deeside 32A	Crumlish, Mrs E.A.	Greenock 15A	Dodd, Miss M.E.	Jedburgh 6A
Connolly, D.	Kirkcaldy 25B	Cubie, J.P.	Paisley 14B	Doherty, A.J.	Stirling 23B
Coogan, J.M.	Lanark 13A	Cullen, W.T.	Glasgow 16B	Donaghy, L.G.	Dumbarton 18A

Donald, A.C.	Falkirk 22A	Dunnett, A.L.	Glasgow 16A-110	Fiddes, G.R.	Ayr 10A
Donald, A.P.	Buchan 34A	Dunnett, W.G.	List 6-R	Fields, J.T.	England 47B
Donald, K.W.	Kirkcaldy 25A	(Dunphy, R.G.	Europe 48)	Finch, G.S.	Glasgow 16A-8
Donald, P.H.	Inverness 37A	Dunsmore, B.W.	England 47A	Findlay, H.J.W.	Hamilton 17A-86
Donald, R.M.	Dunoon 20A	Dupar, K.W.	Ross 39B	Findlay, W.P.	Glasgow 16B
Donald, T.W.	Melrose/Peebles 4B	Dupuy, E.J.	Lothian 3B	Finlay, Mrs J.G.	List 6-I
Donaldson, C.V.	Lothian 3B	Durno, R.C.	Glasgow 16A-89	Finlay, Q.	Angus 30B
Donaldson, D.	Dumbarton 18A	Dutch, M.M.	List 6-I	Finlayson, D.	List 6-H
Donaldson, G.M.	List 6-I	Duthie, G.	Inverness 37A	Finlayson, J.C.	Edinburgh 1B
Donaldson, M.	Inverness 37B	Dutton, D.W.	Wigtown/Stranraer 9A	Finnie, C.J.	Jedburgh 6A
Donaldson, R.B.	Perth 28B			Fisher, D.N.	Annan'/Eskdale 7B
Donn, T.M.	Inverness 37B	Earnshaw, P.	St Andrews 26B	Fisher, K.H.	Ardrossan 12B
Dougall, Mrs E.	Edinburgh 1B	Easton, D.J.C.	Glasgow 16A-6	Fisher, M.L.	Glasgow 16A-150
Dougall, N.J.	Edinburgh 1A-75	Easton, I.A.G.	Dumbarton 18B	Fisk, Mrs E.A.	Dunfermline 24A
Douglas, A.B.	Edinburgh 1A-4	Easton, Mrs L.C.	Edinburgh 1A-16	Fleming, A.F.	Stirling 23B
Douglas, A.M.	List 6-R	Eddie, D.C.	Aberdeen 31A	Fleming, H.K.	Perth 28B
Douglas, A.M.	Aberdeen 31B	Edgar, W.M.G.	List 6-R	Fleming, T.G.	List 6-I
Douglas, Mrs C.A.	Moray 35B	Edington, G.L.	St Andrews 26B	Fletcher, G.G.	Glasgow 16A-57
Douglas, C.R.	West Lothian 2A	Edwards, M.S.	Glasgow 16A-82	Fletcher, T.	England 47A
Douglas, Miss F.C.	Dundee 27B	Elder, A.B.	Dum'/K'cudbright 8B	Flockhart, D.R.	List 6-I
Douglas, I.M.	Angus 30A	Elders, I.A.	Edinburgh 1A-6	Foggitt, E.W.	Lothian 3A
Douglas, I.P.	Buchan 34B	Elliot, G.	Edinburgh 1B	Forbes, G.A.R.	Glasgow 16B
Douglas, J.D.	St Andrews 26B	Elliott, G.J.	Lanark 13A	Forbes, I.M.	Aberdeen 31A
Douglas, P.C.	St Andrews 26B	Elliott, K.C.	Ayr 10A	Forbes, J.W.A.	Kincard'/Deeside 32B
Downie, A.A.	Irv'/K'marnock 11B	Ellis, D.W.	List 6-I	Ford, A.A.	Glasgow 16A-143
Downie, A.F.M.	Stirling 23A	Elston, I.	Kirkcaldy 25A	Forrest, A.B.	Dunoon 20B
Downie, A.S.	Ardrossan 12B	Elston, P.K.	Kirkcaldy 25B	Forrest, G.W.	Glasgow 16B
Dowswell, J.A.M.	Shetland 46A	Embleton, B.M.	Edinburgh 1A-68	Forrest, M.R.	South Argyll-19A
Doyle, D.W.	Hamilton 17A-63	Embleton, Mrs S.R.	Edinburgh 1A-43	Forrester, D.B.	Edinburgh 1B
Doyle, I.B.	Edinburgh 1B	Erskine, A.U.	Dunoon 20B	Forrester, I.L.	Kirkcaldy 25B
Drake, Mrs W.F.	Lothian 3A	Erskine, M.J.	South Argyll 19A	Forrester, Mrs M.R.	Edinburgh 1A-80
Drummond, A.G.	Perth 28A	Evans, J.W.	Moray 35B	Forrester-Paton, C.	List 6-H
Drummond, J.S.	England 47B	Eve, J.C.	Glasgow 16A-7	Forsyth, A.R.	Kirkcaldy 25A
Drummond, J.W.	Glasgow 16A-39	Ewart, J.C.	Glasgow 16A-3	Forsyth, D.S.	Dunkeld/Meigle 27B
Drummond, N.W.	List 6-I	Ewing, J.	Ardrossan 12B	Forsyth, J.	Ross 39B
Drummond, R.H.	Edinburgh 1B			Foster, M.	Edinburgh 1A-23
Dryden, I.	Gordon 33B	Fair, W.M.	Angus 30A	Fowler, A.J.R.	Paisley 14A
Drysdale, J.H.D.C.	Falkirk 22A	Fairful, J.	Hamilton 17A-9	Fowler, R.C.A.	List 6-I
Drysdale, J.P.R.	Angus 30B	Fairlie, G.	St Andrews 26B	Fox, G.D.A.	Jedburgh 6B
Duff, S.M.	Glasgow 16A-100	Fairweather, I.C.M.	Glasgow 16B	Fraser, Mrs A.G.	St Andrews 26A
Duff, T.M.F.	Glasgow 16A-117	Falconer, A.D.	Europe 48A	Fraser, A.M.	Glasgow 16A-17
Duff, Miss V.J.	Glasgow 16A-80	Falconer, J.B.	Aberdeen 31B	Fraser, D.W.	Dundee 29A
Duffin, G.L.	Lothian 3A	Faris, Mrs J.M.	Mel'/Peebles 4A	Fraser, I.C.	Glasgow 16A-129
Dunbar, Ms L.J.	Kirkcaldy 25A	Farquhar, W.E.	Dunfermline 24A	Fraser, I.M.	List 6-I
Duncan, A.S.	Dumbarton 18A	Farquharson, G.	Kin'/Deeside 32A	Fraser, J.P.	Hamilton 17B
Duncan, C.A.	Melrose/Peebles 4B	Faulds, N.L.	Edinburgh 1B	Fraser, J.W.	Lothian 3A
Duncan, D.M.	England 47B	Fawkes, G.M.A.	Buchan 34B	Fraser, J.W.	Lothian 3B
Duncan, G.A.	Falkirk 22A	Fenemore, J.C.	Dunoon 20B	Fraser, Miss S.A.	Edinburgh 1B
Duncan, J.	Dunkeld/Meigle 27B	Fenton, R.J.	Glasgow 16B	Frater, A.	Dumbarton 18A
Duncan, J.C.	Kirkcaldy 25B	Ferguson, A.M.	Dumbarton 18A	Frazer, R.E.	Aberdeen 31A
Duncan, Mrs M.M.	Irv'/K'nock 11A	Ferguson, D.J.	Moray 35B	Frew, J.M.	List 6-I
Duncan, R.F.	Angus 30B	Ferguson, J.	Lochcarron/Skye 42B	Frew, M.W.	Lanark 13A
Dundas, T.B.S.	West Lothian 2B	Ferguson, J.A.	Aberdeen 31A	Frew, Mrs R.	St Andrews 26A
Dunleavy, Miss S.	Paisley 14A	Ferguson, J.B.	Glasgow 16A-30	Frizzell, R.S.	Inverness 37B
Dunlop, A.J.	South Argyll 19A	Ferguson, J.F.	Perth 28B	Froude, K.	Kirkcaldy 25A
Dunlop, M.W.B.	Buchan 34B	Ferguson, R.	List 6-H	Fulton, F.H.	Dunkeld/Meigle 27B
Dunn, J.F.	List 6-R	Ferguson, S.B.	Glasgow 16A-126	Fulton, R.S.M.	Falkirk 22B
Dunn, W.I.C.	Edinburgh 1B	Ferguson, W.B.	Glasgow 16A-54	Fulton, Mrs S.F.	Falkirk 22A
Dunn, W.S.	Hamilton 17A-58	Fergusson, D.A.S.	Edinburgh 1B	Fyall, R.S.	England 47B

Gaddes, D.R.   Duns 5B
Galbraith, D.   Edinburgh 1B
Galbraith, N.W.   Glasgow 16A-63
Galbraith, W.J.L.   Perth 28B
Gale, R.A.A.   Duns 5B
Gall, R.   Kincard'/Deeside 32A
Gallacher, Miss J.W.   Falkirk 22A
Gallan, A.   Stirling 23B
Galloway, A.D.   Glasgow 16B
Galloway, I.F.   Glasgow 16A-81
Galloway, Mrs K.   List 6-I
Galloway, R.W.C.   St Andrews 26B
Gammack, G.   Dundee 29B
Garden, Miss M.J.   Gordon 33A
Gardner, A.   Hamilton 17A-3
Gardner, B.K.   Kin'/Deeside 32A
Gardner, Mrs F.   Glasgow 16A-142
Gardner, F.J.   Greenock 15A
Gardner, J.V.   Angus 30A
Gardner, N.N.   Dunkeld/Meigle 27A
Gardner, P.M.   Glasgow 16A-118
Garrity, T.A.W.   Ayr 10B
Gaston, A.R.C.   Stirling 23B
Gatherer, J.F.   Dumbarton 18A
Gatt, D.W.   Kirkcaldy 25B
Gauld, B.G.D.D.   Lanark 13A
Gauld, Mrs K.   Moray 35A
Gauld, R.S.R.   Moray 35A
Geddes, A.J.   Dum'/K'cudbright 8B
Gehrke, R.   Glasgow 16A-48
Gemmell, D.R.   Ayr 10A
Gemmell, J.   Ross 39A
Gibb, J.D.   Stirling 23A
Gibbons, R.   Inverness 37B
Gibson, A.C.   Inverness 37B
Gibson, A.W.   Hamilton 17A-73
Gibson, F.S.   South Argyll 19B
Gibson, H.M.   Glasgow 16B
Gibson, H.M.   St Andrews 26B
Gibson, I.   Kirkcaldy 25B
Gibson, J.C.L.   Edinburgh 1B
Gibson, J.M.   Hamilton 17A-16
Gibson, M.   Glasgow 16B
Gilchrist, E.J.   Perth 28A
Gilchrist, G.R.   List 6-R
Gilchrist, Miss K.   Hamilton 17B
Gilfillan, J.   Lothian 3B
Gillespie, Miss A.M. Dum'/K'cud 8B
Gillespie, Mrs I.C.   Stirling 23A
Gillies, Mrs J.E.   Lothian 3A
Gillon, C.B.   Glasgow 16A-88
Gillon, D.R.M.   Paisley 14A
Gillon, J.B.   Edinburgh 1B
Gilmour, I.Y.   Edinburgh 1A-45
Gilmour, R.M.   List 6-I
Gilmour, W.M.   Stirling 23A
Gisbey, J.E.   Dunoon 20B
Glass, A.   Ross 39B
Glen, G.E.D.   Gordon 33A

Glencross, W.M.   Ayr 10B
Glover, R.L.   Lothian 3A
Goldie, Miss C.   Glasgow 16A-67
Goldie, G.D.   Aberdeen 31B
Goodman, R.A.   Falkirk 22B
Gordon, A.B.   List 6-H
Gordon, D.C.   Ardrossan 12B
Gordon, Miss E.J.   Perth 28B
Gordon, I.D.   Kirkcaldy 25B
Gordon, J.A.   Ross 39A
Gordon, L.Y.   Aberdeen 31B
Gordon, P.M.   St Andrews 26B
Gordon, T.   Edinburgh 1B
Goring, I.M.   Stirling 23A
Goring, J.M.   List 6-R
Goskirk, J.L.   Sutherland 40A
Goss, A.J.   Glasgow 16B
Goss, M.S.   Dundee 29A
Goudie, S.M.   Irv'/K'marnock 11B
Gough, I.G.   Angus 30A
Gow, N.   Gordon 33A
Graham, A.D.M.   Aberdeen 31A
Graham, A.F   Moray 35A
Graham, A.G.   Angus 30A
Graham, D.J.   Lothian 3A
Graham, S.S.   Dundee 29A
Graham, W.P.   Edinburgh 1B
Grahame, R.P.   Ardrossan 12A
Grainger, H.L.   Aberdeen 31A
Grainger, I.G.   Lorn and Mull 21B
Grant, A.R.   List 6-R
Grant, D.I.M.   Ardrossan 12A
Grant, G.V.R.   List 6-R
Grant, J.   Dum'/K'cudbright 8B
Grant, J.G.   Ayr 10B
Grant, N.M.   Dunfermline 24A
Gray, A.H.   South Argyll 19A
Gray, J.A.   List 6-F
Gray, K.N.   Paisley 14A
Gray, R.   Kincard'/Deeside 32B
Gray, W.   Lorn and Mull 21A
Greaves, A.T.   Dundee 29A
Green, A.H.   Stirling 23A
Greenshields, I.M.   Lochcarron/
                           Skye 42A
Greer, A.D.C.   Dum'/K'cudbright 8B
Gregory, J.C.   Perth 28B
Gregson, Mrs E.M.   Glasgow 16B
Greig, A.   Gordon 33A
Greig, C.H.M.   Shetland 46A
Greig, J.   List 6-R
Greig, J.C.G.   List 6-H
Greig, R.G.   West Lothian 2A
Grier, J.   Hamilton 17A-26
Grieve, D.S.A.   Dunkeld/Meigle 27B
Griffiths, M.J.   Sutherland 40A
Grimson, J.A.   Perth 28B
Grimstone, A.F.   Glasgow 16B
Groves, I.B.   Gordon 33A

Grubb, A.J.   Aberdeen 31B
Grubb, G.D.W.   Edinburgh 1B
Gunn, A.M.   Dunkeld/Meigle 27A
Gunn, F.D.   List 6-I
Guthrie, J.A.   Dum'/K'cudbright 8A
Guy, S.C.   Aberdeen 31A

Haddow, A.H.   Aberdeen 31B
Haddow Mrs M.M.   Kin/Deeside 32A
Hair, P.R.   Edinburgh 1A-34
Haley, D.   Glasgow 16B
Hall, K.F.   Dundee 29A
Hall, W.M.   Irv'/Kilmarnock 11A
Halliday, A.R.   Perth 28B
Hamill, R.   Dum'/K'cudbright 8B
Hamilton, D.G.   Dunkeld/Meigle 27A
Hamilton, D.S.M.   Dumbarton 18B
Hamilton, Miss H.   Glasgow 16A-127
Hamilton, I.W.F.   Inverness 37A
Hamilton, J.   Dundee 29B
Hamilton, P.J.R.   Dunoon 20B
Hamilton, R.   Jedburgh 6B
Hamilton, R.A.   Hamilton 17A-8
Hamilton, R.G.   Dumbarton 18A
Hamilton, W.D.   Greenock 15A
Hammond, R.J.   Falkirk 22A
Handley, J.   Hamilton 17B
Hannah, W.   Ayr 10B
Harbison, D.J.H.   Ardrossan 12B
Harbison, Mrs K.E.   Hamilton 17A-51
Hardie, H.W.   West Lothian 2A
Hardie, R.K.   Falkirk 22A
Hardy, B.G.   Edinburgh 1B
Hare, M.M.W.   Irv'/Kilmarnock 11B
Harkes, G.   Wigtown/Stranraer 9B
Harkness, J.   Edinburgh 1B
Harper, Miss A.J.M.   Glasgow 16B
Harper, D.L.   Ayr 10A
Harries, D.A.   Ross 39B
Harris, J.W.F.   Dumbarton 18A
Harris, S.McC.   Wigtown/Stranraer 9A
Harvey, W.J.   Edinburgh 1A-12
Haslett, H.J.   Lothian 3A
Hastie, G.I.   Kincard'/Deeside 32A
Hastie, J.S.G.   Hamilton 17A-55
Haston, C.B.   Annan/Eskdale 7A
Haughton, F.   Glasgow 16B
Hawdon, J.E.   Dundee 29B
Hawthorn, D.   Gordon 33A
Hay, B.J.L.   Duns 5B
Hay, J.W.   Edinburgh 1A-2
Hay, W.J.R.   Irv'/K'marnock 11B
Hebenton, D.J.   Ardrossan 12B
Hegarty, J.D.   Moray 35A
Helon, G.G.   Ayr 10B
Henderson, Mrs C.   List 6-R
Henderson, C.M.   South Argyll 19B
Henderson, D.C.   Angus 30B

Henderson, Miss E.M.	Edinb' 1A-69	Houston, W.R.	Hamilton 17A-4
Henderson, G.M.	Ross 39A	Howe, A.Y.	Ross 39B
Henderson, J.D.	Dunkeld/Meigle 27B	Howie, Mrs M.L.K.	Ardrossan 12A
Henderson, Miss J.M.	St Andrews 26A	Howie, W.	List 6-H
Henderson, R.B.	Inverness 37B	Howieson, R.A.	St Andrews 26B
Henderson, R.J.M.	Glasgow 16A-98	Howitt, Miss J.M.	List 6-I
Hendrie, B.R.	Perth 28A	Hudson, E.V.	Dumbarton 18A
Hendrie, Mrs Y.	List 6-I	Hudson, H.R.	Glasgow 16A-53
Henig, G.	Moray 35A	Hudson, J.H.	Dundee 29B
Henney, W.	St Andrews 26B	Huggett, Miss J.A.	Irv'/K'nock 11B
Henry, M.N.	Perth 28B	Hughes, C.E.	Perth 28B
Hepburn, Miss C.A.	Kincard'/Deeside 32A	Hughes, D.W.	Hamilton 17A-59
Hepburn, J.L.	Edinburgh 1B	Hughes, O.T.	England 47B
Heriot, C.R.	Falkirk 22B	Huie, D.F.	Europe 48B
Herkes, Mrs M.	Angus 30A	Humphris, P.M.	Inverness 37A
(Heron, A.I.C.	Europe 48)	Hunt, T.G.	Orkney 45A
Heron, J.	List 6-R	Hunter, A.G.	Glasgow 16B
Herron, A.	Glasgow 16B	Hunter, G.	Glasgow 16B
Hetherington, R.M.	Paisley 14A	Hunter, G.L.	Dumbarton 18B
Hewitt, W.C.	Greenock 15A	Hunter, J.E.	Hamilton 17B
Hibbert, F.W.	Jerusalem 49A	Hunter, W.F.	Glasgow 16A-120
Higgins, G.K.	List 6-I	Hurst, F.R.	Sutherland 40A
Higham, R.D.	Duns 5B	Hutcheson, J.M.	Glasgow 16B
Hill, A.T.	Lothian 3B	Hutcheson, N.M.	Dum'/K'cud 8A
Hill, J.W.	Edinburgh 1B	Hutchison, Mrs A.M.	Aberdeen 31B
Hill, R.	St Andrews 26B	Hutchison, A.S.	Aberdeen 31B
Hill, R.S.	List 6-R	Hutchison, D.S.	Aberdeen 31B
Hill, S.	Falkirk 22B	Hutchison, H.	Glasgow 16B
Hilsley, B.C.	Edinburgh 1A-46	Hutchison, Mrs M.	Dum'/K'cud 8B
Hobson, Mrs D.	Dundee 29A		
Hodge, W.N.T.	Angus 30B	Inglis, Mrs A.	List 6-I
Hogg, T.	Lothian 3A	Inglis, C.G.	List 6-R
Hogg, W.T.	Dum'/K'cudbright 8A	Inglis, D.B.C.	Dunoon 20B
Holland, J.C.	Falkirk 22B	Ingram, J.R.	Dundee 29B
Holland, M.	Dum'/K'cudbright 8A	Ireland, A.	List 6-I
Hollins, R.M.	Ayr 10B	Irvine, Mrs E.H.C.	Glasgow 16B
Holroyd, G.	Ross 39B	Irving, D.R.	Dum'/K'cudbright 8A
Holt, J.	Kincard'/Deeside 32A	Irving, G.D.	Greenock 15A
Homewood, I.M.	Edinburgh 1A-24	Irving, W.D.	Lothian 3A
Hood, A.J.J.	England 47B	Izett, W.A.F.	Stirling 23B
Hood, D.	Glasgow 16A-103		
Hood, E.C.P.	Kincard'/Dee' 32B	Jack, Mrs A.M.	List 6-I
Hood, Mrs E.L.	Paisley 14A	Jack, D.	Aberdeen 31B
Hood, H.S.C.	South Argyll 19B	Jack, J.A.P.	Edinburgh 1A-25
Hope, Miss E.P.	Glasgow 16B	Jack, R.	Dumbarton 18B
Hope, Mrs G.H.	Duns 5A	Jackson, Mrs C.	Dundee 29A
Horne, A.M.	Falkirk 22A	Jackson, J.	Duns 5B
Horne, D.A.	Ross 39A	Jackson, J.A.	Hamilton 17A-22
Horsburgh, A.G.	England 47A	Jackson, W.	Glasgow 16A-12
Horsburgh, G.E.	Irv'/K'marnock 11A	Jaffrey, Mrs A.	Buchan 34A
Hosain, S.	Irv'/K'marnock 11A	Jamieson, D.B.	Dundee 29A
Hosie, J.	List 6-H	Jamieson, Mrs E.M.M.	List 6-I
Houghton, Mrs C.	Angus 30A	Jamieson, G.D.	Edinburgh 1B
Houston, A.M.	Perth 28B	Jamieson, G.T.	Stirling 23B
Houston, Miss E.W.	Dumbarton 18A	Jamieson, Mrs H.E.	Lanark 13A
Houston, G.R.	Lanark 13A	Jamieson, J.	Stirling 23B
Houston, P.M.	Dumbarton 18B	Jamieson, R.C.	Irv'/K'marnock 11B
Houston, T.C.	Glasgow 16A-116	Jarvie, J.W.	St Andrews 26A
		Jarvie, T.W.	Irv'/K'marnock 11A

Jeffrey, E.W.S.	Edinburgh 1B		
Jeffrey, K.	St Andrews 26A		
Jeffrey, S.D.	Buchan 34B		
Jenkins, G.F.C.	Dunfermline 24A		
Jenkinson, J.J.	Falkirk 22A		
Jessamine, A.L.	Dunfermline 24A		
Job, A.J.	Kirkcaldy 25A		
Johnson, C.I.W.	Greenock 15A		
Johnston, C.D.	List 6-L		
Johnston, J.	Dum'/K'cudbright 8B		
Johnston, J.P.N.	Hamilton 17A-15		
Johnston, K.L.	Ayr 10B		
Johnston, Miss M.H.	Glasgow 16A-95		
Johnston, R.W.M.	Glasgow 16B		
Johnston, T.N.	Edinburgh 1A-65		
Johnston, W.R.	Ardrossan 12A		
Johnston, W.B.	Edinburgh 1B		
Johnstone, B.	Lochaber 38A		
Johnstone, D.	List 6-R		
Johnstone, D.B.	List 6-I		
Johnstone, H.M.J.	Glasgow 16B		
Johnstone, M.E.	Glasgow 16A-28		
Johnstone, R.	List 6-I		
Johnstone, R.	Caithness 41A		
Johnstone, W.	Aberdeen 31B		
Jolly, A.J.	England 47B		
Jolly, J.	Glasgow 16B		
Jones, Mrs A.M.	List 6-I		
Jones, E.G.	Glasgow 16B		
Jones, J.D.	List 6-R		
Jones, J.O.	Glasgow 16A-97		
Jones, P.H.	Lanark 13B		
Jones, R.	Ross 39A		
Jones, R.A.	Gordon 33B		
Jones, W.	Angus 30B		
Jones, W.G.	Ayr 10A		
Kant, E.W.	Edinburgh 1B		
Kavanagh, J.A.	Glasgow 16A-32		
Kay, D.	Paisley 14A		
Kay, Miss E.	Dundee 29A		
Keating, Mrs G.J.	Edinburgh 1A-39		
Keddie, D.A.	Glasgow 16A-99		
Keil, A.H.	Edinburgh 1A-71		
Keith, D.	Angus 30B		
Kellas, D.J.	Dunoon 20A		
Kellet, J.M.	Melrose/Peebles 4B		
Kellock, C.N.	Falkirk 22B		
Kelly, A.F.	Edinburgh 1A-1		
Kelly, E.R.	Edinburgh 1B		
Kelly, Miss I.J.M.	Greenock 15A		
Kelly, T.A.D.	Irvine/Kilmarnock 11B		
Kelly, T.C.	Perth 28B		
Kelly, W.	Dum'/K'cudbright 8A		
Kennedy, D.A.	List 6-R		
Kennedy, G.	Wigtown/Stranraer 9A		
Kennedy, H.M.	List 6-I		
Kennedy, Mrs L.J.	Dundee 29A		
Kennon, S.	Melrose/Peebles 4B		

Phoenix Glass Co.

STAINED GLASS ARTISTS AND RESTORERS

EXPERTS IN CONSERVATION AND PROTECTION OF
STAINED LEADED GLASS (WIRE MESH, LEXAN, PLATE)

0131-557 6132

FREE ESTIMATES   **42 ST MARY STREET, EDINBURGH**

Kenny, Mrs C.G. Duns 5A
Kenny, Miss E. Dunfermline 24A
Kent, A.F.S. Ayr 10B
Kent, R.M. Hamilton 17A-49
Kerr, A. Duns 5B
Kerr, A. Glasgow 16A-35
Kerr, B. Lanark 13A
Kerr, H.F. Aberdeen 31A
Kesting, S.M. Edinburgh 1B
Keyes, Mrs J.A. Orkney 45A
King, C.S. Hamilton 17B
Kingston, D.V.F. Europe 48B
Kinniburgh, Miss E.B. Kincard'/Dee' 32B
Kinnis, R.L. St Andrews 26B
Kinsey, L. Aberdeen 31A
Kirby, P.S. List 6-I
Kirk, W.L. Annan/Eskdale 7B
Kirkland, S. Falkirk 22A
Kirkpatrick, Miss A.H. Shetland 46B
Kirkwood, G. List 6-I
Kirkwood, H. Ardrossan 12B
Knight, B. Ardrossan 12A
Knox, J.W. Dunkeld/Meigle 27B
Knox, R.A. Shetland 46A

Lacey, E.R. Inverness 37B
Lacy, D.W. Irv'/K'marnock 11A
Lafferty, J.M.M. Ardrossan 12A
Laidlaw, J.J. Dundee 29B
Laidlaw, V.W.N. Edinburgh 1A-72
Laing, D.J.H. St Andrews 26A
Laing, I.A. Glasgow 16A-2
Laing, W.F. Melrose/Peebles 4B
Lamb, A.D. Ardrossan 12B
Lamb, A.H.W. Lochaber 38A
Lambie, A.E. List 6-H
Lamont, A. Lorn/Mull 21B
Lamont, A.D. Edinburgh 1B
(Lamont, S.J. Europe 48)
Landels, J. Stirling 23A
Lane, Ms C.M. Irv'/K'marnock 11B
Lang, Miss I.P. Dunoon 20A
Langlands, C.H. Glasgow 16B
Law, A. St Andrews 26B
Lawrie, B.B. Moray 35A
Lawrie, R.M. List 6-I
Lawson, A.H. Dumbarton 18B
Lawson, D.G. Perth 28A
Lawson, J.B. Perth 28B
Lawson, K.C. Edinburgh 1B
Lawson, R.G. Perth 28B
Learmonth, A.J. Hamilton 17B
Learmonth, W. St Andrews 26B
Leask, Mrs R.M. Glasgow 16B
Leckie, J.L. List 6-I
Ledgard, J.C. Gordon 33B
Lees, A.P. Dumbarton 18A
Legge, Mrs R. South Argyll 19A

Leishman, J.S. Dum'/K'cudbright 8B
Leitch, D.G. Edinburgh 1A-3
Leitch, Mrs M. Paisley 14A
Lennox, L.I. Kincard'/Deeside 32A
Levison, C.L. Glasgow 16B
Levison, L.D. Lothian 3B
Levison, Mrs M.I. List 6-H
Lewis, E.M.H. Glasgow 18B
Liddell, M. Glasgow 16B
Liddell, Miss M. Ross 39B
Liddiard, F.G.B. List 6-I
Lillie, Mrs F.L. Orkney 45A
Lincoln, J. Stirling 23A
Lind, G.K. Annan/Eskdale 7A
Lind, M.J. South Argyll 19A
Lindsay, D.G. Duns 5A
Lindsay, J.A. List 6-R
Lindsay, W.D. Glasgow 16A-15
Lister, D. Gordon 33B
Lithgow, Mrs A.R. Lothian 3A
Lithgow, T. St Andrews 26B
Livesley, A. Inverness 37B
Lloyd, J.M. Glasgow 16A-69
Lochrie, J.S. Ayr 10A
Locke, D. Glasgow 16A-50
Lodge, B.P. Glasgow 16A-83
Logan, Mrs A.T. Edinburgh 1A-85
Logan, R.J.V. Inverness 37B
Logan, T.M. List 6-I
Longmuir, T.G. Gordon 33A
Longmuir, W. Jedburgh 6B
Low, Mrs N. Hamilton 17A-69
Low, J.E.S. Dunkeld/Meigle 27B
Lowe, E. Paisley 14B
Lugton, G.L. England 47B
Lunan, D.W. Glasgow 16B
Lunn, D. England 47A
Lusk, A.S. Hamilton 17A-33
Lyall, D. Edinburgh 1B
Lyall, J.E. List 6-R
Lyall, M.G. Hamilton 17A-80
Lynn, Mrs J. List 6-H
Lynn, R. Ayr 10A
Lyon, B.A. Buchan 34A
Lyon, D.H.S. Edinburgh 1B

McAdam, D.J. Glasgow 16A-14
McAlister, D.J.B. D'keld/Meigle 27B
MacAlister, Mrs E.E. Gordon 33A
Macallan, G.B. Gordon 33B
MacAlpine, A.G. List 6-R
McAlpine, J. Hamilton 17A-66
McAlpine, R.H.M. Irv'/K'nock 11B
McAlpine, R.J. Kirkcaldy 25B
McAreavey, W. Glasgow 16B
MacArthur, A. List 6-R
Macarthur, A.J. Lochcarron/Skye 42B
Macarthur, J.M.M. Glasgow 16B
Macarthur, Ms M. Stirling 23A

Macaskill, D. Glasgow 16B
Macaskill, D. Inverness 37B
Macaskill, Mrs M. Glasgow 16B
McAspurren, A.T. Ardrossan 12A
Macaulay, A.H. Moray 35B
Macaulay, D. Lewis 44B
Macaulay, G. Falkirk 22A
MacBain, F.J. Lewis 44A
MacBain, I.W. Glasgow 16B
McCabe, G. Hamilton 17B
McCafferty, A. Orkney 45A
McCallum, A.D. Ardrossan 12A
McCallum, J. Falkirk 22B
McCallum, J. Gordon 33A
McCance, A. Ardrossan 12A
McCann, G.McD. Mel'/Peebles 4B
McCartney, A.C. St Andrews 26B
McCaskill, G.I.L. List 6-H
McClenaghan, L.P. Buchan 34A
MacColl, J. Paisley 14B
MacColl, J.C. Paisley 14B
McConnell, R. Jedburgh 6B
McCool, Mrs A.C. Paisley 14A
McCorkindale, D.G.B. Dunf'line 24A
McCormick, A.F. Perth 28B
McCormick, J.A. Lorn/Mull 21A
MacCormick, Ms M.G. Stirling 23A
McCormick, W.C. Lanark 13B
McCracken, G.A. Ardrossan 12A
McCreadie, D.W. Wigtown/Stran' 9B
McCree, I.W. Sutherland 40A
McCrum, R. Angus 30A
McCulloch, A.J.R. L'carron/Skye 42A
McCulloch, J.D. Irv'/K'marnock 11A
McCulloch, W.B. Europe 48A
McCutcheon, G.A. List 6-R
McDonald, A. Paisley 14B
Macdonald, A. Paisley 14A
Macdonald, A. Lewis 44B
MacDonald, A. Uist 43B
McDonald, A.D. St Andrews 26A
MacDonald, A.I. Inverness 37A
Macdonald, C.D. Glasgow 16A-20
Macdonald, D.M. List 6-R
Macdonald, F.A.J. Edinburgh 1B
MacDonald, I. L'carron/Skye 42A
MacDonald, I.D. Orkney 45A
McDonald, I.J.M. Kirkcaldy 25B
Macdonald, I.U. Ayr 10B
Macdonald, J. List 6-R
Macdonald, J. Lewis 44B
Macdonald J. Lochcarron/Skye 42A
McDonald, J.A. Hamilton 17B
Macdonald, I.M.M. Lewis 44A
MacDonald, J.F. D'keld/Meigle 27B
McDonald, J.I.H. Edinburgh 1B
MacDonald, J.M. Irv'/K'nock 11B
MacDonald, J.W. Perth 28A
MacDonald, K. Glasgow 16A-152

MacDonald, K.	L'carron/Skye 42B	McIntosh, C.G.	Stirling 23A	MacKichan, A.J.	Glasgow 16A-74
Macdonald, M.	Buchan 34A	McIntosh, H.	Edinburgh 1B	Mackie, J.F.	Sutherland 40A
MacDonald, Ms M.	Hamilton 17A-81	McIntosh, H.N.M.	Stirling 23B	Mackie, S.G.	Edinburgh 1B
McDonald, Ms M.	Lothian 3A	McIntyre, A.G.	Greenock 15A	McKillop, A.	Kincard'/Deeside 32A
MacDonald M.C.	Buchan 34A	McIntyre, G.	Dumbarton 18A	McKillop, K.	Glasgow 16A-119
Macdonald, M.E.	Glasgow 16B	McIntyre, G.J.	Stirling 23A	McKimmon, E.G.	Falkirk 22A
Macdonald, P.J.	Edinburgh 1A-76	McIntyre, J.	Edinburgh 1B	MacKinnon, A.W.	Angus 30B
MacDonald, R.I.T.	Glasgow 16A-131	McIntyre, J.A.	Dumbarton 18B	Mackinnon, C.	Glasgow 16A-49
McDonald, R.J.	Glasgow 16B	Macintyre, T.	Paisley 14A	MacKinnon, C.M.	Glasgow 16A-23
Macdonald, R.M.	List 6-R	Macintyre, W.J.	St Andrews 26B	Mackinnon, D.	L'carron/Skye 42B
McDonald, T.	Jedburgh 6A	Maciver, N.	Aberdeen 31A	McKinnon, Miss E.W.	List 6-L
McDonald, W.G.	Falkirk 22B	MacIver, N.	Uist 43A	McKinnon, Mrs L.F.	Glasgow 16A-25
Macdonald, W.J.	Edinburgh 1B	McIvor, Miss A.	South Argyll 19A	MacKinnon, N.	Falkirk 22A
McDonald, W.J.G.	Edinburgh 1B	Mack, Miss E.	Dum'/K'cudbright 8A	Mackinnon, R.M.	Ross 39B
Macdonald, W.U.	Perth 28B	Mack, J.C.	Gordon 33A	Mackinnon, T.J.R.	Uist 43A
Macdonell, A.W.	Lothian 3B	Mack, K.L.	Lothian 3A	McLachlan, D.	Paisley 14B
MacDougall, A.	L'carron/Skye 42B	McKaig, W.G.	Falkirk 22A	McLachlan, D.N.	Paisley 14A
MacDougall, Miss M.I.	Dundee 29A	McKane, W.	St Andrews 26B	McLachlan, E.	Glasgow 16A-56
Macdougall, M.M.	Mel'/Peebles 4A	MacKay, A.H.	Glasgow 16A-104	McLachlan, F.C.	Greenock 15B
McDowall, R.J.	Falkirk 22B	MacKay, D.	Dum'/K'cudbright 8B	McLachlan, I.K.	Ayr 10A
McDowall, W.B.	Hamilton 17A-79	McKay, D.M.	Annan'/Eskdale 7A	McLachlan, T.A.	Glasgow 16A-24
McDowell, B.	Edinburgh 1B	MacKay, G.C.	Paisley 14A	Maclagan, D.W.	Ardrossan 12B
McEnhill, P.	England 47B	McKay, J.R.	Ardrossan 12B	MacLaine, Mrs M.	Paisley 14A
MacEwan D.G.	St Andrews 26A	Mackay, K.J.	Edinburgh 1A-81	McLaren, D.M.	Glasgow 16B
MacEwan, J.A.I.	Abernethy 36A	McKay, Mrs M.	Buchan 34A	McLaren, J.R.	Aberdeen 31A
MacFadyen, Mrs A.M.	Glasgow 16B	Mackay, Mrs M.H.	Ardrossan 12A	Maclaren, W.B.	Falkirk 22B
McFadyen, G.J.	St Andrews 26B	Mackay, M.M.	Aberdeen 31B	McLarty, R.R.	Glasgow 16A-132
McFadzean, I.	Dumbarton 18B	McKay, Mrs V.C.C.	Dunfermline 24A	McLauchlan, Mrs M.C.	Ayr 10A
Macfarlane, A.J.C.	List 6-H	McKean, A.T.	Gordon 33A	MacLaughlan, G.	Edinburgh 1A-56
Macfarlane, D.	List 6-H	McKean, D.	List 6-H	McLay, A.D.	Glasgow 16A-138
MacFarlane, D.C.	Mel'/Peebles 4B	McKean, M.J.	List 6-I	Maclean, Mrs A.G.	Edinburgh 1B
Macfarlane, J.	Dunoon 20A	MacKechnie, J.M.	Lorn/Mull 21B	MacLean, A.T.	Greenock 15A
Macfarlane, K.	List 6-H	McKee, N.B.	Hamilton 17A-78	MacLean, E.	Glasgow 16A-101
Macfarlane, P.T.	England 47B	McKenna, E.C.	Aberdeen 31A	MacLean, Ms G.P.	West Lothian 2A
McFarlane, R.G.	Glasgow 16A-107	McKenna, S.S.	Edinburgh 1A-51	MacLean, H.A.M.	Lochaber 38B
Macfarlane, T.G.	Glasgow 16B	McKenzie, A.	Hamilton 17A-10	MacLean, I.A.	Aberdeen 31A
Macfarlane, W.J.E.	Dumbarton 18B	Mackenzie, A.C.	St Andrews 26B	McLean, J.	West Lothian 2A
McGill, Ms S.	Hamilton 17A-77	Mackenzie, A.I.	Ross 39B	McLean, J.	Glasgow 16B
McGill, T.W.	Wigtown/Stran' 9B	Mackenzie, C.	Lothian 3A	Maclean, J.P.	Kirkcaldy 25A
McGillivray, A.G.	Edinburgh 1B	McKenzie, D.M.	Kirkcaldy 25B	Maclean, M.	Glasgow 16A-58
McGlynn, Mrs M.	Glasgow 16A-77	MacKenzie, D.W.	Perth 28B	MacLean, Miss M.A.	Edinburgh 1B
McGowan, A.T.B.	Ross 39B	Mackenzie, G.R.	Dundee 29A	McLean, Ms M.G.	Annan'/Eskdale 7B
Macgregor, A.	Buchan 34A	Mackenzie, G.R.R.	Dundee 29B	MacLean, N.R.	Perth 28B
McGregor, A.G.C.	Edinburgh 1A-42	Mackenzie, I.	Dunoon 20B	McLean-Foreman, A.	List 6-L
McGregor, D.J.	St Andrews 26B	Mackenzie, I.C.	Glasgow 16A-78	McLeish, D.N.	Perth 28B
MacGregor, J.	Ross 39A	Mackenzie, I.M.	Dumbarton 18B	McLeish, R.S.	Gordon 33B
McGregor, J.B.	Glasgow 16A-149	Mackenzie, J.A.R.	St Andrews 26B	McLellan, A.R.C.	Edinburgh 1A-70
MacGregor, Miss M.S.	Edinburgh 1B	Mackenzie, J.G.	England 47A	MacLennan, A.J.	Ross 39B
MacGregor, N.I.M.	Gordon 33A	Mackenzie, K.	Hamilton 17A-39	MacLennan, D.A.	Lewis 44A
McGregor, T.S.	Edinburgh 1B	MacKenzie, K.I.	Europe 48A	Maclennan, W.	Ross 39B
McGregor, W.	Perth 28A	McKenzie, M.G.	Angus 30B	Macleod, A.D.	Perth 28A
McGurk, A.F.	Ardrossan 12A	McKenzie, Miss M.O.	Dunoon 20B	Macleod, A.J.	Europe 48B
McHaffie, R.D.	Jedburgh 6A	Mackenzie, R.A.	Europe 48A	Macleod, A.M.	Duns 5B
McIlroy, A.M.	List 6-R	McKenzie, R.D.	Hamilton 17A-42	MacLeod, C.A.	England 47B
McIlroy, I.	Wigtown/Stranraer 9A	Mackenzie, R.K.	Dunoon 20A	MacLeod, D.	Dunkeld/Meigle 27A
McIndoe, J.H.	England 47B	MacKenzie, R.P.	Dunfermline 24B	MacLeod, D.	L'carron/Skye 42B
MacInnes, D.	Uist 43B	Mackenzie, S.L.	Buchan 34B	MacLeod, D.C.	Dundee 29B
MacInnes, D.M.	Glasgow 16A-123	McKenzie, W.M.	Dum'/K'cud 8B	MacLeod, I.	Ardrossan 12A
McInnes, I.M.S.	Glasgow 16A-52	McKeown, P.	Glasgow 16B		

MacLeod, I.I.S.	Angus 30B	MacPherson, D.	Inverness 37A	Marten, Mrs S.	England 47A
Macleod, J.	Irv/K'marnock 11A	McPherson, D.C.	Hamilton 17A-30	Martin, A.M.	England 47B
McLeod, J.	Ross 39B	Macpherson, D.J.	Annan'/Esk' 7B	Martin, D.N.	Buchan 34A
MacLeod, K.	Kincard'/Deeside 32B	Macpherson, F.	List 6-R	Martin, F.	Dunkeld/Meigle 27B
Macleod, K.D.	Ross 39A	MacPherson, G.C.	List 6-I	Martin, G.M.	Lochcarron/Skye 42A
MacLeod, M.	Irv'/K'marnock 11A	MacPherson, J.	Sutherland 40A	Martin, J.	Hamilton 17B
MacLeod, N.	South Argyll 19A	Macpherson, K.J.	Uist 43A	Martin, R.A.K.	Irv'/K'marnock 11A
McLeod, N.	Kirkcaldy 25B	Macpherson, N.J.	D'keld/Meigle 27B	Martindale, J.P.F.	Glasgow 16A-136
McLeod, R.	Edinburgh 1B	McPherson, S.M.	Edinburgh 1A-73	Massie, R.W.	Dundee 29A
MacLeod, R.	South Argyll 19A	Macpherson, S.M.	Dunfermline 24B	Masson, J.D.	List 6-I
MacLeod, R.A.R.	England 47B	McPherson, W.	Falkirk 22A	Mathers, D.L.	Falkirk 22B
MacLeod, R.N.	England 47B	MacQuarrie, D.A.	Lochaber 38A	Mathers, J.A.C.	Paisley 14B
Macleod, W.	Lewis 44A	McQuarrie, I.A.	Edinburgh 1A-11	Matheson, Mrs A.P.	Lothian 3A
MacLeod, W.J.	Glasgow 16B	MacQuarrie, S.	Glasgow 16B	Matheson, I.G.	List 6-I
MacLeod-Mair, A.	Falkirk 22A	McQuilken, J.E.	Perth 28B	Matheson, J.G.	L'carron/Skye 42B
McLuskey, J.F.	List 6-H	Macrae, D.A.	Uist 43B	Mathew, J.G.	Stirling 23A
McMahon, Miss E.J.	Paisley 14A	MacRae, Mrs E.H.	Stirling 23B	Mathieson, A.R.	Edinburgh 1B
McMahon, J.K.S.	Edinburgh 1A-61	MacRae, G.	Stirling 23A	Mathieson, Mrs F.M.	Edinburgh 1A-8
MacMahon, Mrs J.P.H.	Glasgow 16A-62	Macrae, Mrs J.	Glasgow 16A-92	Matthews, J.C.	Glasgow 16A-121
McMahon, R.J.	Lanark 13B	McRae, M.H.	Stirling 23B	Maule-Brown, R.	Lothian 3B
McMillan, C.D.	Moray 35A	Macrae, N.C.	Lothian 3B	Maxton, R.M.	Falkirk 22B
McMillan, Mrs E.F.	Dundee 29A	MacRae, N.I.	Inverness 37A	Maxwell, I.D.	Edinburgh 1A-40
Macmillan, G.	Edinburgh 1A-34	MacRitchie, I.A.M.	Inverness 37B	May, A.	Glasgow 16A-37
McMillan, H.G.	Dundee 29B	MacRitchie, M.	Lewis 44B	Mayes, R.	Ayr 10A
MacMillan, J.	Kirkcaldy 25A	McRoberts, T.D.	Moray 35A	Mayne, K.	Hamilton 17A-38
MacMillan, Mrs R.M.	Perth 28B	MacSween, D.A.	Ross 39A	Mead, J.M.	Wigtown/Stran' 9A
McMillan, S.	Dundee 29A	MacSween, N.	Lewis 44B	Meager, P.	St Andrews 26B
Macmillan, W.B.R.	Edinburgh 1B	MacVicar, K.	Dunkeld/Meigle 27B	Mealyea, H.B.	Ayr 10A
McMillan, W.J.	Shetland 46A	McWhirter, T.M.	Wigtown/Stran' 9A	Mechie, W.M.	List 6-R
MacMillan, W.M.	Annan'/Eskdale 7B	McWilliam, A.	Glasgow 16A-151	Meikle, Mrs A.A.	Lanark 13A
McMullin, J.A.	Falkirk 22B	McWilliam, S.W.	List 6-R	Mellis, R.J.	Gordon 33B
MacMurchie, Miss F.L.	Edinburgh 1A-29	McWilliam, T.M.	Ross 39A	Melrose, J.H.L.	Hamilton 17B
McNab, D.G.	Ayr 10A	Mailer, C.	Falkirk 22A	Melville, D.D.	Dum'/K'cudbright 8A
MacNab, H.S.D.	St Andrews 26B	Main, A.	Aberdeen 31B	Merchant, M.C.	Gordon 33A
McNab, J.L.	Orkney 45A	Main, A.W.A.	List 6-I	Meredith, I.	List 6-I
Macnab, S.G.	List 6-R	Main, D.M.	Kin'/Deeside 32A	Middleton, J.R.H.	Edinburgh 1A-22
McNaught, N.A.	Ayr 10A	Mair, J.	List 6-I	Middleton, P.	Edinburgh 1A-20
McNaught, S.M.	Kirkcaldy 25A	Mair, M.V.A.	Dundee 29A	Mill, D.	Greenock 15A
McNaughtan, J.	Irv'/K'marnock 11A	Majcher, P.L.	England 47B	Mill, J.S.	List 6-I
McNaughton, D.J.H.	Perth 28B	Malcolm, A.	Inverness 37A	Millar, A.E.	Perth 28B
Macnaughton, G.F.H.	Orkney 45A	Malcolm, J.W.	List 6-H	Millar, A.M.	Perth 28B
Macnaughton, J.A.	Glasgow 16B	Malcolm, M.	Lothian 3A	Millar, D.A.R.	Glasgow 16B
Macnee, I.	Caithness 41A	Malloch, P.R.M.	Stirling 23A	Millar, J.	Glasgow 16B
McNeil, J.N.R.	Stirling 23A	Malloch, R.J.	Dum'/K'cudbright 8A	Millar, J.L.	Lochaber 38B
MacNeil, T.	Lewis 44A	Mann, J.T.	Sutherland 40A	Millar, Mrs J.M.	List 6-H
McNeill, C.C.	Europe 48B	Manners, S.	Edinburgh 1A-86	Millar, Miss M.R.M.	Lorn/Mull 21A
McNicol, B.	Jedburgh 6A	Manson, Mrs E.	Greenock 15A	Miller, A.	Kirkcaldy 25A
McNidder, R.H.	Ayr 10B	Manson, I.A.	Europe 48A	Miller, C.W.	Dundee 29B
McPake, J.L.	Hamilton 17A-34	Manson, J.A.	Lothian 3A	Miller, H.G.	Dunoon 20B
McPake, J.M.	Edinburgh 1A-48	Manson, Mrs N.	West Lothian 2B	Miller, Mrs I.B.	List 6-H
McPhail, A.M.	Ayr 10A	Mappin, M.G.	Caithness 41B	Miller, I.D.	List 6-R
McPhail, P.	St Andrews 26B	Marr, E.R.	Paisley 14B	Miller, I.H.	Dumbarton 18A
McPhee, D.C.	Edinburgh 1B	Marr, I.	List 6-I	Miller, J.D.	Glasgow 16A-61
MacPhee, D.P.	Perth 28B	Marshall, A.S.	West Lothian 2A	Miller, J.G.	Greenock 15A
MacPherson, A.J.	Stirling 23A	Marshall, Mrs F.	Lorn/Mull 21A	Miller, J.R.	Dum'/K'cudbright 8B
MacPherson, A.S.	Edinburgh 1B	Marshall, F.J.	Greenock 15B	Miller, W.B.	Moray 35B
MacPherson, C.C.	Edinburgh 1B	Marshall, J.S.	Dunoon 20B	Milligan, R.	Gordon 33B
		Marshall, J.S.	List 6-H	Milloy, A.M.	England 47B
		Marshall, T.E.	Paisley 14A	Mills, A.	List 6-I

Mills, P.W.   England 47B
Milne, R.B.   Annan'/Eskdale
Milroy, T.   Dundee 29B
Milton, A.L.   England 47B
Milton, E.G.   Angus 30B
Mirrilees, J.B.   Aberdeen 31B
Mitchell, A.B.   Dunfermline 24A
Mitchell, A.S.   List 6-R
Mitchell, D.   Glasgow 16B
Mitchell, D.R.   Ardrossan 12A
Mitchell, J.   Lothian 3A
Mitchell, J.   Dundee 29B
Mitchell, Miss S.M.   Ayr 10B
Moffat, R.   Aberdeen 31A
Moffat, T.   Dunfermline 24A
Moffet, J.R.   Paisley 14B
Moir, I.A.   Edinburgh 1B
Monro, G.D.   List 6-H
Montgomerie, Miss J.B.   Angus 30A
Montgomery, D.   South Argyll 19A
Montgomery, R.A.   Greenock 15B
Moore, Miss A.A.   Hamilton 17A-12
Moore, J.W.   West Lothian 2B
Moore, Ms N.   Hamilton 17A-48
Moore, W.H.   Melrose/Peebles 4B
Morrice, A.A.   List 6-I
Morrice, A.M.   Angus 30B
Morrice, C.S.   West Lothian 2B
Morrice, W.G.   Edinburgh 1B
Morris, G.C.   List 6-H
Morris, W.   Glasgow 16A-65
Morrison, A.   Lewis 44A
Morrison, A.   Lewis 44A
Morrison, A.H.   Paisley 14A
Morrison, A.W.   South Argyll 19B
Morrison, Mrs C.M.   Kirkcaldy 25A
Morrison, D.   Lochcarron/Skye 42A
Morrison, D.J.   Uist 43B
Morrison, H.   Inverness 37B
Morrison, I.   Glasgow 16A-85
Morrison, I.C.   West Lothian 2A
Morrison, J.G.   Dum'/Kircudbright 8B
Morrison, Mrs M.B.   Edinburgh 1B
Morrison, R.   Glasgow 16A-79
Morrison, R.   Ross 39A
Morton, A.J.   Melrose/Peebles 4B
Morton, A.Q.   Dumbarton 18B
Morton, A.R.   Edinburgh 1B
Morton, Mrs G.   Melrose/Peebles 4B
Morton, R.C.M.   Edinburgh 1B
Morton, T.   Glasgow 16B
Mowat, G.M.   Dundee 29B
Moyes, A.   West Lothian 2B
Muckart, G.W.M.   Aberdeen 31A
Muir, A.   Uist 43B
Muir, Miss E.D.   Stirling 23A
Muir, F.C.   Glasgow 16B
Muir, Miss M.A.   Lanark 13A
Munro, A.   Kirkcaldy 25B
Munro, A.W.   List 6-I
Munro, D.P.   Dumbarton 18B
Munro, Mrs F.J.   Aberdeen 31A
Munro, Miss G.   Aberdeen 31B
Munro, G.A.M.   Edinburgh 1B
Munro, J.A.   Greenock 15A
Munro, J.P.L.   Perth 28A
Munro, J.R.   Edinburgh 1A-26
Munro, Mrs M.   Wigtown/Stran' 9B
Munro, Ms S.   Dunfermline 24A
Munroe, H.   Falkirk 22B
Munson, Ms W.   Shetland 46A
Munton, J.G.   Hamilton 17B
Murdoch, I.C.   Hamilton 17A-82
Murdoch, J.A.H.   Lorn and Mull 21A
Murdoch, W.M.   Hamilton 17A-52

Murison, W.G.   Edinburgh 1B
Murning, J.   Dunoon 20A
Murray, A.   Aberdeen 31A
Murray, B.I.   Dunkeld/Meigle 27A
Murray, D.   Moray 35B
Murray, D.M.   List 6-R
Murray, D.R.   Europe 48A
Murray, E.J.   Falkirk 22B
Murray, G.M.   Glasgow 16A-130
Murray, R.N.G.   West Lothian 2B
Murrie, J.   Edinburgh 1B
Musgrave, C.W.   Jerusalem 49
Myers, F.   Glasgow 16B

Neill, B.F.   Melrose/Peebles 4A
Neilson, P.   Edinburgh 1A-74
Neilson, R.   Buchan 34A
Nelson, Mrs G.   West Lothian 2B
Nelson, J.   List 6-H
Nelson, J.R.   Hamilton 17A-20
Nelson, R.C.   Lorn and Mull 21A
Nelson, T.   Glasgow 16A-34
Ness, D.T.   Ayr 10A
Newell, Mrs A.M.   Edinburgh 1B
Newell, J.P.   Edinburgh 1B
Newlands, G.M.   Glasgow 16B
Nicholas, M.S.   Lothian 3A
Nicholson, T.S.   Duns 5A
Nicholson, W.   Kincard'/Deeside 32B
Nicol, D.A.O.   Edinburgh 1B
Nicol, D.M.   Glasgow 16A-116
Nicol, G.G.   Dunfermline 24A
Nicol, J.C.   Stirling 23A
Nicol, R.M.   St Andrews 26B
Nicol, Mrs S.E.C.   Edinburgh 1A-18
Nicolson, J.M.   L'carron/Skye 42A
Nimmo, P.W.   Glasgow 16A-84
Ninian, Ms E.   Paisley 14A
Nisbet, G.C.   Perth 28A
Niven, H.   Hamilton 17B
Niven, W.W.   Ross 39B
Noble, A.B.   Buchan 34A
Noble, G.S.   Buchan 34B
Norman, Miss N.M.   Mel'/Peebles 4A
Norrie, G.   Angus 30A
Norwood, D.W.   England 47B
Notman, J.R.   Kincard'/Deeside 32A

O'Brien, H.   Gordon 33A
O'Donnell, C.T.   List 6-I
Ogilvie, Mrs C.   Falkirk 22A
Ogilvie, K.G.   List 6-H
Ogilvy, O.M.   Wigtown/Stran' 9B
Ogston, D.D.   Perth 28A
Ogston, E.J.   Shetland 46A
O'Leary, T.   Paisley 14B
Oliver, G.   Shetland 46A
Olsen, Miss H.C.   Sutherland 40A
O'Neill, J.C.   Edinburgh 1B
Ord, J.K.   St Andrews 26B
Ormiston, H.C.   Dunkeld/Meigle 27A
Orr, J.M.   Dunfermline 24B
Orrock, A.A.   Stirling 23B
Osbeck, J.R.   Aberdeen 31A
Ostler, J.H.   List 6-I
Oswald, J.   Perth 28A
Ott, Mrs V.J.   Dum'/Kirkcudbright 8A
Ovens, S.B.   Stirling 23B
Owen, Mrs C.W.   List 6-I
Owen, J.J.C.   Annandale/Eskdale 7B
Oxburgh, B.H.   Ardrossan 12A

Pacitti, S.A.   Lanark 13A
Page, J.R.   Europe 48A
Page, R.   Edinburgh 1B

Palmer, G.R.   Edinburgh 1A-83
Palmer, S.W.   Paisley 14B
Park, C.D.   Glasgow 16A-66
Park, P.B.   Dunfermline 24A
Parker, A.H.   List 6-I
Parker, N.   Aberdeen 31A
Paterson, A.E.   Dunfermline 24A
Paterson, D.S.   Ardrossan 12A
Paterson, I.M.   Edinburgh 1B
Paterson, J.H.   Ardrossan 12B
Paterson, J.L.   West Lothian 2A
Paterson, J.M.K.   Edinburgh 1B
Paterson, J.W.   Ayr 10A
Paterson, Mrs M.   Kirkcaldy 25A
Paterson, S.J.   Hamilton 17A-21
Paterson, W.   Duns 5B
Patience, D.   Irv'/K'marnock 11B
Paton, A.S.   Hamilton 17A-35
Paton, I.F.   St Andrews 26A
Paton, J.H.   South Argyll 19A
Paton, Miss M.J.   St Andrews 26A
Patterson, J.M.   Edinburgh 1B
Patterson, J.W.   St Andrews 26B
Pattison, K.J.   Ross 39A
Paul, Miss A.   Dumbarton 18B
Paul, I.   Falkirk 22B
Peat, S.W.   List 6-I
Penman, I.D.   Edinburgh 1A-38
Penny, R.F.   Dunkeld/Meigle 27A
Perry, J.B.   Angus 30B
Peterkin, W.N.   List 6-R
Petrie, I.D.   Dundee 29A
Petrie, K.L.   Aberdeen 31A
Petty, P.W.P.   List 6-H
Philip, A.J.   Glasgow 16A-125
Philip, D.S.   Europe 48B
Philip, G.M.   Glasgow 16B
Philip, J.   Edinburgh 1B
Philip, M.R.   Falkirk 22A
Philip, Miss C.   Edinburgh 1B
Philp, R.A.   Glasgow 16B
Pickering, J.M.   Perth 28A
Pieterse, B.   Angus 30A
Pirie, D.   Lothian 3A
Pitkeathly, D.G.   Buchan 34A
Pitkeathly, T.C.   Europe 48A
Pittendreigh, I.   Lochaber 38A
Plate, Miss M.A.G.   Edinburgh 1B
Pogue, V.C.   Dunfermline 24B
Pollock, T.L.   Hamilton 17A-2
Pollock, W.   Lorn/Mull 21B
Poole, Mrs A.M.   Moray 35A
Pope, D.H.N.   Hamilton 17A-61
Portchmouth, R.J.   St Andrews 26B
Porteous, A.   Greenock 15B
Porteous, J.K.   St Andrews 26B
Porteous, N.W.   Edinburgh 1B
Porter, J.C.   Moray 35B
Porter, R.   Glasgow 16B
Pot, J.   Europe 48A
Povey, J.M.   West Lothian 2A
Powrie, J.E.   Dundee 29B
Prentice, D.K.   Inverness 37B
Prentice, G.   Paisley 14B
Preston, T.   West Lothian 2A
Price, Mrs A.E.   Orkney 45A
Price, P.O.   Hamilton 17B
Provan, I.W.   List 6-I
Pryce, S.F.A.   Stirling 23B
Pryde, W.K.   St Andrews 26A
Purves, J.P.S.   Stirling 23A
Purves, J.S.   Glasgow 16A-73
Pyper, J.S.   Greenock 15B

Quigley, Mrs B.D.   List 6-I

Raby, S.	Hamilton 17A-84	Robertson, I.M.	Dunkeld/Meigle 27B	Scott, J.	Kincard'/Deeside 32A
Rae, A.W.	Melrose/Peebles 4B	Robertson, I.W.	Dum'/K'cud 8B	Scott, J.F.	Stirling 23B
Rae, D.L.	Edinburgh 1B	Robertson, J.	Lothian 3B	Scott, J.L.	List 6-H
Rae, P.C.	Lochaber 38B	Robertson, J.H.	Inverness 37A	Scott, J.M.	St Andrews 26B
Rae, R.	Dundee 29B	Robertson, J.T.	Moray 35B	Scott, J.W.	Dum'/K'cudbright 8A
Rae, S.M.	Dumbarton 18B	Robertson, M.	Dunkeld/Meigle 27B	Scott, M.	Edinburgh 1B
Raeburn, A.C.	Glasgow 16A-51	Robertson, Miss N.	St Andrews 26B	Scott, R.	Hamilton 17A-6
Raemonn, P.	Europe 48A	Robertson, T.G.M.	St Andrews 26A	Scott, T.T	Irvine/K'marnock 11B
Ramage, A.E.	Dumbarton 18A	Robertson, T.P.	Dundee 29B	Scott, W.D.	Buchan 34B
Ramsay, A.	Lochaber 38A	Robertson, T.R.	Dum'/K'cud 8B	Scoular, J.M.	Stirling 23A
Ramsay, B.	Angus 30A	Robson, G.K.	Dundee 29A	Scoular, S.	Dundee 29B
Ramsay, M.	Dunkeld/Meigle 27A	Rodger, M.A.	Gordon 33B	Scouler, M.D.	Melrose/Peebles 4A
Ramsay, R.J.	Dundee 29A	Rodwell, Mrs A.S.	Greenock 15A	Scouller, H.	List 6-I
Ramsay, W.G.	Glasgow 16B	Rogers, J.M.	Dundee 29B	Scroggie, J.C.	Dundee 29B
Ramsden I.	Ross 39A	Rogerson, S.D.	Hamilton 17B	Seaman, R.S.	Annan'/Eskdale 7A
Randall, D.J.	Buchan 34A	Rollo, G.B.	Moray 35A	Searle, D.C.	Edinburgh 1B
Redmayne, D.	Dunfermline 24A	Rooney, M.I.G.	Angus 30A	Seath, T.J.G.	Lanark 13B
Redmayne, G.	Irv'/K'marnock 11A	Rose, D.S.	Dum'/K'cud 8A	Sefton, H.R.	Aberdeen 31B
Redpath, J.G.	Paisley 14A	Ross, A.C.	Edinburgh 1B	Selfridge, J.	Ardrossan 12B
Reid, A.A.S.	Stirling 23B	Ross, A.C.	Annan'/Eskdale 7B	Sewell, P.M.N.	Stirling 23A
Reid, A.B.	Angus 30B	Ross, Mrs A.J.	List 6-I	Shackleton, S.J.S.	England 47B
Reid, A.D.	Jedburgh 6A	Ross, D.M.	Glasgow 16B	Shackleton, W.	Glasgow 16B
Reid, A.G.	Dunfermline 24A	Ross, D.S.	Buchan 34A	Shanks, N.J.	Glasgow 16B
Reid, D.	Dunfermline 24B	Ross, Ms E.J.B.	Edinburgh 1A-79	Shannon, W.G.	Dunkeld/Meigle 27B
Reid, D.T.	Stirling 23B	Ross, E.J.	Dunfermline 24B	Sharp, A.	Kirkcaldy 25A
Reid, I.M.A.	Glasgow 16B	Ross, Ms F.C.	Ardrossan 12A	Sharp, J.C.	Hamilton 17A-36
Reid, J.	Kirkcaldy 25A	Ross, J.	Glasgow 16B	Sharp, S.	Falkirk 22A
Reid, Miss J.G.	Glasgow 16A-122	Ross, Miss J.	Falkirk 22A	Shaw, A.	List 6-R
Reid, J.K.S.	List 6-R	Ross, J.H.G.	List 6-H	Shaw, A.N.	List 6-I
Reid, M.R.B.C.	Kirkcaldy 25B	Ross, K.R.	Edinburgh 1B	Shaw, C.A.M.	Irv'/K'marnock 11A
Reid, R.G.	Falkirk 22A	Ross, K.W.	Edinburgh 1A-20	Shaw, D.	West Lothian 2A
Reid, S.	Lanark 13A	Ross, M.Z.	St Andrews 26A	Shaw, D.	St Andrews 26B
Reid, W.M.	Europe 48A	Ross, R.A.	List 6-I	Shaw, D.	List 6-H
Reid, W.S.	Edinburgh 1B	Ross, W.B.	Dundee 29A	Shaw, D.W.D.	St Andrews 26B
Rennie, A.M.	England 47B	Roy, A.A.	Caithness 41A	Shedden, J.	Lorn and Mull 21A
Rennie, C.A.J.	Falkirk 22A	Roy, A.J.	St Andrews 26B	Sheppard, M.J.	Wigtown/Stranraer 9A
Rennie, D.B.	Kincard'/Deeside 32B	Roy, I.M.	Ardrossan 12B	Sheret, B.S.	Glasgow 16A-72
Rennie, J.B.	Stirling 23B	Roy, J.	Irv'/K'marnock 11B	Sherrard, H.D.	Dumbarton 18A
Rennie, J.D.	Annan'/Eskdale 7B	Roy, J.A.	Dundee 29A	Sherratt, A.	Paisley 14A
Rennie, Mrs M.	Edinburgh 1A-14	Rule, J.A.	Paisley 14B	Sherry, G.T.	Stirling 23A
Rennie, S.	Angus 30	Rushton, J.	Glasgow 16A-126	Shewan, F.D.F.	Edinburgh 1A-54
Renton, I.P.	Edinburgh 1B	Russell, A.	West Lothian 2B	Shewan, M.R.R.	Perth 28A
Renton, J.P.	Gordon 33A	Russell, A.C.	Angus 30B	Shields, J.M.	Melrose/Peebles 4A
Renwick, C.C.	Glasgow 16A-90	Russell, A.M.	Aberdeen 31B	Shields, R.B.	Dumbarton 18A
Rettie, J.A.	Inverness 37B	Russell, J.	Dunkeld/Meigle 27B	Shirra, J.	Perth 28B
Ribbons, F.	Lothian 3A	Russell, K.G.	Stirling 23A	Silcox, J.R.	Stirling 23B
Richard, Mrs F.	Dunfermline 24A	Russell, P.R.	Ayr 10A	Silver, R.M.	Glasgow 16A-42
Richardson, T.C.	Aberdeen 31A	Rutherford, B.C.	Aberdeen 31A	Sim, J.G.	Edinburgh 1B
Richmond, J.	England 47B			Sime, Mrs C.	Dum'/K'cudbright 8A
Riddell, J.A.	Jedburgh 6A			Simpson, E.V.	Glasgow 16A-19
Riddell, T.S.	West Lothian 2A	Salmond, J.S.	Hamilton 17A-53	Simpson, G.M.	Kirkcaldy 25B
Ridland, A.K.	Edinburgh 1B	Salters, R.B.	St Andrews 26B	Simpson, J.A.	Perth 28B
Risby, Mrs L.	Ardrossan 12B	Samuel, R.	Dunoon 20B	Simpson, J.H.	Greenock 15A
Ritchie, A.	Edinburgh 1A-17	Sanderson, A.M.	Ayr 10A	Simpson, J.H.	Dundee 29A
Ritchie, B.	Perth 28B	Sanderson, W.R.	Lothian 3B	Simpson, N.A.	Glasgow 16B
Ritchie, Mrs C.	Lothian 3A	Sandilands, I.S.	Edinburgh 1B	Simpson, R.R.	Lothian 3A
Ritchie, G.W.M.	Jedburgh 6B	Sangster, E.G.	Stirling 23B	Sinclair, C.A.M.	Edinburgh 1A-59
Ritchie, J.	Aberdeen 31A	Saunders, C.M.	Ayr 10B	Sinclair, D.I.	St Andrews 26B
Ritchie, J.McL.	Lothian 3B	Saunders, K.	Glasgow 16B	Sinclair, J.H.	Dum'/K'cudbright 8A
Ritchie, M.A.	South Argyll 19B	Savage, G.M.A.	Dum'/K'cud 8A	Sinclair, T.S.	Lewis 44A
Ritchie, W.M.	Lochcarron/Skye 42B	Sawers, E.A.H.	Lothian 3B	Skakle, G.S.	Aberdeen 31B
Robb, N.J.	St Andrews 26B	Sawers, H.	List 6-I	Skinner, D.M.	Edinburgh 1B
Robb, R.P.T.	Stirling 23A	Schluter, Miss L.	Hamilton 17A-57	Skinner, S.	Kincard'/Deeside 32B
Robertson, A.	Glasgow 16B	Schofield, M.F.	Edinburgh 1B	Slack, J.W.	Melrose/Peebles 4B
Robertson, A.	Stirling 23B	Scobie, A.J.	Dumbarton 18A	Sloan, J.	Ayr 10A
Robertson, B.	Glasgow 16B	Scotland, R.J.	Moray 35A	Sloan, R.	Perth 28A
Robertson, B.	Europe 48B	Scott, A.D.	Gordon 33B	Sloan, R.P.	Kincard'/Deeside 32A
Robertson, C.	Edinburgh 1A-7	Scott, D.D.	Dumbarton 18A	Slorach, A.	Duns 5B
Robertson, C.	List 6-H	Scott, D.H.	Falkirk 22B	Smart, D.D.	Aberdeen 31A
Robertson, Miss C.	Angus 30A	Scott, D.S.	Dundee 29A	Smart, G.H.	Falkirk 22A
Robertson, D.M.	Ayr 10B	Scott, D.V.	Lochcarron/Skye 42A	Smillie, A.M.	Glasgow 16B
Robertson, E.	West Lothian 2B	Scott, E.M.	Greenock 15B	Smith, A.	Aberdeen 31B
Robertson, Miss E.M.D.	Stirling 23A	Scott, G.G.	Dundee 29A	Smith, A.E.	Gordon 33A
Robertson, F.A.	Inverness 37A	Scott, I.G.	Edinburgh 1A-30	Smith, A.M.	Glasgow 16B
Robertson, G.R.	Gordon 33A	Scott, J.	Dunfermline 24B	Smith, D.J.	Kirkcaldy 25A

Smith, Mrs E.	West Lothian 2A	
Smith, G.S.	Glasgow 16A-94	
Smith, G.W.	West Lothian 2A	
Smith, Miss H.C.	Glasgow 16B	
Smith, H.G.	Angus 30B	
Smith, H.M.C.	Moray 35A	
Smith, Miss H.W.	Mel/Peebles 4A	
Smith, J.A.W.	Kincard'/Deeside 32B	
Smith, J.M.	Uist 43B	
(Smith, J.R.	Edinburgh 1A-53)	
Smith, J.R.	Glasgow 16B	
Smith, J.S.A.	Glasgow 16B	
Smith, M.	Abernethy 36A	
Smith, M.	Uist 43A	
Smith, N.A.	Buchan 34A	
Smith, R.	Dum'/K'cudbright 8B	
Smith, R.	Falkirk 22B	
Smith, R.	Ross 39A	
Smith, Ms R.A.	Hamilton 17A-14	
Smith, R.W.	Falkirk 22A	
Smith, S.J.	Glasgow 16A-111	
Smith, S.J.	Ardrossan 12A	
Smith, T.F.	Dunfermline 24B	
Smith, W.E.	West Lothian 2B	
Sorensen, A.K.	Greenock 15A	
Souter, D.I.	Perth 28A	
Speed, D.K.	Glasgow 16A-140	
Speirs, A.	List 6-I	
Spence, A.	Moray 35B	
Spence, C.K.O.	Dumbarton 18B	
Spence, Miss E.G.B.	Glasgow 16B	
Spence, Mrs S.M.	Hamilton 17A-54	
Spencer, J.	Lorn and Mull 21B	
Spiers, J.M.	Glasgow 16A-18	
Spowart, Mrs M.G.	St Andrews 26B	
Squires, J.F.R.	List 6-I	
Steel, D.	Edinburgh 1B	
Steel, G.H.B.	Glasgow 16A-45	
Steele, H.D.	Wigtown/Stran' 9A	
Steele, L.M.	Melrose/Peebles 4A	
Steele, Miss M.	West Lothian 2A	
Steell, S.C.	Paisley 14A	
Steenbergen, Ms P.	Gordon 33A.	
Stein, J.	Dunfermline 24A	
Stein, Mrs M.E.	Dunfermline 24A	
Stenhouse, W.D.	Perth 28A	
Stephen, A.	Kin'/Deeside 32B	
Stephen, D.M.	Edinburgh 1B	
Steven, H.A.M.	Dumbarton 18B	
Stevens, D.	Angus 30B	
Stevenson, A.	List 6-R	
Stevenson, A.L.	St Andrews 26B	
Stevenson, D.F.	Abernethy 36A	
Stevenson, J.	Edinburgh 1B	
Stevenson, J.	Glasgow 16A-11	
Stewart, Mrs A.	Perth 28B	
Stewart, A.T.	Edinburgh 1A-15	
Stewart, A.T.	Stirling 23B	
Stewart, C.E.	England 47B	
Stewart, D.	Paisley 14A	
Stewart, D.	Dunoon 20A	
Stewart, Ms D.E.	Glasgow 16A-33	
Stewart, D.J.	Kin'/Deeside 32A	
Stewart, F.J.	List 6-R	
Stewart, F.M.C.	Dundee 29A	
Stewart, G.C.	Gordon 33B	
Stewart, G.G.	Perth 28B	
Stewart, J.	Dunoon 20A	
Stewart, Mrs J.	South Argyll 19B	
Stewart, J.C.	Perth 28A	
Stewart, J.C.	Aberdeen 31B	
Stewart, J.M.	Lanark 13B	
Stewart, L.	Dunkeld/Meigle 27A	
Stewart, Mrs M.L.	List 6-I	
Stewart, M.S.	Abernethy 36B	
Stewart, Ms N.D.	Glasgow 16B	
Stewart, R.J.	Perth 28B	
Stewart, Miss U.B.	Hamilton 17A-76	
Stewart, W.T.	Hamilton 17A-40	
Stewart, W.T.A.	Dunkeld/Meigle 27B	
Stirling, A.D.	West Lothian 2B	
Stirling, G.A.S.	Inverness 37B	
Stirling, I.R.	Ayr 10B	
Stirling, J.	Stirling 23B	
Stitt, R.J.M.	Hamilton 17A-44	
Stiven, I.K.	Edinburgh 1B	
Stobie, C.I.G.	List 6-H	
Stoddart, A.C.	Annan/Eskdale 7A	
Stoddart, A.G.	Gordon 33B	
Stoddart, D.L.	St Andrews 26B	
Stone, W.V.	Greenock 15B	
Storrar, W.F.	Edinburgh 1B	
Stott, K.D.	Dundee 29A	
Strachan, A.E.	Dum'/K'cudbright 8B	
Strachan, D.G.	List 6-I	
Strachan, G.	List 6-I	
Strachan, I.M.	Aberdeen 31B	
Strickland, A.	St Andrews 26A	
Strong, C.	St Andrews 26B	
Strong, C.A.	Edinburgh 1A-84	
Stuart, J.T.	Moray 35B	
Sutcliffe, Miss C.B.	Irv'/K'nock 11A	
Sutherland, A.S.	Ayr 10B	
Sutherland, C.A.	Ardrossan 12A	
Sutherland, D.	Dundee 29A	
Sutherland, D.G.	List 6-H	
Sutherland, D.I.	Glasgow 16B	
Sutherland, Miss E.W.	Glasgow 16B	
Sutherland, I.A.	Buchan 34A	
Sutherland, W.	Kirkcaldy 25B	
Swan, A.	List 6-H	
Swan, A.F.	Lothian 3B	
Swinburne, N.	Annan/Eskdale 7B	
Swindells, Mrs A.J.	Aberdeen 31A	
Swindells, S.	Aberdeen 31A	
Swinton, J.	Aberdeen 31B	
Symington, A.H.	Ayr 10A	
Symington, R.C.	Stirling 23B	
Tait, A.	Glasgow 16B	
Tait, H.A.G.	Perth 28B	
Tait, J.M.	Edinburgh 1A-60	
Tait, T.W.	Dunkeld/Meigle 27B	
Tallach, J.	Ross 39A	
Talman, H.	Falkirk 22B	
(Tamas, B.	Europe 48A)	
Taverner, D.J.	Angus 30A	
Taverner, G.R.	Melrose/Peebles 4B	
Taylor, A.H.S.	Perth 28B	
Taylor, A.S.	Ardrossan 12B	
Taylor, A.T.	Lorn/Mull 21A	
Taylor, A.T.H.	List 6-H	
Taylor, C.G.	Dundee 29A	
Taylor, D.J.	Dum'/K'cudbright 8A	
Taylor, G.J.A.	Paisley 14A	
Taylor, H.G.	Edinburgh 1B	
Taylor, I.	Stirling 23A	
Taylor, I.	St Andrews 26B	
Taylor, Miss J.C.	Irv'/K'marnock 11A	
Taylor, J.H.B.	Irv'/K'marnock 11A	
Taylor, J.T.H.	Kirkcaldy 25B	
Taylor, P.R.	Kincard'/Deeside 32B	
Taylor, W.	Buchan 34B	
Taylor, W.R.	Jedburgh 6A	
Telfer, A.B.	Ayr 10A	
Telfer, I.J.M.	Edinburgh 1B	
Templeton, J.L.	Kirkcaldy 25A	
Thain, W.G.M.	Glasgow 16A-5	
Thom, D.J.	Annan'/Eskdale 7A	
Thom, I.G.	Hamilton 17A-71	
Thomas, M.R.H.	Angus 30B	
Thomas, Mrs S.	Angus 30B	
Thomas, W.C.	List 6-I	
Thompson, W.M.D.	Jedburgh 6B	
Thomson, A.	Glasgow 16A-36	
Thomson, A.	Hamilton 17A-1	
Thomson, D.M.	Kirkcaldy 25A	
Thomson, E.P.L.	Jedburgh 6A	
Thomson, G.F.M.	Melrose/Peebles 4B	
Thomson, G.L.	Kirkcaldy 25B	
Thomson, I.U.	Gordon 33A	
Thomson, J.B.	Perth 28A	
Thomson, J.D.	Kirkcaldy 25A	
Thomson, J.G.S.S.	Edinburgh 1B	
Thomson, J.M.	Moray 35B	
Thomson, J.M.A.	Hamilton 17A-47	
Thomson, J.S.	Lanark 13B	
Thomson, M.	Wigtown/Stran' 9A	
Thomson, Mrs M.	Ardrossan 12B	
Thomson, P.D.	Perth 28A	
Thomson, P.G.	St Andrews 26B	
Thomson, R.	Falkirk 22A	
Thomson, S.	Caithness 41A	
Thomson, W.	Perth 28A	
Thomson, W.H.	Lothian 3B	
Thorburn, R.J.	Ardrossan 12A	
Thorne, L.W.	Hamilton 17B	
Thornthwaite, A.P.	Edinburgh 1A-87	
Thrower, C.G.	St Andrews 26A	
Tierney, J.P.	Kincard'/Deeside 32B	
Todd, A.S.	Stirling 23B	
Todd, J.F.	Caithness 41A	
Tollick, F.	List 6-I	
Tomlinson, B.L.	Kirkcaldy 25A	
Torrance, A.	St Andrews 26B	
Torrance, D.J.	Glasgow 16A-13	
Torrance, D.W.	Lothian 3B	
Torrance, I.R.	Aberdeen 31B	
Torrance, J.B.	Edinburgh 1B	
Torrance, T.F.	Edinburgh 1B	
Torrens, S.	Ross 39A	
Travers, R.	Irv'/K'marnock 11A	
Trevorrow, J.A.	Glasgow 16A-68	
Troup, H.J.G.	Lorn/Mull 21B	
Turnbull, J.	Stirling 23A	
Turnbull, J.J.	St Andrews 26B	
Turnbull, J.S.	List 6-I	
Turner, A.	Glasgow 16B	
Turner, D.M.	List 6-R	
Turner, F.K.	Hamilton 17A-50	
Tuton, R.M.	Glasgow 16B	
Twaddle, L.H.	Lothian 3A	
Tyre, R.	Angus 30B	
Underwood, Mrs F.A.	Lothian 3A	
Underwood, G.H.	Lothian 3B	
Urie, D.M.L.	Kincard'/Deeside 32B	
Urquhart, J.	Glasgow 16A-14	
Urquhart, J.A.	Irv'/K'marnock 11A	
Urquhart, J.D.	Uist 43	
Urquhart, J.M.	List 6-R	
Urquhart, N.	Irv'/K'marnock 11A	
Varwell, A.P.J.	Lochaber 38A	
Vincent, C.R.	Dum'/K'cudbright 8B	
Vint, A.S.	Glasgow 16A-47	
Waddell, Mrs E.A.	Irv'/K'nock 11A	
Walker, A.L.	Glasgow 16B	
Walker, C.D.	Buchan 34B	
Walker, D.K.	Kincard'/Deeside 32A	
Walker, D.S.	Ardrossan 12B	
Walker, I.	West Lothian 2B	
Walker, J.B.	St Andrews 26B	
Walker, K.D.F.	Lothian 3A	

Walker, R.F.   England 47B
Walker, R.W.   Edinburgh 1B
Wallace, C.   Dum'/K'cudbright 8A
Wallace, D.S.   England 47B
Wallace, D.W.   Hamilton 17A-37
Wallace, H.M.   Glasgow 16A-105
Wallace, J.H.   Melrose/Peebles 4A
Wallace, R.J.S.   Gordon 33B
Wallace, W.F.   Caithness 41A
Walton, A.   Aberdeen 31B
Wandrum, D.   Falkirk 22A
Ward, A.H.   Greenock 15A
Ward, M.J.   Orkney 45B
Wardlaw, E.G.S.   West Lothian 2A
Wark, A.C.   Paisley 14A
Warner, K.   Caithness 41A
Warnock, D.   Angus 30B
Warnock, J.   List 6-R
Warwick, I.C.   Ross 39A
Watson, Mrs E.R.L.   Ardrossan 12A
Watson, I.M.   Hamilton 17A-18
Watson, J.   Dunoon 20B
Watson, J.M.   Aberdeen 31A
Watson, Miss J.S.   Stirling 23A
Watson, Mrs K.K.   Edinburgh 1A-50
Watson, T.D.   Ayr 10A
Watson, Miss V.G.C.   Jedburgh 6A
Watt, A.G.N.   Sutherland 40A
Watt, H.F.   Inverness 37A
Watt, J.H.I.   List 6-I
Watt, R.   Stirling 23B
Watt, R.J.   Dumbarton 18A
Watt, W.D.   Kincard'/Deeside 32B
Watt, W.G.   Aberdeen 31B
Watts, A.   Kincard/Deeside 32A
Waugh, J.L.   Inverness 37B
Weatherhead, J.L.   Angus 30B
Webster, A.F.   Angus 30A
Webster, B.G.   Stirling 23A
Webster, J.G.   Glasgow 16B
Webster, P.   Edinburgh 1A-63
Weighton, Mrs G.   Ayr 10A
Weir, D.G.   List 6-R
Weir, J.   Hamilton 17A-19
Weir, Mrs M.K.   List 6-I
Wells, I.J.   Edinburgh 1A-67
Wells, J.R.   Edinburgh 1A-52

Welsh, A.M.   List 6-I
Westmarland, C.A.   Europe 48B
White, B.A.   Dunkeld/Meigle 27B
White, C.P.   Glasgow 16A-135
White, D.M.   Glasgow 16A-26
White, E.M.   England 47B
Whitecross, Mrs J.   Dumbarton 18A
Whiteford, A.   Inverness 37A
Whiteford, D.H.   Lothian 3B
Whiteford, J.D.   Glasgow 16A-108
Whiteford, R.S.   Falkirk 22B
Whitelaw, W.D.   List 6-R
Whiteman, D.   Ayr 10A
Whitley, L.A.B.   Angus 30A
Whitson, W.S.   Perth 28B
Whitton, J.P.   England 47B
Whyte, D.W.   Abernethy 36A
Whyte, G.J.   Edinburgh 1A-10
Whyte, I.A.   Edinburgh 1B
Whyte, Mrs I.H.   Dunfermline 24B
Whyte, J.   Glasgow 16A-5
Whyte, J.A.   St Andrews 26B
Whyte, J.H.   Greenock 15B
Whyte, Mrs M.A.   Glasgow 16A-113
Whyte, N.R.   Moray 35A
Whyte, R.C.   Abernethy 36A
Whyte, W.B.   Inverness 37A
Wigglesworth, J.C.   Edinburgh 1B
Wilkie, G.D.   List 6-H
Wilkie, I.   Dumbarton 18A
Wilkie, J.L.   Edinburgh 1B
Wilkie, J.R.   Dum'/K'cudbright 8B
Wilkie, W.E.   Aberdeen 31B
Wilkinson, A.D.   Ayr 10A
Wilkinson, J.   Edinburgh 1B
Wilkinson, W.B.   South Argyll 19A
Williams, Miss J.M.   Edinburgh 1B
Williams, Mrs L.   List 6-I
Williams, T.C.   Annan'/Eskdale 7A
Williamson, C.R.   Perth 28A
Williamson, J.   Dum'/K'cud 8A
Williamson, M.J.C.   Shetland 46A
Williamson, T.   L'carron/Skye 42B
Wilson, A.G.N.   Aberdeen 31A
Wilson, G.   L'carron/Skye 42A
Wilson, Ms H.   Perth 28A
Wilson, I.M.   Edinburgh 1B

Wilson, J.   Glasgow 16A-144
Wilson, J.H.   Hamilton 17B
Wilson, J.L.   Dundee 29A
Wilson, J.M.   Sutherland 40A
Wilson, J.M.   Inverness 37B
Wilson, Miss M.   Kirkcaldy 25A
Wilson Mrs M.D.   Sutherland 40B
Wilson, Mrs P.M.   Hamilton 17A-64
Wilson, R.   Dumbarton 18A
Wilson, R.M.   St Andrews 26B
Wilson, T.F.   List 6-I
Wilson, W.T.S.   Glasgow 16A-71
Wilson, W.S.   Shetland 46B
Winn, Mrs F.M.M.   List 6-I
Winning, Miss A.A.   Lochaber 38A
Wishart, J.   Buchan 34A
Wood, C.R.   South Argyll 19A
Wood, G.M.   Moray 35A
Wood, J.L.K.   Aberdeen 31B
Wood, P.J.   List 6-I
Wotherspoon, I.G.   Hamilton 17A-28
Wotherspoon, R.C.   Dum'/K'cud 8B
Wright, D.L.   Moray 35B
Wright, J.P.   Stirling 23B
Wright, M.   Dumbarton 18A
Wylie, W.A.   List 6-H
Wyllie, H.R.   Hamilton 17B

Yorke, K.B.   Ayr 10A
Young, A.W.   Edinburgh 1B
Young, D.A.   Lanark 13A
Young, Mrs E.M.   Dunoon 20A
Young, G.S.   Dunkeld/Meigle 27B
Young, H.J.   List 6-R
Young, J.   Dum/K'cudbright 8B
Young, J.N.   Edinburgh 1A-47
Young, Mrs R.M.   Ayr 10A
Young, W.F.   Kirkcaldy 25B
Younger, Mrs A.   Glasgow 16A-71
Younger, A.S.   Inverness 37A
Youngson, P.   Angus 30B
Yule, Mrs M.J.B.   Dumbarton 18A
Yule, R.F.   Buchan 34A

Zambonini, J.   Hamilton 17A-24

INDEX OF PARISHES AND PLACES

NOTE: Numbers on the right of the column refer to the Presbytery in which the district lies. Names in brackets are given for ease of identification. They either refer to the name of the Parish, which may be different from that of the district, or they distinguish places with the same name, or they indicate the first named charge in a union.

Abdie and Dunbog	26	Arisaig and the		Beith	12	Breich Valley	2
Abercorn	2	Small Isles	38	Belhaven	3	Bressay (Lerwick)	46
Aberdeen	31	Armadale	2	Belhelvie	33	Bridge of Allan	23
Aberdour (Fife)	24	Arngask	28	Bellie	35	Bridge of Earn	
Aberdour (Buchan)	34	Arnsheen Barrhill	10	Bellshill	17	(Dunbarney)	28
Aberfeldy	27	Arrochar	18	Benbecula	43	Bridge of Weir	14
Aberfoyle	23	Ashkirk	4	Bendochy	27	Brightons	22
Aberlady	3	Assynt and Stoer	40	Berneray and		Broadford (Strath)	42
Aberlemno	30	Athelstaneford	3	Lochmaddy	43	Brodick	12
Aberlour	35	Auchaber	34	Berriedale and		Broom	16
Aberluthnott	32	Auchencairn and Rerrick	8	Dunbeath	41	Broughton, Glenholm	
Abernethy and Dron	28	Auchengray (Carnwath)	13	Bervie	32	and Kilbucho	4
Abernethy	36	Auchinleck	10	Berwick-upon-Tweed		Broughty Ferry	
Abernyte	29	Auchterarder	28	and Lowick	5	(Dundee)	29
Aboyne-Dinnet	32	Auchterderran	25	Biggar	13	Broxburn	2
Acharacle	38	Auchtergaven and		Birnie	35	Bruan (Lybster)	41
Advie (Cromdale)	36	Moneydie	28	Birsay, Harray and		Brydekirk	7
Airdrie	17	Auchterhouse	29	Sandwick	45	Buchanan	23
Airlie Ruthven		Auchterless	34	Birse and Feughside	32	Buchlyvie	23
Kingoldrum	30	Auchtermuchty	26	Bishopbriggs	16	Buckhaven	25
Airth	22	Auchtertool	25	Bishopton	14	Buckie	35
Aithsting (Sandsting)	46	Auldearn and Dalmore	37	Blackbraes and		Bucksburn Stoneywood	31
Alexandria	18	Aviemore		Shieldhill	22	Buittle and Kelton	8
Allanton (Edrom)	5	(Rothiemurchus)	36	Blackburn and Seafield	2	Bunessan	
Alloa	23	Avoch	39	Blackford	28	(Kilfinichen)	21
Alloway	10	Avonbridge	2	Black Mount	13	Burghead (Alves)	35
Almondbank Tibbermore	28	Ayr	10	Blackridge	2	Burnmouth (Ayton)	5
Alness	39	Ayton and Burnmouth	5	Blair Atholl and Struan	27	Burnside	16
Altnaharra and Farr	40			Blairbeth	16	Burntisland	25
Alva	23	Baldernock	18	Blairdaff	33	Burra Isle	46
Alves and Burghead	35	Balfron	23	Blairgowrie	27	Burray	
Alvie and Insh	36	Balgonie (Kennoway)	25	Blairingone (Saline)	24	(South Ronaldsay)	45
Alyth	27	Ballantrae	10	Blantyre	17	Burrelton (Cargill)	28
Amulree and		Ballingry and Lochcraig	24	Boarhills and Dunino	26	Busby	16
Strathbraan	27	Balloch (Jamestown)	18	Boat of Garten and		Bute United	20
Ancrum	6	Balmaclellan and Kells	8	Kincardine	36		
Annan	7	Balmaghie	8	Boharm (Keith)	35	Cabrach (Mortlach)	35
Annbank	10	Balmedie (Belhelvie)	33	Boleskine (Dores)	37	Cadder	16
Anstruther	26	Balmerino	26	Bolton and Saltoun	3	Caddonfoot	4
Anwoth and Girthon	8	Balquhidder	23	Bona (Inverness)	37	Caerlaverock	8
Appin	21	Banchory-Devenick		Bonar Bridge (Creich)	40	Cairneyhill	24
Applecross, Lochcarron		and Maryculter/		Bo'ness	22	Cairngryffe	13
and Torridon	42	Cookney	32	Bonhill	18	Cairnie-Glass (Huntly)	33
Applegarth and		Banchory-Ternan	32	Bonkle (Newmains)	17	Calder, Kirk of	2
Sibbaldbie	7	Banff	34	Bonkyl and Preston	5	Calderbank	17
Arbirlot	30	Bankfoot (Auchtergaven)	28	Bonnybridge	22	Caldercruix and	
Arbroath	30	Bannockburn	23	Bonnyrigg	3	Longriggend	17
Arbuthnott	32	Banton	16	Borgue	8	Caldwell	14
Archiestown		Bargeddie	17	Borthwick	3	Callander	23
(Knockando)	35	Barr	10	Bothkennar and		Cambusbarron	23
Ardchattan	21	Barra	43	Carronshore	22	Cambuslang	16
Ardclach	37	Barrhead	14	Bothwell	17	Cambusnethan (Wishaw)	17
Ardentinny (Strone)	20	Barrhill (Arnsheen)	10	Botriphnie (Keith)	35	Cameron	26
Ardeonaig (Killin)	23	Barry	30	Bourtie (Meldrum)	33	Campbeltown	19
Ardersier	37	Barthol Chapel	33	Bowden	4	Campsie	16
Ardgay (Kincardine)	40	Barvas	44	Bower	41	Canisbay	41
Ardgour	38	Bathgate	2	Bowling		Canonbie	7
Ardler, Kettins and		Bearsden	18	(Old Kilpatrick)	18	Caputh and Clunie	27
Meigle	27	Beath	24	Bowmore (Kilarrow)	19	Cara (Gigha)	19
Ardnamurchan	38	Beattock		Bracadale and Duirinish	42	Cardross	18
Ardoch	28	(Kirkpatrick Juxta)	7	Braemar	32	Careston (Fern)	30
Ardrishaig	19	Beauly (Kilmorack)	37	Braes of Rannoch	27	Carfin	17
Ardrossan	12	Bedrule	6	Brechin	30	Cargill Burrelton	28

Carinish	43	Coupar Angus	27	Deer	34	Dyke	35
Carlisle	7	Cove (Craigrownie)	18	Deerness	45	Dysart	25
Carlops	4	Cowdenbeath	24	Delting	46		
Carloway	44	Cowie	23	Denbeath	25	Eaglesfield (Kirtle)	7
Carluke	13	Coylton	10	Denholm	6	Eaglesham	16
Carmunnock (Glasgow)	16	Craigie	10	Denny	22	Earlston	4
Carmyllie	30	Craignish	19	Deskford (Cullen)	35	Eassie and Nevay	30
Carnbee	26	Craigrownie	18	Devonside (Fossoway)	28	East Calder	
Carnock and Oakley	24	Crail	26	Dingwall	39	(Kirknewton)	2
Carnoustie	30	Crailing and Eckford	6	Dinnet (Aboyne)	32	East Kilbride	17
Carnwath	13	Cranstoun, Crichton		Dirleton	3	East Linton (Traprain)	3
Carradale (Saddell)	19	and Ford	3	Dollar	23	Eccles	5
Carriden	22	Crathie	32	Dores and Boleskine	37	Echt	33
Carrington (Cockpen)	3	Creich	40	Dornoch	40	Eckford (Crailing)	6
Carron (Stenhouse)	22	Creich, Flisk and		Dornock	7	Eday	45
Carronshore		Kilmany	26	Douglas	13	Edderton (Kincardine)	40
(Bothkennar)	22	Crichton (Cranstoun)	3	Douglas Water and		Eddleston	4
Carsphairn	8	Crieff	28	Rigside	13	Eddrachillis	40
Carstairs	13	Crimond	34	Doune (Kilmadock)	23	Edenshead and	
Carstairs Junction	13	Croick (Kincardine)	40	Dreghorn and Springside	11	Strathmiglo	26
Castle Douglas	8	Cromar	32	Dron (Abernethy)	28	Edgerston (Jedburgh)	6
Castletown (Olrig)	41	Cromarty	39	Drongan	10	Edinburgh	1
Cathkin (Glasgow		Cromdale and Advie	36	Drumblade	33	Edinkillie	35
Fernhill)	16	Cross, Ness	44	Drumclog (Strathaven)	17	Ednam (Kelso North)	6
Catrine	10	Crossbost (Lochs)	44	Drumelzier (Stobo)	4	Edrom Allanton	5
Cavers and Kirkton	6	Crossford	13	Drummore (Kirkmaiden)	9	Edzell-Lethnot	30
Cawdor	37	Crosshill	10	Drumnadrochit		Elchies (Knockando)	35
Cellardyke	26	Crosshouse	11	(Urquhart)	37	Elderslie	14
Ceres and Springfield	26	Crossmichael and		Drumoak and Durris	32	Elgin	35
Channelkirk	4	Parton	8	Drymen	23	Elie	26
Chapel of Garioch	33	Croy and Dalcross	37	Dufftown (Mortlach)	35	Ellon	33
Chapelhall	17	Cruden	34	Duffus, Spynie and		Enzie	35
Chapelton	17	Cullen and Deskford	35	Hopeman	35	Erchless (Kilmorack)	37
Chirnside	5	Culloden	37	Duirinish (Bracadale)	42	Errol	28
Chryston	16	Culross and Torryburn	24	Dull and Weem	27	Erskine	14
Clackmannan	23	Culsalmond and Rayne	33	Dulnain Bridge	36	Ervie Kirkcolm	9
Cleish	28	Culter	13	Dumbarton	18	Eskdalemuir	7
Cleland	17	Cults	31	Dumfries	8	Ettrick and Yarrow	4
Closeburn	8	Cumbernauld	22	Dun	30	Evanton (Kiltearn)	39
Clunie (Caputh)	27	Cumbrae	12	Dunbar	3	Evie	45
Cluny	33	Cuminestown		Dunbarney	28	Ewes (Langholm)	7
Clydebank	18	(Monquhitter)	34	Dunbeath (Berriedale)	41	Eyemouth	5
Clyne	40	Cumlodden		Dunblane	23		
Coalburn	13	Lochfyneside and		Dunbog (Abdie)	26	Fair Isle (Dunrossness)	46
Coalsnaughton (Sauchie)	23	Lochgair	19	Dundee	29	Fairlie	12
Coatbridge	17	Cummertrees	8	Dundonald	10	Fala and Soutra	3
Cockenzie and		Cumnock	10	Dundonnell (Gairloch)	42	Falkirk	22
Port Seton	3	Cunningsburgh		Dundrennan (Rerrick)	8	Falkland	26
Cockpen and Carrington	3	(Sandwick)	46	Dundurn	28	Fallin	23
Coldingham and St Abb's	5	Cushnie and Tough	33	Dunfermline	24	Farnell	30
Coldstream	5	Cupar	26	Dunglass	3	Farr (Altnaharra)	40
Colinsburgh				Dunino (Boarhills)	26	Fauldhouse	2
(Kilconquhar)	26	Dailly	10	Dunipace (Denny)	22	Fearn Abbey and Nigg	39
Colintraive (Kilmodan)	20	Dairsie	26	Dunkeld	27	Fenwick	11
Coll	21	Dalarossie (Moy)	37	Dunlichity (Daviot)	37	Fergushill	12
Collace	28	Dalavich (Kilchrennan)	21	Dunlop	11	Ferintosh	39
Colliston	30	Dalbeattie	8	Dunnet	41	Fern, Careston and	
Colmonell	10	Dalcross (Croy)	37	Dunnichen, Letham		Menmuir	30
Colonsay and Oronsay	21	Dalgety	24	and Kirkden	30	Fernhill and Cathkin	16
Colvend, Southwick		Dalkeith	3	Dunnottar (Stonehaven)	32	Fetlar	46
and Kirkbean	8	Dallas	35	Dunoon	20	Fetteresso (Stonehaven)	32
Comrie	28	Dalmally (Glenorchy)	21	Dunrossness	46	Feughside (Birse)	32
Condorrat		Dalmellington	10	Duns	5	Findhorn (Kinloss)	35
(Cumbernauld)	22	Dalmeny	1	Dunscore	8	Findochty	35
Connel	21	Dalmore (Auldearn)	37	Duntocher	18	Fintray and Kinellar	33
Contin	39	Dalmuir	18	Dunure (Fisherton)	10	Fintry	23
Cookney		Dalry (Ayrshire)	12	Dunvegan (Bracadale		Firth	45
(Banchory-Devenick)	32	Dalry (St John's Town)	8	and Duirinish)	42	Fisherton	10
Corby	47	Dalrymple	10	Durisdeer	8	Fishwick (Hutton)	5
Cornhill (Ordiquhill)	34	Dalserf	17	Durness and		Flisk (Creich)	26
Corpach (Kilmallie)	38	Dalton	7	Kinlochbervie	40	Flotta	45
Corrie (Arran)	12	Dalziel (Motherwell)	17	Duror	38	Fodderty and	
Corrie (Hutton)	7	Darvel	11	Durris (Drumoak)	32	Strathpeffer	39
Corsock and		Daviot	33	Duthil	36	Fogo and Swinton	5
Kirkpatrick Durham	8	Daviot and Dunlichity	37	Dyce	31	Ford (Cranstoun)	3

Ford (Glassary)	19	Glenrothes	25
Fordyce	34	Glens, The and	
Forfar	30	Kirriemuir Old	30
Forgandenny	28	Glenshee (Kirkmichael)	27
Forglen (Turriff)	34	Golspie	40
Forres	35	Gordon	5
Fort Augustus	38	Gorebridge	3
Forth	13	Gourock	15
Fortingall and		Grange (Keith)	35
Glenlyon	27	Grangemouth	22
Fortrose and		Grantown-on-Spey	36
Rosemarkie	39	Grantshouse and	
Fort William	38	Houndwood and	
Foss and Rannoch	27	Reston	5
Fossoway and Devonside	28	Grantully, Logierait	
Foulden and		and Strathtay	27
Mordington	5	Greenbank (Edinburgh)	1
Foveran	33	Greenbank (Glasgow)	16
Fowlis and Liff	29	Greengairs	17
Fowlis Wester	28	Greenlaw	5
Fraserburgh	34	Greenock	15
Freuchie	26	Gretna, Half Morton and	
Friockheim Kinnell	30	Kirkpatrick-Fleming	7
Fyvie	34	Guernsey	47
		Gullane	3
Gairloch and		Guthrie and Rescobie	30
Dundonnell	42		
Galashiels	4	Haddington	3
Galston	11	Haggs	22
Gardenstown	34	Half Morton (Gretna)	7
Garelochhead	18	Halkirk and Westerdale	41
Gargunnock	23	Halladale (Strathy)	41
Gartcosh	16	Hamilton	17
Gartmore	23	Harray (Birsay)	45
Gartocharn		Harthill	2
(Kilmaronock)	18	Harwood (Polbeth)	2
Garvald and Morham	3	Hawick	6
Gask	28	Helensburgh	18
Gateside (Edenshead)	2	Helmsdale (Kildonan)	40
Giffnock	16	Heriot (Stow)	4
Gifford (Yester)	3	Hightae	7
Gigha and Cara	19	Hillside	30
Gilmerton (Edinburgh)	1	Hobkirk and	
Gilmerton (Monzie)	28	Southdean	6
Girthon (Anwoth)	8	Hoddam	7
Girvan	10	Holm	45
Gladsmuir	3	Holytown	17
Glamis Inverarity and		Holywood	8
Kinnettles	30	Hopeman (Duffus)	35
Glasford	17	Houndwood	
Glasgow	16	(Grantshouse)	5
Glass (Huntly)	33	Houston and Killellan	14
Glassary, Kilmartin and		Howe of Fife	26
Ford	19	Howe Trinity	33
Glasserton and		Howgate	3
Isle of Whithorn	9	Hownam (Morebattle)	6
Glenaray and Inveraray	19	Howwood	14
Glenboig	16	Hoy and Walls	45
Glencairn and Moniaive	8	Hume (Stichill)	6
Glencaple	13	Humbie	3
Glencoe	38	Huntly	33
Glencorse	3	Hurlford	11
Glendaruel (Kilmodan)	20	Hutton and Corrie	7
Glendevon	23	Hutton and Fishwick	
Glenelg and Kintail	38	and Paxton	5
Glenesk	30		
Glengarry	38	Inch	9
Glenholm (Broughton)	4	Inchbrayock	30
Glenisla Kilry		Inchinnan	14
Lintrathen	30	Inchture and Kinnaird	29
Glenlivet (Tomintoul)	36	Innellan	20
Glenlyon (Fortingall)	27	Innerleithen, Traquair	
Glenmoriston (Urquhart)	37	and Walkerburn	4
Glenmuick	32	Innerleven	25
Glenorchy and Innishael	21	Innishael (Glenorchy)	21

Insch-Leslie-		Kilmacolm	15
Premnay-Oyne	33	Kilmadock	23
Insh (Alvie)	36	Kilmallie	38
Inverallochy and		Kilmany (Creich)	26
Rathen East	34	Kilmarnock	11
Inveraray (Glenaray)	19	Kilmaronock Gartocharn	18
Inverarity (Glamis)	30	Kilmartin (Glassary)	19
Inveraven (Tomintoul)	36	Kilmaurs	11
Inverbervie (Bervie)	32	Kilmelford (Kilninver)	19
Invergordon	39	Kilmeny	19
Invergowrie	29	Kilmodan and	
Inverkeilor and Lunan	30	Colintraive	20
Inverkeithing	24	Kilmonivaig	38
Inverkip	15	Kilmorack and Erchless	37
Inverness	37	Kilmore and Oban	21
Inverurie	33	Kilmore (Kilninian)	21
Iona	21	Kilmorich	
Irongray, Lochrutton and		(Lochgoilhead)	20
Teregles	8	Kilmory	12
Irvine	11	Kilmuir and	
Isle of Whithorn		Logie Easter	39
(Glasserton)	9	Kilmuir and Stenscholl	
		(Skye)	42
Jamestown	18	Kilmuir and Paible	43
Jedburgh	6	Kilmun	20
Jersey	47	Kilninian and Kilmore	21
Johnstone (Annandale)	7	Kilninver and	
Johnstone (Paisley)	14	Kilmelford	19
Jura	19	Kilrenny	26
		Kilry (Glenisla)	30
Keir (Penpont)	8	Kilspindie and Rait	28
Keiss	41	Kilsyth	16
Keith	35	Kiltarlity	37
Keithhall	33	Kiltearn	39
Kells (Balmaclellan)	8	Kilvickeon (Kilfinichen)	21
Kelso	6	Kilwinning	12
Kelton (Buittle)	8	Kincardine (Tulliallan)	24
Kelty	24	Kincardine	
Kemback	26	(Boat of Garten)	36
Kemnay	33	Kincardine, Croick	
Kenmore and Lawers	27	and Edderton	40
Kennoway, Windygates		Kincardine in Menteith	23
and Balgonie	25	Kinclaven	27
Kettins (Ardler)	27	Kinellar (Fintray)	33
Kilarrow	19	Kinfauns (St Madoes)	28
Kilbarchan	14	King Edward	34
Kilberry	19	Kinghorn	25
Kilbirnie	12	Kinglassie	25
Kilbrandon and		Kingoldrum (Airlie)	30
Kilchattan	21	Kingsbarns	26
Kilbucho (Broughton)	4	Kingscavil (Pardovan)	2
Kilcalmonell	19	Kingswells	31
Kilchattan		Kingussie	36
(Kilbrandon)	21	Kinkell (Trinity Gask)	28
Kilchenzie (Killean)	19	Kinloch	44
Kilchoman	19	Kinlochbervie (Durness)	40
Kilchrenan and		Kinlochleven	38
Dalavich	21	Kinlochspelvie	
Kilchrist (Urray)	39	(Torosay)	21
Kilconquhar and		Kinloss and Findhorn	35
Colinsburgh	26	Kinnaird (Inchture)	29
Kilcreggan		Kinneff	32
(Craigrownie)	18	Kinnell (Friockheim)	30
Kildalton and Oa	19	Kinnettles (Glamis)	30
Kildonan (Whiting Bay)	12	Kinross	28
Kildonan and Loth,		Kintail (Glenelg)	42
Helmsdale	40	Kintore	33
Kilfinan	20	Kippen	23
Kilfinichen, Kilvickeon		Kirkbean (Colvend)	8
and the Ross of Mull	21	Kirkcaldy	25
Killean and Kilchenzie	19	Kirkcolm (Ervie)	9
Killearn	23	Kirkconnel	8
Killearnan	39	Kirkcowan	9
Killellan (Houston)	14	Kirkcudbright	8
Killin and Ardeonaig	23	Kirkden (Dunnichen)	30

Kirkfieldbank 13
Kirkgunzeon 8
Kirkhill 37
Kirkinner 9
Kirkintilloch 16
Kirkliston (Edinburgh) 1
Kirkmabreck 9
Kirkmahoe 8
Kirkmaiden 9
Kirkmichael (Ayr) 10
Kirkmichael, Tinwald
and Torthorwald 8
Kirkmichael, Straloch
and Glenshee 27
Kirkmichael and
Tomintoul 36
Kirkmuirhill 13
Kirknewton and
East Calder 2
Kirk of Calder 2
Kirk of Lammermuir 5
Kirk o' Shotts 17
Kirkoswald 10
Kirkpatrick Durham
(Corsock) 8
Kirkpatrick Fleming
(Gretna) 7
Kirkpatrick Juxta 7
Kirkton (Cavers) 6
Kirkurd and Newlands 4
Kirkwall 45
Kirn 20
Kirriemuir 30
Kirtle Eaglesfield 7
Knock 44
Knockando, Elchies
and Archiestown 35
Knockbain 39
Knoydart (Mallaig) 38
Kyle of Lochalsh
(Lochalsh) 42
Kyles 20

Ladykirk 5
Laggan 36
Lairg 40
Lamlash 12
Lammermuir, Kirk of 5
Lanark 13
Langbank 15
Langholm, Ewes and
Westerkirk 7
Langton and Polwarth 5
Larbert 22
Largo 26
Largoward 26
Largs 12
Larkhall 17
Lasswade 3
Latheron 41
Lauder 4
Laurencekirk 32
Law 13
Lawers (Kenmore) 27
Lecropt 23
Legerwood 5
Leith (Edinburgh) 1
Leithholm 5
Lennoxtown (Campsie) 16
Lenzie 16
Lerwick and Bressay 46
Leslie 25
Leslie (Insch) 33
Lesmahagow 13
Leswalt 9

Letham (Dunnichen) 30
Lethnot (Edzell) 30
Leuchars 26
Leven 25
Levern (Barrhead) 14
Lhanbryd (St Andrew's) 35
Libberton and
Quothquan 13
Liddesdale 6
Liff (Fowlis) 29
Lilliesleaf 6
Limekilns 24
Linlithgow 2
Linton 6
Lintrathen (Glenisla) 30
Linwood 14
Lismore 21
Liverpool 47
Livingston 2
Loanhead 3
Lochalsh 42
Lochbroom and
Ullapool 39
Lochcarron
(Applecross) 42
Lochcraig (Ballingry) 24
Lochend 8
Lochfyneside
(Cumlodden) 19
Lochgair (Cumlodden) 19
Lochgelly 24
Lochgilphead 19
Lochgoilhead and
Kilmorich 20
Lochinver (Assynt) 40
Lochmaben 7
Lochmaddy (Berneray) 43
Lochranza and
Pirnmill 12
Lochrutton (Irongray) 8
Lochs in Bernera 44
Lochs-Crossbost 44
Lochwinnoch 14
Lockerbie 7
Logie 23
Logiealmond (Methven) 28
Logie Easter (Kilmuir) 39
Logierait (Grantully) 27
London 47
Longforgan 29
Longniddry 3
Longriggend
(Caldercruix) 17
Longside 34
Longtown 7
Lonmay 34
Lossiemouth 35
Loth (Kildonan) 40
Loudoun (Newmilns) 11
Lowick (Berwick) 5
Lowther (Glencaple) 13
Lugar 10
Lunan (Inverkeilor) 30
Lundie and
Muirhead of Liff 29
Lunnasting (Nesting) 46
Luss 18
Lybster and Bruan 41
Lyne and Manor 4

Macduff 34
Madderty 28
Makerstoun and
Smailholm 6
Mallaig and Knoydart 38

Manish Scarista 43
Manor (Lyne) 4
Markinch 25
Marnoch 34
Maryculter (Banchory-
Devenick) 32
Mauchline 10
Maud and Savoch 34
Maxton and Mertoun 4
Maxwell Mearns Castle 16
Maybole 10
Mearns (Glasgow) 16
Mearns Coastal 32
Meigle (Ardler) 27
Meldrum and Bourtie 33
Melness and Tongue 40
Melrose 4
Menmuir (Fern) 30
Menstrie 23
Mertoun (Maxton) 4
Methil 25
Methilhill 25
Methlick 33
Methven and
Logiealmond 28
Mid Calder
(Kirk of Calder) 2
Middlebie 7
Midmar 33
Milngavie 18
Milton of Campsie 16
Minto 6
Mochrum 9
Moffat 7
Moneydie
(Auchtergaven) 28
Moniaive (Glencairn) 8
Monifieth 29
Monigaff 9
Monikie and
Newbigging 29
Monimail 26
Monkton and Prestwick 10
Monquhitter and
New Byth 34
Montrose 30
Monymusk 33
Monzie 28
Mordington (Foulden) 5
Morebattle and
Hownam 6
Morham (Garvald) 3
Mortlach and Cabrach 35
Morvern 38
Motherwell 17
Mouswald 8
Moy, Dalarossie and
Tomatin 37
Muckairn 21
Muckhart 23
Muiravonside 22
Muirhead of Liff
(Lundie) 29
Muirkirk 10
Mull, Isle of 21
Murroes and Tealing 29
Musselburgh 3
Muthill 28

Nairn 37
Neilston 14
Nenthorn (Stichill) 6
Ness (Cross) 44
Nesting and Lunnasting 46
Netherlee 16

Nether Lochaber 38
Nevay (Eassie) 30
New Abbey 8
Newarthill 17
Newbattle 3
Newbigging (Monikie) 29
Newburgh 26
Newburgh (Foveran) 33
Newburn (Largo) 26
New Byth
(Monquhitter) 34
Newcastle 47
New Cumnock 10
New Deer 34
New Galloway (Kells) 8
Newhills 31
New Kilpatrick
(Bearsden) 18
Newlands (Kirkurd) 4
New Luce 9
New Machar 33
Newmains 17
Newmill (Keith) 35
Newmilns 11
New Monkland (Airdrie) 17
New Pitsligo 34
Newport on Tay 26
New Stevenston 17
Newton 3
Newtongrange 3
Newtonhill 32
Newton Mearns 16
Newtonmore 36
Newtown 4
Newtyle 30
Nigg (Fearn) 39
Norrieston 23
North Berwick 3
North Knapdale 19
Northmavine 46
North Queensferry 24
North Ronaldsay 45
Noth 33

Oa (Kildalton) 19
Oakley (Carnock) 24
Oathlaw Tannadice 30
Oban (Kilmore) 21
Ochiltree 10
Old Cumnock 10
Old Kilpatrick Bowling 18
Old Luce 9
Old Monkland
(Coatbridge) 17
Olrig 41
Onich (Nether Lochaber) 38
Ordiquhill and Cornhill 34
Ormiston 3
Oronsay (Colonsay) 21
Orphir 45
Orwell 28
Overtown 17
Oxnam 6
Oxton (Channelkirk) 4
Oyne (Insch) 33

Paible (Kilmuir) 43
Paisley 14
Panbride (Carnoustie) 30
Papa Westray 45
Pardovan, Kingscavil
and Winchburgh
(Abercorn) 2
Parton (Crossmichael) 8
Pathhead (Cranstoun) 3

Patna Waterside	10	Ross of Mull		South Knapdale	19
Paxton (Hutton)	5	(Kilfinichen)	21	South Queensferry	
Peebles	4	Rosyth	24	(Queensferry)	1
Pencaitland	3	Rothes	35	South Ronaldsay and	
Penicuik	3	Rothesay	20	Burray	45
Penninghame	9	Rothiemay (Keith)	35	South Uist	43
Penpont, Keir and		Rothiemurchus and		Southwick (Colvend)	8
Tynron	8	Aviemore	36	Soutra (Fala)	3
Perth	28	Rothienorman	34	Spean Bridge	
Peterculter	31	Rousay	45	(Kilmonivaig)	38
Peterhead	34	Roxburgh	6	Speymouth	35
Petty	37	Rutherglen	16	Spott	3
Pirnmill (Lochranza)	12	Ruthven (Airlie)	30	Springfield (Ceres)	26
Pitlochry	27	Ruthwell	8	Springside (Dreghorn)	11
Pitmedden (Udny)	33			Sprouston (Kelso Old)	6
Pitsligo	34	Saddell and Carradale	19	Spynie (Duffus)	35
Pittenweem	26	St Abb's (Coldingham)	5	Stair	10
Plean	23	St Andrews	26	Stamperland	16
Pluscarden	35	St Andrew's Lhanbryd		Stanley	28
Polbeth Harwood	2	and Urquhart	35	Stenhouse and Carron	22
Polmont	22	St Andrew's (Orkney)	45	Stenness (Orphir)	45
Polwarth (Langton)	5	St Boswells	4	Stenscholl (Kilmuir)	42
Port Charlotte		St Fergus	34	Stepps	16
(Kilchoman)	19	St Fillan's (Dundurn)	28	Stevenston	12
Port Glasgow	15	St Madoes		Stewarton	11
Portknockie	35	and Kinfauns	28	Stewartry of	
Portlethen	32	St Martin's	28	Strathearn, The	28
Portmahomack (Tarbat)	39	St Monans	26	Stichill Hume	
Portmoak	28	St Mungo	7	and Nenthorn	6
Portnahaven	19	St Ninians		Stirling	23
Port of Menteith	23	(Dunrossness)	46	Stobo and Drumelzier	4
Portpatrick	9	St Quivox (Ayr)	10	Stoer (Assynt)	40
Portree	42	Salen and Ulva	21	Stonehaven	32
Port Seton (Cockenzie)	3	Saline and Blairingone	24	Stonehouse	17
Premnay (Insch)	33	Saltcoats	12	Stoneykirk	9
Preston (Bonkyl)	5	Saltoun (Bolton)	3	Stoneywood	
Prestonpans	3	Sanday	45	(Buscksburn)	31
Prestwick	10	Sandbank	20	Stornoway	44
		Sandhaven	34	Stow	4
Quarff (Sandwick)	46	Sandness (Walls)	46	Strachur and	
Quarter	17	Sandsting and Aithsting	46	Strathlachlan	20
Queensferry (Edinburgh)	1	Sandwick (Birsay)	45	Straiton	10
Quothquan (Libberton)	13	Sandwick Cunningsburgh		Straloch (Kirkmichael)	27
		and Quarff	46	Stranraer	9
Rafford	35	Sandyhills (Glasgow)	16	Strath and Sleat	42
Rait (Kilspindie)	28	Sanquhar	8	Strathaven	17
Rannoch (Foss)	27	Sauchie and		Strathblane	28
Rathen	34	Coalsnaughton	23	Strathbraan (Amulree)	27
Ratho (Edinburgh)	1	Savoch (Maud)	34	Strathbrock	2
Rathven	35	Scarista (Manish)	43	Strathfillan	21
Rattray	27	Scone	28	Strathkinness	26
Rayne (Culsalmond)	33	Seafield (Blackburn)	2	Strathlachlan (Strachur)	20
Reay	41	Selkirk (Ashkirk)	4	Strathmiglo (Edenshead)	26
Redding and		Shandon (Rhu)	18	Strathpeffer (Fodderty)	39
Westquarter	22	Shapinsay	45	Strathtay (Grantully)	27
Redgorton	28	Shieldhill (Blackbraes)	22	Strathy and Halladale	41
Rendall	45	Shiskine	12	Strichen	34
Renfrew	14	Shotts	17	Stromness	45
Renton	18	Sibbaldbie (Applegarth)	7	Strone and Ardentinny	20
Rerrick (Auchencairn)	8	Skelmorlie and		Stronsay	45
Rescobie (Guthrie)	30	Wemyss Bay	15	Strontian	38
Resolis and Urquhart	39	Skene	33	Struan (Blair Atholl)	27
Reston (Grantshouse)	5	Skerries (Whalsay)	46	Swinton (Fogo)	5
Rhu and Shandon	18	Skipness	19	Symington (Ayr)	10
Riccarton (Kilmarnock)	11	Skirling	4	Symington (Lanark)	13
Rigside (Douglas Water)	13	Slamannan	22		
Roberton (Hawick		Sleat (Strath)	42	Tain	39
Teviot)	6	Smailholm		Tannadice (Oathlaw)	30
Rogart	40	(Mackerstoun)	6	Tarbat	39
Rosehall	40	Small Isles (Arisaig)	38	Tarbert (South Argyll)	19
Rosemarkie (Fortrose)	39	Snizort	42	Tarbert (Uist)	43
Rosewell	3	Sorbie	9	Tarbolton	10
Roslin	3	Sorn	10	Tarbrax (Carnwath)	13
Rosneath	18	Southdean (Hobkirk)	6	Tarff and Twynholm	8
Rosskeen	39	Southend	19	Tarves	33

Taynuilt (Muckairn)	21
Tayport	26
Tealing (Murroes)	29
Tenandry	27
Terregles (Irongray)	8
Teviothead	6
Thornhill (Dumfries)	8
Thornhill (Norrieston)	23
Thornliebank	16
Thornton	25
Thrumster (Wick)	41
Thurso	41
Tibbermore	
(Almondbank)	28
Tillicoultry	23
Tingwall	46
Tinwald (Kirkmichael)	8
Tiree	21
Tobermory	21
Tomatin (Moy)	37
Tomintoul, Glenlivet and	
Inveraven	36
Tongue (Melness)	40
Torosay and	
Kinlochspelvie	21
Torphichen	2
Torrance	16
Torridon (Applecross)	42
Torryburn (Culross)	24
Torthorwald	
(Kirkmichael)	8
Tough (Cushnie)	33
Toward	20
Tranent	3
Traprain	3
Traquair (Innerleithen)	4
Trinity Gask and	
Kinkell	28
Troon	10
Troqueer (Dumfries)	8
Tulliallan and	
Kincardine	24
Tullibody	23
Tundergarth	7
Turriff	34
Twechar	16
Tweedsmuir	4
Twynholm (Tarff)	8
Tyninghame (Whitekirk)	3
Tynron (Penpont)	8
Tyrie	34
Uddingston	17
Udny and Pitmedden	33
Uig	44
Ullapool (Lochbroom)	39
Ulva (Salen)	21
Unst	46
Uphall	2
Uplawmoor (Caldwell)	14
Upper Donside	33
Urquhart and	
Glenmoriston	
(Inverness)	37
Urquhart (Resolis)	39
Urquhart (St Andrew's	
Lhanbryd)	35
Urr	8
Urray and Kilchrist	39
Walkerburn	
(Innerleithen)	4
Walls (Hoy)	45
Walls and Sandness	
(Shetland)	46

Wamphray	7	Westhill (Skene)	33	Whitekirk and
Waterbeck	7	West Kilbride	12	Tyninghame
Waterside (Patna)	10	West Linton	4	Whithorn
Watten	41	West Mearns	32	Whiting Bay and
Weem (Dull)	27	Westquarter		Kildonan
Wemyss	25	(Redding)	22	Whitsome
Wemyss Bay		Westray	45	Wick
(Skelmorlie)	15	Westruther	5	Wigtown
West Calder	2	Whalsay and		Williamwood
Westerdale (Halkirk)	41	Skerries	46	Wilton (Hawick)
Westerkirk		Whitburn	2	Winchburgh
(Langholm)	7	Whitehills	34	(Pardovan)

		Windygates	
Tyninghame	3	(Kennoway)	25
Whithorn	9	Wishaw	17
		Woolfords	
Kildonan	12	(Carnwath)	13
Whitsome	5	Wormit	26
Wick	41		
Wigtown	9	Yarrow (Ettrick)	4
Williamwood	16	Yell	46
Wilton (Hawick)	6	Yester	3
Winchburgh		Yetholm	6
(Pardovan)	2		

3

2
363

INDEX OF FORMER PARISHES AND CONGREGATIONS

The following index is based on the 'Supplementary Index of the Lost Parish Names of Scotland' printed in the previous edition of the *Year Book*, which has now been expanded to cover towns and cities as well as rural areas. It contains the names of parishes of the Church of Scotland and of congregations of the Free Church, the United Free Church and the United Presbyterian Church (and its constituent denominations) which no longer have a separate existence, largely as a consequence of union.

It should be stressed that this index is not intended to be a comprehensive guide to readjustment in the Church of Scotland and does not therefore include the names of *all* parishes and congregations which no longer exist as independent entities. Its purpose is rather to assist those who are trying to identify the present successor of some former parish or congregation whose name may no longer be recognisable. Where a connection between the former name and the present name may easily be established, the former name has not been included, as the following examples will illustrate.

- Where all the former congregations in a town have been united into one, as in the case of Melrose or Selkirk, the names of these former congregations have not been included; but in the case of towns with more than one congregation, such as Galashiels or Hawick, the names of the various constituent congregations are listed.
- Where a prefix such as North, Old, Little, Mid or the like has been lost but the substantive part of the name has been retained, the former name has not been included: it is assumed that someone searching for Little Dalton or Mid Yell will have no difficulty in connecting these with Dalton or Yell.
- Where the present name of a united congregation includes the names of some or all of its constituent parts, these former names do not appear in the index: thus, neither Glasgow: Anderston nor Glasgow: Kelvingrove appears, since both names are easily traceable to Glasgow: Anderston Kelvingrove.
- Some parishes and congregations have disappeared, and their names have been lost, as a consequence of suppression, dissolution or secession. The names of rural parishes in this category have been included, together with the names of their Presbyteries to assist with identification, but those in towns and cities have not been included, as there will clearly be no difficulty in establishing the general location of the parish or congregation in question.

Since 1929, a small number of rural parishes have adopted a new name (for example Whitehills, formerly Boyndie). The former names of these parishes have been included, but it would have been too unwieldy to include either the vast numbers of such changes of name in towns and cities, especially those which occurred at the time of the 1900 and 1929 unions, or the very many older names of pre-Reformation parishes which were abandoned in earlier centuries (however fascinating a list of such long-vanished names as Fothmuref, Kinbathock and Toskertoun might have been).

In this index, the following abbreviations have been used:

C of S	Church of Scotland
FC	Free Church
R	Relief Church
RP	Reformed Presbyterian Church
UF	United Free Church
UP	United Presbyterian Church
US	United Secession Church

Name no longer used	Present name of parish
Abbey St Bathan's	Kirk of Lammermuir
Abbotrule	charge suppressed: Presbytery of Jedburgh
Aberchirder	Marnoch
Aberdalgie	The Stewartry of Strathearn
Aberdeen: Belmont Street	Aberdeen: St Mark's
Aberdeen: Bon Accord	Aberdeen: Denburn
Aberdeen: Carden Place	Aberdeen: Queen's Cross
Aberdeen: Causewayend	Aberdeen: St Stephen's
Aberdeen: East	Aberdeen: St Mark's
Aberdeen: Gallowgate	Aberdeen: St Mary's
Aberdeen: Gilcomston St Colm's	Aberdeen: Denburn
Aberdeen: Hilton	Aberdeen: Woodside
Aberdeen: King Street	Aberdeen: North of St Andrew
Aberdeen: Melville	Aberdeen: Queen's Cross
Aberdeen: Nelson Street	Aberdeen: North of St Andrew
Aberdeen: North	Aberdeen: North of St Andrew
Aberdeen: Pittodrie	Aberdeen: St Mary's
Aberdeen: Powis	Aberdeen: St Stephen's
Aberdeen: Rutherford	Aberdeen: Rosemount
Aberdeen: South (C of S)	Aberdeen: St Nicholas South of Kincorth
Aberdeen: South (FC)	Aberdeen: St Mark's
Aberdeen: St Columba's	Aberdeen: High Hilton
Aberdeen: St Mary's	Aberdeen: St Machar's Cathedral
Aberdeen: St Paul's	Aberdeen: Denburn
Aberdeen: Trinity (C of S)	Aberdeen: St Nicholas
Aberdeen: Trinity (FC)	Aberdeen: St Mark's
Aberdeen: Union	Aberdeen: Denburn
Aberuthven	The Stewartry of Strathearn
Abington	Glencaple
Addiewell	Breich Valley
Afton	New Cumnock
Airdrie: West	Airdrie: New Wellwynd
Aldbar	Aberlemno
Aldcambus	Dunglass
Alford	Howe Trinity
Alloa: Chalmers	Alloa: North
Alloa: Melville	Alloa: North
Alloa: St Andrew's	Alloa: North
Altries	charge dissolved: Presbytery of Kincardine and Deeside
Altyre	Rafford
Alvah	Banff
Annan: Erskine	Annan: St Andrew's
Annan: Greenknowe	Annan: St Andrew's
Arbroath: East	Arbroath: St Andrew's
Arbroath: Erskine	Arbroath: West Kirk
Arbroath: High Street	Arbroath: St Andrew's
Arbroath: Hopemount	Arbroath: St Andrew's
Arbroath: Ladyloan	Arbroath: West Kirk
Arbroath: Princes Street	Arbroath: West Kirk
Arbroath: St Columba's	Arbroath: West Kirk

Name no longer used	Present name of parish
Arbroath: St Margaret's	Arbroath: West Kirk
Arbroath: St Ninian's	Arbroath: St Andrew's
Arbroath: St Paul's	Arbroath: St Andrew's
Ardallie	Deer
Ardwell	Stoneykirk
Ascog	Bute United
Auchindoir	Upper Donside
Auchmithie	Arbroath: St Vigean's
Auldcathie	Dalmeny
Aultbea	Gairloch and Dundonnell
Ayr: Cathcart	Ayr: St Columba
Ayr: Darlington New	Ayr: Auld Kirk of Ayr
Ayr: Darlington Place	Ayr: Auld Kirk of Ayr
Ayr: Lochside	Ayr: St Quivox
Ayr: Martyrs'	Ayr: Auld Kirk of Ayr
Ayr: Sandgate	Ayr: St Columba
Ayr: St John's	Ayr: Auld Kirk of Ayr
Ayr: Trinity	Ayr: St Columba
Ayr: Wallacetown South	Ayr: Auld Kirk of Ayr
Back	charge dissolved: Presbytery of Lewis
Badcall	Edrachillis
Balbeggie	Collace
Balfour	charge dissolved: Presbytery of Dundee
Balgedie	Portmoak
Baliasta	Unst
Ballachulish	Nether Lochaber
Ballater	Glenmuick
Balmacolm	Howe of Fife
Balmullo	charge dissolved: Presbytery of St Andrews
Balnacross	Tarff and Twynholm
Baltasound	Unst
Banchory Ternan: North	Banchory Ternan: West
Banchory Ternan: South	Banchory Ternan: West
Bandry	Luss
Bara	Garvald and Morham
Bargrennan	Penninghame
Barnweil	Tarbolton
Barrhead: Westbourne	Barrhead: Arthurlie
Barrock	Dunnet
Beith: Hamilfield	Beith: Trinity
Beith: Head Street	Beith: Trinity
Beith: Mitchell Street	Beith: Trinity
Belkirk	Liddesdale
Benholm	Mearns Coastal
Benvie	Fowlis and Liff
Binny	Linlithgow: St Michael's
Blackburn	Fintray and Kinellar
Blackhill	Longside
Blairlogie	congregation seceded: Presbytery of Stirling
Blanefield	Strathblane

Name no longer used	Present name of parish
Blantyre: Anderson	Blantyre: St Andrew's
Blantyre: Burleigh Memorial	Blantyre: St Andrew's
Blantyre: Stonefield	Blantyre: St Andrew's
Blyth Bridge	Kirkurd and Newlands
Boddam	Peterhead: Trinity
Bonhill: North	Alexandria
Bothwell: Park	Uddingston: Viewpark
Bourtreebush	Newtonhill
Bow of Fife	Monimail
Bowmore	Kilarrow
Boyndie	Whitehills
Brachollie	Petty
Braco	Ardoch
Braehead	Forth
Brechin: East	Brechin: Gardner Memorial
Brechin: Maison Dieu	Brechin: Cathedral
Brechin: St Columba's	Brechin: Gardner Memorial
Brechin: West	Brechin: Gardner Memorial
Breich	Breich Valley
Bridge of Allan: St Andrew's	Bridge of Allan: Holy Trinity
Bridge of Allan: Trinity	Bridge of Allan: Holy Trinity
Bridge of Teith	Kilmadock
Brora	Clyne
Buccleuch	Ettrick and Yarrow
Burnhead	Penpont, Keir and Tynron
Cairnryan	charge dissolved: Presbytery of Wigtown and Stranraer
Cambuslang: Rosebank	Cambuslang: St Andrew's
Cambuslang: West	Cambuslang: St Andrew's
Cambusmichael	St Martin's
Campbeltown: Longrow	Campbeltown: Lorne and Lowland
Campsail	Rosneath St Modan's
Canna	Mallaig St Columba and Knoydart
Carbuddo	Guthrie and Rescobie
Cardenden	Auchterderran St Fothad's
Carmichael	Cairngryffe
Carnoch	Contin
Carnousie	Turriff: St Ninian's and Forglen
Carnoustie: St Stephen's	Carnoustie
Carrbridge	Duthil
Carruthers	Middlebie
Castle Kennedy	Inch
Castleton	Liddesdale
Caterline	Kinneff
Chapelknowe	congregation seceded: Presbytery of Annandale and Eskdale
Clatt	Noth
Clayshant	Stoneykirk
Climpy	charge dissolved: Presbytery of Lanark
Clola	Deer
Clousta	Sandsting and Aithsting

Name no longer used	Present name of parish
Clova	The Glens and Kirriemuir: Old
Clydebank: Bank Street	Clydebank: St Cuthbert's
Clydebank: Boquhanran	Clydebank: Kilbowie St Andrew's
Clydebank: Hamilton Memorial	Clydebank: St Cuthbert's
Clydebank: Linnvale	Clydebank: St Cuthbert's
Clydebank: St James'	Clydebank: Abbotsford
Clydebank: Union	Clydebank: Kilbowie St Andrew's
Clydebank: West	Clydebank: Abbotsford
Coatbridge: Cliftonhill	Coatbridge: Clifton
Coatbridge: Coatdyke	Coatbridge: Clifton
Coatbridge: Coats	Coatbridge: Clifton
Coatbridge: Dunbeth	Coatbridge: St Andrew's
Coatbridge: Gartsherrie	Coatbridge: St Andrew's
Coatbridge: Garturk	Coatbridge: Calder
Coatbridge: Maxwell	Coatbridge: St Andrew's
Coatbridge: Trinity	Coatbridge: Clifton
Coatbridge: Whifflet	Coatbridge: Calder
Cobbinshaw	charge dissolved: Presbytery of West Lothian
Cockburnspath	Dunglass
Coigach	charge dissolved: Presbytery of Lochcarron-Skye
Coldstone	Cromar
Collessie	Howe of Fife
Corgarff	Upper Donside
Cortachy	The Glens and Kirriemuir: Old
Coull	Cromar
Covington	Cairngryffe
Cowdenbeath: Cairns	Cowdenbeath: Trinity
Cowdenbeath: Guthrie Memorial	Beath and Cowdenbeath: North
Cowdenbeath: West	Cowdenbeath: Trinity
Craggan	Tomintoul, Glenlivet and Inveraven
Craig	Inchbrayock
Craigdam	Tarves
Craigend	Perth: Moncreiffe
Cranshaws	Kirk of Lammermuir
Crawford	Glencaple
Crawfordjohn	Glencaple
Cray	Kirkmichael, Straloch and Glenshee
Creetown	Kirkmabreck
Crofthead	Fauldhouse St Andrew's
Crombie	Culross and Torryburn
Crossgates	Cowdenbeath: Trinity
Cruggleton	Sorbie
Cuikston	Farnell
Culbin	Dyke
Cullicudden	Resolis and Urquhart
Cults	Howe of Fife
Cumbernauld: Baird	Cumbernauld: Old
Cumbernauld: Bridgend	Cumbernauld: Old
Cumbernauld: St Andrew's	Cumbernauld: Old
Dalgarno	Closeburn

Name no longer used	Present name of parish
Dalguise	Dunkeld
Daliburgh	South Uist
Dalkeith: Buccleuch Street	Dalkeith: St Nicholas Buccleuch
Dalkeith: West (C of S)	Dalkeith: St Nicholas Buccleuch
Dalkeith: West (UP)	Dalkeith: St John's and King's Park
Dalmeath	Huntly Cairnie Glass
Dalreoch	charge dissolved: Presbytery of Perth
Dalry: Courthill	Dalry: Trinity
Dalry: St Andrew's	Dalry: Trinity
Dalry: West	Dalry: Trinity
Denny: Broompark	Denny: Westpark
Denny: West	Denny: Westpark
Dennyloanhead	charge dissolved: Presbytery of Falkirk
Dolphinton	Black Mount
Dowally	Dunkeld
Drainie	Lossiemouth St Gerardine's High
Drumdelgie	Huntly Cairnie Glass
Dumbarrow	charge dissolved: Presbytery of Angus
Dumbarton: Bridgend	Dumbarton: West
Dumbarton: Dalreoch	Dumbarton: West
Dumbarton: High	Dumbarton: Riverside
Dumbarton: Knoxland	Dumbarton: Riverside
Dumbarton: North	Dumbarton: Riverside
Dumbarton: Old	Dumbarton: Riverside
Dumfries: Maxwelltown Laurieknowe	Dumfries: Troqueer
Dumfries: Townhead	Dumfries: St Michael's and South
Dunblane: East	Dunblane: St Blane's
Dunblane: Leighton	Dunblane: St Blane's
Dundee: Albert Square	Dundee: Meadowside St Paul's
Dundee: Baxter Park	Dundee: Trinity
Dundee: Broughty Ferry Union	Dundee: Broughty Ferry St Stephen's and West
Dundee: Chapelshade (C of S)	Dundee: Albany Butterburn
Dundee: Chapelshade (FC)	Dundee: Meadowside St Paul's
Dundee: Downfield North	Dundee: Strathmartine
Dundee: Hawkhill	Dundee: Meadowside St Paul's
Dundee: Lochee East	Dundee: Lochee Old and St Luke's
Dundee: Lochee St Ninian's	Dundee: Lochee Old and St Luke's
Dundee: Martyrs'	Dundee: Balgay
Dundee: Maryfield	Dundee: Stobswell
Dundee: McCheyne Memorial	Dundee: West
Dundee: Ogilvie	Dundee: Stobswell
Dundee: Park	Dundee: Stobswell
Dundee: Roseangle	Dundee: West
Dundee: Rosebank	Dundee: Albany Butterburn
Dundee: Ryehill	Dundee: West
Dundee: St Andrew's (FC)	Dundee: Meadowside St Paul's
Dundee: St Clement's Steeple	Dundee: Steeple
Dundee: St David's (C of S)	Dundee: Steeple
Dundee: St Enoch's	Dundee: Steeple
Dundee: St George's	Dundee: Meadowside St Paul's

Name no longer used	Present name of parish
Dundee: St John's	Dundee: West
Dundee: St Mark's	Dundee: West
Dundee: St Matthew's	Dundee: Trinity
Dundee: St Paul's	Dundee: Steeple
Dundee: St Peter's	Dundee: West
Dundee: Tay Square	Dundee: Meadowside St Paul's
Dundee: Victoria Street	Dundee: Stobswell
Dundee: Wallacetown	Dundee: Trinity
Dundee: Wishart Memorial	Dundee: Steeple
Dundurcas	Keith: North, Newmill, Boharm and Rothiemay
Duneaton	Glencaple
Dunfermline: Chalmers Street	Dunfermline: St Andrew's Erskine
Dunfermline: Maygate	Dunfermline: Gillespie Memorial
Dunfermline: Queen Anne Street	Dunfermline: St Andrew's Erskine
Dungree	Kirkpatrick Juxta
Duninald	Inchbrayock
Dunlappie	Brechin: Cathedral
Dunning	The Stewartry of Strathearn
Dunoon: Gaelic	Dunoon: St John's
Dunrod	Kirkcudbright
Dunsyre	Black Mount
Dupplin	The Stewartry of Strathearn
Ecclefechan	Hoddam
Ecclesjohn	Dun
Ecclesmachan	Strathbrock
Ecclesmoghriodan	Abernethy and Dron
Edinburgh: Abbey	Edinburgh: Greenside
Edinburgh: Abbeyhill	Edinburgh: Holyrood Abbey
Edinburgh: Arthur Street	Edinburgh: Kirk o' Field
Edinburgh: Barony	Edinburgh: Greenside
Edinburgh: Belford	Edinburgh: Palmerston Place
Edinburgh: Bruntsfield	Edinburgh: Barclay
Edinburgh: Buccleuch	Edinburgh: Kirk o' Field
Edinburgh: Cairns Memorial	Edinburgh: Gorgie
Edinburgh: Candlish	Edinburgh: Polwarth
Edinburgh: Canongate (FC,UP)	Edinburgh: Holy Trinity
Edinburgh: Chalmers	Edinburgh: Barclay
Edinburgh: Charteris Memorial	Edinburgh: Kirk o' Field
Edinburgh: College	Edinburgh: Muirhouse St Andrew's
Edinburgh: College Street	Edinburgh: Muirhouse St Andrew's
Edinburgh: Cowgate (FC)	Edinburgh: Muirhouse St Andrew's
Edinburgh: Cowgate (R)	Edinburgh: Barclay
Edinburgh: Cowgate (US)	Edinburgh: Mayfield Salisbury
Edinburgh: Dalry	Edinburgh: St Colm's
Edinburgh: Davidson	Edinburgh: Stockbridge
Edinburgh: Dean (FC)	Edinburgh: Palmerston Place
Edinburgh: Dean Street	Edinburgh: Stockbridge
Edinburgh: Fountainhall Road	Edinburgh: Mayfield Salisbury
Edinburgh: Grange (C of S)	Edinburgh: Marchmont St Giles
Edinburgh: Grange (FC)	Edinburgh: St Catherine's Argyle

Name no longer used	Present name of parish
Edinburgh: Guthrie Memorial	Edinburgh: Greenside
Edinburgh: Haymarket	Edinburgh: St Colm's
Edinburgh: Henderson (C of S)	Edinburgh: Craigmillar Park
Edinburgh: Henderson (UP)	Edinburgh: Richmond Craigmillar
Edinburgh: Hillside	Edinburgh: Greenside
Edinburgh: Holyrood	Edinburgh: Holyrood Abbey
Edinburgh: Hope Park	Edinburgh: Mayfield Salisbury
Edinburgh: Hopetoun	Edinburgh: Greenside
Edinburgh: John Ker Memorial	Edinburgh: Polwarth
Edinburgh: Knox's	Edinburgh: Holy Trinity
Edinburgh: Lady Glenorchy's North	Edinburgh: Greenside
Edinburgh: Lady Glenorchy's South	Edinburgh: Holy Trinity
Edinburgh: Lady Yester's	Edinburgh: Greyfriars Tolbooth and Highland
Edinburgh: Lauriston	Edinburgh: Barclay
Edinburgh: Lochend	Edinburgh: St Margaret's
Edinburgh: Lothian Road	Edinburgh: Palmerston Place
Edinburgh: Mayfield North	Edinburgh: Mayfield Salisbury
Edinburgh: Mayfield South	Edinburgh: Craigmillar Park
Edinburgh: McCrie	Edinburgh: Kirk o' Field
Edinburgh: McDonald Road	Edinburgh: Broughton St Mary's
Edinburgh: Moray	Edinburgh: Holy Trinity
Edinburgh: Morningside High	Edinburgh: Morningside Braid
Edinburgh: New North (C of S)	Edinburgh: Marchmont St Giles
Edinburgh: New North (FC)	Edinburgh: Greyfriars Tolbooth and Highland
Edinburgh: Newington East	Edinburgh: Kirk o' Field
Edinburgh: Newington South	Edinburgh: Mayfield Salisbury
Edinburgh: Nicolson Street	Edinburgh: Kirk o' Field
Edinburgh: North Morningside	Edinburgh: Morningside United
Edinburgh: North Richmond Street	Edinburgh: Richmond Craigmillar
Edinburgh: Pleasance (FC)	Edinburgh: Muirhouse St Andrew's
Edinburgh: Pleasance (UF)	Edinburgh: Kirk o' Field
Edinburgh: Prestonfield	Edinburgh: Priestfield
Edinburgh: Queen Street (FC)	Edinburgh: St Andrew's and St George's
Edinburgh: Queen Street (UP)	Edinburgh: Stockbridge
Edinburgh: Restalrig (C of S)	Edinburgh: St Margaret's
Edinburgh: Restalrig (FC)	Edinburgh: New Restalrig
Edinburgh: Rosehall	Edinburgh: Priestfield
Edinburgh: Roxburgh	Edinburgh: Kirk o' Field
Edinburgh: Roxburgh Terrace	Edinburgh: Kirk o' Field
Edinburgh: South Morningside	Edinburgh: Cluny
Edinburgh: St Bernard's	Edinburgh: Stockbridge
Edinburgh: St Bride's	Edinburgh: St Colm's
Edinburgh: St Columba's	Edinburgh: Greyfriars Tolbooth and Highland
Edinburgh: St David's (C of S)	Edinburgh: Viewforth
Edinburgh: St David's (FC)	Edinburgh: St David's Broomhouse
Edinburgh: St James' (C of S)	Edinburgh: Greenside
Edinburgh: St James' (FC)	Edinburgh: Inverleith
Edinburgh: St James' Place	Edinburgh: Greenside
Edinburgh: St John's	Edinburgh: Greyfriars Tolbooth and Highland
Edinburgh: St Luke's	Edinburgh: St Andrew's and St George's

Name no longer used	Present name of parish
Edinburgh: St Matthew's	Edinburgh: Cluny
Edinburgh: St Oran's	Edinburgh: Greyfriars Tolbooth and Highland
Edinburgh: St Oswald's	Edinburgh: Viewforth
Edinburgh: St Paul's	Edinburgh: Kirk o' Field
Edinburgh: St Stephen's (C of S)	Edinburgh: Stockbridge
Edinburgh: St Stephen's (FC)	Edinburgh: St Stephen's Comely Bank
Edinburgh: Tolbooth (C of S)	Edinburgh: Greyfriars Tolbooth and Highland
Edinburgh: Tolbooth (FC)	Edinburgh: St Andrew's and St George's
Edinburgh: Trinity College	Edinburgh: Holy Trinity
Edinburgh: Tynecastle	Edinburgh: Gorgie
Edinburgh: Warrender	Edinburgh: Marchmont St Giles
Edinburgh: West St Giles	Edinburgh: Marchmont St Giles
Eigg	Arisaig and the Small Isles
Eilean Finain	Ardnamurchan
Elgin: Moss Street	Elgin: St Giles and St Columba's South
Elgin: South Street	Elgin: St Giles and St Columba's South
Ellem	Kirk of Lammermuir
Elsrickle	Black Mount
Eshaness	Northmavine
Essie	Noth
Essil	Speymouth
Ethie	Inverkeilor and Lunan
Ettiltoun	Liddesdale
Ewes Durris	Langholm, Ewes and Westerkirk
Falkirk: Graham's Road	Falkirk: Grahamston United
Farnua	Kirkhill
Ferryden	Inchbrayock
Fetterangus	Deer
Fettercairn	West Mearns
Fetternear	Chapel of Garioch
Finzean	Birse and Feughside
Fochabers	Bellie
Forbes	Howe Trinity
Fordoun	West Mearns
Forfar: South	Forfar: St Margaret's
Forfar: St James'	Forfar: St Margaret's
Forfar: West	Forfar: St Margaret's
Forgan	Newport-on-Tay
Forgue	Auchaber United
Forres: Castlehill	Forres: St Leonard's
Forres: High	Forres: St Leonard's
Forteviot	The Stewartry of Strathearn
Forvie	Ellon
Foula	Walls and Sandness
Galashiels: East	Galashiels: St Ninian's
Galashiels: Ladhope	Galashiels: St Aidan's
Galashiels: South	Galashiels: St Aidan's
Galashiels: St Andrew's	Galashiels: St Ninian's
Galashiels: St Columba's	Galashiels: St Ninian's
Galashiels: St Cuthbert's	Galashiels: St Aidan's

Name no longer used	Present name of parish
Galashiels: St Mark's	Galashiels: St Ninian's
Galashiels: Trinity	Galashiels: St Aidan's
Galtway	Kirkcudbright
Gamrie	charge dissolved: Presbytery of Buchan
Garmouth	Speymouth
Gartly	Noth
Garvell	Kirkmichael, Tinwald and Torthorwald
Garvock	Mearns Coastal
Gatehouse	Anwoth and Girthon
Gauldry	Balmerino
Gelston	Buittle and Kelton
Giffnock: Orchard Park	Giffnock: The Park
Girvan: Chalmers	Girvan: North (Old and St Andrew's)
Girvan: Trinity	Girvan: North (Old and St Andrew's)
Glasgow: Abbotsford	Glasgow: Gorbals
Glasgow: Auldfield	Glasgow: Pollokshaws
Glasgow: Baillieston Old	Glasgow: Baillieston St Andrew's
Glasgow: Baillieston Rhinsdale	Glasgow: Baillieston St Andrew's
Glasgow: Balornock North	Glasgow: Wallacewell
Glasgow: Barmulloch	Glasgow: Wallacewell
Glasgow: Barrowfield (C of S)	Glasgow: Bridgeton St Francis in the East
Glasgow: Barrowfield (RP)	Glasgow: St Luke's and St Andrew's
Glasgow: Bath Street	Glasgow: Renfield St Stephen's
Glasgow: Battlefield West	Glasgow: Langside
Glasgow: Bellahouston	Glasgow: Ibrox
Glasgow: Bellgrove	Glasgow: Dennistoun Blackfriars
Glasgow: Belmont	Glasgow: Kelvinside Hillhead
Glasgow: Berkeley Street	Glasgow: Renfield St Stephen's
Glasgow: Bluevale	Glasgow: Dennistoun Central
Glasgow: Blythswood	Glasgow: Renfield St Stephen's
Glasgow: Bridgeton East	Glasgow: Bridgeton St Francis in the East
Glasgow: Bridgeton West	Glasgow: St Luke's and St Andrew's
Glasgow: Buccleuch	Glasgow: Renfield St Stephen's
Glasgow: Burnbank	Glasgow: Lansdowne
Glasgow: Calton New	Glasgow: St Luke's and St Andrew's
Glasgow: Calton Old	Glasgow: Calton Parkhead
Glasgow: Calton Relief	Glasgow: St Luke's and St Andrew's
Glasgow: Cambridge Street	Bishopbriggs: Springfield Cambridge
Glasgow: Candlish Memorial	Glasgow: Govanhill Trinity
Glasgow: Central	Glasgow: St Luke's and St Andrew's
Glasgow: Cessnock	Glasgow: Kinning Park
Glasgow: Chalmers (C of S)	Glasgow: St Luke's and St Andrew's
Glasgow: Chalmers (FC)	Glasgow: Gorbals
Glasgow: Claremont	Glasgow: Anderston Kelvingrove
Glasgow: College	Glasgow: Anderston Kelvingrove
Glasgow: Cowcaddens	Glasgow: Renfield St Stephen's
Glasgow: Cowlairs	Glasgow: Springburn
Glasgow: Crosshill	Glasgow: Queen's Park
Glasgow: Dalmarnock (C of S)	Glasgow: Calton Parkhead
Glasgow: Dalmarnock (UF)	Rutherglen: Old

Name no longer used	Present name of parish
Glasgow: Dean Park	Glasgow: New Govan
Glasgow: Dennistoun South	Glasgow: Dennistoun Blackfriars
Glasgow: Dowanhill	Glasgow: Partick Trinity
Glasgow: Dowanvale	Glasgow: Partick South
Glasgow: Drumchapel Old	Glasgow: Drumchapel St Andrew's
Glasgow: East Campbell Street	Glasgow: Dennistoun Central
Glasgow: East Park	Glasgow: Kelvin Stevenson Memorial
Glasgow: Edgar Memorial	Glasgow: St Luke's and St Andrew's
Glasgow: Eglinton Street	Glasgow: Govanhill Trinity
Glasgow: Elder Park	Glasgow: Govan Old
Glasgow: Elgin Street	Glasgow: Govanhill Trinity
Glasgow: Erskine	Glasgow: Langside
Glasgow: Fairbairn	Rutherglen: Old
Glasgow: Fairfield	Glasgow: New Govan
Glasgow: Finnieston	Glasgow: Anderston Kelvingrove
Glasgow: Garnethill	Glasgow: Renfield St Stephen's
Glasgow: Garscube Netherton	Glasgow: Knightswood St Margaret's
Glasgow: Gillespie	Glasgow: St Luke's and St Andrew's
Glasgow: Gordon Park	Glasgow: Whiteinch
Glasgow: Govan Copland Road	Glasgow: New Govan
Glasgow: Govan Trinity	Glasgow: New Govan
Glasgow: Grant Street	Glasgow: Renfield St Stephen's
Glasgow: Greenhead	Glasgow: St Luke's and St Andrew's
Glasgow: Hall Memorial	Rutherglen: Old
Glasgow: Hamilton Crescent	Glasgow: Partick South
Glasgow: Highlanders' Memorial	Glasgow: Knightswood St Margaret's
Glasgow: Hyndland (UF)	Glasgow: St John's Renfield
Glasgow: John Knox's	Glasgow: Gorbals
Glasgow: Johnston	Glasgow: Springburn
Glasgow: Jordanvale	Glasgow: Whiteinch
Glasgow: Kelvinhaugh	Glasgow: Anderston Kelvingrove
Glasgow: Kelvinside Botanic Gardens	Glasgow: Kelvinside Hillhead
Glasgow: Kelvinside Old	Glasgow: Kelvin Stevenson Memorial
Glasgow: Kingston	Glasgow: Carnwadric
Glasgow: Lancefield	Glasgow: Anderston Kelvingrove
Glasgow: Langside Avenue	Glasgow: Shawlands
Glasgow: Langside Hill	Glasgow: Battlefield East
Glasgow: Langside Old	Glasgow: Langside
Glasgow: Laurieston (C of S)	Glasgow: Gorbals
Glasgow: Laurieston (FC)	Glasgow: Carnwadric
Glasgow: London Road	Glasgow: Bridgeton St Francis in the East
Glasgow: Lyon Street	Glasgow: Renfield St Stephen's
Glasgow: Macgregor Memorial	Glasgow: Govan Old
Glasgow: Macmillan	Glasgow: St Luke's and St Andrew's
Glasgow: Milton	Glasgow: Renfield St Stephen's
Glasgow: Netherton St Matthew's	Glasgow: Knightswood St Margaret's
Glasgow: Newhall	Glasgow: Bridgeton St Francis in the East
Glasgow: Newton Place	Glasgow: Partick South
Glasgow: Nithsdale	Glasgow: Queen's Park
Glasgow: Old Partick	Glasgow: Partick Trinity

Name no longer used	Present name of parish
Glasgow: Paisley Road	Glasgow: Kinning Park
Glasgow: Partick Anderson	Glasgow: Partick South
Glasgow: Partick East	Glasgow: Partick Trinity
Glasgow: Partick High	Glasgow: Partick South
Glasgow: Phoenix Park	Glasgow: Springburn
Glasgow: Plantation	Glasgow: Kinning Park
Glasgow: Pollok St Aidan's	Glasgow: St James' Pollok
Glasgow: Pollok Street	Glasgow: Kinning Park
Glasgow: Polmadie	Glasgow: Govanhill Trinity
Glasgow: Queen's Cross	Glasgow: Ruchill
Glasgow: Renfield (C of S)	Glasgow: Renfield St Stephen's
Glasgow: Renfield (FC)	Glasgow: St John's Renfield
Glasgow: Renfield Street	Glasgow: Renfield St Stephen's
Glasgow: Renwick	Glasgow: Gorbals
Glasgow: Robertson Memorial	Glasgow: The Martyrs'
Glasgow: Rockcliffe	Rutherglen: Old
Glasgow: Rockvilla	Glasgow: Possilpark
Glasgow: Rose Street	Glasgow: Langside
Glasgow: Rutherford	Glasgow: Dennistoun Central
Glasgow: Shamrock Street	Glasgow: Renfield St Stephen's
Glasgow: Shawholm	Glasgow: Pollokshaws
Glasgow: Shawlands Cross	Glasgow: Shawlands
Glasgow: Shawlands Old	Glasgow: Shawlands
Glasgow: Sighthill	Glasgow: Springburn
Glasgow: Somerville	Glasgow: Springburn
Glasgow: Springbank	Glasgow: Lansdowne
Glasgow: St Clement's	Glasgow: Bridgeton St Francis in the East
Glasgow: St Columba Gaelic	Glasgow: New Govan
Glasgow: St Cuthbert's	Glasgow: Ruchill
Glasgow: St Enoch's (C of S)	Glasgow: St Enoch's Hogganfield
Glasgow: St Enoch's (FC)	Glasgow: Anderston Kelvingrove
Glasgow: St George's (C of S)	Glasgow: St George's Tron
Glasgow: St George's (FC)	Glasgow: Anderston Kelvingrove
Glasgow: St George's Road	Glasgow: Renfield St Stephen's
Glasgow: St James' (C of S)	Glasgow: St James' Pollok
Glasgow: St James' (FC)	Glasgow: St Luke's and St Andrew's
Glasgow: St John's (C of S)	Glasgow: St Luke's and St Andrew's
Glasgow: St John's (FC)	Glasgow: St John's Renfield
Glasgow: St Kiaran's	Glasgow: New Govan
Glasgow: St Mark's	Glasgow: Anderston Kelvingrove
Glasgow: St Mary's Govan	Glasgow: New Govan
Glasgow: St Mary's Partick	Glasgow: Partick South
Glasgow: St Matthew's (C of S)	Glasgow: Renfield St Stephen's
Glasgow: St Matthew's (FC)	Glasgow: Knightswood St Margaret's
Glasgow: St Ninian's	Glasgow: Gorbals
Glasgow: St Peter's	Glasgow: Anderston Kelvingrove
Glasgow: Steven Memorial	Glasgow: Ibrox
Glasgow: Strathbungo	Glasgow: Queen's Park
Glasgow: Summerfield	Rutherglen: Old
Glasgow: Summertown	Glasgow: New Govan

Name no longer used	Present name of parish
Glasgow: Sydney Place	Glasgow: Dennistoun Cental
Glasgow: The Park	Giffnock: The Park
Glasgow: Titwood	Glasgow: Pollokshields
Glasgow: Tradeston	Glasgow: Gorbals
Glasgow: Trinity	Glasgow: St Luke's and St Andrew's
Glasgow: Trinity Duke Street	Glasgow: Dennistoun Central
Glasgow: Tron St Anne's	Glasgow: St George's Tron
Glasgow: Union	Glasgow: Carnwadric
Glasgow: Victoria	Glasgow: Queen's Park
Glasgow: Wellfield	Glasgow: Springburn
Glasgow: Wellpark	Glasgow: Dennistoun Cental
Glasgow: West Scotland Street	Glasgow: Kinning Park
Glasgow: White Memorial	Glasgow: Kinning Park
Glasgow: Whitehill	Glasgow: Dennistoun Blackfriars
Glasgow: Whitevale (FC)	Glasgow: St Thomas' Gallowgate
Glasgow: Whitevale (UP)	Glasgow: Dennistoun Central
Glasgow: Wilton	Glasgow: Kelvin Stevenson Memorial
Glasgow: Woodlands	Glasgow: Wellington
Glasgow: Woodlands Road	Glasgow: Wellington
Glasgow: Woodside	Glasgow: Lansdowne
Glasgow: Wynd (C of S)	Glasgow: St Luke's and St Andrew's
Glasgow: Wynd (FC)	Glasgow: Gorbals
Glasgow: Young Street	Glasgow: Dennistoun Blackfriars
Glen Convinth	Kiltarlity
Glen Ussie	Fodderty and Strathpeffer
Glenapp	Ballantrae
Glenbervie	West Mearns
Glenbuchat	Upper Donside
Glenbuck	Muirkirk
Glencaple	Caerlaverock
Glendoick	St Madoes and Kinfauns
Glenfarg	Arngask
Glengairn	Glenmuick
Glengarnock	Kilbirnie: Auld Kirk
Glenluce	Old Luce
Glenmoriston	Fort Augustus
Glenprosen	The Glens and Kirriemuir Old
Glenrinnes	Mortlach and Cabrach
Glenshiel	Glenelg and Kintail
Glentanar	Aboyne – Dinnet
Gogar	Edinburgh: Corstorphine Old
Gordon	Monquhitter and New Byth
Graemsay	Stromness
Grangemouth: Grange	Grangemouth: Zetland
Grangemouth: Old	Grangemouth: Zetland
Greenloaning	Ardoch
Greenock: Augustine	Greenock: Cartsdyke
Greenock: Cartsburn	Greenock: Cartsdyke
Greenock: Crawfordsburn	Greenock: Cartsdyke
Greenock: Gaelic	Greenock: St Luke's

Name no longer used	Present name of parish
Greenock: Greenbank	Greenock: St Luke's
Greenock: Martyrs'	Greenock: St George's North
Greenock: Middle	Greenock: St George's North
Greenock: Mount Park	Greenock: Mount Kirk
Greenock: Mount Pleasant	Greenock: Mount Kirk
Greenock: North (C of S)	Greenock: Old West Kirk
Greenock: North (FC)	Greenock: St George's North
Greenock: Sir Michael Street	Greenock: Ardgowan
Greenock: South	Greenock: Mount Kirk
Greenock: South Park	Greenock: Mount Kirk
Greenock: St Andrew's	Greenock: Ardgowan
Greenock: St Columba's Gaelic	Greenock: Old West Kirk
Greenock: St Mark's	Greenock: St Luke's
Greenock: St Thomas'	Greenock: St George's North
Greenock: The Old Kirk	Greenock: St Luke's
Greenock: The Union Church	Greenock: Ardgowan
Greenock: Trinity	Greenock: Ardgowan
Greenock: Union Street	Greenock: Ardgowan
Greenock: West	Greenock: St Luke's
Gress	Stornoway: St Columba
Guardbridge	Leuchars St Athernase
Haddington: St John's	Haddington: West
Hamilton: Auchingramont North	Hamilton: North
Hamilton: Avon Street	Hamilton: St Andrew's
Hamilton: Brandon	Hamilton: St Andrew's
Hamilton: Saffronhall Assoc. Anti-B.	Hamilton: North
Hardgate	Urr
Hassendean	Minto
Hawick: East Bank	Hawick: Trinity
Hawick: Orrock	Hawick: St Mary's and Old
Hawick: St Andrew's	Hawick: Trinity
Hawick: St George's	Hawick: Teviot
Hawick: St George's West	Hawick: Teviot
Hawick: St John's	Hawick: Trinity
Hawick: St Margaret's	Hawick: Teviot
Hawick: West Port	Hawick: Teviot
Hawick: Wilton South	Hawick: Teviot
Haywood	Forth
Helensburgh: Old	Helensburgh: The West Kirk
Helensburgh: St Andrew's	Helensburgh: The West Kirk
Helensburgh: St Bride's	Helensburgh: The West Kirk
Heylipol	Tiree
Hillside	Unst
Hillswick	Northmavine
Hilton	Whitsome
Holywell	Longtown
Hope Kailzie	charge suppressed: Presbytery of Melrose and Peebles
Horndean	Ladykirk
Howford	charge dissolved: Presbytery of Inverness
Howmore	South Uist

Name no longer used	Present name of parish
Huntly: Princes Street	Huntly: Strathbogie
Inchkenneth	Kilfinichen and Kilvickeon and the Ross of Mull
Inchmartin	Errol
Innerwick	Dunglass
Inverallan	Grantown-on-Spey
Inverchaolain	Toward
Inverkeithny	Auchaber United
Inverness: Merkinch St Mark's	Inverness: Trinity
Inverness: Queen Street	Inverness: Trinity
Inverness: St Mary's	Inverness: Dalneigh and Bona
Irving	Gretna, Half Morton and Kirkpatrick Fleming
Jedburgh: Abbey	Jedburgh: Trinity
Jedburgh: Blackfriars	Jedburgh: Trinity
Jedburgh: Boston	Jedburgh: Trinity
Johnshaven	Mearns Coastal
Johnstone: East	Johnstone: St Paul's
Johnstone: West	Johnstone: St Paul's
Kames	Kyles
Kearn	Upper Donside
Keig	Howe Trinity
Keith Marischal	Humbie
Keith: South	Keith: North, Newmill, Boharm and Rothiemay
Kelso: East	Kelso: North and Ednam
Kelso: Edenside	Kelso: North and Ednam
Kelso: St John's	Kelso: North and Ednam
Kelso: Trinity	Kelso: North and Ednam
Kennethmont	Noth
Kettle	Howe of Fife
Kilbirnie: Barony	Kilbirnie: Auld Kirk
Kilbirnie: East	Kilbirnie: St Columba's
Kilbirnie: West	Kilbirnie: St Columba's
Kilblaan	Southend
Kilblane	Kirkmahoe
Kilbride (Dumfries and Kirkcudbright)	Sanquhar
Kilbride (Dunoon)	Kyles
Kilbride (Lorn and Mull)	Kilmore and Oban
Kilbride (Stirling)	Dunblane: Cathedral
Kilchattan Bay	Bute United
Kilchousland	Campbeltown: Highland
Kilcolmkill (Lochaber)	Morvern
Kilcolmkill (South Argyll)	Southend
Kildrummy	Upper Donside
Kilkerran	Campbeltown: Highland
Kilkivan	Campbeltown: Highland
Killintag	Morvern
Kilmacolm: St James'	Kilmacolm: St Columba
Kilmahew	Cardross
Kilmahog	Callander
Kilmarnock: King Street	Kilmarnock: Howard St Andrew's
Kilmarnock: Portland Road	Kilmarnock: Howard St Andrew's

Name no longer used	Present name of parish
Kilmarrow	Killean and Kilchenzie
Kilmichael (Inverness)	Urquhart and Glenmoriston
Kilmichael (South Argyll)	Campbeltown: Highland
Kilmoir	Brechin: Cathedral
Kilmore	Urquhart and Glenmoriston
Kilmoveonaig	Blair Atholl and Struan
Kilmun: St Andrew's	Strone and Ardentinny
Kilpheder	South Uist
Kinairney	Midmar
Kincardine O'Neil	Mid Deeside
Kincraig	Alvie and Insh
Kingarth	Bute United
Kininmonth	charge dissolved: Presbytery of Buchan
Kinkell	Keithhall
Kinloch	Caputh and Clunie
Kinlochewe	Applecross, Lochcarron and Torridon
Kinlochluichart	Contin
Kinlochrannoch	Foss and Rannoch
Kinneil	Bo'ness: Old
Kinnettas	Fodderty and Strathpeffer
Kinnoir	Huntly Cairnie Glass
Kinrossie	Collace
Kirkandrews	Borgue
Kirkapol	Tiree
Kirkcaldy: Abbotsrood	Kirkcaldy: St Andrew's
Kirkcaldy: Bethelfield	Kirkcaldy: Linktown
Kirkcaldy: Dunnikeir	Kirkcaldy: St Andrew's
Kirkcaldy: Gallatown	Kirkcaldy: Viewforth
Kirkcaldy: Invertiel	Kirkcaldy: Linktown
Kirkcaldy: Old	Kirkcaldy: St Bryce Kirk
Kirkcaldy: Raith	Kirkcaldy: Abbotshall
Kirkcaldy: Sinclairtown	Kirkcaldy: Viewforth
Kirkcaldy: St Brycedale	Kirkcaldy: St Bryce Kirk
Kirkcaldy: Victoria Road	Kirkcaldy: St Andrew's
Kirkchrist	Tarff and Twynholm
Kirkconnel	Gretna, Half Morton and Kirkpatrick Fleming
Kirkcormick	Buittle and Kelton
Kirkdale	Kirkmabreck
Kirkforthar	Markinch
Kirkhope	Ettrick and Yarrow
Kirkintilloch: St Andrew's	Kirkintilloch: St Columba's
Kirkintilloch: St David's	Kirkintilloch: St Columba's
Kirkmadrine (Machars)	Sorbie
Kirkmadrine (Rhinns)	Stoneykirk
Kirkmaiden	Glasserton and Isle of Whithorn
Kirkmichael	Tomintoul, Glenlivet and Inveraven
Kirkpottie	Abernethy and Dron
Kirkwall: King Street	Kirkwall: East
Kirkwall: Paterson	Kirkwall: East
Kirriemuir: Bank Street	The Glens and Kirriemuir Old

Name no longer used	Present name of parish
Kirriemuir: Barony	The Glens and Kirriemuir Old
Kirriemuir: Livingstone	Kirriemuir: St Andrew's
Kirriemuir: South	Kirriemuir: St Andrew's
Kirriemuir: St Ninian's	The Glens and Kirriemuir Old
Kirriemuir: West	The Glens and Kirriemuir Old
Ladybank	Howe of Fife
Lagganallochie	Dunkeld
Lamberton	Foulden and Mordington
Lamington	Glencaple
Lanark: Broomgate	Lanark: Greyfriars
Lanark: Cairns	Lanark: Greyfriars
Lanark: St Kentigern's	Lanark: Greyfriars
Lanark: St Leonard's	Lanark: St Nicholas'
Largieside	Killean and Kilchenzie
Lassodie	Dunfermline: Townhill and Kingseat
Lathones	Largoward
Laurieston	Balmaghie
Laxavoe	Delting
Leadhills	Lowther
Leith: Bonnington	Edinburgh: Leith North
Leith: Claremont	Edinburgh: Leith St Andrew's
Leith: Dalmeny Street	Edinburgh: Pilrig St Paul's
Leith: Elder Memorial	Edinburgh: St John's Oxgangs
Leith: Harper Memorial	Edinburgh: Leith North
Leith: Kirkgate	Edinburgh: Leith South
Leith: South (FC)	Edinburgh: Leith St Andrew's
Leith: St Andrew's Place	Edinburgh: Leith St Andrew's
Leith: St John's	Edinburgh: St John's Oxgangs
Leith: St Nicholas	Edinburgh: Leith North
Leith: St Ninian's	Edinburgh: Leith North
Lemlair	Kiltearn
Lempitlaw	Kelso: Old and Sprouston
Leny	Callander
Leochel	Cushnie and Tough
Lesmahagow: Cordiner	Lesmahagow: Abbey Green
Lethendy	Caputh and Clunie
Lindowan	Craigrownie
Linlithgow: East	Linlithgow: St Ninian's Craigmailen
Linlithgow: Trinity	Linlithgow: St Ninian's Craigmailen
Livingston: Tulloch	Livingston: Old
Livingston: West	Livingston: Old
Lochaline	Morvern
Lochdonhead	Torosay and Kinlochspelvie
Lochearnhead	Balquhidder
Lochlee	Glenesk
Lochryan	Inch
Logie Buchan	Ellon
Logie Mar	Cromar
Logie Pert	charge dissolved: Presbytery of Angus
Logie Wester	Ferintosh

Name no longer used	Present name of parish
Logie (Dundee)	Fowlis and Liff
Logie (St Andrews)	charge dissolved: Presbytery of St Andrews
Logiebride	Auchtergaven and Moneydie
Longcastle	Kirkinner
Longformacus	Kirk of Lammermuir
Longnewton	Ancrum
Longridge	Breich Valley
Luce	Hoddam
Lude	Blair Atholl and Struan
Lumphanan	Mid Deeside
Lumphinnans	Beath and Cowdenbeath: North
Lumsden	Upper Donside
Luncarty	Redgorton
Lund	Unst
Lynturk	Cushnie and Tough
Mailor	The Stewartry of Strathearn
Mainsriddle	Colvend, Southwick and Kirkbean
Maryburgh	Ferintosh
Marykirk	Aberluthnott
Maryton	Inchbrayock
Meadowfield	Caldercruix and Longriggend
Meathie	Glamis, Inverarity and Kinnettles
Megget	Lyne and Manor
Melville	charge suppressed: Presbytery of Lothian
Memus	The Glens and Kirriemuir: Old
Methil: East	Innerleven: East
Mid Calder: Bridgend	Kirk of Calder
Mid Calder: St John's	Kirk of Calder
Midholm	congregation seceded: Presbytery of Jedburgh
Migvie	Cromar
Millbrex	Fyvie
Millerston	charge dissolved: Presbytery of Glasgow
Millport	Cumbrae
Milnathort	Orwell
Monecht	charge dissolved: Presbytery of Gordon
Monifeith: North	Monikie and Newbigging
Montrose: Knox's	Montrose: Melville South
Montrose: St George's	Montrose: St Andrew's
Montrose: St John's	Montrose: St Andrew's
Montrose: St Luke's	Montrose: St Andrew's
Montrose: St Paul's	Montrose: Melville South
Montrose: Trinity	Montrose: St Andrew's
Monzievaird	Crieff
Moonzie	charge dissolved: Presbytery of St Andrews
Morton	Thornhill
Mossbank	Delting
Mossgreen	Cowdenbeath: Trinity
Motherwell: Brandon	Motherwell: Crosshill
Motherwell: Cairns	Motherwell: Crosshill
Moulin	Pitlochry

Name no longer used	Present name of parish
Mount Kedar	Ruthwell
Mow	Morebattle and Hownam
Moy	Dyke
Moyness	charge dissolved: Presbytery of Moray
Muckersie	The Stewartry of Strathearn
Muirton	Aberluthnott
Murthly	Caputh and Clunie
Musselburgh: Bridge Street	Musselburgh: St Andrew's High
Musselburgh: Millhill	Musselburgh: St Andrew's High
Nairn: High	Nairn: St Ninian's
Nairn: Rosebank	Nairn: St Ninian's
Navar	Edzell Lethnott
New Leeds	charge dissolved: Presbytery of Buchan
New Liston	Edinburgh: Kirkliston
Newcastleton	Liddesdale
Newdosk	Edzell Lethnott
Newmills	Culross and Torryburn
Newseat	Rothienorman
Newton Stewart	Penninghame
Nigg	charge dissolved: Presbytery of Aberdeen
Nisbet	Crailing and Eckford
North Bute	Bute United
Norwick	Unst
Ogston	Lossiemouth: St Gerardine's High
Old Kilpatrick: Barclay	Dalmuir Barclay
Oldhamstocks	Dunglass
Ollaberry	Northmavine
Olnafirth	Delting
Ord	Ordiquhill and Cornhill
Paisley: Canal Street	Paisley: Castlehead
Paisley: George Street	Paisley: Glenburn
Paisley: High	Paisley: Oakshaw Trinity
Paisley: Merksworth	Paisley: Wallneuk North
Paisley: Middle	Paisley: Castlehead
Paisley: Mossvale	Paisley: Wallneuk North
Paisley: New Street	Paisley: Glenburn
Paisley: North	Paisley: Wallneuk North
Paisley: Oakshaw West	Paisley: St Luke's
Paisley: Orr Square	Paisley: Oakshaw Trinity
Paisley: South	Paisley: St Luke's
Paisley: St Andrew's	Paisley: Laigh
Paisley: St George's	Paisley: Laigh
Paisley: St John's	Paisley: Oakshaw Trinity
Papa Stour	Walls and Sandness
Park	Kinloch
Pathhead	Ormiston
Pathstruie	The Stewartry of Strathearn
Pearston	Dreghorn and Springside
Peebles: West	Peebles: St Andrew's Leckie
Pennersaughs	Middlebie

Name no longer used	Present name of parish
Pentland	Lasswade
Persie	Kirkmichael, Straloch and Glenshee
Perth: Bridgend	Perth: St Matthew's
Perth: East	Perth: St Leonard's-in-the-Fields and Trinity
Perth: Knox's	Perth: St Leonard's-in-the-Fields and Trinity
Perth: Middle	Perth: St Matthew's
Perth: St Andrew's	Perth: Riverside
Perth: St Columba's	Perth: North
Perth: St Leonard's	Perth: North
Perth: St Stephen's	Perth: Riverside
Perth: West	Perth: St Matthew's
Perth: Wilson	Perth: St Matthew's
Perth: York Place	Perth: St Leonard's-in-the-Fields and Trinity
Peterhead: Charlotte Street	Peterhead: Trinity
Peterhead: East	Peterhead: St Andrew's
Peterhead: South	Peterhead: St Andrew's
Peterhead: St Peter's	Peterhead: Trinity
Peterhead: West Associate	Peterhead: Trinity
Pettinain	Cairngryffe
Pitcairn (CofS)	Redgorton
Pitcairn (UF)	Almondbank Tibbermore
Pitlessie	Howe of Fife
Pitroddie	St Madoes and Kinfauns
Plockton	Lochalsh
Polmont South	Brightons
Poolewe	Gairloch and Dundonnell
Port Bannatyne	Bute United
Port Ellen	Kildalton and Oa
Port Glasgow: Clune Park	Port Glasgow: St Andrew's
Port Glasgow: Newark	Port Glasgow: St Andrew's
Port Glasgow: Old	Port Glasgow: St Andrew's
Port Glasgow: Princes Street	Port Glasgow: St Andrew's
Port Glasgow: West	Port Glasgow: St Andrew's
Port Sonachan	Glenorchy and Inishail
Port William	Mochrum
Portobello: Regent Street	Edinburgh: Portobello Old
Portobello: Windsor Place	Edinburgh: Portobello Old
Portsoy	Fordyce
Prestonkirk	Traprain
Prinlaws	Leslie Trinity
Quarrier's Mount Zion	Kilmacolm: St Columba
Raasay	Portree
Rathillet	Creich, Flisk and Kilmany
Rathmuriel	Noth
Redcastle	Killearnan
Restenneth	Forfar: East and Old
Rhynd	Perth: Moncreiffe
Rhynie	Noth
Rickarton	charge dissolved: Presbytery of Kincardine and Deeside
Rigg	Gretna, Half Morton and Kirkpatrick Fleming

Name no longer used	Present name of parish
Rinpatrick	Gretna, Half Morton and Kirkpatrick Fleming
Roberton	Glencaple
Rosehearty	Pitsligo
Rossie	Inchture and Kinnaird
Rothesay: Bridgend	Bute United
Rothesay: Craigmore High	Rothesay: Trinity
Rothesay: Craigmore St Brendan's	Bute United
Rothesay: High	Bute United
Rothesay: New	Bute United
Rothesay: St James'	Rothesay: Trinity
Rothesay: St John's	Bute United
Rothesay: West	Rothesay: Trinity
Rutherglen: East	Rutherglen: Old
Rutherglen: Greenhill	Rutherglen: Old
Rutherglen: Munro	Ritherglen: West
Ruthven	Huntly Cairnie Glass
Saltcoats: Erskine	Saltcoats: New Trinity
Saltcoats: Landsborough	Saltcoats: New Trinity
Saltcoats: Middle	Saltcoats: New Trinity
Saltcoats: Trinity	Saltcoats: New Trinity
Saltcoats: West	Saltcoats: New Trinity
Sandhead	Stoneykirk
Saughtree	Liddesdale
Saulseat	Inch
Scalloway	Tingwall
Scatsta	Delting
Sclattie	Blairdaff
Scone: Abbey	Scone: New
Scone: West	Scone: New
Scoonie	Leven
Scourie	Edrachillis
Seafield	Findochty, Portknockie and Rathven
Sennick	Borgue
Seton	Tranent
Shawbost	Carloway
Shebster	Reay
Sheuchan	Stranraer: High
Shieldaig	Applecross, Lochcarron and Torridon
Shiels	Belhelvie
Shottsburn	Kirk o' Shotts
Shurrery	Reay
Simprin	Fogo and Swinton
Skerrols	Kilarrow
Skinnet	Halkirk and Westerdale
Slains	Ellon
South Ballachulish	charge dissolved: Presbytery of Lochaber
Spittal (Caithness)	Halkirk and Westerdale
Spittal (Duns)	charge dissolved: Presbytery of Duns
Springfield	Gretna, Half Morton and Kirkpatrick Fleming
St Cyrus	Mearns Coastal

Name no longer used	Present name of parish
St Ola	Kirkwall: St Magnus Cathedral
Stenton	Traprain
Stewartfield	Deer
Stewarton: Cairns	Stewarton: St Columba's
Stewarton: Laigh	Stewarton: St Columba's
Stirling: Craigs	Stirling: St Columba's
Stirling: North (FC)	Stirling: St Columba's
Stobhill	Gorebridge
Stockbridge	Dunglass
Stonehaven: North	Stonehaven: South
Stoneyburn	Breich Valley
Stornoway: James Street	Stornoway: Martin's Memorial
Stracathro	Brechin: Cathedral
Strachan	Birse and Feughside
Stranraer: Bellevilla	Stranraer: St Ninian's
Stranraer: Bridge Street	Stranraer: St Ninian's
Stranraer: Ivy Place	Stranraer: St Andrew's
Stranraer: St Margaret's	Stranraer: High
Stranraer: St Mark's	Stranraer: St Andrew's
Strathconon	Contin
Strathdeveron	Mortlach and Cabrach
Strathdon	Upper Donside
Stratherrick	Dores and Boleskine
Strathgarve	Contin
Strathglass	Kilmorack and Erchless
Strathmartine (C of S)	Dundee: Mains
Strowan	Comrie
Suddie	Knockbain
Tarfside	Glenesk
Tarland	Cromar
Tarvit	Cupar: Old and St Michael of Tarvit
Temple	Gorebridge
Thankerton	Cairngryffe
The Bass	North Berwick: St Andrew Blackadder
Tighnabruaich	Kyles
Tongland	Tarff and Twynholm
Torphins	Mid Deeside
Torrance	East Kilbride: Old
Towie	Upper Donside
Trailflat	Kirkmichael, Tinwald and Torthorwald
Trailtrow	Cummertrees
Trefontaine	Kirk of Lammermuir
Trossachs	Callander
Trumisgarry	Berneray and Lochmaddy
Tullibole	Fossoway St Serf's and Devonside
Tullich	Glenmuick
Tullichetil	Comrie
Tullynessle	Howe Trinity
Tummel	Foss and Rannoch
Tushielaw	Ettrick and Yarrow

Name no longer used	Present name of parish
Uddingston: Aitkenhead	Uddingston: Viewpark
Uddingston: Chalmers	Uddingston: Old
Uddingston: Trinity	Uddingston: Old
Uig	Snizort
Uphall: North	Strathbrock
Uyeasound	Unst
Walston	Black Mount
Wandel	Glencaple
Wanlockhead	Lowther
Waternish	Bracadale and Duirinish
Wauchope	Langholm, Ewes and Westerkirk
Waulkmill	Insch-Leslie-Premnay-Oyne
Weisdale	Tingwall
West Kilbride: Barony	West Kilbride: St Andrew's
West Kilbride: St Bride's	West Kilbride: St Andrew's
Wheelkirk	Liddesdale
Whitehill	New Pitsligo
Whiteness	Tingwall
Whittingehame	Traprain
Wick: Central	Wick: Pultneytown and Thrumster
Wick: Martyrs'	Wick: Pultneytown and Thrumster
Wick: St Andrew's	Wick: Pultneytown and Thrumster
Wilkieston	Edinburgh: Ratho
Wilsontown	Forth
Wiston	Glencaple
Wolfhill	Cargill Burrelton
Wolflee	Hobkirk and Southdean
Woomet	Newton
Ythan Wells	Auchaber United

INDEX OF SUBJECTS

Action of Churches Together in Scotland
(ACTS) — xvi, 42
Adult Adviser (Parish Education) — 43–44
Alcohol/Drug Dependency Units — 31ff.
Apologetics Committee — 26
Artistic Matters Committee — 18
Assembly Council — 2, 16
Associations (and Societies) — 60
Auxiliary Ministry — 19, 21, 260

Badenoch Christian Centre — xvi, 24
Baptism — 74
Bible Societies — 62
Broadcasting (see Local Broadcasting) — 49

Carberry — xvi
Central Co-ordinating Committee — 6
Chaplaincies Committee — 3, 23, 27
Chaplains to HM Forces — 22, 261
Chaplains, Hospital — 28, 263
Chaplains, Industrial
(Church and Industry) — 3, 28, 272
Chaplains, Prison — 3, 28, 272
Chaplains to the Queen — 71
Chaplains, University and College — 28, 274
Child Protection — 43, 45
Children's Ministry — 44
Christian Aid — xvi, 40
Church and Nation Committee — 16
Church of Scotland Investors Trust — 11
Church of Scotland Societies — 61
Church of Scotland Trust — 49
Church and Society Commission (CEC) — 42
Church music — 72
Church Pastoral Aid Society — 27
Churches, Overseas — 53
Churches Together in Britain and Ireland — 42
Churches in the United Kingdom, Other — 52
Communication Board — xvi, 47
Conference of European Churches — 42
Congregational Liaison (Social Responsibility) — 37
Council Education Committees
Church Representatives on — 302
Counselling and Support — 31, 33, 35

Deeds of Covenant — 13
Dementia Units — 32, 35, 36
Design Services — 48
Diaconate, Membership of — 274
Divinity Faculties, Scottish — 56
Doctrine, Panel on — 17
Drug Dependency Units — 31ff.

Ecclesiastical Buildings — 10
Ecumenical Relations Committee — 2, 40
Education Committee — 2, 46
Elder Training — 45
Endowment Grants — 20
Epilepsy Unit — 32

European Churches, Conference of — 42

Forces Registers — 22
Funds (and Trusts) — 64

General Assembly (2002)
Decisions of — 82
Moderator of — xiv, xviii, 80
Officials — 80
General Assembly (2003)
Date of — xvii
General Treasurer's Department — 7
General Trustees — 2, 9
Gift Aid — 13
Glasgow Lodging House Mission — xvi, 24
Glebes — 2, 10
Guild, Church of Scotland — 14

Healthcare Chaplaincies — 28
HIV/AIDS Project — 39
Home Support Service — 36
Homelessness Centres — 31, 34, 36
Housing and Loan Fund — 2, 21

Impact Teams — 27
Index of Former Parishes and Congregations — 363
Index of Ministers — 344
Index of Parishes and Places — 357
Information Technology Department — 7
Insurance — 10
Investors Trust, Church of Scotland — 11
Iona Community Board — 23, 28
Israel, Accommodation in — 40

John Knox House and Museum — 26
Joint Faiths Advisory Board on Criminal
Justice — 3, 23, 24
Judicial Commission — 5

Kirk Care — xvi

Law Department — 8
Lay Agents, Retired — 303
Learn to Live Programme — 44, 46
Learning Disability Centres — 31–35
Libraries of the Church — 72
Life & Work — 47, 48
Local Broadcasting — 49
Local Broadcasting,
Association of Christians in (ACB) — 49
Local Broadcasting,
Churches Advisory Council for (CACLB) — 49
Long Service Certificates — 72
Lord High Commissioners (List) — 69

Marriage — 75
Marriage Services, Conduct of — 77
Media Relations Unit (Press Office) — xvi, 47

Meetings (Boards/Committees)
Dates of   2
Mental Illness Centres   31–35
Ministers deceased   304
Ministers having resigned Membership of
Presbytery   279
Ministers holding Practising Certificates   280
Ministers' Forum   47
Ministers ordained sixty years and upwards   305
Ministry Department   2, 19
Mission and Evangelism, Advisers in   283
Mission and Evangelism Resources
Committee   3, 23, 26
Mission Projects   27
Moderator of the General Assembly
(see General Assembly)   xvi, xviii, 80
Moderator of the General Assembly
Committee to Nominate   5
Moderators of the General Assembly (List)   70

National Mission Board   xvi, 2, 22
Netherbow, The   xvi, 26
New Charge Development Committee   3, 23, 25
Nomination Committee   11

Offenders' Hostels   31
Office Manager (121 George Street)   xvi, 8
Office Manager's Department   8
Older People, Services for   31ff.
Overseas Appointments   283
Overseas Locations   284
Overseas, Resigned and Retired Mission
Partners   289
Overseas Vacancies   39

Panel on Doctrine   17
Panel on Worship   17
Parish Assistance Committee   3, 23, 26
Parish Assistants   292
Parish Development Fund   29
Parish Education Board   xvi, 43
Parish Reappraisal Committee   2, 23, 24–25
Parliamentary Office (Scottish Churches)   xvi, 43
Pathway Productions   xvi, 48
Pension Trustees   14
Personnel Department   3, 9
Practice and Procedure Board   2, 5
Practising Certificates   280
Presbytery Lists   88–258

Press Office (Media Relations Unit)   xvi, 47
Project Rejoice   24
Project Workers   292
Properties   10
Pulpit Supply   20

Readers   45, 293
Records of the Church   72
Residential Schools   33
Rural Committee   27

Saint Andrew Press   48
St Francis in the East Church House   xvi, 26
Scottish Christian Press   46
Scottish Churches Community Trust   29
Scottish Churches Open College   46
Scottish Churches Parliamentary Office   xvi, 43
Scottish Storytelling Centre   26–27
Social Interests   36
Social Responsibility Board   xvi, 3, 29
Social Responsibility Board
(Media & Public Relations)   36
Societies (and Associations)   60
Society, Religion and Technology Project   xvi, 27
Statistics, Congregational   310–343
Statistics, Summary   310
Stewardship and Finance Board   3, 12
Stipend   20
Study Leave Scheme   20
Summer Missions   27
Supported Accommodation Projects   31, 36

Travelling Expenses   20
Trusts (and Funds)   64

Urban Priority Areas Committee   27

Vacancy Procedure   xviii

Well Asian Information and Advice Centre   27
Wills   13, 78
World Alliance of Reformed Churches   42
World Council of Churches   41
World Mission Board   3, 38
Worship, Panel on   17

Year Book, Information on   xvii, xviii
Youth Ministry   44

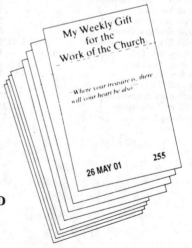

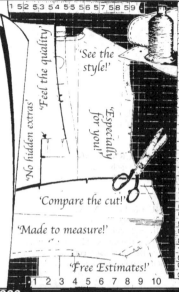
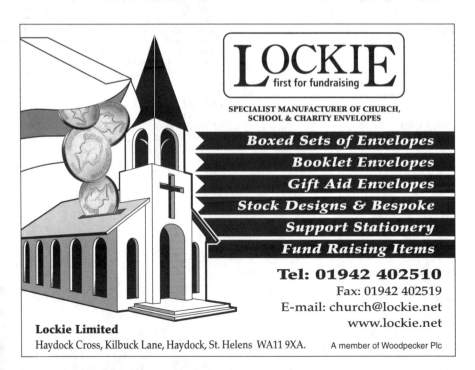

INDEX OF ADVERTISERS

BOOKSHOPS
Wesley Owen .... OBC

CHURCH CLOCKS
James Ritchie 352

CHURCH FURNISHINGS
Hayes & Finch .... IBC
James Chase & Sons i

CHURCH MAINTENANCE
A. Alexander & Son 393
Balmore Specialist Contracts 50
Fleming Buildings Ltd 351
National Specialist Steeplejacks 396
Richardson & Starling 388

CLERICAL TAILORS
Ede & Ravenscroft ix
J. & M. Paterson v
J & M Sewing Service 389

EQUIPMENT
A and C Audio Visual 395

FUND RAISING
Christian Blind Mission xx
Erskine Hospital iii

INSURANCE
Autosave xii

MONUMENTAL MASON
Monkland Memorials 347

MUSICAL SUPPLIES
Allen Organs xiii

PRINTERS AND PUBLISHERS
Acorn 391
Life & Work .... IFC
St Andrew Press viii

REGULAR GIVING ENVELOPES
Church Finance Supplies Ltd 388
Donation Envelopes Ltd xi
Lockie Envelopes 389

SILVERSMITHS
A. Edward Jones Ltd 393
Avon Silversmiths Ltd 392
Eleanor Macdougall 346

SOCIAL WORKS
Borderline x
Christian Aid Scotland vi
Carberry vii
Housing & Loan Fund 86
National Church Association 395
Scottish Bible Society iv
Scottish Churches Open College 394
Stewardship & Finance ii
The Boys' Brigade 345

STAINED GLASS
Les Barrie 350
Phoenix Glass 349
Roland Mitton 348